COMPREHENSIVE RENEWABLE ENERGY

COMPREHENSIVE RENEWABLE ENERGY

EDITOR-IN-CHIEF
Ali Sayigh
*Chairman of WREC, Director General of WREN, and
Chairman of IEI, Brighton, UK*

VOLUME 4
FUEL CELLS AND HYDROGEN TECHNOLOGY

VOLUME EDITOR
Andrew J. Cruden
University of Strathclyde, Glasgow, U.K.

ELSEVIER

AMSTERDAM BOSTON HEIDELBERG LONDON NEW YORK OXFORD
PARIS SAN DIEGO SAN FRANCISCO SINGAPORE SYDNEY TOKYO

Elsevier
Radarweg 29, PO Box 211, 1000 AE Amsterdam, The Netherlands
The Boulevard, Langford Lane, Kidlington, Oxford OX5 1GB, UK
225 Wyman Street, Waltham, MA 02451, USA

Copyright © 2012 Elsevier Ltd. All rights reserved.

4.04 Hydrogen Safety Engineering: The State-of-the-Art and Future Progress
Copyright © 2012 V Molkov

5.16 Renewable Fuels: An Automotive Perspective
Copyright © 2012 Lotus Cars Limited

The following articles are US Government works in the public domain and not subject to copyright:
1.19 Cadmium Telluride Photovoltaic Thin Film: CdTe
1.37 Solar Power Satellites
4.02 Current Perspective on Hydrogen and Fuel Cells
5.02 Historical Perspectives on Biofuels

No part of this publication may be reproduced, stored in a retrieval system or transmitted in any form or by any means electronic, mechanical, photocopying, recording or otherwise without the prior written permission of the publisher

Permissions may be sought directly from Elsevier's Science & Technology Rights Department in Oxford, UK: phone (+44) (0) 1865 843830; fax (+44) (0) 1865 853333; email: permissions@elsevier.com. Alternatively you can submit your request online by visiting the Elsevier web site at http://elsevier.com/locate/permissions, and selecting *Obtaining permission to use Elsevier material*

Notice
No responsibility is assumed by the publisher for any injury and/or damage to persons or property as a matter of products liability, negligence or otherwise, or from any use or operation of any methods, products, instructions or ideas contained in the material herein. Because of rapid advances in the medical sciences, in particular, independent verfication of diagnoses and drug dosages should be made.

British Library Cataloguing in Publication Data
A catalogue record for this book is available from the British Library

The Library of Congress Control Number: 2012934547

ISBN: 978-0-08-087872-0

For information on all Elsevier publications
visit our website at books.elsevier.com

Printed and bound in Italy

11 12 13 14 10 9 8 7 6 5 4 3 2 1

Working together to grow
libraries in developing countries

www.elsevier.com | www.bookaid.org | www.sabre.org

ELSEVIER   BOOK AID International   Sabre Foundation

Editorial: Gemma Mattingley, Joanne Williams
Production: Edward Taylor, Maggie Johnson

EDITOR-IN-CHIEF

Professor Ali Sayigh, BSc, DIC, PhD, CEng, a British citizen, graduated from Imperial College London and the University of London in 1966. He is a fellow of the Institute of Energy, a fellow of the Institution of Electrical Engineers, and is a chartered engineer.

From 1966 to 1985, Prof. Sayigh taught in the College of Engineering at the University of Baghdad and at King Saud University, Saudi Arabia, as a full-time professor, and also at Kuwait University as a part-time professor. From 1981 to 1985, he was Head of the Energy Department at the Kuwait Institute for Scientific Research (KISR) and expert in renewable energy at the Arab Organization of Petroleum Exporting Countries (AOPEC), Kuwait.

He started working in solar energy in September 1969. In 1984, he established links with Pergamon Press and became Editor-in-Chief of his first international journal, *Solar & Wind Technology*. Since 1990 he has been Editor-in-Chief of *Comprehensive Renewable Energy* incorporating *Solar & Wind Technology*, published by Elsevier Science Ltd., Oxford, UK. He is the editor of several international journals published in Morocco, Iran, Bangladesh, and Nigeria.

He has been a member of the International Society for Equitation Science (ISES) since 1973, founder and chairman of the ARAB Section of ISES since 1979, chairman of the UK Solar Energy Society for 3 years, and consultant to many national and international organizations, among them, the British Council, the Islamic Educational, Scientific and Cultural Organization (ISESCO), the United Nations Educational, Scientific and Cultural Organization (UNESCO), the United Nations Development Programme (UNDP), the Economic and Social Commission for Western Asia (ESCWA), and the United Nations Industrial Development Organization (UNIDO).

Since 1977 Prof. Sayigh has founded and directed several renewable energy conferences and workshops in the International Centre for Theoretical Physics (ICTP) – Trieste, Italy, Canada, Colombia, Algeria, Kuwait, Bahrain, Malaysia, Zambia, Malawi, India, the West Indies, Tunisia, Indonesia, Libya, Taiwan, UAE, Oman, the Czech Republic, Germany, Australia, Poland, the Netherlands, Thailand, Korea, Iran, Syria, Saudi Arabia, Singapore, China, the United States, and the United Kingdom.

In 1990 he established the World Renewable Energy Congress (WREC) and, in 1992, the World Renewable Energy Network (WREN), which hold their Congresses every 2 years, attracting more than 100 countries each time. In 2000, he and others in UAE, Sharjah, founded the Arab Science and Technology Foundation (ASTF) and regional conferences have been held in Sweden, Malaysia, Korea, Indonesia, Australia, UAE, and Libya, to name but a few. Prof. Sayigh has been running an annual international seminar on all aspects of renewable energy since 1990 in the United Kingdom and abroad. In total, 85 seminars have been held.

Prof. Sayigh supervised and graduated more than 34 PhD students and 64 MSc students at Reading University and the University of Hertfordshire when he was a professor from 1986 to 2004.

He has edited, contributed, and written more than 32 books and published more than 500 papers in various international journals and conferences.

In 2000–09, he initiated and worked closely with Sovereign Publication Company to produce the most popular magazine at annual bases called *Renewable Energy*, which was distributed freely to more than 6000 readers around the world. Presently, he is the editor-in-chief of *Comprehensive Renewable Energy*, coordinating 154 top scientists', engineers', and researchers' contributions in eight volumes published by Elsevier Publishing Company, Oxford, UK.

VOLUME EDITORS

Dr. Wilfried G. J. H. M. van Sark graduated from Utrecht University, the Netherlands, with an MSc in experimental physics in 1985, and with an MSc thesis on measurement and analysis of I–V characteristics of c-Si cells. He received his PhD from Nijmegen University, the Netherlands; the topic of his PhD thesis was III–V solar cell development, modeling, and processing. He then spent 7 years as a postdoc/senior researcher at Utrecht University and specialized in a-Si:H cell deposition and analysis. He is an expert in plasma chemical vapor deposition, both radio frequency and very high frequency. After an assistant professor position at Nijmegen University, where he worked on III–V solar cells, he returned to Utrecht University, with a focus on (single-molecule) confocal fluorescence microscopy of nanocrystals. In 2002, he moved to his present position as assistant professor at the research group Science, Technology and Society of the Copernicus Institute at Utrecht University, the Netherlands, where he performed and coordinated research on next-generation photovoltaic devices incorporating nanocrystals; for example, luminescent solar concentrators, as well as photovoltaic performance, life cycle analysis, socioeconomics, and policy development. He is member of the editorial board of Elsevier's scientific journal *Renewable Energy*, and member of various organizing committees of the European Union, the Institute of Electrical and Electronics Engineers (IEEE), and the SPIE PV conferences. He is author or coauthor of over 200 peer-reviewed journal and conference paper publications and book chapters. He has (co-)edited three books, including the present one.

Professor John K. Kaldellis holds a mechanical engineering degree from the National Technical University of Athens (NTUA) and a business administration diploma from the University of Piraeus. He obtained his PhD from NTUA (Fluid Sector) sponsored by Snecma–Dassault, France, and Bodossakis Foundation, Greece. He is currently the head of the Mechanical Engineering Department and since 1991 the director of the Soft Energy Applications and Environmental Protection Laboratory of the Technological Education Institute (TEI) of Piraeus. Prof. Kaldellis is also the scientific director (for TEI of Piraeus) of the MSc in Energy program organized by Heriot-Watt University and TEI of Piraeus. His scientific expertise is in the fields of energy and the environment. His research interests include feasibility analysis of energy sector applications; technological progress in wind, hydro, and solar energy markets; hybrid energy systems; energy storage issues; social attitudes toward renewable energy applications; and environmental technology–atmospheric pollution. He has participated in numerous research projects, funded by the European Union, European/Greek Industries, and the Greek State. Prof. Kaldellis has published six books concerning renewable energy applications and environmental protection. He is also the author of more than 100 scientific/research papers in international peer-reviewed journals and more than 300 papers for international scientific conferences. During the last decade, he was also a member of the Scientific Committee of the Hellenic Society of Mechanical–Electrical Engineers as well as a member of the organizing and scientific committee of several national and international conferences. He is currently a member of the editorial board of the *Renewable Energy International* journal and reviewer in more than 40 international journals in the energy and environment sector. He is the editor of the book *Stand-Alone and Hybrid Wind Energy Systems: Technology, Energy Storage and Applications* that has recently been published.

Dr. Soteris A. Kalogirou is a senior lecturer at the Department of Mechanical Engineering and Materials Science and Engineering at the Cyprus University of Technology, Limassol, Cyprus. He received his Higher Technical Institute (HTI) degree in mechanical engineering in 1982, his MPhil in mechanical engineering from the Polytechnic of Wales in 1991, and his PhD in mechanical engineering from the University of Glamorgan in 1995. In June 2011, he received the title of DSc from the University of Glamorgan.

For more than 25 years, he has been actively involved in research in the area of solar energy and particularly in flat-plate and concentrating collectors, solar water heating, solar steam generating systems, desalination, and absorption cooling. Additionally, since 1995, he has been involved in pioneering research dealing with the use of artificial intelligence methods, such as artificial neural networks, genetic algorithms, and fuzzy logic, for the modeling and performance prediction of energy and solar energy systems.

He has 29 books and book contributions and published 225 papers, 97 in international scientific journals and 128 in refereed conference proceedings. To date he has received more than 2550 citations on this work. He is Executive Editor of *Energy*, Associate Editor of *Renewable Energy*, and Editorial Board Member of another 11 journals. He is the editor of the book *Artificial Intelligence in Energy and Renewable Energy Systems*, published by Nova Science Inc.; coeditor of the book *Soft Computing in Green and Renewable Energy Systems*, published by Springer; and author of the book *Solar Energy Engineering: Processes and Systems*, published by Academic Press of Elsevier.

He has been a member of the World Renewable Energy Network (WREN) since 1992 and is a member of the Chartered Institution of Building Services Engineers (CIBSE), the American Society of Heating Refrigeration and Air-Conditioning Engineers (ASHRAE), the Institute of Refrigeration (IoR), and the International Solar Energy Society (ISES).

Dr. Andrew Cruden, a British citizen, was born in 1968. He obtained his BEng, MSc, and PhD in electrical engineering from the University of Strathclyde and CEng, MIEE Dr. Cruden is a past member of BSI GEL/105 Committee on Fuel Cells and Committee member of the IET Scotland Power Section. He is Director of the Scottish Hydrogen and Fuel Cell Association (SHFCA; www.shfca.org.uk) and Director of Argyll, Lomond and the Islands Energy Agency (www.alienergy.org.uk).

Dr. Cruden has been active in the field of hydrogen and fuel cells since 1995, when he acted as a consultant for Zevco Ltd., providing assistance with power electronic interfaces for early fuel cell systems. Later in 1998, he helped found the Scottish Fuel Cell Consortium (SFCC), supported by the Scottish Enterprise Energy Team, which ultimately developed a battery/fuel cell hybrid electric vehicle based on an AC Cobra kit car. The experience and contacts from the SFCC eventually gave rise to the formation of the Scottish Hydrogen and Fuel Cell Association (SHFCA), a trade body for the industry to promote and commercialize Scottish expertise in this field. Dr. Cruden was the founding chairman of the SHFCA.

Dr. Cruden is currently investigating alkaline electrolyzers in terms of improving their part load efficiency and lifetime when powered by variable renewable power sources, for example, wind turbines, as part of a £5 million EPSRC Supergen project on the 'Delivery of Sustainable Hydrogen' (EP/G01244X/1). He is also working with a colleague within Electronic and Electrical Engineering (EEE) at Strathclyde, studying the concept of vehicle-to-grid energy storage, as a mechanism not only to allow controlled load leveling on the power system, but also to potentially 'firm' up renewable energy generation. This work is supported by two research grants, an international E.On Research Initiative 2007 award and an ESPRC grant (EP/F062133/1).

Dr. Cruden is a senior lecturer within the Department of Electronic and Electrical Engineering at the University of Strathclyde. His current fields of research are modeling fuel cell and electrolyzer systems, fuel cell combined heat and power (CHP) systems, power electronic devices for interfacing both vehicular and stationary fuel cell systems, condition monitoring systems for renewable energy sources (i.e., wind turbines as part of EPSRC Supergen on Wind Energy Technologies, EP/D034566/1), and energy management systems for hybrid electric vehicles.

His areas of expertise include hydrogen-powered fuel cells and electrolyzers, energy storage for electric vehicles, and renewable energy generation.

Professor Dermot J. Roddy, BSc, PhD, CEng, FIET, joined Newcastle University as Science City Professor of Energy in 2008 after a period of some 20 years in the energy industry and petrochemical sectors. He is also Director of the Sir Joseph Swan Centre for Energy Research, which integrates energy research across Newcastle University and links with a powerful external industrial base in the energy sector. Outside of the university he is Chairman of Northeast Biofuels, Finance Director of the UK Hydrogen Association, and Vice-President of the Northern England Electricity Supply Companies Association. Prior to coming to Newcastle University, he was Chief Executive of Renew Tees Valley Ltd. – a company which he set up in 2003 to create a viable and vibrant economy in the Tees Valley based on renewable energy and recycling – where he was instrumental in a wide range of major renewable energy and low-carbon projects relating to biomass, biofuels, hydrogen, carbon capture and storage, wind, and advanced waste processing technologies. From 1998 to 2002, he ran the crude oil refinery on Teesside as a site director for a $5 billion turnover facility before moving to the Netherlands to work on Petroplus' international growth plans. Roddy's experience in the petrochemical industry began in 1985, involving a variety of UK and international roles in operations, engineering, and technology with ICI and others. Prior to that he developed leading-edge technology at Queen's University, Belfast, for optimization and control in aerospace applications.

André G. H. Lejeune was born on 2 August 1942 in Belgium. He was graduated in 1967 as a civil engineer, in 1972 as doctor in applied sciences (PhD), and in 1973 as master in oceanography in the University of Liège in Belgium. He was appointed full-time professor in the same university in 1976, and was visitor professor at the UNESCO–IHE Institute for Water Education in the Netherlands and Ecole Polytechnique Fédérale de Lausanne (EPFL) in Switzerland. Within the framework of his activities of professor, director of the Hydraulic Constructions and Hydraulic Research Laboratory, and expert, he took part in studies of dams and hydraulic structures and went on site in more than 90 countries of the world. In particular, he was for the last 6 years the chairman of the Technical Committee on Hydraulics for Dams in ICOLD (International Commission of Large Dams). He is a member of the Belgian Royal Academy of Sciences. He made his PhD thesis in hydraulic numerical modelization. This thesis received the Lorenz G. Straub Award in Minneapolis, USA (H. Einstein Jr. was a member of the Jury), and was used in particular by Chinese colleagues in the Three Gorges Project. Due to his practice and experience, he has a very complete knowledge of the hydraulic phenomena modelizations through both numerical and physical means.

With his wife, he has 3 children and 11 grandchildren. He likes books, tennis, and diving.

Thorsteinn I. Sigfusson is an internationally recognised physicist, educated in Copenhagen, Denmark, and Cambridge, UK. He is Director-General of the Innovation Center, Iceland and Professor of physics at the University of Iceland. He has been a visiting professor at Columbia University, New York, and he is currently the lead scientist in a prize-winning energy technology project performed at Tomsk Polytechnic University in Tomsk, Russia.

He has been a key figure in the introduction of new ideas and opportunities in the further greening of Icelandic society through the energy industry, and instrumental in the challenge of saving imported hydrocarbons by focusing on hydrogen from renewable energy.

He has started over a dozen start-up companies from research in Iceland and chaired various international societies in alternative energy. Among his achievements in geothermal energy is the construction of the world's largest solid-state thermoelectric generator powered with geothermal steam in southern Iceland. At the Innovation Center, Iceland, efforts are made to develop materials to withstand erosion in geothermal environments.

AbuBakr S. Bahaj is Professor of Sustainable Energy at the University of Southampton. After completing his PhD, he was employed by the University, progressing from a researcher to a personnel chair of Sustainable Energy. Over the past 20 years, Prof. Bahaj has established the energy theme within the University and directed his Sustainable Energy Research Group (SERG, www.energy.soton.ac.uk), which is now considered to be one of the United Kingdoms's leading university-based research groups in renewable energy and energy in buildings. He initiated and managed research in ocean energy conversion (resources, technologies, and impacts), photovoltaics, energy in buildings, and impacts of climate change on the built environment in the University. This work has resulted in over 230 articles published in academic refereed journals and conference series of international standing (see www.energy.soton.ac.uk).

Prof. Bahaj is the head of the Energy and Climate Change Division (ECCD) within the highly rated Faculty of Engineering and the Environment – Civil Engineering and the Environment – (www.civil.soton.ac.uk/research/divisions/divlist.asp?ResearchGroupID=1) (second in the United Kingdom, Research Assessment Exercise in 2008, with 80% of research judged to be either 'World Leading' or 'Internationally Excellent'). The aims of the Division and SERG are to promote and execute fundamental and applied research and preindustrial development in the areas of energy resources, technologies, energy efficiency, and the impact of climate change.

Prof. Bahaj is an experienced research team director and has many internationally focused research projects including collaborative projects in China, the European Union, the Middle East, and Africa. He also coordinated (2006–10) the United Kingdom's Engineering and Physical Sciences Research Council (EPSRC), Ecoregion Research Networks that aim to develop research themes and projects to study eco-city development encompassing resource assessment, technology pathways for the production and conservation of energy, planning, and social and economic studies required in establishing eco-regions in China and elsewhere (http://www.eco-networks.org). He is a founding member of the Sino-UK Low Carbon City Development Cooperation (LCCD) which aims to promote and undertake research into pathways for low-carbon development in Chinese cities. His work also encompasses an ongoing multimillion pound program in Africa, 'Energy for Development' for promoting and implementing village electrification systems, addressing villager's needs, and establishing coherent approaches to the commercial sustainability of the projects. This program is funded by the Research Councils and the UK Department for International Development (DFID; www.energyfordevelopment.net).

Prof. Bahaj is the editor-in-chief of the *International Journal of Sustainable Energy* and associate Editor of the *Renewable & Sustainable Energy Review*. He was on the editorial boards of the journals *Sustainable Cities and Society* and *Renewable Energy* (2005–11), and the United Kingdom's Institute of Civil Engineering journal Energy (2006–09). He was a member of the Tyndall Centre for Climate Change Research Supervisory Board (2005–10), and from 2001 to 2007 he was a member of the UK Government Department of Business, Enterprise and Regulatory Reform (now Department for Business Innovations and Skills, BIS), Technology Programmes Panels on Water (including ocean energy) and Solar Energy, now being administered by the Technology Strategy Board (TSB). Prof. Bahaj was the chair of the Technical Committees of the World Renewable Energy Congress – held in Glasgow (July 2008) and in Abu Dhabi (September 2010). He was a member of the Technical Committee of the 27th International Conference on Offshore Mechanics and Arctic Engineering (OMAE, 2008), a member of the management and technical committees of the European Wave and Tidal Energy Conferences (EWTEC, Porto, Portugal, September 2007; and Uppsala, Sweden, September 2009). He is also a member of the British Standards Institution (BSI) Committee GEL/82 on PV Energy Systems. Recently, at the invitation of the International Energy Agency, he has completed the 2008 status report on tidal stream energy conversion and in September 2009 was elected to chair the next EWTEC conference in the series – EWTEC2011 which was held in Southampton, 5–9 September 2011, and attended by around 500 participants.

To address training in the areas of energy and climate change Prof. Bahaj has coordinated and developed a set of MSc programs under the banner 'Energy and Sustainability' that address Energy Resources and Climate Change and Energy, Environment and Buildings.

CONTRIBUTORS FOR ALL VOLUMES

P Agnolucci
Imperial College London, London, UK

EO Ahlgren
Chalmers University of Technology, Gothenburg, Sweden

D Aklil
Pure Energy Center, Unst, Shetland Isles, UK

D-C Alarcón Padilla
Centro de Investigaciones Energéticas Medioambientales y Tecnológicas (CIEMAT), Plataforma Solar de Almeria, Almeria, Spain

K Alexander
University of Canterbury, Christchurch, New Zealand

S Alexopoulos
Aachen University of Applied Sciences, Jülich, Germany

A Altieri
UNICA – Brazilian Sugarcane Industry Association, São Paulo, Brazil

A Anthrakidis
Aachen University of Applied Sciences, Jülich, Germany

E Antolín
Universidad Politécnica de Madrid, Madrid, Spain

P Archambeau
University of Liège, Liège, Belgium

H Ármannsson
Iceland GeoSurvey (ISOR), Reykjavík, Iceland

MF Askew
Wolverhampton, UK

A Athienitis
Concordia University, Montreal, QC, Canada

G Axelsson
University of Iceland, Reykjavik, Iceland

V Badescu
Polytechnic University of Bucharest, Bucharest, Romania

AS Bahaj
The University of Southampton, Southampton, UK

P Banda
Instituto de Sistema Fotovoltaicos de Concentración (ISFOC), Puertollano, Spain

VG Belessiotis
'DEMOKRITOS' National Center for Scientific Research, Athens, Greece

P Berry
ADAS High Mowthorpe, Malton, UK

F Bidault
Imperial College London, London, UK

D Biro
Fraunhofer Institute for Solar Energy Systems, Freiburg, Germany

G Boschloo
Uppsala University, Uppsala, Sweden

C Boura
Aachen University of Applied Sciences, Jülich, Germany

E Bozorgzadeh
Iran Water and Power Resources Development Company (IWPCO), Tehran, Iran

CE Brewer
Iowa State University, Ames, IA, USA

M Börjesson
Chalmers University of Technology, Gothenburg, Sweden

RC Brown
Iowa State University, Ames, IA, USA

F Bueno
University of Burgos, Burgos, Spain

K Burke
NASA Glenn Research Center, Cleveland, OH, USA

LF Cabeza
GREA Innovació Concurrent, Universitat de Lleida, Lleida, Spain

L Candanedo
Dublin Institute of Technology, Dublin, Ireland

YG Caouris
University of Patras, Patras, Greece

UB Cappel
Uppsala University, Uppsala, Sweden

JA Carta
Universidad de Las Palmas de Gran Canaria, Las Palmas de Gran Canaria, Spain

P Chen
Dalian Institute of Chemical Physics, Dalian, China

DG Christakis
Wind Energy Laboratory, Technological Educational Institute of Crete, Crete, Greece

DA Chwieduk
Warsaw University of Technology, Warsaw, Poland

J Clark
University of York, York, UK

G Conibeer
University of New South Wales, Sydney, NSW, Australia

AJ Cruden
University of Strathclyde, Glasgow, UK

MC da Silva

B Davidsdottir
University of Iceland, Reykjavík, Iceland

O de la Rubia
Instituto de Sistema Fotovoltaicos de Concentración (ISFOC), Puertollano, Spain

E Despotou
Formerly of the European Photovoltaic Industry Association, Brussels, Belgium

BJ Dewals
University of Liège, Liège, Belgium

AL Dicks
The University of Queensland, Brisbane, QLD, Australia

R DiPippo
University of Massachusetts Dartmouth, Dartmouth, MA, USA

E Dunlop
European Commission DG Joint Research Centre, Ispra, Italy

NM Duteanu
Newcastle University, Newcastle upon Tyne, UK;
University 'POLITEHNICA' Timisoara, Timisoara, Romania

LM Eaton
Oak Ridge National Laboratory, Oak Ridge, TN, USA

H-J Egelhaaf
Konarka Technologies GmbH, Nürnberg, Germany

T Ehara
Mizuho Information & Research Institute, Tokyo, Japan

B Erable
Newcastle University, Newcastle upon Tyne, UK;
CNRS-Université de Toulouse, Toulouse, France

S Erpicum
University of Liège, Liège, Belgium

G Evans
NNFCC, Biocentre, Innovation Way, Heslington, York, UK

AFO Falcão
Instituto Superior Técnico, Technical University of Lisbon, Lisbon, Portugal

G Faninger
University of Klagenfurt, Klagenfurt, Austria; Vienna University of Technology, Vienna, Austria

GA Florides
Cyprus University of Technology, Limassol, Cyprus

ÓG Flóvenz
Iceland GeoSurvey (ISOR), Reykjavík, Iceland

RN Frese
VU University Amsterdam, Amsterdam, The Netherlands

Þ Friðriksson
Iceland GeoSurvey (ISOR), Reykjavík, Iceland

VM Fthenakis
Columbia University, New York, NY, USA; Brookhaven National Laboratory, Upton, NY, USA

M Fuamba
École Polytechnique de Montréal, Montreal, QC, Canada

A Fuller
University of Canterbury, Christchurch, New Zealand

LMC Gato
Instituto Superior Técnico, Technical University of Lisbon, Lisbon, Portugal

R Gazey
Pure Energy Center, Unst, Shetland Isles, UK

TA Gessert
National Renewable Energy Laboratory (NREL), Golden, CO, USA

MM Ghangrekar
*Newcastle University, Newcastle upon Tyne, UK;
Indian Institute of Technology, Kharagpur, India*

M Giannouli
University of Patras, Patras, Greece

EA Gibson
University of Nottingham, Nottingham UK

A Gil
Hydropower Generation Division of Iberdrola, Salamanca, Spain

SW Glunz
Fraunhofer Institute for Solar Energy Systems, Freiburg, Germany

JC Goldschmidt
Fraunhofer Institute for Solar Energy Systems ISE, Freiburg, Germany

R Gottschalg
Loughborough University, Leicestershire, UK

MA Green
The University of New South Wales, Sydney, NSW, Australia

J Göttsche
Aachen University of Applied Sciences, Jülich, Germany

J Guo
China Institute of Water Resources and Hydropower Research (IWHR), Beijing, China

A Hagfeldt
Uppsala University, Uppsala, Sweden

B Hagin
Ingénieur-Conseil, Lutry, Switzerland

K Hall
Technology Transition Corporation, Ltd., Tyne and Wear, UK

O Hamandjoda
University of Yaounde, Yaounde, Republic of Cameroon

AP Harvey
Newcastle University, Newcastle upon Tyne, UK

JA Hauch
Konarka Technologies GmbH, Nürnberg, Germany

D Heinemann
University of Oldenburg, Oldenburg, Germany

V Heller
Imperial College London, London, UK

GP Hersir
Iceland GeoSurvey (ISOR), Reykjavík, Iceland

T Heyer
Technical University of Dresden, Dresden, Germany

P Hilger
Aachen University of Applied Sciences, Jülich, Germany

B Hillring
Swedish University of Agricultural Sciences, Skinnskatteberg, Sweden

T Hino
CTI Engineering International Co., Ltd., Chu-o-Ku, Japan

LC Hirst
Imperial College London, London, UK

B Hoffschmidt
Aachen University of Applied Sciences, Jülich, Germany

H Horlacher
Technical University of Dresden, Dresden, Germany

N Hughes
Imperial College London, London, UK

SL Hui
Bechtel Civil Company, San Francisco, CA, USA

D Husmann
University of Wisconsin–Madison, Madison, WI, USA

JTS Irvine
University of St Andrews, St Andrews, UK

D Jacobs
Freie Universität Berlin, Berlin, Germany

Y Jestin
Advanced Photonics and Photovoltaics Group, Bruno Kessler Foundation, Trento, Italy

A Jäger-Waldau
Institution for Energy Transport, Ispra, Italy

S Jianxia
Design and Research Institute, Yangzhou City, Jiangsu Province, China

E Johnson
Pure Energy Center, Unst, Shetland Isles, UK

HF Kaan
TNO Energy, Comfort and Indoor Quality, Delft, The Netherlands

JK Kaldellis
Technological Education Institute of Piraeus, Athens, Greece

SA Kalogirou
Cyprus University of Technology, Limassol, Cyprus

HD Kambezidis
Institute of Environmental Research and Sustainable Development, Athens, Greece

M Kapsali
Technological Education Institute of Piraeus, Athens, Greece

M Karimirad
Norwegian University of Science and Technology, Trondheim, Norway

T Karlessi
National and Kapodistrian University of Athens, Athens, Greece

SN Karlsdóttir
Innovation Center Iceland, Iceland

D Al Katsaprakakis
Wind Energy Laboratory, Technological Educational Institute of Crete, Crete, Greece

O Kaufhold
Aachen University of Applied Sciences, Jülich, Germany

CA Kaufmann
Helmholtz Zentrum für Materialien und Energie GmbH, Berlin, Germany

KA Kavadias
Technological Education Institute of Piraeus, Athens, Greece

LL Kazmerski
National Renewable Energy Laboratory, Golden, CO, USA

A Kazmi
University of York, York, UK

K Kendall
University of Birmingham, Birmingham, UK

J Kenfack
University of Yaounde, Yaounde, Republic of Cameroon

R Kenny
European Commission DG Joint Research Centre, Ispra, Italy

HC Kim
Brookhaven National Laboratory, Upton, NY, USA

L Kloo
KTH—Royal Institute of Technology, Stockholm, Sweden

G Knothe
USDA Agricultural Research Service, Peoria, IL, USA

FR Kogler
Konarka Technologies GmbH, Nürnberg, Germany

D Kolokotsa
Technical University of Crete, Crete, Greece

K Komoto
Mizuho Information & Research Institute, Tokyo, Japan

E Kondili
Technological Education Institute of Piraeus, Athens, Greece

H Kristjánsdóttir
University of Iceland, Reykjavík, Iceland

LA Lamont
Petroleum Institute, Abu Dhabi, UAE

GA Landis
NASA Glenn Research Center, Cleveland, OH, USA

JGM Lee
Newcastle University, Newcastle upon Tyne, UK

G Leftheriotis
University of Patras, Patras, Greece

A Lejeune
University of Liège, Liège, Belgium

T Leo
FuelCell Energy Inc., Danbury, CT, USA

E Lester
The University of Nottingham, Nottingham, UK

E Lorenz
University of Oldenburg, Oldenburg, Germany

JW Lund
Geo-Heat Center, Oregon Institute of Technology, Klamath Falls, OR, USA

A Luque
Universidad Politécnica de Madrid, Madrid, Spain

BP Machado
Intertechne, Curitiba, PR, Brazil

EBL Mackay
GL Garrad Hassan, Bristol, UK

T-F Mahdi
École Polytechnique de Montréal, Montreal, QC, Canada

GG Maidment
London South Bank University, London, UK

A Malmgren
BioC Ltd, Cirencester, UK

C Manson-Whitton
Progressive Energy Ltd., Stonehouse, UK

Á Margeirsson
Magma Energy Iceland, Reykjanesbaer, Iceland

A Martí
Universidad Politécnica de Madrid, Madrid, Spain

M Martinez
Instituto de Sistema Fotovoltaicos de Concentración (ISFOC), Puertollano, Spain

S Mathew
University of Brunei Darussalam, Gadong, Brunei Darussalam

PH Middleton
University of Agder, Grimstad, Norway

R Mikalsen
Newcastle University, Newcastle upon Tyne, UK

D Milborrow
Lewes, East Sussex, UK

H Müllejans
European Commission DG Joint Research Centre, Ispra, Italy

V Molkov
University of Ulster, Newtownabbey, Northern Ireland, UK

M Moner-Girona
Joint Research Centre, European Commission, Institute for Energy and Transport, Ispra, Italy

PE Morthorst
Technical University of Denmark, Roskilde, Denmark

N Mortimer
North Energy Associates Ltd, Sheffield, UK

E Mullins
Teagasc, Oak Park Crops Research Centre, Carlow, Republic of Ireland

P Mulvihill
Pioneer Generation Ltd., Alexandra, New Zealand

DR Myers
National Renewable Energy Laboratory, USA

D Nash
University of Strathclyde, Glasgow, UK

GF Nemet
University of Wisconsin–Madison, Madison, WI, USA

H Nfaoui
Mohammed V University, Rabat, Morocco

T Nikolakakis
Columbia University, New York, NY, USA

X Niu
Changjiang Institute of Survey, Planning, Design and Research, Wuhan, China

B Norton
Dublin Institute of Technology, Dublin, Ireland

A Nuamah
The University of Nottingham, Nottingham, UK; RWE npower, Swindon, UK

B O'Connor
Aachen University of Applied Sciences, Jülich, Germany

O Olsson
Swedish University of Agricultural Sciences, Skinnskatteberg, Sweden

V Ortisi
Pure Energy Center, Unst, Shetland Isles, UK

H Ossenbrink
European Commission DG Joint Research Centre, Ispra, Italy

AG Paliatsos
Technological Education Institute of Piraeus, Athens, Greece

A Pandit
VU University Amsterdam, Amsterdam, The Netherlands

E Papanicolaou
'DEMOKRITOS' National Center for Scientific Research, Athens, Greece

A Paurine
London South Bank University, London, UK

N Pearsall
Northumbria University, Newcastle, UK

RJ Pearson
Lotus Engineering, Norwich, UK

RD Perlack
Oak Ridge National Laboratory, Oak Ridge, TN, USA

H Pettersson
Swerea IVF AB, Mölndal, Sweden

GS Philip
KCAET, Malapuram, Kerala, India

S Pillai
The University of New South Wales, Sydney, NSW, Australia

M Pirotton
University of Liège, Liège, Belgium

BG Pollet
University of Birmingham, Birmingham, UK

D Porter
Association of Electricity Producers, London, UK

A Pouliezos
Technical University of Crete, Hania, Greece

R Preu
Fraunhofer Institute for Solar Energy Systems, Freiburg, Germany

CM Ramos

C Rau
Aachen University of Applied Sciences, Jülich, Germany

AA Refaat
Cairo University, Giza, Egypt

TH Reijenga
BEARiD Architecten, Rotterdam, The Netherlands

AHME Reinders
*Delft University of Technology, Delft, The Netherlands;
University of Twente, Enschede, The Netherlands*

G Riley
RWE npower, Swindon, UK

DJ Roddy
Newcastle University, Newcastle upon Tyne, UK

S Rolland
Alliance for Rural Electrification, Brussels, Belgium

A Roskilly
Newcastle University, Newcastle upon Tyne, UK

F Rubio
Instituto de Sistema Fotovoltaicos de Concentración (ISFOC), Puertollano, Spain

F Rulot
University of Liège, Liège, Belgium

L Rybach
GEOWATT AG, Zurich, Switzerland

M Santamouris
National and Kapodistrian University of Athens, Athens, Greece

J Sattler
Aachen University of Applied Sciences, Jülich, Germany

M Sauerborn
Aachen University of Applied Sciences, Jülich, Germany

TW Schmidt
The University of Sydney, Sydney, NSW, Australia

N Schofield
University of Manchester, Manchester, UK

REI Schropp
Utrecht University, Utrecht, The Netherlands

K Scott
Newcastle University, Newcastle upon Tyne, UK

SP Sen
NHPC Ltd., New Delhi, India

TI Sigfusson
Innovation Center, Reykjavik, Iceland

L Sims
*Konarka Technologies GmbH, Nürnberg, Germany;
Universität Augsburg, Augsburg, Germany*

C Smith
NNFCC, Biocentre, Innovation Way, Heslington, York, UK

K Sæmundsson
Iceland GeoSurvey (ISOR), Reykjavík, Iceland

BK Sovacool
Vermont Law School, South Royalton, VT, USA

J Spink
Teagasc, Oak Park Crops Research Centre, Carlow, Republic of Ireland

JN Sørensen
Technical University of Denmark, Lyngby, Denmark

T Stallard
The University of Manchester, Manchester, UK

GS Stavrakakis
Technical University of Crete, Chania, Greece

R Steim
Konarka Technologies GmbH, Nürnberg, Germany

BJ Stokes
CNJV LLC, Washington, DC, USA

L Sun
*KTH—Royal Institute of Technology, Stockholm, Sweden;
Dalian University of Technology (DUT), Dalian, China*

L Suo
Science and Technology Committee of the Ministry of Water Resources, Beijing, China

DT Swift-Hook
*Kingston University, London, UK;
World Renewable Energy Network, Brighton, UK*

A Synnefa
National and Kapodistrian University of Athens, Athens, Greece

S Szabo
Joint Research Centre, European Commission, Institute for Energy and Transport, Ispra, Italy

MJY Tayebjee
The University of Sydney, Sydney, NSW, Australia

A Tesfai
University of St Andrews, St Andrews, UK

P Thornley
The University of Manchester, Manchester, UK

Y Tripanagnostopoulos
University of Patras, Patras, Greece

L Tsakalakos
General Electric – Global Research Center, New York, NY, USA

JWG Turner
Lotus Engineering, Norwich, UK

E Tzen
Centre for Renewable Energy Sources and Saving (CRES), Pikermi, Attica, Greece

T Unold
Helmholtz Zentrum für Materialien und Energie GmbH, Berlin, Germany

J van der Heide
imec vzw, Leuven, Belgium

P van der Vleuten
Free Energy Consulting, Eindhoven, The Netherlands

F Van Hulle
XP Wind Consultancy, Leuven, Belgium

GC van Kooten
University of Victoria, Victoria, BC, Canada

WGJHM van Sark
Utrecht University, Utrecht, The Netherlands

I Waller
FiveBarGate Consultants Ltd, Cleveland, UK

I Walsh
Opus International Consultants Ltd., New Zealand

Y Wang
Newcastle University, Newcastle upon Tyne, UK

T Wizelius
Gotland University, Visby, Sweden; Lund University, Lund, Sweden

LL Wright
University of Tennessee, Knoxville, TN, USA

H Xie
Changjiang Institute of Survey, Planning, Design and Research, Wuhan, China

M Yamaguchi
Toyota Technological Institute, Tempaku, Nagoya, Japan

P Yianoulis
University of Patras, Patras, Greece

EH Yu
Newcastle University, Newcastle upon Tyne, UK

H Yu
Newcastle University, Newcastle upon Tyne, UK

DP Zafirakis
Technological Education Institute of Piraeus, Athens, Greece

G Zaragoza
Centro de Investigaciones Energéticas Medioambientales y Tecnológicas (CIEMAT), Plataforma Solar de Almeria, Almeria, Spain

M Zeman
Delft University of Technology, Delft, The Netherlands

PREFACE

Comprehensive Renewable Energy is the only multivolume reference work of its type at a time when renewable energy sources are increasingly in demand and realistically sustainable, clean, and helping to combat climate change and global warming. Renewable energy investment has exceeded US$10 billion per year during the past 5 years. The World Renewable Energy Network (WREN) predicts that this figure is set to increase to US$20 billion per year by 2015.

As Editor-in-Chief, I have assembled an impressive world-class team of 154 volume editors and contributing authors for the eight volumes. They represent policy makers, researchers, industrialists, financiers, and heads of organizations from more than 80 countries to produce this definitive complete work in renewable energy covering the past, explaining the present, and giving the ideas and prospects of development for the future. There are more than 1000 references from books, journals, and the Internet within the eight volumes. *Comprehensive Renewable Energy* is full of color charts, illustrations, and photographs of real projects and research results from around the world. Each chapter has been painstakingly reviewed and checked for consistent high quality. The result is an authoritative overview that ties the literature together and provides the user with reliable background information and a citation resource.

The field of renewable energy research and development is represented by many journals that are directly and indirectly concerned with the field. But no reference work encompasses the entire field and unites the different areas of research through in-depth foundational reviews. *Comprehensive Renewable Energy* fills this vacuum, and is the definitive work for this subject area. It will help users apply context to diverse journal literature, aiding them in identifying areas for further research and development.

Research into renewable energy is spread across a number of different disciplines and subject areas. These areas do not always share a unique identifying factor or subject themselves to clear and concise definitions. This work unites the different areas of research and allows users, regardless of their background, to navigate through the most essential concepts with ease, saving them time and vastly improving their understanding so that they can move forward, whether in their research, development, manufacturing, or purchase of renewable energy.

The first volume is devoted to Photovoltaic Technology and is edited by Mr. Wilfried G. J. H. M. van Sark from the Netherlands. It consists of 38 chapters, written by 41 authors from Europe, the United States, Japan, China, India, Africa, and the Middle East. The topics covered range from the smallest applications to MW projects. A brief introduction and history is followed by chapters on finance and economics, solar resources, up- and downconversion, crystalline photovoltaic (PV) cells, luminescent concentrators, thin-film and multiple-junction plastic solar cells, dye-sensitized solar cells, bio-inspired converters, application of micro- and nanotechnology, building integrated photovoltaics (BIPV) application in architecture, and very large-scale PV systems. Without doubt, this is an impressive tour of an immense field.

Volume 2 is devoted to Wind Energy and is edited by Professor John K. Kaldellis from Greece. It consists of 22 chapters written by 22 authors, again from various parts of the world, covering all aspects of wind energy from small wind mills to very large wind farms. The volume includes chapters on the history of wind power, the potential of wind power, wind turbine development, aerodynamic analysis, mechanical and electrical loads, control systems, noise and testing, onshore and offshore wind systems, policy, industry, and special wind power applications.

Volume 3 is devoted to Solar Thermal Applications and the editor is Professor Soteris A. Kalogirou from Cyprus. It consists of 19 chapters written by 17 authors. All aspects of solar thermal energy and its applications are covered. The volume begins with solar energy as a source of heat and goes on to describe the history of thermal applications, low-temperature and high-temperature storage systems, selective coating, glazing, modeling and simulation, hot water systems, space heating and cooling, water desalination, industrial and agricultural applications, concentration power, heat pumps, and passive solar architecture. The authors have looked at the Sun from the thermal energy aspect and put together a very informative and up-to-date volume from which every interested person, no matter what their level of knowledge, can benefit.

Volume 4 is on Fuel Cells and Hydrogen Technology and is edited by Dr. Andrew Cruden from the United Kingdom. It consists of 14 chapters covering the following topics: introduction and perspectives on hydrogen and fuel cells; theory and application of alkaline fuel cells; application of proton exchange membrane (PEM) fuel cells; molten carbonate fuel cells; solid oxide fuel cells; microbial and biological fuel cells; storage of compressed gas and hydrogen; the economy and policy of hydrogen technology; hydrogen safety engineering and future progress; the use of hydrogen for transport; and hydrogen and fuel cell power electronics. The 14 chapters were written by 16 authors. All aspects of practice, innovative technology, and future guidelines for researchers and industry have been addressed in this definitive volume.

Volume 5 deals with the huge field of Biomass and Biofuels and is edited by Professor Dermot J. Roddy from the United Kingdom. This work consists of 21 chapters written by 23 authors, again covering all aspects of biomass and biofuels, including their past, present, and future. The volume explains the history and prospective future of biofuels; bioethanol development in Brazil; power generation from biomass; biomass co-firing stations; biomass world market; a critical assessment of biomass – combined heat and power (CHP) energy systems; the ethics of biofuel production – issues, constraints, and limitations; greenhouse gases life cycle analysis; six different solutions from gasification and pyrolysis; new processes in biomass-to-liquid technology; new processes in biofuel production; biofuels from waste materials; novel feedstocks and woody biomass; feedstocks with the potential of yield improvement; renewable fuels – an automotive prospective; and novel use of biofuels in a range of engine configurations. Under Expanding the Envelope, there are chapters on biochar, extracting additional value from biomass, and biomass to chemicals. Finally, the chapter on bioenergy policy development concludes the volume.

Volume 6 is concerned with Hydro Power and is edited by Professor André G. H. Lejeune from Belgium. This is the oldest of all the renewable energy applications and has progressed over the ages from pico-hydro of a few hundred watts to large- and mega-scale dams generating more than 3000 MW with innovative civil engineering capability. This volume consists of 18 chapters prepared by 21 authors. It contains introduction – benefits and constraints of hydropower, recent developments and achievements in hydraulic research in China, and the management of hydropower and its impacts through construction and operation. The volume then assesses nine hydropower schemes around the world: the Three Gorges Project in China; large hydropower plants of Brazil; hydropower in Iran – vision and strategy; the recent trend in developing hydropower in India; the evolution of hydropower in Spain; hydropower in Japan; hydropower in Canada; an overview of institutional structure reform of the Cameroon power sector and assessment; and hydropower reliability in Switzerland. Other important issues are covered: pumped storage power plants; simplified generic axial-flow microhydro turbines; the development of a small hydroelectric scheme at Horseshoe Bend, Teviot River, New Zealand; concrete durability in dam design structure; and long-term sediment management for sustainable hydropower.

Volume 7 deals with Geothermal Energy. The editor of this volume is Professor Thorsteinn I. Sigfusson from Iceland. The volume consists of 10 chapters, which are written by 15 different authors. It covers the following areas: introduction and the physics of geothermal resources and management during utilization; geothermal shallow systems – heat pumps; geothermal exploration techniques; corrosion, scaling, and material selection in geothermal power production; direct heat utilization of geothermal energy; geothermal power plants; geochemical aspects of geothermal utilization; geothermal cost and investment factors; and the role of sustainable geothermal development.

Volume 8 is devoted to Generating Electricity from the Oceans, edited by Professor AbuBakr S. Bahaj from the United Kingdom. It consists of six chapters written by five authors. The volume covers the historical aspects of wave energy conversion, resource assessment for wave energy, development of wave devices from initial conception to commercial demonstration, air turbines, and the economics of ocean energy.

One chapter is totally devoted to Renewable Energy Policy and Incentives. It is included in the first volume only. The author of this chapter is Mr. David Porter, Chief Executive of the Association of Electricity Producers in the United Kingdom, an author who has had vast experience of dealing with electricity generation in the United Kingdom over many years. He has advised the British Government on how to meet supply and demand of electricity and coordinate with all electricity producers regarding their sources and supply. The chapter outlines the types of mechanisms used to promote renewable energy and their use, the impact on their deployment, ensuring investor certainty, the potential for harmonizing support schemes, and the conclusion.

In short, my advice to anyone who wants to acquire comprehensive knowledge concerning renewable energy, no matter which subject or application, is that they should acquire this invaluable resource for their home, research center and laboratory, company, or library.

Professor Ali Sayigh BSc, DIC, PhD, FIE, FIEE, CEng
Chairman of WREC (World Renewable Energy Congress)
Director General of WREN (World Renewable Energy Network)
Chairman of IEI (The Institution of Engineers (India))
Editor-in-Chief of *Renewable Energy*
Editor-in-Chief of *Renewable Energy Magazine*

CONTENTS

Editor-in-Chief	v
Volume Editors	vii
Contributors for All Volumes	xi
Preface	xix

Volume 1 Photovoltaic Solar Energy

Renewable Energy

1.01	Renewable Energy Policy and Incentives *D Porter*	1

Photovoltaic Solar Energy

1.02	Introduction to Photovoltaic Technology *WGJHM van Sark*	5
1.03	Solar Photovoltaics Technology: No Longer an Outlier *LL Kazmerski*	13
1.04	History of Photovoltaics *LA Lamont*	31

Economics and Environment

1.05	Historical and Future Cost Dynamics of Photovoltaic Technology *GF Nemet and D Husmann*	47
1.06	Feed-In Tariffs and Other Support Mechanisms for Solar PV Promotion *D Jacobs and BK Sovacool*	73
1.07	Finance Mechanisms and Incentives for Photovoltaic Technologies in Developing Countries *M Moner-Girona, S Szabo, and S Rolland*	111
1.08	Environmental Impacts of Photovoltaic Life Cycles *VM Fthenakis and HC Kim*	143
1.09	Overview of the Global PV Industry *A Jäger-Waldau*	161
1.10	Vision for Photovoltaics in the Future *E Despotou*	179

1.11	Storage Options for Photovoltaics VM Fthenakis and T Nikolakakis	199

Resource and Potential

1.12	Solar Radiation Resource Assessment for Renewable Energy Conversion DR Myers	213
1.13	Prediction of Solar Irradiance and Photovoltaic Power E Lorenz and D Heinemann	239

Basics

1.14	Principles of Solar Energy Conversion LC Hirst	293
1.15	Thermodynamics of Photovoltaics V Badescu	315

Technology

1.16	Crystalline Silicon Solar Cells: State-of-the-Art and Future Developments SW Glunz, R Preu, and D Biro	353
1.17	Thin-Film Silicon PV Technology M Zeman and REI Schropp	389
1.18	Chalcopyrite Thin-Film Materials and Solar Cells T Unold and CA Kaufmann	399
1.19	Cadmium Telluride Photovoltaic Thin Film: CdTe TA Gessert	423
1.20	Plastic Solar Cells L Sims, H-J Egelhaaf, JA Hauch, FR Kogler, and R Steim	439
1.21	Mesoporous Dye-Sensitized Solar Cells A Hagfeldt, UB Cappel, G Boschloo, L Sun, L Kloo, H Pettersson, and EA Gibson	481
1.22	Multiple Junction Solar Cells M Yamaguchi	497
1.23	Application of Micro- and Nanotechnology in Photovoltaics L Tsakalakos	515
1.24	Upconversion TW Schmidt and MJY Tayebjee	533
1.25	Downconversion MJY Tayebjee, TW Schmidt, and G Conibeer	549
1.26	Down-Shifting of the Incident Light for Photovoltaic Applications Y Jestin	563
1.27	Luminescent Solar Concentrators JC Goldschmidt	587
1.28	Thermophotovoltaics J van der Heide	603
1.29	Intermediate Band Solar Cells E Antolín, A Martí, and A Luque	619
1.30	Plasmonics for Photovoltaics S Pillai and MA Green	641
1.31	Artificial Leaves: Towards Bio-Inspired Solar Energy Converters A Pandit and RN Frese	657

Applications

1.32	Design and Components of Photovoltaic Systems *WGJHM van Sark*	679
1.33	BIPV in Architecture and Urban Planning *TH Reijenga and HF Kaan*	697
1.34	Product-Integrated Photovoltaics *AHME Reinders and WGJHM van Sark*	709
1.35	Very Large-Scale Photovoltaic Systems *T Ehara, K Komoto, and P van der Vleuten*	733
1.36	Concentration Photovoltaics *M Martinez, O de la Rubia, F Rubio, and P Banda*	745
1.37	Solar Power Satellites *GA Landis*	767
1.38	Performance Monitoring *N Pearsall and R Gottschalg*	775
1.39	Standards in Photovoltaic Technology *H Ossenbrink, H Müllejans, R Kenny, and E Dunlop*	787

Volume 2 Wind Energy

2.01	Wind Energy – Introduction *JK Kaldellis*	1
2.02	Wind Energy Contribution in the Planet Energy Balance and Future Prospects *JK Kaldellis and M Kapsali*	11
2.03	History of Wind Power *DT Swift-Hook*	41
2.04	Wind Energy Potential *H Nfaoui*	73
2.05	Wind Turbines: Evolution, Basic Principles, and Classifications *S Mathew and GS Philip*	93
2.06	Energy Yield of Contemporary Wind Turbines *DP Zafirakis, AG Paliatsos, and JK Kaldellis*	113
2.07	Wind Parks Design, Including Representative Case Studies *D Al Katsaprakakis and DG Christakis*	169
2.08	Aerodynamic Analysis of Wind Turbines *JN Sørensen*	225
2.09	Mechanical-Dynamic Loads *M Karimirad*	243
2.10	Electrical Parts of Wind Turbines *GS Stavrakakis*	269
2.11	Wind Turbine Control Systems and Power Electronics *A Pouliezos*	329
2.12	Testing, Standardization, Certification in Wind Energy *F Van Hulle*	371
2.13	Design and Implementation of a Wind Power Project *T Wizelius*	391
2.14	Offshore Wind Power Basics *M Kapsali and JK Kaldellis*	431

2.15	Wind Energy Economics D Milborrow	469
2.16	Environmental-Social Benefits/Impacts of Wind Power E Kondili and JK Kaldellis	503
2.17	Wind Energy Policy GC van Kooten	541
2.18	Wind Power Integration JA Carta	569
2.19	Stand-Alone, Hybrid Systems KA Kavadias	623
2.20	Wind Power Industry and Markets PE Morthorst	657
2.21	Trends, Prospects, and R&D Directions in Wind Turbine Technology JK Kaldellis and DP Zafirakis	671
2.22	Special Wind Power Applications E Kondili	725

Volume 3 Solar Thermal Systems: Components and Applications

Solar Thermal Systems

3.01	Solar Thermal Systems: Components and Applications – Introduction SA Kalogirou	1
3.02	Solar Resource HD Kambezidis	27
3.03	History of Solar Energy VG Belessiotis and E Papanicolaou	85

Components

3.04	Low Temperature Stationary Collectors YG Caouris	103
3.05	Low Concentration Ratio Solar Collectors SA Kalogirou	149
3.06	High Concentration Solar Collectors B Hoffschmidt, S Alexopoulos, J Göttsche, M Sauerborn, and O Kaufhold	165
3.07	Thermal Energy Storage LF Cabeza	211
3.08	Photovoltaic/Thermal Solar Collectors Y Tripanagnostopoulos	255
3.09	Solar Selective Coatings P Yianoulis, M Giannouli, and SA Kalogirou	301
3.10	Glazings and Coatings G Leftheriotis and P Yianoulis	313
3.11	Modeling and Simulation of Passive and Active Solar Thermal Systems A Athienitis, SA Kalogirou, and L Candanedo	357

Applications

3.12	Solar Hot Water Heating Systems G Faninger	419
3.13	Solar Space Heating and Cooling Systems SA Kalogirou and GA Florides	449
3.14	Solar Cooling and Refrigeration Systems GG Maidment and A Paurine	481
3.15	Solar-Assisted Heat Pumps DA Chwieduk	495
3.16	Solar Desalination E Tzen, G Zaragoza, and D-C Alarcón Padilla	529
3.17	Industrial and Agricultural Applications of Solar Heat B Norton	567
3.18	Concentrating Solar Power B Hoffschmidt, S Alexopoulos, C Rau, J Sattler, A Anthrakidis, C Boura, B O'Connor, and P Hilger	595
3.19	Passive Solar Architecture D Kolokotsa, M Santamouris, A Synnefa, and T Karlessi	637

Volume 4 Fuel Cells and Hydrogen Technology

4.01	Fuel Cells and Hydrogen Technology – Introduction AJ Cruden	1
4.02	Current Perspective on Hydrogen and Fuel Cells K Burke	13
4.03	Hydrogen Economics and Policy N Hughes and P Agnolucci	45
4.04	Hydrogen Safety Engineering: The State-of-the-Art and Future Progress V Molkov	77
4.05	Hydrogen Storage: Compressed Gas D Nash, D Aklil, E Johnson, R Gazey, and V Ortisi	111
4.06	Hydrogen Storage: Liquid and Chemical P Chen	137
4.07	Alkaline Fuel Cells: Theory and Application F Bidault and PH Middleton	159
4.08	PEM Fuel Cells: Applications AL Dicks	183
4.09	Molten Carbonate Fuel Cells: Theory and Application T Leo	227
4.10	Solid Oxide Fuel Cells: Theory and Materials A Tesfai and JTS Irvine	241
4.11	Biological and Microbial Fuel Cells K Scott, EH Yu, MM Ghangrekar, B Erable, and NM Duteanu	257
4.12	Hydrogen and Fuel Cells in Transport K Kendall and BG Pollet	281
4.13	H_2 and Fuel Cells as Controlled Renewables: FC Power Electronics N Schofield	295
4.14	Future Perspective on Hydrogen and Fuel Cells K Hall	331

Volume 5 Biomass and Biofuel Production

Biomass and Biofuels

5.01	Biomass and Biofuels – Introduction *DJ Roddy*	1
5.02	Historical Perspectives on Biofuels *G Knothe*	11

Case Studies

5.03	Bioethanol Development in Brazil *A Altieri*	15
5.04	Biomass Power Generation *A Malmgren and G Riley*	27
5.05	Biomass Co-Firing *A Nuamah, A Malmgren, G Riley, and E Lester*	55

Issues, Constraints & Limitations

5.06	A Global Bioenergy Market *O Olsson and B Hillring*	75
5.07	Biomass CHP Energy Systems: A Critical Assessment *M Börjesson and EO Ahlgren*	87
5.08	Ethics of Biofuel Production *I Waller*	99
5.09	Life Cycle Analysis Perspective on Greenhouse Gas Savings *N Mortimer*	109

Technology Solutions – New Processes

5.10	Biomass Gasification and Pyrolysis *DJ Roddy and C Manson-Whitton*	133
5.11	Biomass to Liquids Technology *G Evans and C Smith*	155
5.12	Intensification of Biofuel Production *AP Harvey and JGM Lee*	205
5.13	Biofuels from Waste Materials *AA Refaat*	217

Technology Solutions – Novel Feedstocks

5.14	Woody Biomass *LL Wright, LM Eaton, RD Perlack, and BJ Stokes*	263
5.15	Potential for Yield Improvement *J Spink, E Mullins, and P Berry*	293

Technology Solutions – Novel End Uses

5.16	Renewable Fuels: An Automotive Perspective *RJ Pearson and JWG Turner*	305
5.17	Use of Biofuels in a Range of Engine Configurations *A Roskilly, Y Wang, R Mikalsen, and H Yu*	343

Expanding the Envelope

5.18	Biochar *CE Brewer and RC Brown*	357
5.19	Extracting Additional Value from Biomass *MF Askew*	385
5.20	Biomass to Chemicals *A Kazmi and J Clark*	395
5.21	Bioenergy Policy Development *P Thornley*	411

Volume 6 Hydro Power

Hydro Power

| 6.01 | Hydro Power – Introduction
A Lejeune | 1 |

Constraints of Hydropower Development

| 6.02 | Hydro Power: A Multi Benefit Solution for Renewable Energy
A Lejeune and SL Hui | 15 |
| 6.03 | Management of Hydropower Impacts through Construction and Operation
H Horlacher, T Heyer, CM Ramos, and MC da Silva | 49 |

Hydropower Schemes Around the World

6.04	Large Hydropower Plants of Brazil *BP Machado*	93
6.05	Overview of Institutional Structure Reform of the Cameroon Power Sector and Assessments *J Kenfack and O Hamandjoda*	129
6.06	Recent Hydropower Solutions in Canada *M Fuamba and TF Mahdi*	153
6.07	The Three Gorges Project in China *L Suo, X Niu, and H Xie*	179
6.08	The Recent Trend in Development of Hydro Plants in India *SP Sen*	227
6.09	Hydropower Development in Iran: Vision and Strategy *E Bozorgzadeh*	253
6.10	Hydropower Development in Japan *T Hino*	265
6.11	Evolution of Hydropower in Spain *A Gil and F Bueno*	309
6.12	Hydropower in Switzerland *B Hagin*	343

Design Concepts

6.13	Long-Term Sediment Management for Sustainable Hydropower *F Rulot, BJ Dewals, S Erpicum, P Archambeau, and M Pirotton*	355
6.14	Durability Design of Concrete Hydropower Structures *S Jianxia*	377
6.15	Pumped Storage Hydropower Developments *T Hino and A Lejeune*	405

6.16	Simplified Generic Axial-Flow Microhydro Turbines *A Fuller and K Alexander*	435
6.17	Development of a Small Hydroelectric Scheme at Horseshoe Bend, Teviot River, Central Otago, New Zealand *P Mulvihill and I Walsh*	467
6.18	Recent Achievements in Hydraulic Research in China *J Guo*	485

Volume 7 Geothermal Energy

7.01	Geothermal Energy – Introduction *TI Sigfusson*	1
7.02	The Physics of Geothermal Energy *G Axelsson*	3
7.03	Geothermal Energy Exploration Techniques *ÓG Flóvenz, GP Hersir, K Sæmundsson, H Ármannsson, and Þ Friðriksson*	51
7.04	Geochemical Aspects of Geothermal Utilization *H Ármannsson*	95
7.05	Direct Heat Utilization of Geothermal Energy *JW Lund*	169
7.06	Shallow Systems: Geothermal Heat Pumps *L Rybach*	187
7.07	Geothermal Power Plants *R DiPippo*	207
7.08	Corrosion, Scaling, and Material Selection in Geothermal Power Production *SN Karlsdóttir*	239
7.09	Geothermal Cost and Investment Factors *H Kristjánsdóttir and Á Margeirsson*	259
7.10	Sustainable Energy Development: The Role of Geothermal Power *B Davidsdottir*	271

Volume 8 Ocean Energy

8.01	Generating Electrical Power from Ocean Resources *AS Bahaj*	1
8.02	Historical Aspects of Wave Energy Conversion *AFO Falcão*	7
8.03	Resource Assessment for Wave Energy *EBL Mackay*	11
8.04	Development of Wave Devices from Initial Conception to Commercial Demonstration *V Heller*	79
8.05	Air Turbines *AFO Falcão and LMC Gato*	111
8.06	Economics of Ocean Energy *T Stallard*	151
Index		171

4.01 Fuel Cells and Hydrogen Technology – Introduction

AJ Cruden, University of Strathclyde, Glasgow, UK

© 2012 Elsevier Ltd.

4.01.1	Introduction	1
4.01.2	Volume Introduction	2
4.01.3	Introduction to Basic Electrochemistry	10
4.01.4	Conclusions	11
References		11

4.01.1 Introduction

Hydrogen is the most abundant material in the Universe, forming over 75% of known matter, although it does not commonly exist on Earth in its natural form, due to its highly reactive nature, but within other compounds, most notably water and hydrocarbons.

The discovery of hydrogen gas is credited to the famous English philosopher Henry Cavendish (although he was actually born in Nice, France!) who, in 1766, wrote a seminal paper entitled *Experiments on Factitious Airs* [1] (**Figure 1**) after carrying out experiments dissolving different metals (e.g., zinc) in acidic solutions.

These experiments produced a gas, the 'factitious air', that was observed to "takes fire and goes off with an explosion" (see an extract from the Cavendish's 1766 paper in **Figure 2**), which is now a common high school test for hydrogen gas – set fire to it and it goes 'pop'!

Cavendish further established that this gas was significantly lighter than air. Although he was credited with isolating this new inflammable gas, it was another Frenchman, Antoine Lavoisier, who named this gas as hydrogen in 1783. Indeed the name 'hydrogen' itself is from the Greek words *hydros* (meaning 'water') and *generos* (meaning to 'make' or 'create'), hence the name hydrogen means 'to make water' or 'water former'.

The story of hydrogen took a step forward around this time when the Englishman, William Nicholson, correctly identified it following his earlier experiments on electrolysis. **Figure 3** shows an extract of Nicholson's famous 1800 paper [2], where he proves that water is composed of hydrogen and oxygen.

Of course the discovery and naming of hydrogen at this time is all the more challenging due to its properties which at standard temperature and pressure (stp) render it odorless, colorless, tasteless, nontoxic, and highly flammable (within its flammability limits of 4–74% in air). It is a highly reactive substance (hence it does not naturally occur but is found bonded within many other compounds) and is the lightest element in the periodic table.

Hydrogen at stp is in the form of a molecular gas. It was not until 1898 that the Scotsman Sir James Dewar liquefied hydrogen for the first time (see **Figure 4**, showing a repeat of this first experiment in 1899), achieving temperatures of 20 K or −253 °C. Even at such extreme low temperatures, hydrogen formed a colorless liquid.

Dewar continued his pursuit of ever colder temperatures and was the first to produce solid hydrogen, at temperatures below 14 K (−259 °C) in 1899.

From around this time, hydrogen gas had been in use as a constituent of coal gas. Coal gas, as opposed to natural gas (naturally occurring gas containing methane as a major component), was a manufactured gas from the 'cracking' of coal, that is, the break-up of the long, coal hydrocarbon molecules into different compounds. This cracking was achieved by controlled combustion (with limited air) to produce a gas containing up to 50% hydrogen, methane, carbon monoxide, and other gaseous elements. This gas was produced locally and used for lighting and heat/cooking [3].

The manufacture of coal gas in the United Kingdom decreased rapidly following the discovery and extraction of natural gas, principally methane, from the North Sea, which could be both extracted and used in a much environmentally clean fashion, with less remediation required than coal gas production [4].

Coal gas was used for various purposes and was supplied from large gas holders (or gasometers), which stored the gas, to households in many towns and cities via piped distribution system. These containers (an example is shown in **Figure 5**) were a common site and are now being replaced by high pressure storage in modern, underground, plastic high-pressure natural gas pipeline system.

Thus, for well over a century, hydrogen gas has been in use, albeit in a mixed dilute form within a coal gas mix. Hydrogen also has many industrial and specialty uses: as a product in semiconductor processing, petroleum refining, ammonia production for fertilizer, heat treatment of metals; as a coolant in large electrical generators in power stations; and as a rocket fuel for space missions! However, this volume will concentrate on the technologies that aim to use pure hydrogen as a fuel.

Hydrogen is not a source of 'primary energy' as it requires to be produced/released or manufactured as a pure gas and also requires further treatment to liberate energy when being converted to useful work. It is also not a form of renewable energy, rather it should be viewed as an 'energy vector', in a similar fashion to electricity that does not naturally occur, requires to be produced (generated) from primary energy sources/fuels, and is then reconverted to useful work in our electric lights, heaters, machinery,

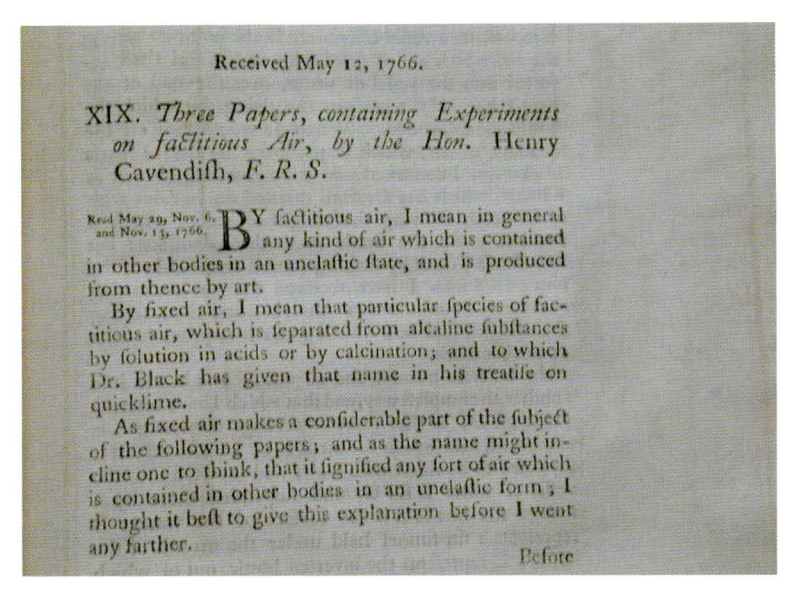

Figure 1 Cavendish's 1799 paper on 'Factitious Air'. Image from http://www.theworldsgreatbooks.com/images/Science/cavtext.jpg [2].

Figure 2 Extract from Cavendish's 1766 philosophical transactions paper. Source: http://books.google.co.uk/books?id=1kJFAAAAcAAJ&pg=PA141&lpg=PA141&dq=philosophical+transactions+of+the+royal+society+1766+cavendish&source=bl&ots=IGBnzpS7_e&sig=5cTcFhZXXJQZLHV7Nf6NVx3sJfo&hl=en&ei=alO6TsywKMi3hAfinZjBBw&sa=X&oi=book_result&ct=result&resnum=7&ved=0CEQQ6AEwBg#v=onepage&q=philosophical%20transactions%20of%20the%20royal%20society%201766%20cavendish&f=false [3].

computers, and so on. However, hydrogen is a unique type of energy vector in which it can be stored in large volumes, unlike electricity, and this unique feature will enable its use to support development and implementation of other forms of renewable energy reported in this *Comprehensive Renewable Energy* series.

This capacity for hydrogen to be used as both an energy store and a fuel is particularly relevant to the transport sector, a sector dominated by fossil fuels and hence carbon emission concerns, and a sector that forms of renewable energy like wind or solar (unless biofuels) is not frequently linked to. The use of hydrogen as an intermediate energy store and fuel will allow wind energy and other forms of renewables to power water electrolysis plants, to produce hydrogen gas for use in vehicles thereby creating a 'double benefit': increase the usage of renewable energy and replace vehicle fossil fuel consumption with a zero-emission alternative.

Discuss: Brief history of fuel cells

4.01.2 Volume Introduction

This section introduces the various chapters in the volume, with the prose to 'hang them together' as a coherent volume. It covers aspects not specifically covered by chapters, such as electrolysis, phosphoric acid fuel cells, regenerative fuel cells, and alternative forms of hydrogen production (e.g., thermal, biological, etc.) (**Table 1** and **Figures 6–21**).

Experiments with a new Electrical or Galvanic Apparatus. 183

clock standing in the room. The product of gas, during the whole two hours and a half, was two-thirtieths of a cubic inch. It was then mixed with an equal quantity of common air, and exploded by the application of a lighted waxed thread.

It might seem almost unnecessary to have reversed the order of the pile in building up, as reversing the tube must have answered exactly the same purpose. We chose, however, to do this, and found that when the zinc was at the bottom, its effects were reversed, that is to say, the gas still came from the wire communicating with the silver, &c.

We had been led by our reasoning on the first appearance of hydrogen to expect a decomposition of the water; but it was with no little surprize that we found the hydrogen extricated at the contact with one wire, while the oxigen fixed itself in combination with the other wire at the distance of almost two inches. This new fact still remains to be explained, and seems to point at some general law of the agency of electricity in chemical operations. As the distance between the wires formed a striking feature in this result, it became desirable to ascertain whether it would take place to greater distances. When a tube three quarters of an inch in diameter, and thirty-six inches long, was made use of, the effect failed, though the very same wires, inserted into a shorter tube, operated very briskly. The solicitation of other objects of enquiry prevented trial being made of all the various intermediate distances; but from the general tenor of experiments, it appears to be established, that this decomposition is more effectual the less the distance between the wires, but that it ceases altogether when the wires come into contact.

May 6.—Mr. Carlisle repeated the experiment with copper wires and tincture of litmus. The oxidating wire, namely, from the zinc side, was the lowest in the tube; it changed the tincture red in about ten minutes as high as the upper extremity of the wire. The other portion remained blue. Hence it seems either an acid was formed, or that a portion of the oxigen combined with the litmus, so as produce the effect of an acid.

Figure 3 Extract from Nicholson's 1800 paper, determining the composition of water. Source: http://books.google.co.uk/books?id=TggAAAAAMAAJ&printsec=frontcover&source=gbs_ge_summary_r&cad=0#v=onepage&q&f=false [4].

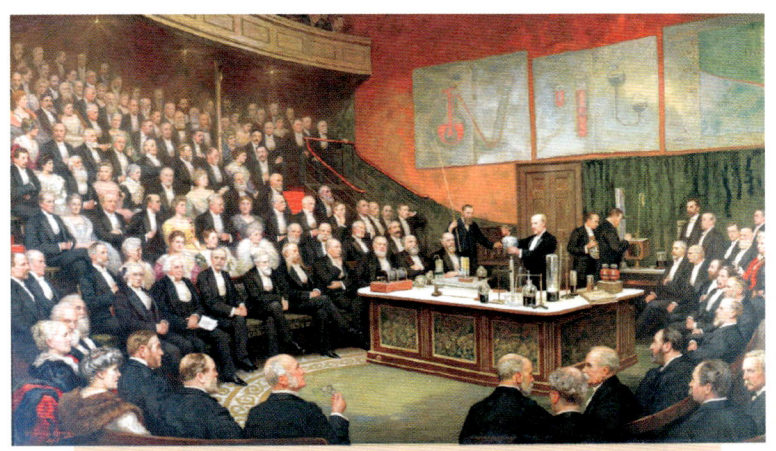

Figure 4 Painting of Sir James Dewar demonstrating liquefaction of hydrogen to the Royal Institution, 1899.

Figure 5 Coal Gas storage container (gasometer). Source: http://www.igg.org.uk/gansg/12-linind/gasworks.htm [8].

Table 1 Specification of NEL Hydrogen Electrolysers

Capacity	
Capacity range ($Nm^3\,H_2\,h^{-1}$)	10–485
Maximum $Nm^3\,H_2$ per cell	2.11
Energy	
Power consumption at 4000 Amp DC (kWh $(Nm^3\,H_2)^{-1}$)	4.1 ± 0.1
Power consumption at 5150 Amp DC (kWh $(Nm^3\,H_2)^{-1}$)	4.3 ± 0.1
Purity	
H_2 purity (%)	99.9 ± 0.1
O_2 purity (%)	99.5 ± 0.1
H_2 purity after purification (%)	99.9998% (2ppm)
Pressure	
H_2 outlet pressure after electrolyser	200–500 mm WG
Maximum H_2 outlet pressure after compressor	440 bar g
Operation	
Operating temperature	80 °C
Operation	Automatic, 20–100% of max capacity
Electrolyte	25% KOH aqueous solution
Feed water consumption	0.9 l $(Nm^3\,H_2)^{-1}$

Figure 6 NEL Hydrogen, 2 MW, alkaline electrolyzer.

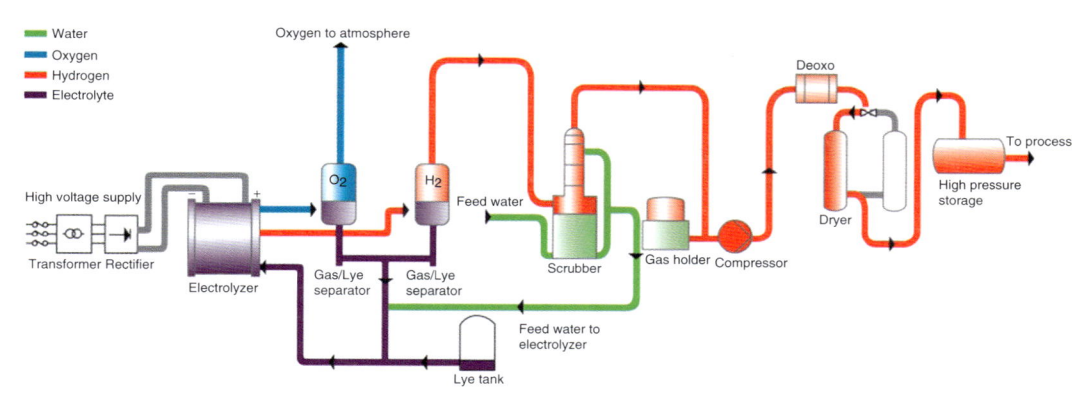

Figure 7 Simplified flow diagram of alkaline electrolyzer.

Figure 8 Electrode of alkaline electrolyzer.

Figure 9 Nonasbestos diaphragm for alkaline electrolyzer.

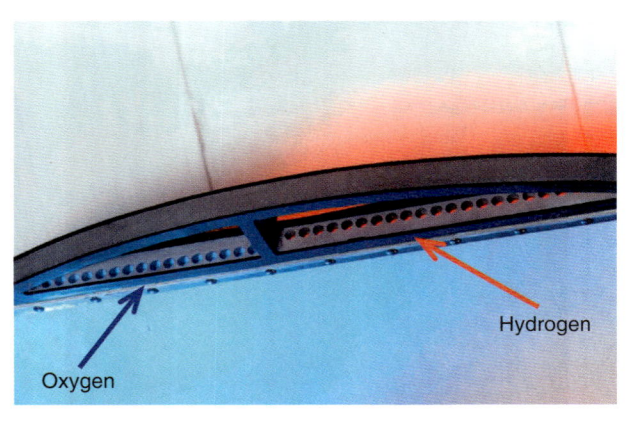

Figure 10 Gas ducts on alkaline electrolyzer (edge view of cell, with ducts on either side of diaphragm).

Figure 11 Hydro's electrolyzer plant for Ammonia production in Glomfjord, Norway.

Figure 12 Water treatment.

Figure 13 Dryer/heater/separator.

Figure 14 Storage tanks.

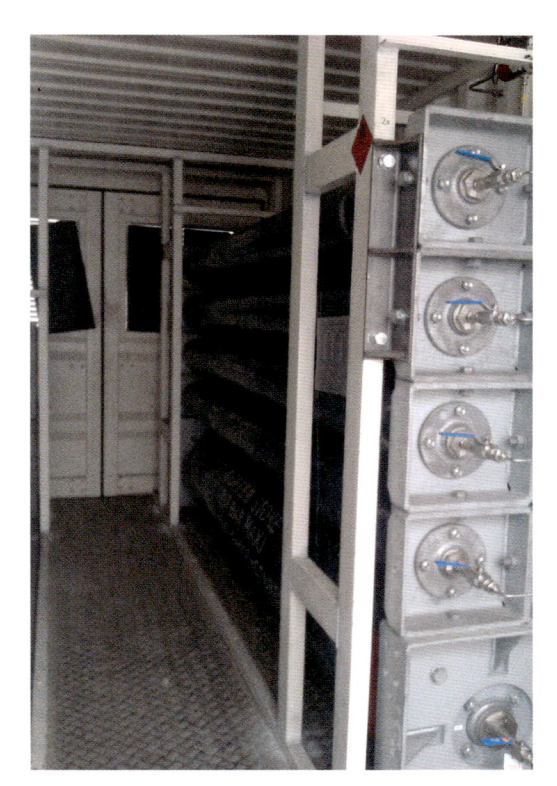

Figure 15 High pressure storage cylinders and bottom buffer store.

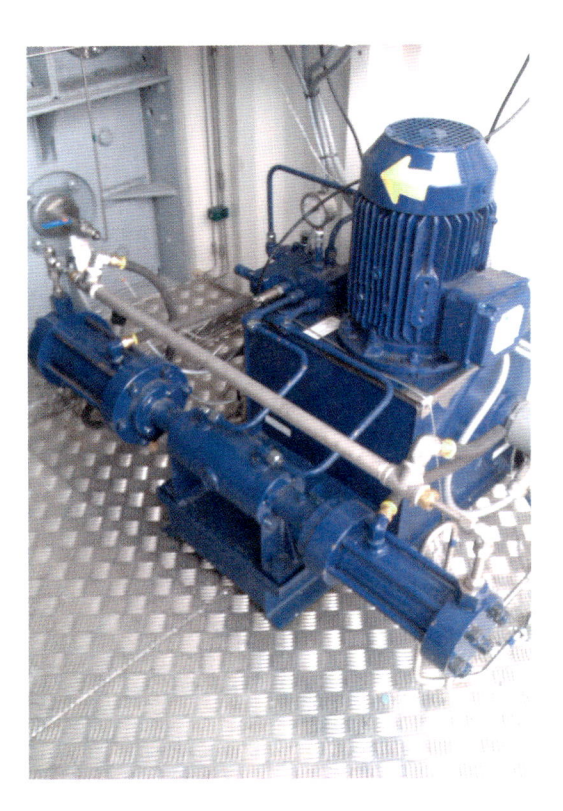

Figure 16 Compressor.

Figure 17 WEH refueller nozzle.

Figure 18 Refueller.

Figure 19 Vehicle receptacle.

Figure 20 HICE van.

Figure 21 Porsgrunn Hydrogen Station.

4.01.3 Introduction to Basic Electrochemistry

Standard Hydrogen Electrode
   Explains the basic theory of a fuel cell and introduces terms that appear in various chapters, to aid reading of subsequent chapters:

1. Oxidation and reduction
2. Anode/cathode
3. Anion/cation
4. Hydrophobic/hydrophilic/lyophobic
5. Dissolution
6. Hydrogenation
7. Intercalation
8. Ligand
9. Contact angle
10. Carbon black
11. Monopolar
12. Bipolar
13. Nucleophilic
14. Hydrolysis
15. Reformation
16. Catalysis and poisoning
17. Hygroscopic

18. Moiety
19. Electroosmotic drag
20. Radiation graft
21. Polymer
22. Aromatic
23. Anhydrous
24. Plasticizer
25. Hydrate
26. Adsorption
27. Facile
28. Bond strength
29. Ppm
30. Hydronium
31. Transition metal
32. Macrocyclic
33. Binary and ternary
34. Heterocyclic
35. Absorbed
36. Joule–Thomson
37. Nernst equation
38. LHV/HHV
39. Electrochemical series and potentials

The properties of hydrogen, compared to other fuels.

4.01.4 Conclusions

It is hoped that the reader enjoys the volume!

It encourages continued development and uptake of hydrogen and fuel cells – it is evident that the diesel engine, although developed in 1893 and used extensively, has only really developed for cars in the last 15–20 years as the result of huge progress/investment. Hence, hydrogen and fuel cells need the same development… we are still at the 'early adopters' stage!

It is suggested that hydrogen and fuel cells could be part of a future energy 'mix'!

References

[1] Cavendish H (1766) Experiments on factitious air. *Philosophical Transactions* LVI: 141–184.
[2] http://www.theworldsgreatbooks.com/images/Science/cavtext.jpg.
[3] http://books.google.co.uk/books?id=1kJFAAAAcAAJ&pg=PA141&lpg=PA141&dq=philosophical+transactions+of+the+royal+society+1766+cavendish&source=bl&ots=IGBnzpS7_e&sig=5cTcFhZXXJQZLHV7Nf6NVx3sJfo&hl=en&ei=aIO6TsywKMi3hAfinZjBBw&sa=X&oi=book_result&ct=result&resnum=7&ved=0CEQQ6AEwBg#v=onepage&q=philosophical%20transactions%20of%20the%20royal%20society%201766%20cavendish&f=false.
[4] http://books.google.co.uk/books?id=TggAAAAAMAAJ&printsec=frontcover&source=gbs_ge_summary_r&cad=0#v=onepage&q&f=false.
[5] Nicholson W (1800) Experiment with a new electrical or Galvanic apparatus. *Journal of Natural Philosophy, Chemistry and the Arts* 4: 179–187.
[6] Cleveland CJ (ed.) (2009) *Concise Encyclopedia of the History of Energy*. Elsevier, ISBN 978-0-12-375117-1.
[7] Gas works, coke works, and other coal carbonisation plants. Department of Environment, Crown copyright, 1995, ISBN 1-85112-232-X.
[8] http://www.igg.org.uk/gansg/12-linind/gasworks.htm.

4.02 Current Perspective on Hydrogen and Fuel Cells

K Burke, NASA Glenn Research Center, Cleveland, OH, USA

Published by Elsevier Ltd.

4.02.1	**Space Applications of Hydrogen**	13
4.02.1.1	Space Propulsion	13
4.02.1.1.1	Atlas-Centaur	13
4.02.1.1.2	Apollo Saturn	14
4.02.1.1.3	Space shuttle	17
4.02.1.1.4	Delta IV	17
4.02.1.1.5	Variable specific impulse magnetoplasma rocket	19
4.02.1.1.6	Other LH$_2$/LOX-powered rockets	20
4.02.1.2	Space Battery Power and Energy Storage – NiH$_2$ Batteries	22
4.02.1.3	Astronaut Environmental Control and Life Support	24
4.02.1.4	Scientific Instrument Cooling	24
4.02.1.4.1	Wide-field infrared survey explorer	24
4.02.1.4.2	Planck	25
4.02.2	**Space Applications of Fuel Cells**	26
4.02.2.1	Gemini	26
4.02.2.2	Apollo	26
4.02.2.3	Space Shuttle	29
4.02.3	**Other Current Uses of Hydrogen and Fuel Cells**	30
4.02.3.1	Current Uses of Hydrogen	31
4.02.3.1.1	Ammonia production	31
4.02.3.1.2	Oil refinery use	31
4.02.3.1.3	Methanol production	32
4.02.3.1.4	Other chemical manufacturing	32
4.02.3.1.5	Other uses	33
4.02.3.2	Current Uses of Fuel Cells	33
4.02.3.2.1	Electric power generation	33
4.02.3.2.2	Backup power supplies	34
4.02.3.2.3	Portable electronics	36
4.02.3.2.4	Motor vehicles	36
4.02.3.2.5	Other markets	40
References		42

4.02.1 Space Applications of Hydrogen

4.02.1.1 Space Propulsion

Hydrogen use as a chemical propellant is unquestionably the most important space application of hydrogen. In terms of mass of hydrogen used, the use of hydrogen propellant dwarfs all other space applications of hydrogen combined. The reason for the use of hydrogen is that hydrogen is the most efficient propellant. Specific impulse is a measure of the change of momentum per unit weight on Earth of the propellant. The higher the specific impulse, the lesser the weight of the propellant needed. **Table 1** shows a comparison of liquid fuel rocket propellants [1].

4.02.1.1.1 Atlas-Centaur

The Atlas-Centaur rocket was the first rocket to use the combination of liquid hydrogen/oxygen (LH$_2$/LOX) for propulsion. This rocket's second stage, Centaur, used the RL10 LH$_2$/LOX rocket engine shown in **Figure 1**. The RL10 was the first engine to use LH$_2$/LOX. The RL10 used liquid hydrogen to cool the engine nozzle, and the heat absorbed by the liquid hydrogen caused the hydrogen to expand. It was this absorbed energy that was then used to turn the turbine and turbopump on the RL10 engine. This simplicity of design made the engine lightweight and very reliable. The RL10 was first run in July 1959 and was first flight tested with the Centaur on 27 November 1963. The test flight was delayed to allow for the mourning of President Kennedy, shot days earlier [2]. Upgraded versions of the RL10 are used to currently launch Atlas-Centaur rockets and on the upper stage of the Delta IV rocket being used currently.

The Centaur rocket's fuel compartment used the pressure of the propellant to rigidize the structure of the rocket. This approach minimized the mass of the rocket structure and was initially demonstrated in an U.S. Air Force missile project called MX-774. Although this project was canceled before the development was completed, Charlie Bossart, the MX-774 designer, applied this knowledge to the

Table 1 Rocket propellant performance comparison

Oxidizer	Fuel	Mixture ratio	Specific impulse (s, sea level)	Density impulse (kg s l^{-1}, S.L.)
Liquid oxygen	Liquid hydrogen	5.00	381	124
	Liquid methane	2.77	299	235
	Ethanol + 25% water	1.29	269	264
	Kerosene	2.29	289	294
	Hydrazine	0.74	303	321
	MMH	1.15	300	298
	UDMH	1.38	297	286

Specific impulses are theoretical maximum assuming 100% efficiency; actual performance will be less.
All mixture ratios are optimum for the operating pressures indicated, unless otherwise noted.
LO$_2$/LH$_2$ and LF$_2$/LH$_2$ mixture ratios are higher than optimum to improve density impulse.
FLOX-70 is a mixture of 70% liquid fluorine and 30% liquid oxygen.
Where kerosene is indicated, the calculations are based on n-dodecane.

Figure 1 Pratt and Whitney RL10. Source: Sloop JL (1978) Liquid hydrogen as a propulsion fuel 1945–1959. The NASA history series, NASA SP-4404 (RL10 Rocket Engine Photo). http://history.nasa.gov/SP-4404/ch10-7.htm [2].

design of the Atlas. Later, this 'pressure-stabilized' approach was used by Krafft Ehricke as a key design element of the Centaur [3]. Together, the RL10 LH$_2$/LOX rocket engine and the lightweight Centaur structure gave NASA a lightweight powerful upper stage. The powerful Centaur upper stage when mated with the lightweight Atlas provided NASA with a launch vehicle capable of putting payloads beyond the low Earth orbit and out into space. **Figures 2** and **3** show the single-engine and dual-engine versions of the Centaur upper stage.

4.02.1.1.2 Apollo Saturn

The Apollo missions to the moon used the Saturn V rocket. The Saturn V was a three-stage rocket. The first stage used kerosene/LOX as propellant. Its second and third stages used LH$_2$/LOX. The payloads to be launched required more powerful LH$_2$/LOX engines (200 000 lbs of thrust) than the RL10 LH$_2$/LOX engine (20 000 lbs of thrust). This requirement led to the development of the J-2 LH$_2$/LOX by Rocketdyne shown in **Figure 4**.

Figure 2 Single-engine Centaur upper stage. Source: Image from NASA. Image from NASA Kennedy Media Archive Collection, Photo No. KSC-05PD-1338. http://images.ksc.nasa.gov/photos/2005/low/KSC-05PD-1338.gif [4].

Figure 3 Dual-engine Centaur upper stage. Source: Image from NASA. Image Exchange, ID No. KSC-00PP-0426, NASA Kennedy Space Center (dual engine Centaur photo). http://images.ksc.nasa.gov/photos/2000/low/KSC-00PP-0426.gif [5].

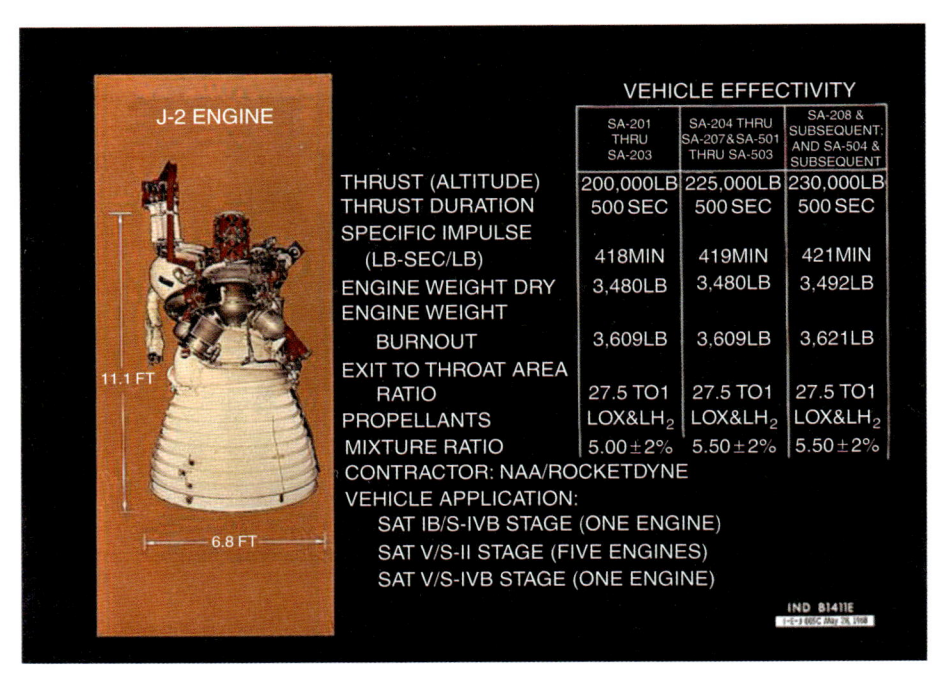

Figure 4 Rocketdyne J-2 rocket engine. Source: Image from NASA Image Exchange, ID No. MSFC-9801770, NASA Marshall Space Flight Center (J2 Engine Slide). http://mix.msfc.nasa.gov/IMAGES/MEDIUM/9801770.jpg [6].

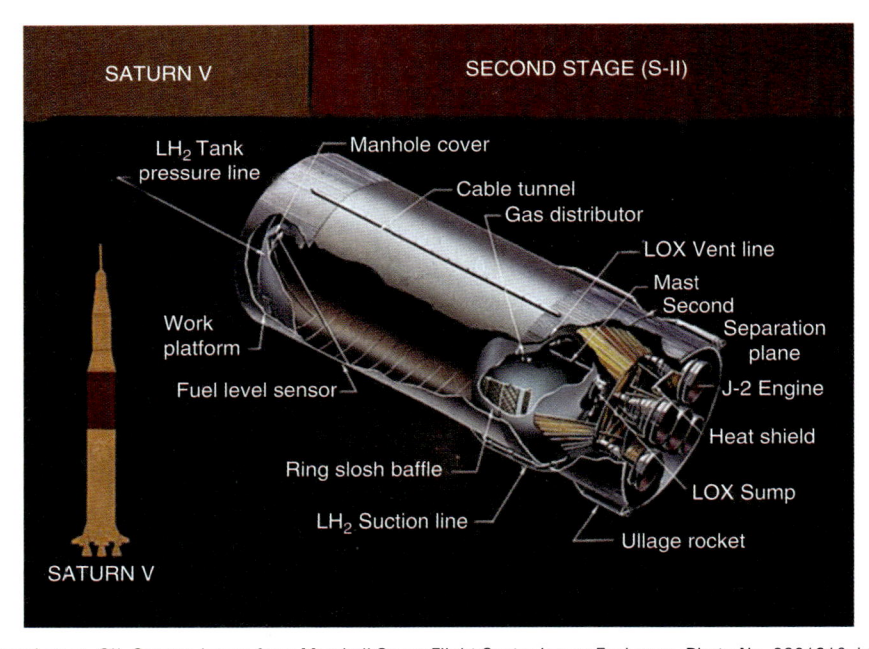

Figure 5 Saturn V second stage, SII. Source: Image from Marshall Space Flight Center Image Exchange, Photo No. 9801810. http://mix.msfc.nasa.gov/IMAGES/MEDIUM/9801810.jpg [8].

The second stage of Saturn V, called SII, used five J-2 engines to provide 1 000 000 lbs of thrust. The SII stage had a diameter of 10 m and a length of approximately 24.9 m. Filled with propellants, its gross mass was approximately 480 000 kg, and empty, a mass of approximately 36 000 kg. The burn time for the second stage was 367 s [7]. **Figure 5** shows an illustration of the SII stage, and **Figure 6** shows the SII stage being hoisted onto a test stand at the NASA Stennis Space Center.

The third stage of Saturn V used one J-2 engine, which provided approximately 200 000 lbs of thrust. The SIII stage had a diameter of 6.6 m and a length of approximately 17.8 m. Filled with propellants, its gross mass was 119 900 kg, and empty, a mass of approximately 11 000 kg. The burn time for the second stage was 475 s [10].

Figure 6 SII lifted onto test stand. Source: Image from NASA Image Exchange, ID No. 67-701-c, NASA Stennis Space Center (SII stage of Saturn V rocket photo). http://www.ssc.nasa.gov/sirs/photos/history/low/67-701-c.jpg [9].

An upgraded version of the J-2 engine, called J-2X, is being developed for NASA for further exploration of the Moon and Mars. The J-2X with 294 000 lbs of thrust will be more powerful than the J-2 engine. The J-2X engine requirements call for an exit diameter of approximately 47 cm, a length of 72.8 cm, and a mass of 2477 kg [11]. The J-2X is to be used for the upper stage of the ARES-1, which will launch the crew capsule. The J-2X is also to be used for the upper stage of the heavy lift launch vehicle ARES-V, which will lift the exploration landing craft into space.

4.02.1.1.3 Space shuttle

The space shuttle is launched using a combination of two solid rocket motors and three LH_2/LOX engines. Unlike Saturn V where the first stage is nearly complete with its burn when the second stage starts its burn, the space shuttle's propulsion combination propels the space shuttle simultaneously until the solid rocket motors complete their burn. The three LH_2/LOX engines then continue to burn, eventually lifting the space shuttle into a low Earth orbit. **Figure 7** shows the space shuttle shortly after liftoff with both the solid rocket motors and LH_2/LOX engines operating. The large orange tank shown in **Figure 7** is the LH_2/LOX storage tank. This tank is the only expendable portion of the Space Transportation System, separating from the space shuttle after the LH_2/LOX engines complete their burn. Unlike Saturn V and all previous rockets, the space shuttle is reuseable. Following its 1–2 week mission, the space shuttle reenters the Earth's atmosphere, gliding, and then landing on a landing strip.

The space shuttle main engine (SSME) is unique, in that it is the only reuseable LH_2/LOX engine in the world. It was designed for 7.5 h of operation over an average life span of 55 starts [13]. The SSME is much more powerful than the J-2 engine (470 000 lbs of thrust (at vacuum) vs. 200 000 lbs). The SSME consumes 12 100 kg min^{-1} of LH_2 and 72 300 kg min^{-1} of LOX for approximately 8.5 min. The SSME has a 229 cm exit diameter, is 427 cm in length, and had a mass of 3039 kg [14]. **Figures 8** and **9** show the SSME [15, 16].

4.02.1.1.4 Delta IV

The Delta family of rockets started with the first launch of a Delta rocket on 13 May 1960. The early Delta rockets did not use LH_2 as a propellant. The Delta rocket evolved through continuous improvements from a Delta A rocket in 1962 through a Delta N rocket in 1972. This improvement continued through 1972–89 with Delta Series 904, 1000, 2000, 3000, 4000, and 5000. This in turn was followed by the Delta II Series 6000 and 7000 from 1989 through 2000. Finally, in 23 August 2000, a Delta III was successfully launched [17]. The Delta III used the Pratt and Whitney RL10 LH_2/LOX engine for the upper stage. This was, however, the only successful launch of the Delta III. A Delta IV series was launched on 20 November 2002 [17]. The Delta IV series continues to be launched. The Delta IV series uses LH_2/LOX engines for its first stage. The Delta IV-4M (medium lift) uses a single LH_2/LOX (heavy lift) uses three LH_2/LOX engines as shown in **Figure 10** [18].

The Delta IV uses the RS-68 LH_2/LOX rocket engine developed by Rocketdyne in 1998. The RS-68 is the largest and most powerful LH_2/LOX engine in the world. The RS-68 is more powerful than the SSME engine (758 000 lbs of thrust vs. 470 000 lbs). The RS-68 is approximately 244 cm in diameter, 521 cm in length, and had a mass of 6761 kg [19, 20]. **Figure 10** shows the RJ-68 being test fired [21]. The RS-68 is planned to be used for a heavy lift launch vehicle for NASA that would use five engines in its first stage.

18 Current Perspective on Hydrogen and Fuel Cells

Figure 7 Space shuttle after liftoff. Source: Image from NASA Image Exchange, ID No. STS062(S)055, NASA Johnson Space Center. http://images.jsc.nasa.gov/lores/STS062(S)055.jpg [12].

Figure 8 Space shuttle main engine. Source: Image from NASA Image Exchange, ID No. KSC-04PD-1643, NASA Kennedy Space Center. http://images.ksc.nasa.gov/photos/2004/low/KSC-04PD-1643.gif [15].

Figure 9 Test firing of the SSME. Source: Image from NASA Image Exchange, Photo No. MSFC-7995081. http://mix.msfc.nasa.gov/IMAGES/MEDIUM/7995081.jpg [16].

Figure 10 RS-68 test firing. Source: Image from NASA Image Exchange, Photo No. MSFC-0700063. http://www.nasa.gov/images/content/148709main_d4_testing_08.jpg [21].

4.02.1.1.5 Variable specific impulse magnetoplasma rocket

Unlike all previous rocket engines that use hydrogen, the variable specific impulse magnetoplasma rocket (VASIMR) does not combust the hydrogen. Instead, the hydrogen is ionized into a plasma using an electric power source. The ionized hydrogen plasma is accelerated through an electric field and using magnetic fields directed out of the end of the VASIMR. The unconventional technique has shown very high specific impulse (the amount of change in momentum per unit mass of propellant), which is a measure of a rocket engine's performance. LH_2/LOX engines have been developed because the specific impulse of LH_2/LOX engines was 400–500 s, which is higher than other conventional propellants. VASIMR has a specific impulse of 4000 to over 10 000 s [22], indicating that 90% or more of the propellant weight could be saved, a tremendous advantage, especially for long space voyages. One drawback to this promising technology is that the VASIMR requires a high-power electric source. Long planetary trips to date have used electric power sources that are much less powerful than what is needed by VASIMR. In the future, possibly high-power nuclear electric sources may

Figure 11 VASIMR engine test. Source: NASA website. http://www.nasa.gov/vision/space/travelinginspace/future_propulsion.html [23].

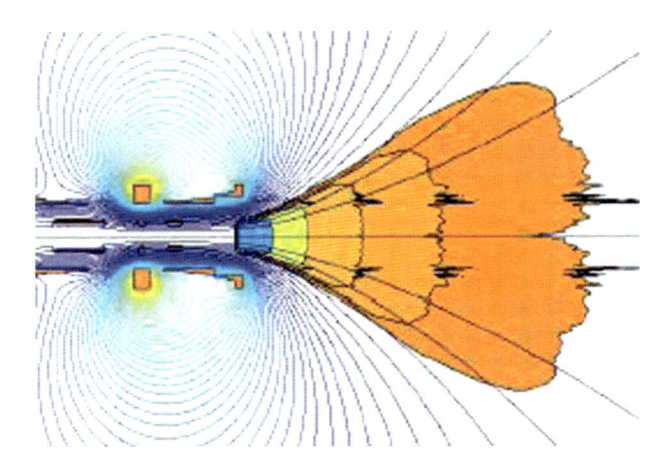

Figure 12 VASIMR magnetic field and plasma analysis.

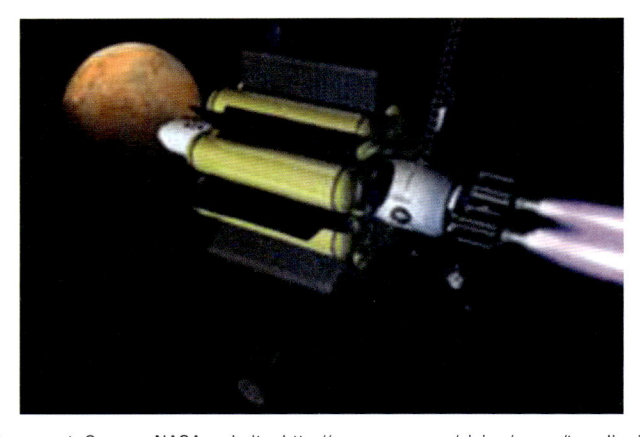

Figure 13 VASIMR-powered rocket concept. Source: NASA website. http://www.nasa.gov/vision/space/travelinginspace/future_propulsion.html [23].

allow this technology to be fully exploited. **Figure 11** shows a VASIMR engine under test. **Figure 12** shows an analysis of the VASIMR magnetic field and plasma. **Figure 13** shows an artist's illustration of a VASIMR-powered spacecraft concept.

4.02.1.1.6 Other LH$_2$/LOX-powered rockets

Only recently have nations other than the United States started to produce LH$_2$/LOX engines. The Japanese have produced two engines that are used for the first and second stages. The LE-5 is used for the second stage and had its first flight in 1986. The LE-5 produces 23 100 lbs of thrust and has a diameter of 2.49 m, a length of 2.68 m, and a mass of 245 kg [24]. **Figure 14** shows the LE-5

Figure 14 Japan's LE-5 LH$_2$/LOX engine. Source: Wikipedia, the Free Encyclopedia File: LE-5.JPG. http://en.wikipedia.org/wiki/File:LE-5.JPG [25].

Figure 15 Japan's LE-7 LH$_2$/LOX engine. Source: Encyclopedia Astronautica info page on the LE-7. http://www.astronautix.com/engines/le7.htm [27].

[25]. Japan also produced the LE-7 designed for a first stage and had its first flight in 1994. The LE-7 produces 242 000 lbs of thrust and has a diameter of 4 m, a length of 3.4 m, and a mass of 1714 kg [26]. **Figure 15** shows the LE-7 [27]. Japan's H-II unmanned expendable launch vehicle uses one LE-7A engines in its first stage and one LE-5 on the upper stage.

Figure 16 Vulcain rocket engine. Source: Wikipedia, the Free Encyclopedia – Vulcain. http://en.wikipedia.org/wiki/File:Moteur-Vulcain.jpg [30].

Snecma Moteurs (France) has produced the Vulcain LH$_2$/LOX engine designed for a first stage and had its first successful flight in 1997 [28]. The Vulcain produces 256 760 lbs of thrust and has a diameter of 1.76 m, a length of 3.0 m, and a mass of 1700 kg [29]. **Figure 16** shows the Vulcain [30]. The Ariane 5 launch vehicle uses a single Vulcain as its first-stage engine.

4.02.1.2 Space Battery Power and Energy Storage – NiH$_2$ Batteries

Nickel hydrogen energy storage was an improvement in rechargeable battery technology over the nickel cadmium cells. The nickel hydrogen cells use a nickel electrode similar to that used in nickel cadmium cells. The electrochemical reaction at the nickel electrode during discharge is

$$NiOOH + H_2O + e^- \rightarrow Ni(OH)_2 + OH^- \quad \text{(during discharge)}$$

The other electrode in the nickel hydrogen cells is a hydrogen gas electrode. During discharge, the electrochemical reaction occurring at the hydrogen electrode is

$$^1/_2 H_2 + OH^- \rightarrow H_2O + e^-$$

The overall reaction during discharging is

$$NiOOH + \,^1/_2 H_2 \rightarrow Ni(OH)_2$$

During charging, the same reactions occur, but in the opposite direction. The hydrogen produced during charging is captured within a pressure vessel that envelopes the nickel hydrogen cells. The nominal operating voltage for the nickel hydrogen cell is 1.25 VDC, about the same as the nickel cadmium cell.

The development of nickel hydrogen cells was started by COMSAT Laboratories in 1970 [31]. The sealed nickel hydrogen cell was a hybrid, combining both battery and fuel cell technologies. The nickel oxide electrodes had previously been developed from nickel cadmium battery cells, and the nickel hydrogen platinum black hydrogen electrode was previously developed as a fuel cell hydrogen electrode. After the initial demonstration of the feasibility of the nickel hydrogen cell, INTELSAT funded COMSAT Laboratories to develop a 50 A h cell, and in 1975 this development had progressed to the point that the U.S. Naval Research Laboratory funded COMSAT Laboratories to develop a 35 A h nickel hydrogen cell for use on the U.S. Navy navigation technology satellite (NTS-2) spacecraft. The NTS-2, launched in 1977, was the first use of the nickel hydrogen battery technology in space (**Figure 17**). Nickel hydrogen cells were then used on the INTELSAT V-B geosynchronous satellites in 1983. In 1990, the Hubble telescope used nickel

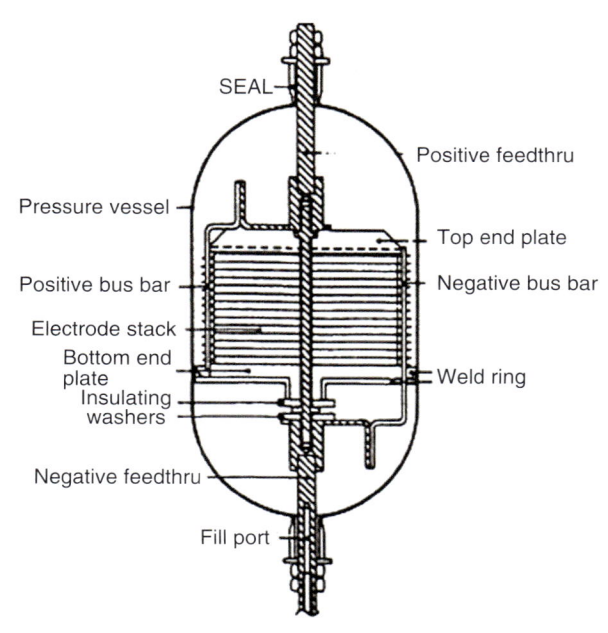

Figure 17 NTS-2 nickel hydrogen cell. Source: Figure taken from 1993 Battery Workshop, NASA Technical Reports Server p. 246. http://ntrs.nasa.gov/archive/nasa/casi.ntrs.nasa.gov/19940023606_1994023606.pdf [32].

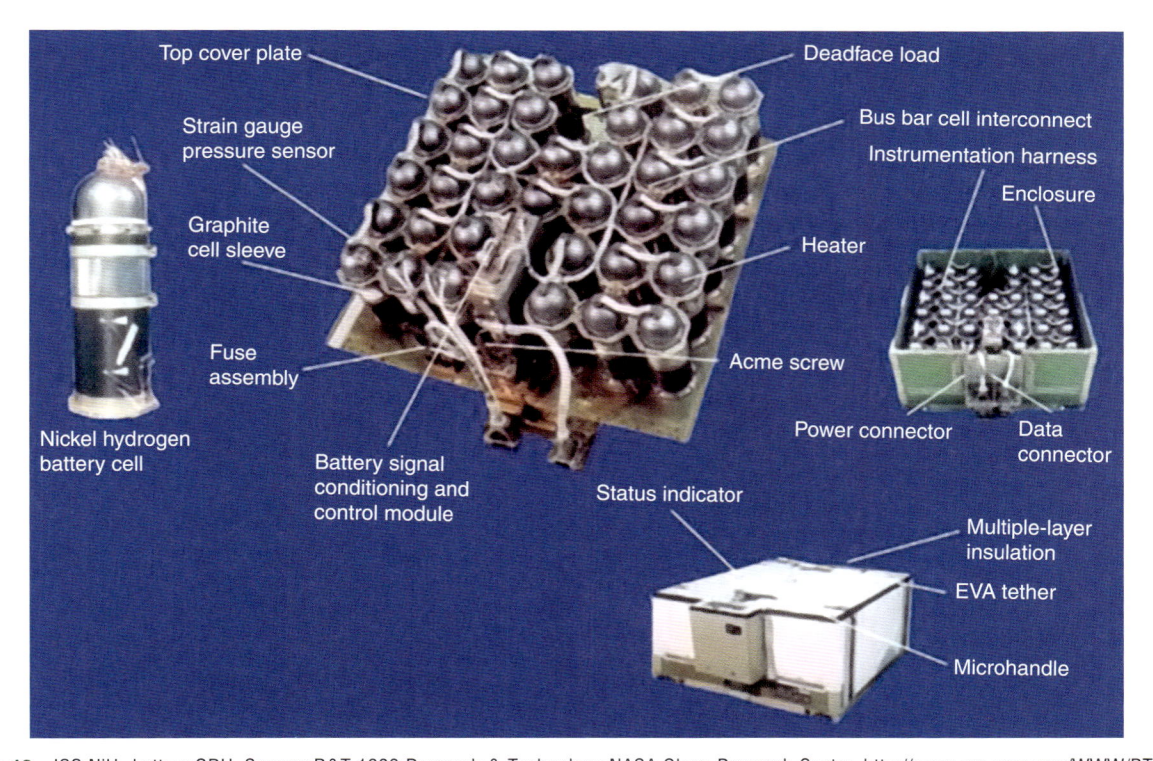

Figure 18 ISS NiH$_2$ battery ORU. Source: R&T 1999 Research & Technology NASA Glenn Research Center. http://www.grc.nasa.gov/WWW/RT/RT1999/5000/5420miller.html [33].

hydrogen cells. Later still, the International Space Station (ISS) power system was designed with nickel hydrogen battery orbital replacement units (ORU) (shown in **Figure 18**) to provide energy storage during the low Earth orbit eclipse period. Originally packaged in individual pressure vessels (IPVs) shown in **Figure 17** [32], subsequent development packaged multiple cells within a single pressure vessel (SPV). These were known as common pressure vessel (CPV) or SPV designs. Nickel hydrogen cell technology started to become obsolete in the 1990s with the introduction of lithium battery technology that had significantly better energy density, lower self-discharge rates, and higher coloumbic efficiency. The simultaneous commercial development of small portable electronics provided the added push toward lithium technology that during the 1990s started to replace nickel hydrogen in space.

4.02.1.3 Astronaut Environmental Control and Life Support

As manned space missions have gradually increased in number of crew and length of time, the advantage of recycling life supporting resources such as water and oxygen versus supplying these resources as expendable (not recycled) becomes more and more compelling when comparing the mass of spacecraft using recycling system with the alternative expendable systems. The disadvantage to recycling systems is that they generally are not as reliable as expendable systems; they also tend to consume another valuable resource, electrical power. Water electrolysis equipment that 'closes the oxygen loop' has been developed and is being used on the ISS. Water electrolysis splits water into hydrogen and oxygen. The oxygen contained within the water is recycled, whereas the hydrogen is vented overboard into space. The ISS has been designed so the hydrogen currently being vented could be used to reduce carbon dioxide. The reduction of carbon dioxide with hydrogen produces water and either methane or amorphous carbon black. The carbon dioxide reduction process that reduces carbon dioxide to water vapor and methane is called the Sabatier CO_2 reduction system. Another alternative carbon dioxide reduction process that reduces carbon dioxide to water vapor and carbon black is called the Bosch CO_2 reduction system. The water vapor produced during the reduction process is subsequently recovered and split into hydrogen and oxygen by water electrolysis. A block diagram of the advanced life support system is shown in **Figure 19**.

4.02.1.4 Scientific Instrument Cooling

Cooling technologies are required for the high-performance detection of electromagnetic radiation of millimeter to nanometer wavelengths. Radiation detectors are subject to background noise that unless substantially reduced can make precise detection impossible. Radiation detectors are cooled to cryogenic temperatures to reduce the background noise, sometimes referred to as the background limit, caused by thermal energy of the detectors themselves. This applies for many types of radiation detectors. For infrared detectors looking through the Earth's atmosphere, the background noise is frequently determined by the atmosphere, but for infrared instruments in space, above the atmosphere, the background limit is determined by the instrument itself that glows with thermal infrared radiation. These infrared instruments are cooled to less than 1 K. To provide this low-temperature cooling requires a refrigerant capable of working at these low temperatures, typically helium or hydrogen.

4.02.1.4.1 Wide-field infrared survey explorer

On 14 December 2009, NASA launched the wide-field infrared survey explorer (WISE). The WISE, shown in **Figure 20**, circles the Earth, from pole to pole, 15 times each day, taking pictures of the sky every 11 s. Its mission is to observe the universe in the 3–25 µm wavelength. The WISE cryostat, shown in **Figure 21**, is a two-stage, solid hydrogen cryostat that cools the satellite's optics to 7.6 K.

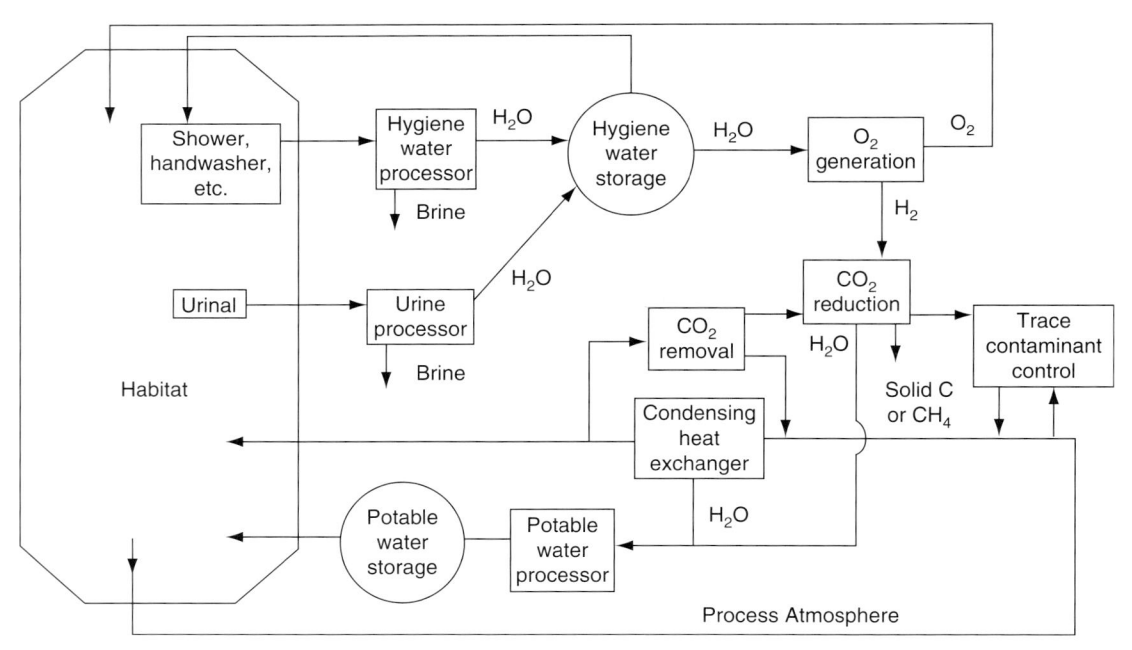

Figure 19 Advanced environmental control and life support for space. Source: Designing for Human Presence in Space, An Introduction to Environmental Control and Life Support Systems, NASA RP-1324 [34].

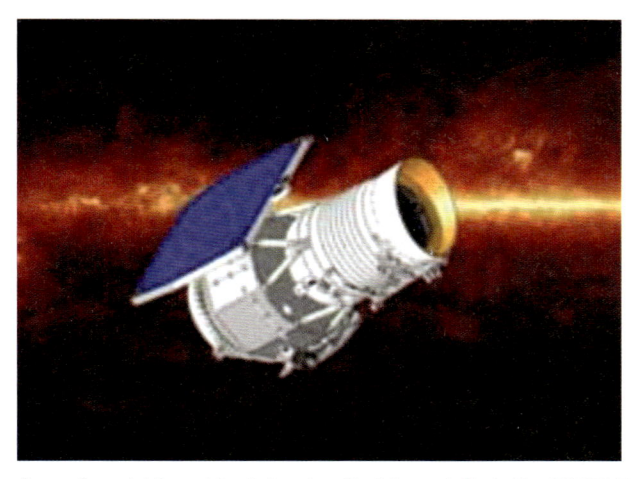

Figure 20 The WISE satellite. Source: Image from Jet Propulsion Laboratory Photojournal, Photo No. PIA12316. http://photojournal.jpl.nasa.gov/jpeg/PIA12011.jpg [35].

Figure 21 WISE hydrogen cryostat. Source: Image from Jet Propulsion Laboratory Photojournal, Photo No. PIA12316. http://photojournal.jpl.nasa.gov/jpegMod/PIA12316_modest.jpg [36].

The solid hydrogen cryostat is expected to last about 10 months after which the satellite's mission will be finished. By cooling the optics and detectors to such a low temperature, WISE will be able to measure the infrared glow of celestial objects with a sensitivity hundreds of times more than any previous spectrometer. WISE will be able to measure the infrared radiation of asteroids in our solar system between Mars and Jupiter and provide the first good estimate of their size distribution.

4.02.1.4.2 Planck

The Planck spacecraft shown in **Figure 22** was launched on 14 May 2009 by the European Space Agency (ESA). Planck's instruments will measure minute differences in the background radiation of space. The background radiation is residual radiation from the Big Bang creation of the universe. These minute differences are measured in millionths of a degree Kelvin about the observable temperature differences measured from Earth of the heat of a rabbit sitting on the moon [37]. To obtain this extraordinary sensitivity, the radiation detectors must be cooled to 0.1 K. The cooling system uses a three-stage cooler. The second stage is a hydrogen sorption cooler where hydrogen is compressed to high pressure, then expanded through a Joule–Thompson expander that cools the detectors to below 20 K. The expanded hydrogen is absorbed by metal hydrides so that it can be recompressed at the start of another cooling cycle.

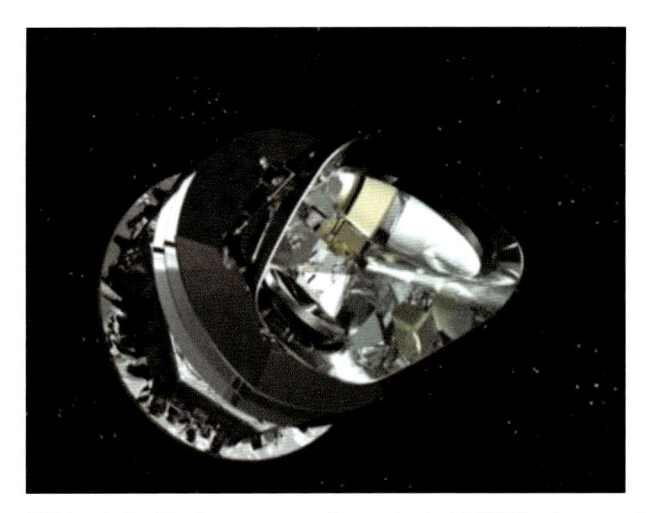

Figure 22 Planck spacecraft. Source: NASA website. http://www.nasa.gov/images/content/323941main_concept.jpg [38].

4.02.2 Space Applications of Fuel Cells

Fuel cell technology was put into the world public spotlight in a dramatic fashion by NASA, which chose to use hydrogen/oxygen fuel cells to provide critical electrical power to its manned spacecraft. While earlier development efforts were looking at fuel cells for various terrestrial power applications, these efforts gained little public notice, but the world public watched as astronauts were launched into space, voyaged to the moon, and return to Earth, powered in no small measure by a mysterious, new 'space age' technology called fuel cells.

NASA first used fuel cells for powering the Gemini spacecraft; fuel cells were also used to provide power for the Apollo spacecraft and space shuttle.

4.02.2.1 Gemini

On 21 August 1965, the Gemini 5 spacecraft launched the use of hydrogen oxygen fuel cells for electrical power generation. The use of fuel cells was still in doubt as late as November 1963 when fuel cell production was stopped due to technical problems. In January 1964, a meeting at the Johnson Space Center was held to review the development status and decide on the further course of action. It was decided to redesign the fuel cells and have them ready for the fifth Gemini flight [39]. The Gemini fuel cell system was used on Gemini 5, 7, 8, 9A, 10, 11, and 12.

The Gemini fuel cell stack, shown in **Figure 23**, consisted of 32 cells in electrical series. Each cell contained an active area of 360 cm^2 (20 cm × 18 cm). Three fuel cell stacks were connected electrically in parallel, shown in **Figure 24**, and housed in a fuel cell section shown in **Figure 25**. Each section was about 66 cm long and 33 cm in diameter and weighed about 31 kg. Two such fuel cell sections plus an associated reactant supply system comprise the Gemini fuel cell system shown in **Figure 26**.

Hydrogen was distributed to each section, and within each section the hydrogen was manifolded to each of the three cell stacks. Oxygen was distributed to each section and within each section was manifolded to each cell stack. The oxygen compartments of the cells were open to the inside of the section container that was filled with oxygen. The hydrogen and oxygen were not circulated through the cell stacks, but were 'dead-ended' and kept at a constant pressure so that as hydrogen and oxygen was consumed by the cells, more hydrogen and oxygen was supplied to the cells to maintain the constant pressure. The water produced by each cell was absorbed by a wick immediately adjacent to the oxygen compartment of each cell. These wicks transferred the water to the bottom of each cell stack where the water was absorbed by a porcelain gas/water separator. The water was pushed out of the gas water separator and outside the fuel cell section by the pressure difference that was controlled between the oxygen and water. Water was collected in an accumulator so that the water could be used by astronauts for drinking. Coolant was distributed to each section and within each section the coolant circulated through the three stacks in series. The coolant was also used to preheat the reactants coming from the supercritical reactant storage tanks. The Gemini 5 mission data showed that the fuel cell stack sections operated at 25.5–28.1 VDC, and the current load varied from 9 to 24 A for each section [42].

4.02.2.2 Apollo

Fuel cells powered the Apollo command and service modules. The first flight for the Apollo fuel cell system was flight AS-202 flown on 25 August 1966. AS-202 was the second test flight of the Apollo Command/Service Module launched with the Saturn IB launch vehicle. This flight was successful and led to the first manned Apollo flight, AS-204 [43]. The AS-204 flight tragically claimed the lives of the first three Apollo astronauts due to a fire in the crew capsule. The flight AS-204 was renamed Apollo 1 in honor of the fallen astronauts. The Apollo fuel cell system flew on all subsequent Apollo missions, Skylab missions, and the Apollo–Soyuz mission. Three Apollo fuel cell systems provided the power for the command and service modules. The fuel cell systems were located inside the service module.

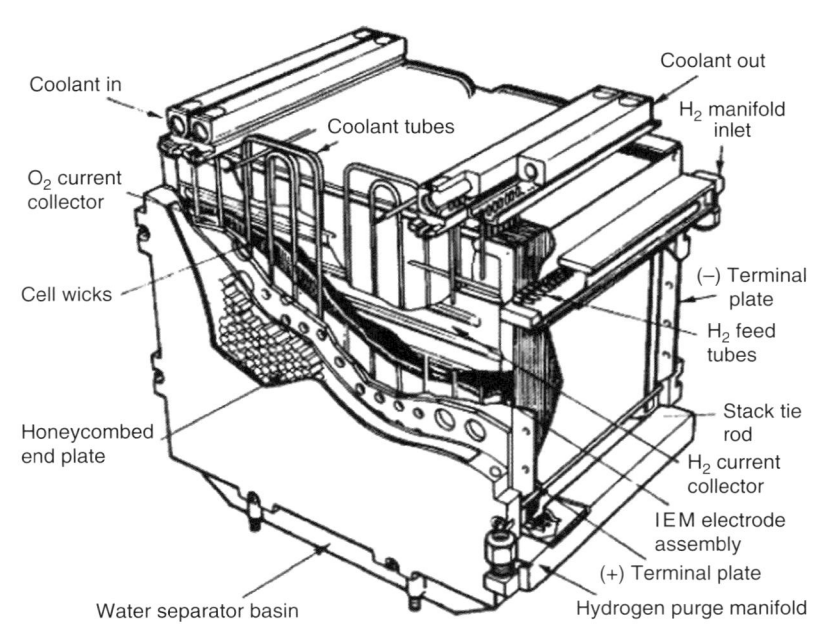

Figure 23 Gemini fuel cell stack. Source: Illustration of Gemini Fuel Cell System from Fuel Cells – A Survey by Bernard Crowe, NASA SP-5115 prepared under Contract NASW-2173, p. 21. http://ntrs.nasa.gov/archive/nasa/casi.ntrs.nasa.gov/19730017318_1973017318.pdf [40].

Figure 24 Gemini stacks before loading into fuel cell section. Source: NASA Photo C-65-3478 from NASA TM X-52149, Swartz, Harvey J., Lewis Research Center. http://ntrs.nasa.gov/archive/nasa/casi.ntrs.nasa.gov/19660005480_1966005480.pdf [41].

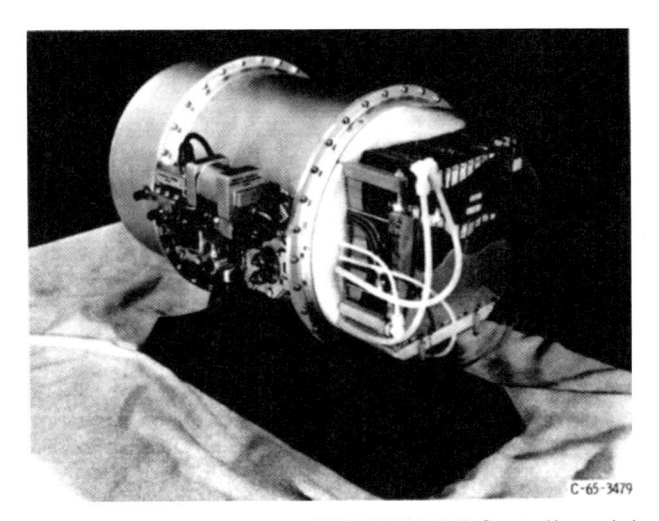

Figure 25 Gemini fuel cell section. Source: NASA Photo C-65-3478 from NASA TM X-52149, Swartz, Harvey J., Lewis Research Center. http://ntrs.nasa.gov/archive/nasa/casi.ntrs.nasa.gov/19660005480_1966005480.pdf [41].

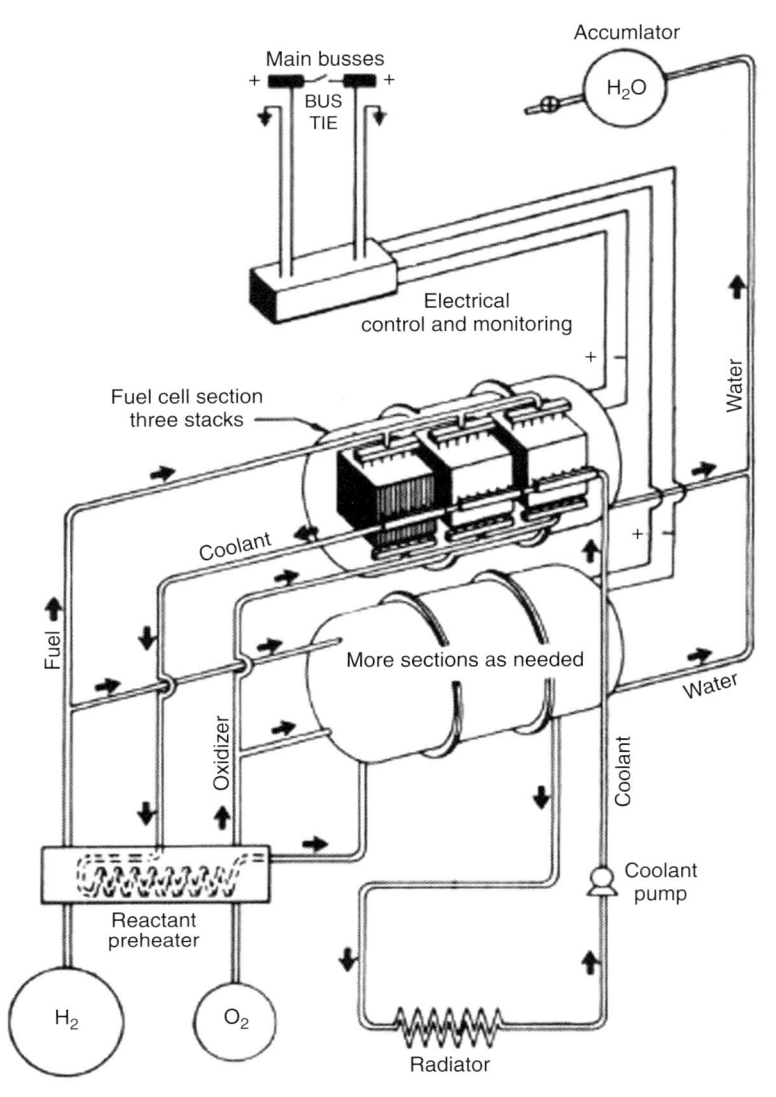

Figure 26 Gemini fuel cell system. Source: NASA Photo C-65-3478 from NASA TM X-52149, Swartz, Harvey J., Lewis Research Center. http://ntrs.nasa.gov/archive/nasa/casi.ntrs.nasa.gov/19660005480_1966005480.pdf [41].

The Apollo fuel cell illustrated in **Figures** 27 and 28 consisted of two nickel plates separated by Teflon gasket that prevented an electrical short between the plates and prevented the electrolyte between the plates from leaking outside the cell. Ceramic insulators in the reactant lines likewise prevented electrical shorting between the cells. A porous nickel electrode within each nickel plate separated the electrolyte from the hydrogen and oxygen reactants. The reactant pressure was 10.5 psi above the electrolyte pressure to maintain the separation between the liquid electrolyte and the gaseous reactants. The Apollo fuel cell system used an 85% KOH electrolyte and operated at a nominal temperature of 213 °C and a pressure of approximately 4 atm. The expansion and contraction of the electrolyte was accommodated by the flexing of the diaphragm that was at the perimeter of each cell. The pressure of the electrolyte was maintained by nitrogen, which bathed the exterior of each cell. The Apollo fuel cell module shown in **Figure 29** consisted of a stack of 31 cells in electrical series. Each cell had a diameter of 20 cm. The stack of cells was placed inside a pressurized nitrogen jacket. Above the stack was an accessory section that contained the hydrogen pump/separator, the coolant pump, coolant accumulator, and the reactant pressure controls. The Apollo fuel cell system shown in **Figures** 30 and 31 was about 112 cm long and 57 cm in diameter and weighed about 109 kg. Three fuel cell systems were connected electrically in parallel to share the electrical load for the Apollo spacecraft. The Apollo fuel cell system flow schematic is shown in **Figure 32**. Each fuel cell system was capable of steadily producing 1420 W within the normal voltage range of the command module voltage bus (27–31 VDC).

The Apollo fuel cell system circulated hydrogen through the cell stack that removed both the water that was formed and the waste heat. The water was condensed from the circulating hydrogen and the condensed water was dynamically separated and pumped out by a hydrogen pump/separator. During the test flights of AS-202, AS-501, AS-502, and the flights of Apollo 7, 8, and 9, approximately 450 kg of potable water was produced by the fuel cell systems. Of this, about 60% was consumed directly by the

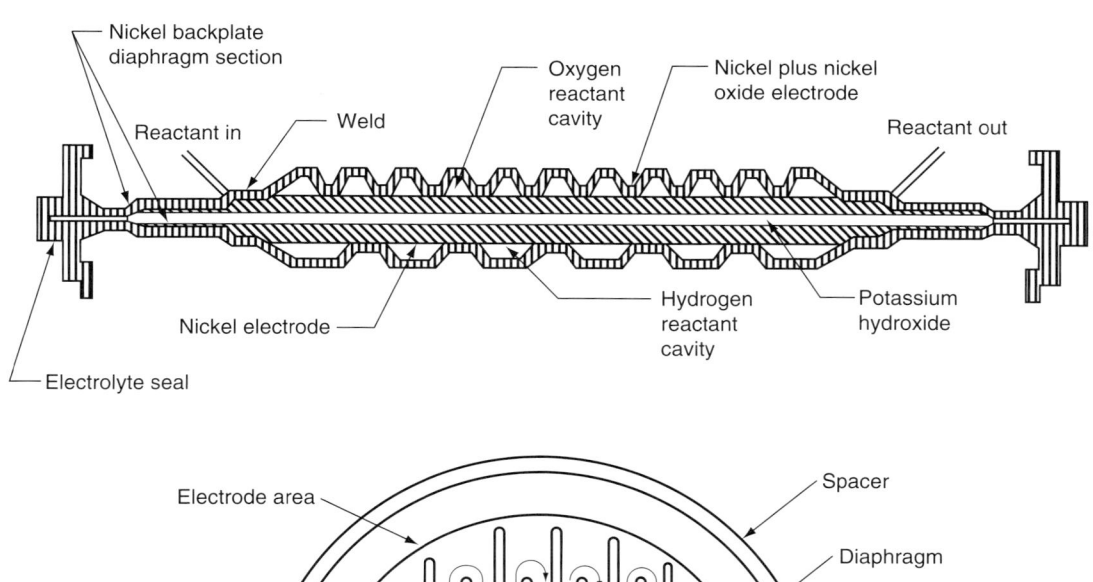

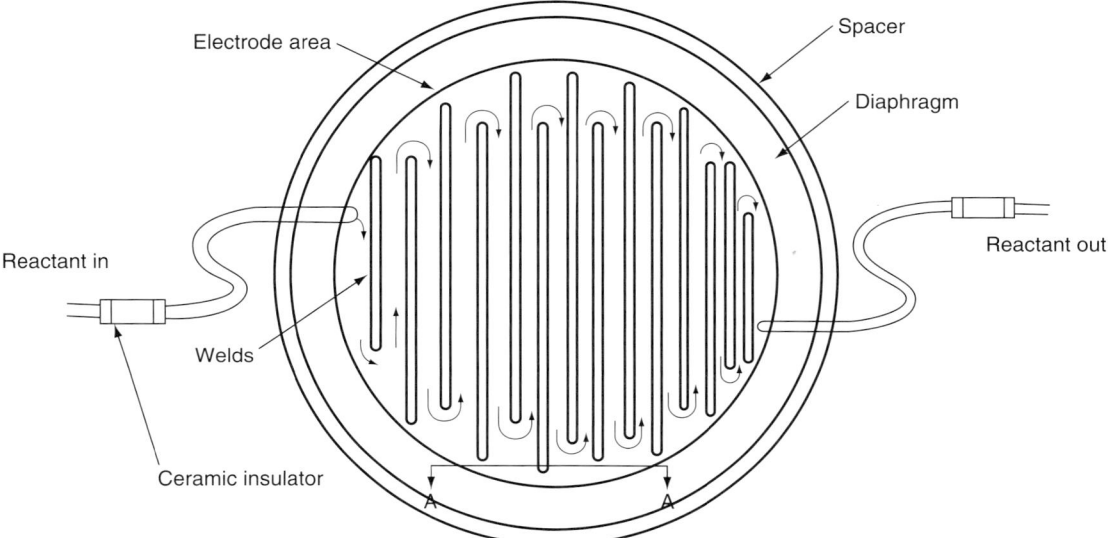

Figure 27 Apollo fuel cell – cross section and top views. Source: Image from Apollo Program Summary Report, JSC-09423, NASA Lyndon B. Johnson Space Center, pp. 4–39. http://history.nasa.gov/apsr/apsr.htm (accessed April 1975) [44] and Image from NASA Apollo Command Module News Reference (1968) North American Aviation, p. 108. http://history.nasa.gov/alsi/CSMNewsRef-Boothman.html [45].

crews. The average mission power level required from each fuel cell system was 600 W, so in the event of two system failures, a single fuel cell system could still meet the power demands of the mission [49].

4.02.2.3 Space Shuttle

The space shuttle fuel cell is shown in **Figures 33** and **34**. Each cell contained an active area of 465 cm^2 (21.6 cm × 21.6 cm). The space shuttle fuel cell used a 35% KOH electrolyte contained within an asbestos matrix and operated at a nominal temperature of 93 °C and a pressure of approximately 4 atm. To accommodate the changing volume of electrolyte, an electrolyte reservoir plate (ERP) made of sintered nickel contacted the fuel cell anode (hydrogen-consuming electrode for alkaline cells). The ERP also formed the hydrogen compartment of the cell. The cell assembly consisted of the cell and two separator plates. The power section of the space shuttle fuel cell powerplant, shown in **Figure 35**, consisted of 96 cells, arranged in three substacks of 32 cells each. The 96 cells used common hydrogen, oxygen, and coolant manifolds. The three substacks of 32 cells each were connected electrically in parallel as shown in **Figure 36**.

At one end of the power section was an accessory section that contained the hydrogen pump/separator, the coolant pump, coolant accumulator, coolant control valves, reactant pressure controls, and electrical control unit. Three fuel cell systems were connected electrically in parallel to share the electrical load for the three power buses onboard the space shuttle. Each space shuttle fuel cell system, shown in **Figures 37** and **38**, was about 101.6 cm long, 35.6 cm high, and 38.1 cm wide and weighed about 116 kg. Each fuel cell system is capable of steadily producing 7000 and 12 000 W for a 15 min period and still operates within the normal voltage range of the space shuttle voltage bus (27.5–32.5 VDC). In the event of two fuel cell system failures, a

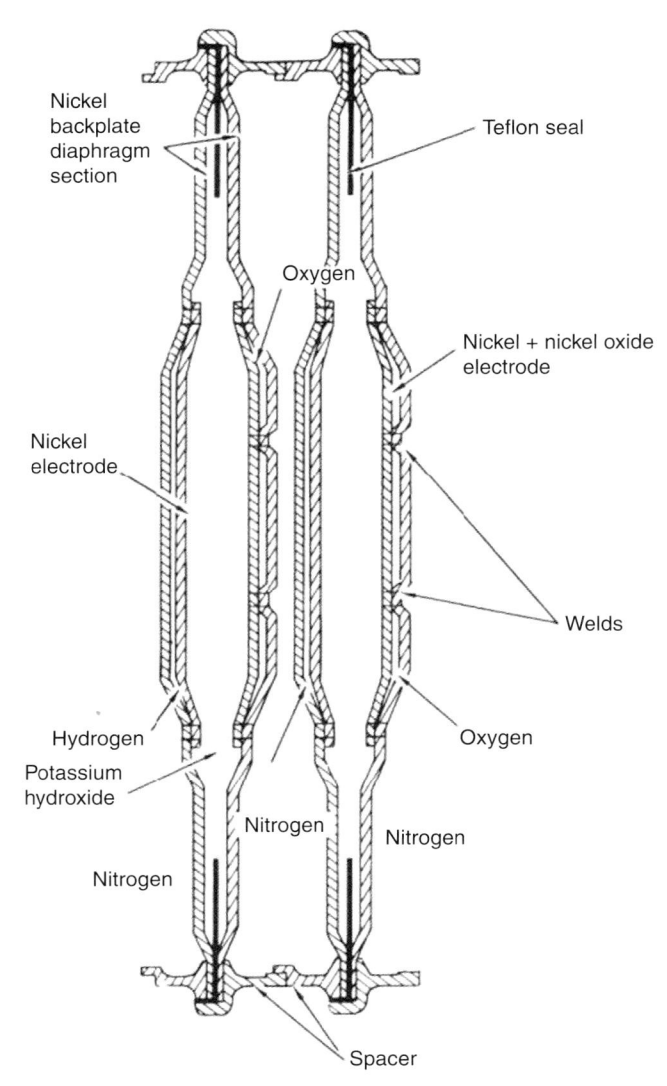

Figure 28 Apollo fuel cell – cross section (two cells). Source: Image from NASA Apollo Command Module News Reference (1968) North American Aviation, p. 108. http://history.nasa.gov/alsj/CSMNewsRef-Boothman.html [45].

single fuel cell system can provide sufficient power to operate the space shuttle. The location of the fuel cell systems aboard the space shuttle is shown in **Figure 39**.

The space shuttle fuel cell system flow schematic is shown in **Figure 40**. Like the Apollo fuel cell system, the space shuttle fuel cell system circulated hydrogen through the cell stack, which removed the water that was formed. The water condensed from the circulating hydrogen, and the condensed water was dynamically separated and pumped out by a hydrogen pump/separator. A liquid coolant (FC-40) was circulated through the cell stack to remove heat. Each fuel cell system was serviced between flights and reused until a total of 2000 h of online service time had been accumulated.

4.02.3 Other Current Uses of Hydrogen and Fuel Cells

Hydrogen and fuel cells are currently being used for purposes other than space applications. **Figure 41** is a summary of the major applications of hydrogen use, the quantity of use, and the approximate value of the economic market for hydrogen. Hydrogen plays a key role in agriculture (the production of ammonia), in energy (oil refining), and in other chemical production (methanol and other chemicals). In many cases, the quantity of hydrogen used is great enough that it is generated on-site as opposed to being delivered to the point of use by pipelines or bottles. This on-site generation and on-site usage is the norm rather than the exception. Fortunately, hydrogen is easily and cheaply produced from either hydrocarbon sources (principally methane) or electrolysis of water.

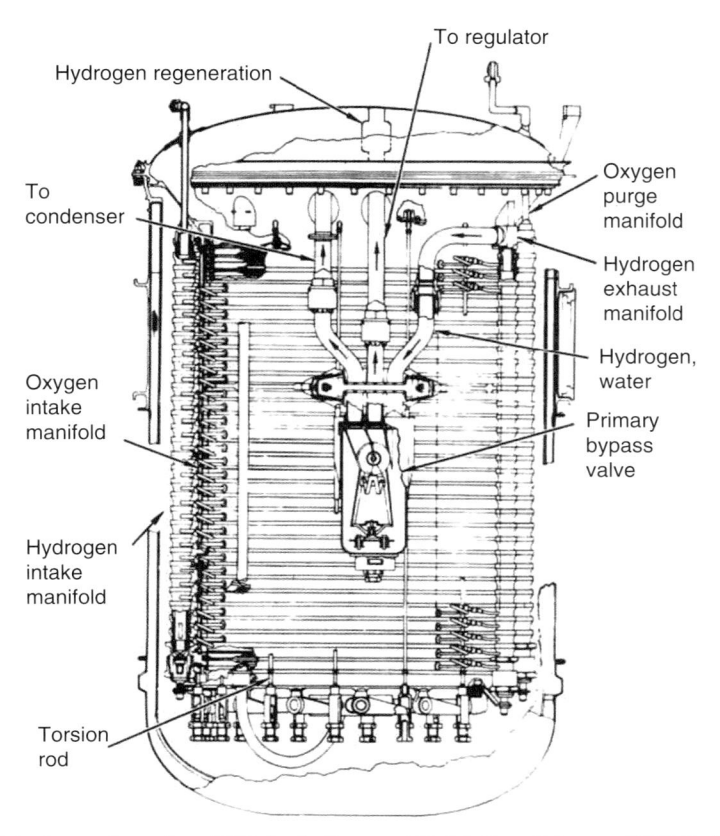

Figure 29 Apollo fuel cell module. Source: Image from NASA Apollo Command Module News Reference (1968) North American Aviation, p. 110. http://history.nasa.gov/alsj/CSMNewsRef-Boothman.html [46].

The fuel cell industry is a new industry that is in the process of commercializing fuel cells. The U.S. Fuel Cell Council, a nonprofit trade association dedicated to the commercialization of fuel cells, was formed in 1998 [58]. Much of the fuel cell industry effort has been in research and development, prototype development, pilot-scale demonstrations, small fleet demonstrations, and the like. Recently, true commercial deployments of fuel cell products has happened, but the industry still faces challenges with incumbent power technologies, lack of public hydrogen infrastructure, underdeveloped municipal codes and safety standards, and a general lack of awareness by the public and industry about the benefits of adopting this alternative power source. Figure 42 is a summary of the US fuel cell market, the major applications that use fuel cells, and the approximate value of the fuel cell economic market. Fuel cells are finding use as stationary electric power generation sources, as backup electrical power sources, in portable electronics, and in motor vehicles. The quiet, nonpolluting characteristics of fuel cells and their ability to produce substantial amounts of power are key to their present adoption.

4.02.3.1 Current Uses of Hydrogen

4.02.3.1.1 Ammonia production

The largest consumption of hydrogen is in the production of ammonia. Almost half of the hydrogen produced in the world is used for this purpose [60]. Hydrogen is typically produced on-site from methane. Methane is reacted with steam in a process called steam reforming. This reaction produces hydrogen and carbon monoxide. The carbon monoxide is then reacted with more steam in a reaction called the water gas shift reaction to produce carbon dioxide and more hydrogen. The hydrogen produced by these processes is used in a process called the Haber process (named after its inventor, Fritz Haber) [61]. This process reacts the hydrogen with nitrogen at high temperature and pressure to produce ammonia for use as a fertilizer. The demand for ammonia is expected to grow as the world population grows.

4.02.3.1.2 Oil refinery use

Hydrogen is used by oil refineries to break down the hydrocarbon in crude oil into lighter hydrocarbons, such as diesel and gasoline. Hydrogen is also used by refineries to remove undesirable contaminants such as sulfur and nitrogen from the hydrocarbons that contain these elements. Hydrogen replaces the sulfur or nitrogen in the hydrocarbon and in the process produces hydrogen sulfide (when removing sulfur) or ammonia (when removing nitrogen). The hydrogen used by refineries is typically produced on-site by

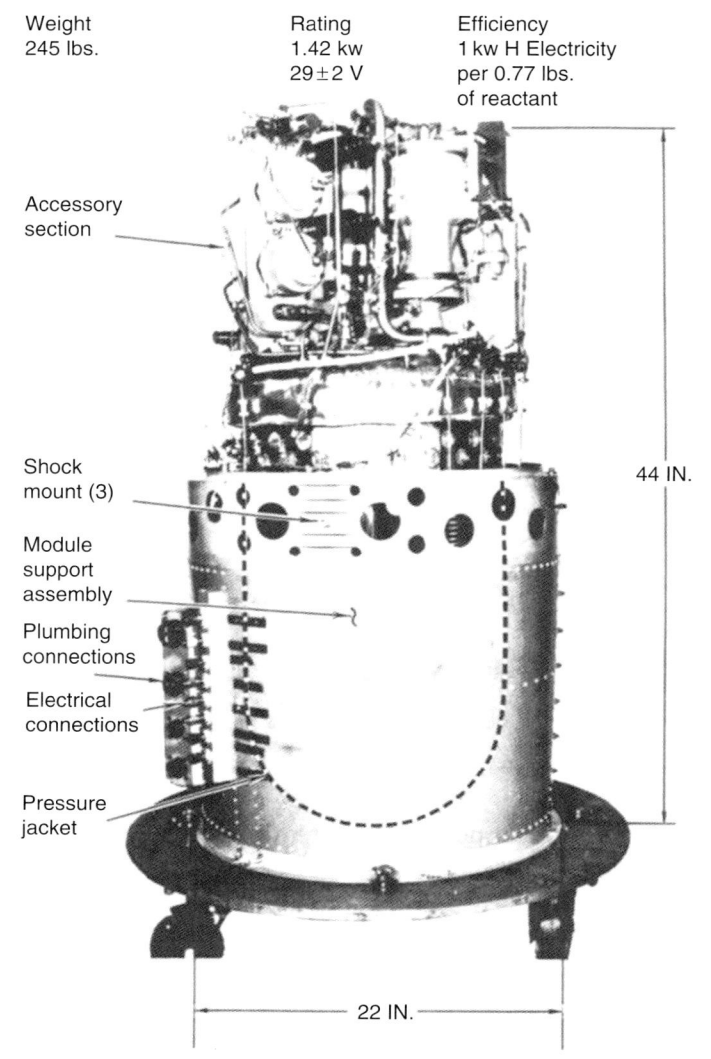

Figure 30 Apollo fuel cell system. Source: Ferguson RB (1969) Apollo fuel cell power system. In: *Proceedings of the Twenty-Third Annual Power Sources Conference*, p. 11, 20–22 May [47].

the same process used by the ammonia producers. Some hydrogen is also produced during the catalytic reforming of naphtha. The use of hydrogen is expected to increase because of the demand for low-sulfur fuel, greater consumption of low-quality crude, and greater consumption of hydrocarbon in developing economies [62].

4.02.3.1.3 Methanol production
Hydrogen is used to make methanol. Hydrogen is typically produced from methane on-site in the same manner as for ammonia production and oil refining. The mixture of hydrogen and carbon monoxide (called syngas) from the steam reforming process is then reacted on a different catalyst to form methanol. Roughly, 4 million tons of methanol is produced in the United States each year. Methanol is a widely used solvent and is used to produce paints, adhesives, inks, varnishes, paint strippers, and other products. About 40% of the methanol is used to produce formaldehyde, which is used to produce plastics, plywood, paints, explosives, and permanent press textiles.

4.02.3.1.4 Other chemical manufacturing
Hydrogen is used for other chemical manufacturing, most notably the hydrogenation of unsaturated carbon bonds. Unsaturated carbon bonds are double bonds between two carbon atoms. The double carbon bond reduces the bonds that exist between carbon and hydrogen in hydrocarbons. These hydrocarbons are referred to as 'unsaturated'. Single bonds between carbon atoms maximize the hydrogen content in hydrocarbons and are referred to as 'saturated'. A common hydrogen application is the hydrogenation of

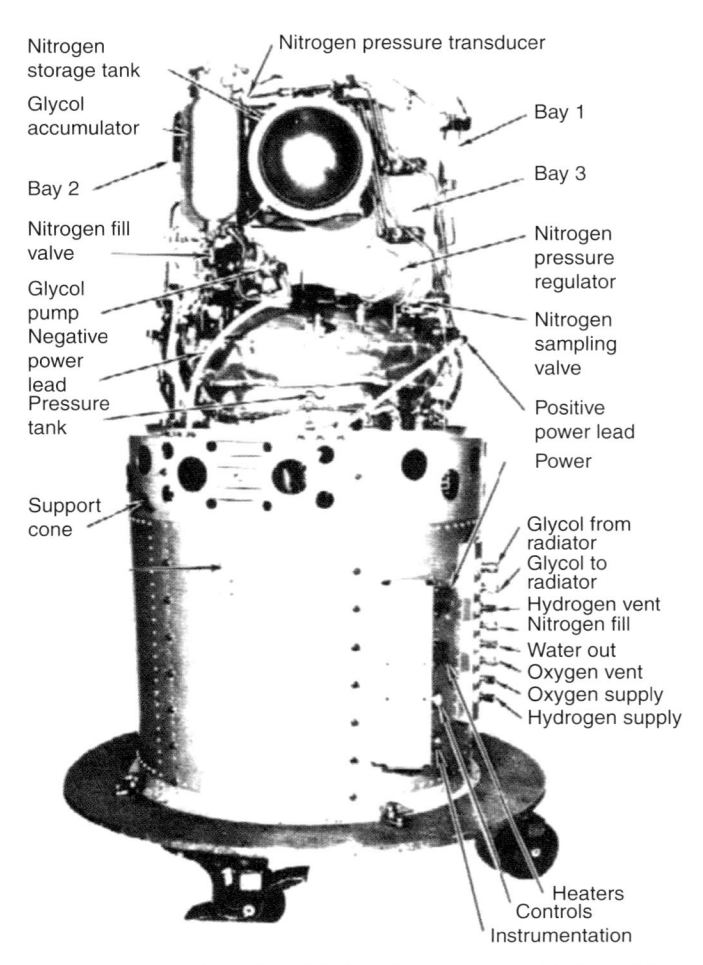

Figure 31 Apollo fuel cell system accessories. Source: Image from NASA Apollo Command Module News Reference (1968) North American Aviation, p. 106. http://history.nasa.gov/alsi/CSMNewsRef-Boothman.html [48].

unsaturated animal fats and oils. The conversion of these unsaturated compounds to saturated compounds increases their melting point and makes them more stable for use in frying foods.

4.02.3.1.5 Other uses

Other hydrogen uses generally do not use the quantities of hydrogen as the applications mentioned above. The methods for obtaining the hydrogen for these other uses are also generally different. In these other applications, the hydrogen is delivered either in bottles or in tube trailers. In some instances, local hydrogen production via water electrolysis provides a better economic solution.

Hydrogen is used in the metal industry to provide a reducing atmosphere to prevent metal oxidation during various metal production or fabrication operations such as annealing, welding, heat treating, sintering, and brazing.

Hydrogen is used in the semiconductor industry. Hydrogen is used as an impurity to change the behavior of semiconductors. Hydrogen binds to native defects or to other impurities that eliminate their electrical activity (a process called passivation). Complementary metal-oxide semiconductor (CMOS) devices require passivation of the Si/SiO_2 interface to provide reliable operation. A hydrogen atmosphere is often used during the growth of semiconductors. Several semiconductor growth techniques such as vapor phase transport, hydrothermal growth, and metal-organic chemical vapor deposition include great quantities of hydrogen in the growth environment [63].

4.02.3.2 Current Uses of Fuel Cells

4.02.3.2.1 Electric power generation

Fuel cells are being used as power generators that are independent of the electrical grid or are supplemental to grid electrical power. These systems are being used for industrial, commercial, and residential electrical power generation. Sometimes, the waste heat produced by the fuel cell system is used for space heating and for producing hot water, which can potentially reduce a user's energy

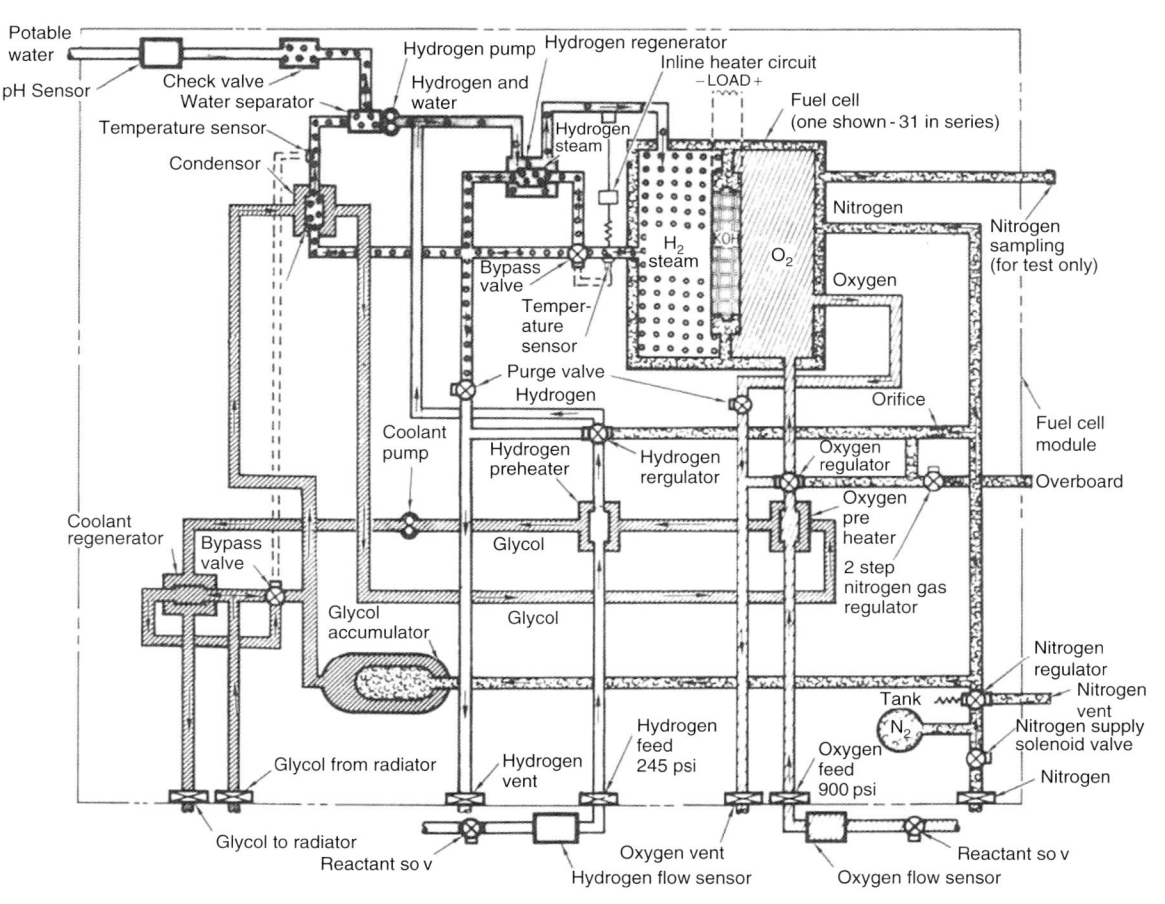

Figure 32 Apollo fuel cell system flow schematic. Source: Image from NASA Apollo Command Module News Reference (1968) North American Aviation p. 109. http://history.nasa.gov/alsj/CSMNewsRef-Boothman.html [50].

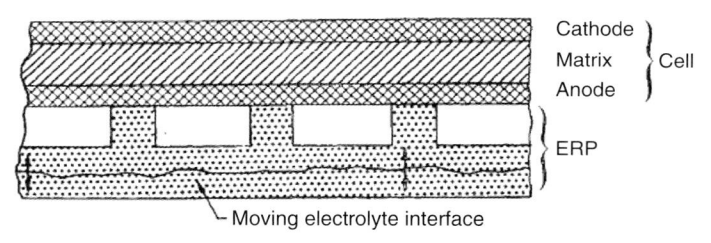

Figure 33 Fuel cell and electrolyte reservoir plate. Source: Images from Orbiter Fuel Cell Powerplant Review and Training Course, presented to United Space Alliance, Houston, TX [51].

service cost by 20–40% over conventional services. The amount of power these systems produce varies depending on the application. **Figure 43** shows a commercial/industrial size unit that produces about 400 kW of electrical power and 500 kW of heat recovery. Typically, these systems use natural gas or propane. Fuel cells are being used industrially in instances where a gas product is being generated that would otherwise be discarded such as landfill gas, anaerobic digester gas, or industrial hydrogen or hydrocarbon by-products. Fuel cells are being used residentially as combined heat and power units, referred to as CHP units. **Figure 44** shows two residential size CHP units. The unit on the left in **Figure 44** produces about 1 kW of electrical power and 2 kW of thermal power and is 55 cm × 55 cm × 160 cm. The unit shown on the right in **Figure 44** produces between 0.5 and 5 kW of electrical power and 7–25 kW of thermal power and is 101 cm × 71 cm × 122 cm.

4.02.3.2.2 *Backup power supplies*

Fuel cell systems are finding use as backup power systems for customers that require high reliability power for such applications as telecommunications, hospitals, computer centers, emergency response systems, national defense, and homeland security. Fuel cell systems are preferred over other alternatives because of their efficient, quiet, and nonpolluting characteristics. These systems are essentially identical to those above, except that in these instances, the fuel cell system is a secondary power source.

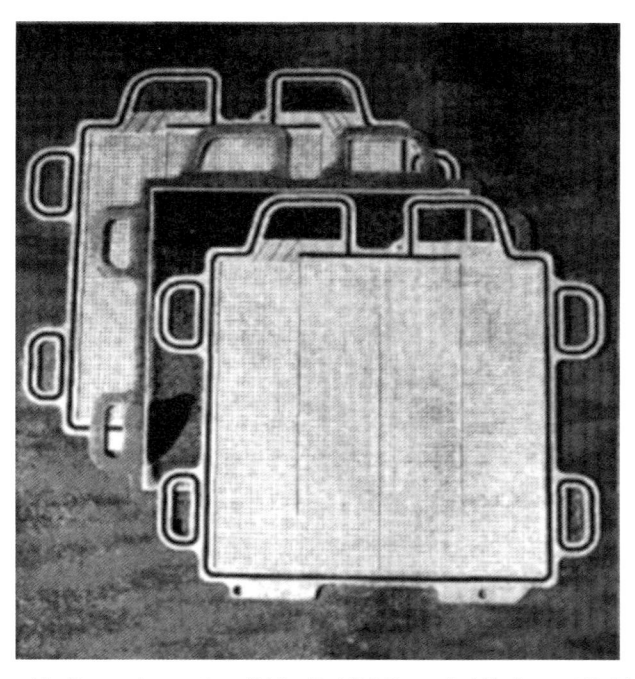

Figure 34 Space shuttle fuel cell assembly. Source: Images from Orbiter Fuel Cell Powerplant Review and Training Course, presented to United Space Alliance, Houston, TX [51].

Figure 35 Space shuttle fuel cell power section. Source: Images from Orbiter Fuel Cell Powerplant Review and Training Course, presented to United Space Alliance, Houston, TX [51].

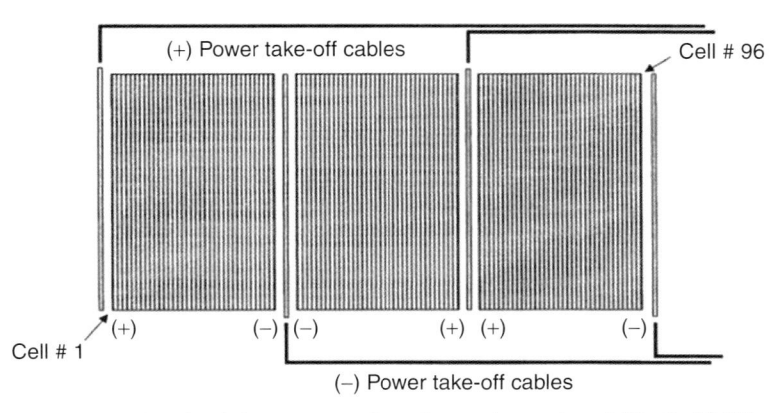

Figure 36 Space shuttle fuel cell power section electrical power connections. Source: Images from Orbiter Fuel Cell Powerplant Review and Training Course, presented to United Space Alliance, Houston, TX [51].

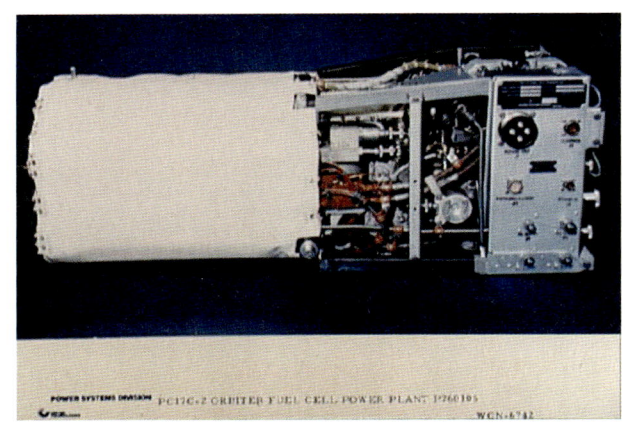

Figure 37 Space shuttle fuel cell system. Source: Image from NASA Image Exchange, NASA Johnson Space Center, Photo No. S83-28219. http://images.jsc.nasa.gov/lores/S83-28219.jpg [52].

Figure 38 Space shuttle fuel cell preflight preparation. Source: Image from Kennedy Space Center Multimedia Gallery, Photo No. KSC-06PD-0005. http://mediaarchive.ksc.nasa.gov/detail.cfm?mediaid=27656 [53].

4.02.3.2.3 Portable electronics

Fuel cell systems are being used for portable applications either as the direct power source for these items or as a portable recharger for the batteries contained in the product. As the power of portable products increases and the desire to have these products run longer between recharges becomes stronger, battery technology is not keeping up with the needs of the marketplace. Fuel cells are finding a niche to fill in this area. **Figure 45** shows two fuel cell-powered portable power sources. The product on the left in **Figure 45** shows a portable fuel cell power system capable of producing 150 W of continuous power for 5 h. It measures 21.6 cm 34.8 cm × 41.1 cm and weighs approximately 10.4 kg. The product on the right in **Figure 45** is designed for recharging of small consumer products. This unit produces 2 W of power and has the energy of 20 typical AA batteries.

Prototype fuel cells are being developed as the power source for small handheld electronics such as cell phones. **Figure 46** shows a prototype of this type of fuel cell that doubles the time between recharges.

4.02.3.2.4 Motor vehicles

There has been significant development of fuel cells, particularly proton exchange membrane (PEM) fuel cells, for motor vehicle applications. The reasons for this are twofold: first, the hydrocarbon fuel for motor vehicles has continued to escalate in cost to the general public, and the adequacy of its future supply is uncertain. Fuel cells that can operate on hydrogen or other renewable fuels offer a solution to this potential worldwide problem. The second reason is that the hydrocarbon fuels used in motor vehicles produce undesirable environmental effects. These effects range from local pollution effects in vehicle-dense metropolitan areas (particularly in developing countries) to worldwide pollution effects from the production and accumulation of greenhouse gases. The low pollution footprint of fuel cells provides an attractive alternative to current technology. **Figure 47** shows a fuel cell-powered bus. Buses are an early adopter market for fuel cells because buses are fleet vehicles that have centralized refueling stations. This makes the issue of hydrogen refueling stations less problematic. Buses are typically owned and operated by municipalities that can subsidize their operation through government grants. Passenger cars are another market for fuel cells. Major car companies have

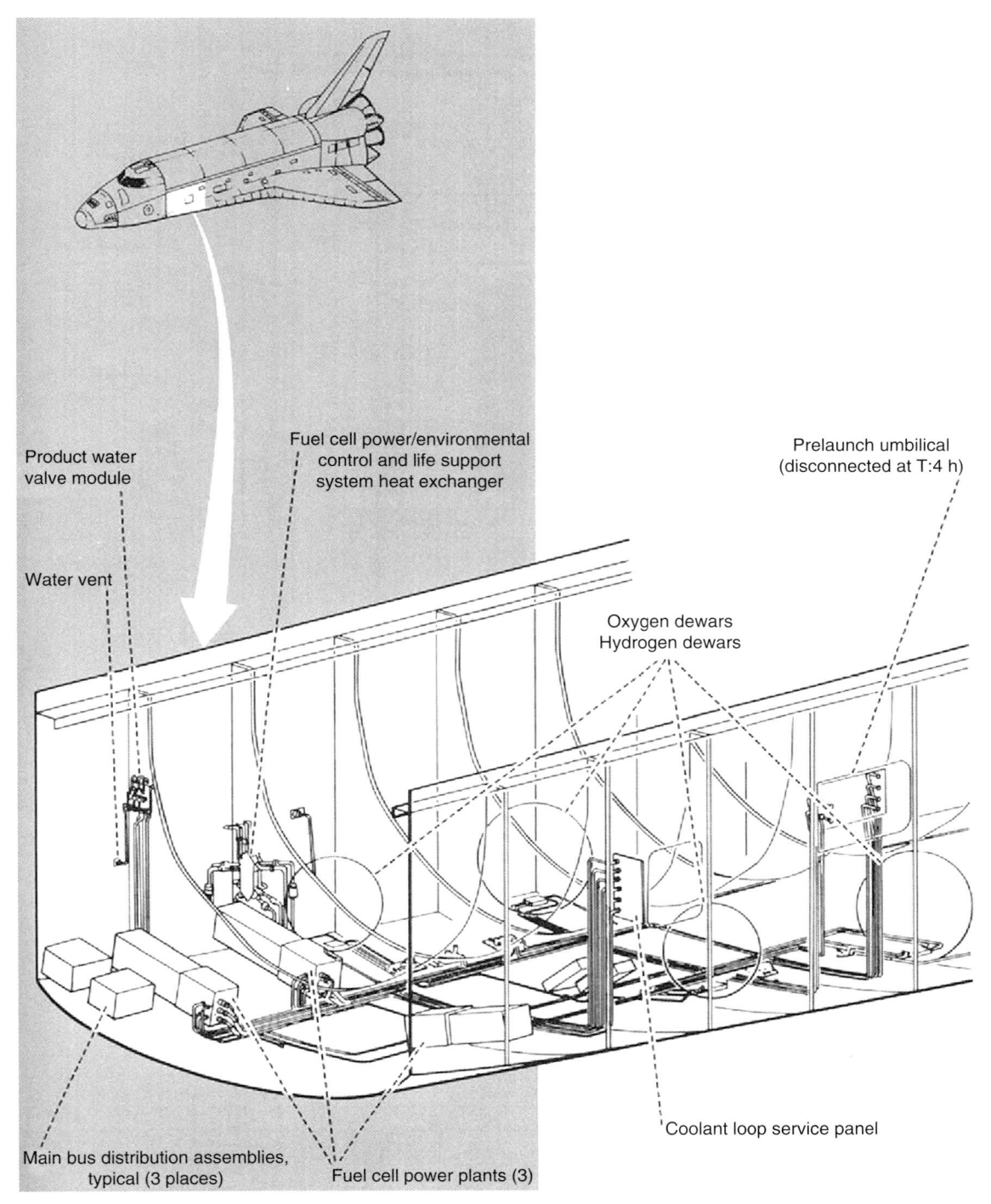

Figure 39 Space shuttle fuel cell powerplant location. Source: Image from National Aeronautics and Space Administration, NASA History Office. SP-407 http://history.nasa.gov/SP-407/p63.htm [54].

developed prototypes and produced small numbers of cars to evaluate performance. Fuel cell-powered passenger cars have been built that have the driving characteristics, speed, and driving range of internal combustion engine-powered automobiles. **Figures 48** and 49 show a pilot production model of fuel cell-powered automobiles.

Forklifts are another promising market area for fuel cells. Fuel cell-powered forklifts are gaining acceptance because these vehicles can be refueled much more rapidly than the recharging of battery-powered forklifts. This allows the forklifts to be put back into service rather than being idled while recharging. Fuel cell-powered forklifts also do not produce the exhaust that hydrocarbon-fueled forklifts produce. **Figure 50** shows two instances of fuel cell-powered forklift use.

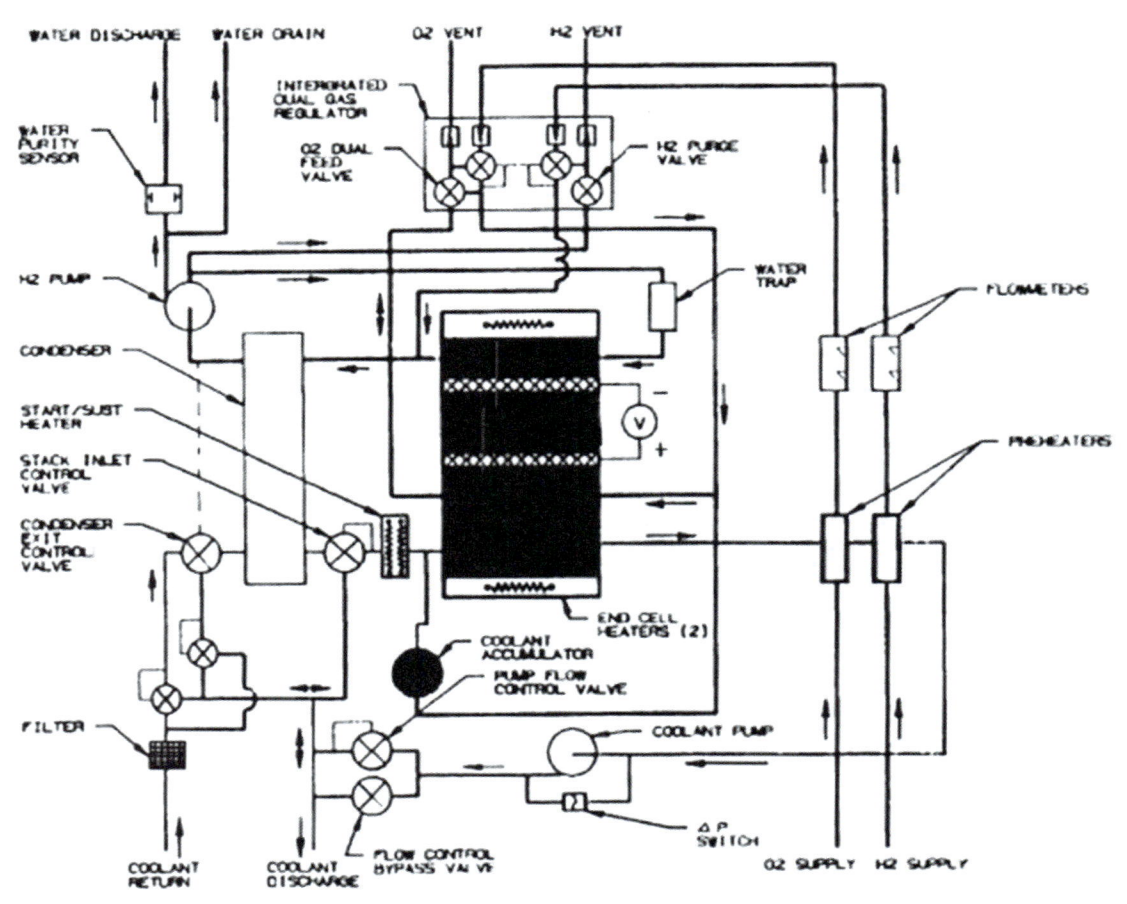

Figure 40 Space shuttle fuel cell powerplant flow schematic. Source: Independent Orbiter Assessment, prepared by McDonnel Douglas Astronautics Company Houston Division, under NASA contract NAS-9-17650. http://ntrs.nasa.gov/archive/nasa/casi.ntrs.nasa.gov/19900001598_1990001598.pdf [55].

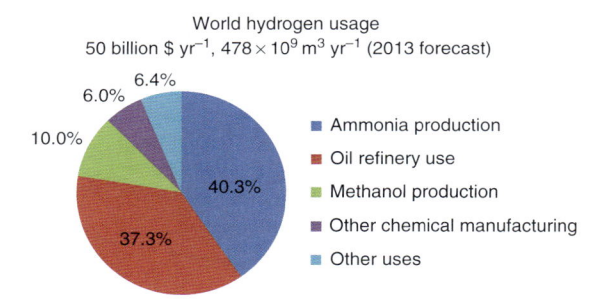

Figure 41 World hydrogen usage. Source: Spath PL and Mann MK (2001) Life cycle assessment of hydrogen production via natural gas steam reforming. National Renewable Energy Laboratory, Revised February 2001. http://www.nrel.gov/docs/fy01osti/27637.pdf [56] and World Hydrogen – Industry Study with Forecasts for 2013 and 2018, Study #2605, The Freedonia Group. http://www.freedoniagroup.com/brochure/26xx/2605smwe.pdf (accessed February 2010) [57].

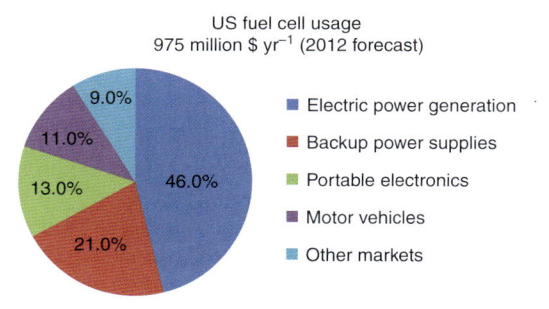

Figure 42 US fuel cell usage. Source: Fuel Cells – US Industry Study with Forecasts for 2012 and 2017, Study #2328, The Freedonia Group. http://www.freedoniagroup.com/brochure/23xx/2328smwe.pdf (accessed April 2008) [59].

Current Perspective on Hydrogen and Fuel Cells 39

(1) Fuel processor (reformer)	(2) Fuel cell stack	(3) Power conditioner
The fuel processor reforms the fuel (natural gas) to hydrogen gas to feed the fuel cell stack.	Hydrogen gas and air are combined in an electrochemical process that produces direct current (DC) power, pure water, and heat. The by-product water is utilized in the operation of the power plant. The useable heat is available for meeting other facility energy requirements (e.g., hot water, space heating, air conditioning, and cooling).	The DC power provided by the fuel cell stack is conditioned to provide high-quality alternating current (AC) power output.

Figure 43 Commercial/industrial 400 kW fuel cell system. Source: UTC Power, a United Technologies Company, 'Purecell ® System – How It Works' Datasheet. http://www.utcpower.com/fs/com/Attachments/data_sheets/DS0118_120608.pdf [64].

Figure 44 Residential size fuel cell systems. Source: Image from Hexis Ltd., Galileo Product Brochure. http://www.hexis.com/downloads/HEXIS_Galileo1000N.jpg [65] and Image from Plug Power Inc., Gensys High Temperature Fuel Cell System for Residential Applications Brochure. http://www.plugpower.com/userfiles/file/GenSysHT-03-09.pdf [66].

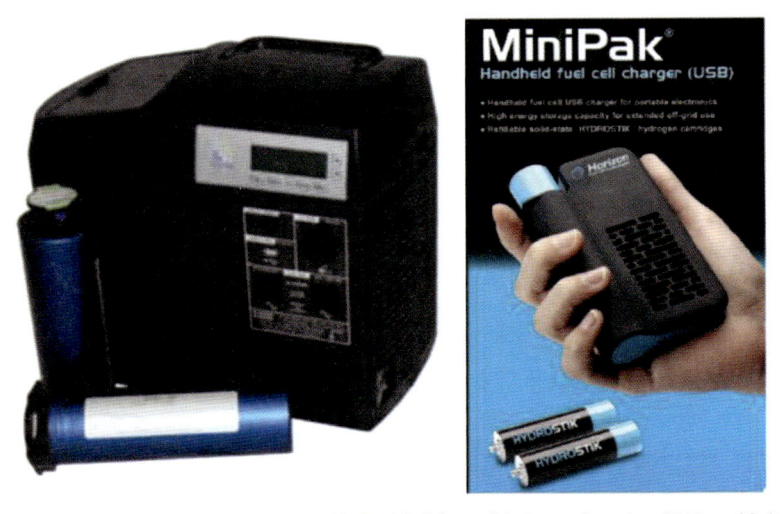

Figure 45 Portable fuel cell power systems. Source: Image from U.S. Fuel Cell Council Industry Overview 2010, p. 22. http://www.usfcc.com/download_a_file/download_a_file/IndustryOverview2010.pdf [67] and Image from Horizon Fuel Cell Technologies Pte. Ltd., Minipak Product Brochure. http://www.horizonfuelcell.com/file/MiniPak_brochure.pdf [68].

Figure 46 Prototype fuel cell for consumer handheld products. Source: Image from U.S. Fuel Cell Council Industry Overview 2010, p. 22. http://www.usfcc.com/download_a_file/download_a_file/IndustryOverview2010.pdf [67].

4.02.3.2.5 Other markets

Fuel cells are being introduced to other markets. The military is considering the use of fuel cells because their quiet operation permits the stealth transport and operation of troops, whereas the use of diesel engines does not. The military is also interested in fuel cells as power sources for unmanned aerial vehicles (UAVs) and unmanned underwater vehicles (UUVs). The use of fuel cells for power generation in space continues to be a highly visible market.

Figure 47 Fuel cell-powered bus. Source: Image from Wikipedia, Fuel Cell Bus. http://en.wikipedia.org/wiki/File:Urbanussplussle_busscar.jpg [69].

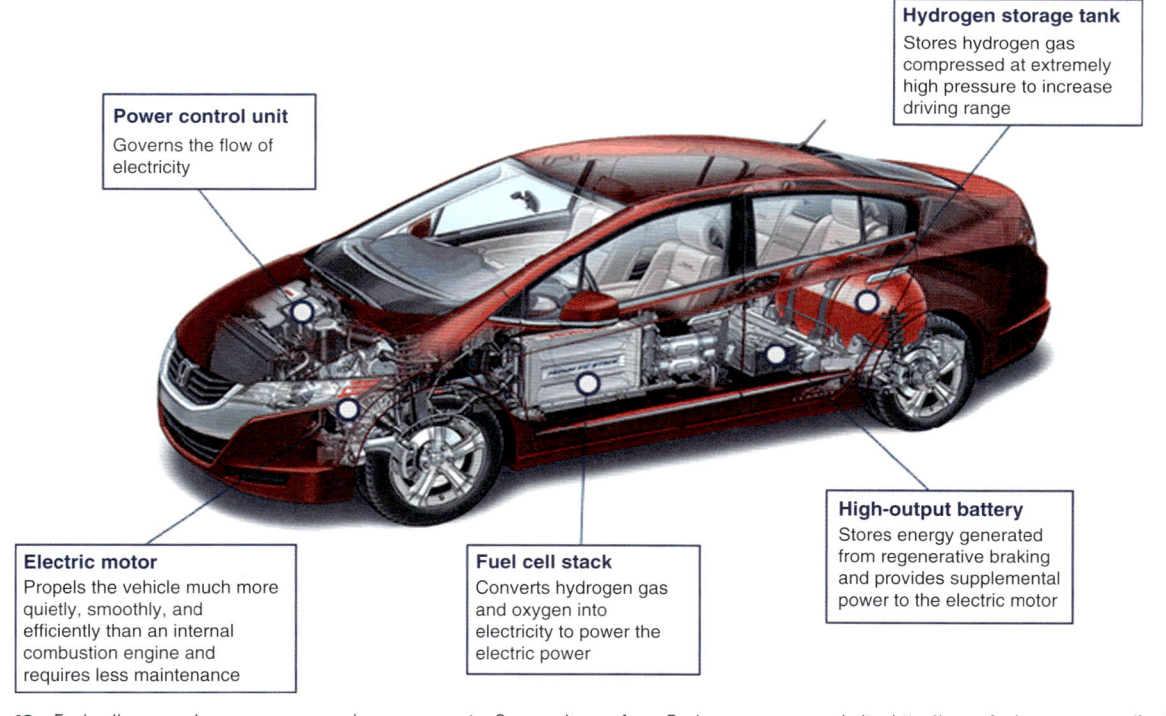

Figure 48 Fuel cell-powered passenger car major components. Source: Image from Fueleconomy.gov website. http://www.fueleconomy.gov/feg/fuelcell.shtml [70].

Figure 49 Fuel cell-powered passenger car on display. Source: Image from Wikipedia, Honda FCX Clarity. http://en.wikipedia.org/wiki/File:FCX_Clarity.jpg [71].

Figure 50 Fuel cell-powered forklifts. Source: Image from U.S. Department of Energy, Energy Efficiency and Renewable Energy website. http://www1.eere.energy.gov/hydrogenandfuelcells/applications.html [72] and Image from U.S. Fuel Cell Council Industry Overview 2010, p. 16. http://www.usfcc.com/download_a_file/download_a_file/IndustryOverview2010.pdf [73].

References

[1] Rocket and Space Technology – Rocket Propellants. http://www.braeuing.us/space/propel.htm.
[2] Sloop JL (1978) Liquid hydrogen as a propulsion fuel 1945–1959. *The NASA History Series, NASA SP-4404 (RL10 Rocket Engine Photo)*. http://history.nasa.gov/SP-4404/ch10-7.htm.
[3] Dawson VP and Bowles MD (2004) Taming liquid hydrogen: The Centaur upper stage rocket 1958–2002. *The NASA History Series, National Aeronautics and Space Administration Office of External Relations*. Washington, DC: NASA SP-2004–4230. http://history.nasa.gov/SP-4230.pdf.
[4] NASA Kennedy Media Archive Collection, Photo No. KSC-05PD-1338. http://images.ksc.nasa.gov/photos/2005/low/KSC-05PD-1338.gif.
[5] NASA Image Exchange, ID No. KSC-00PP-0426, NASA Kennedy Space Center (dual engine Centaur photo). http://images.ksc.nasa.gov/photos/2000/low/KSC-00PP-0426.gif.
[6] NASA Image Exchange, ID No. MSFC-9801770, NASA Marshall Space Flight Center (J2 Engine Slide). http://mix.msfc.nasa.gov/IMAGES/MEDIUM/9801770.jpg.
[7] Wikipedia, the Free Encyclopedia – SII. http://en.wikipedia.org/wiki/S-II.
[8] Marshall Space Flight Center Image Exchange. Photo No. 9801810. http://mix.msfc.nasa.gov/IMAGES/MEDIUM/9801810.jpg.
[9] NASA Image Exchange, ID No. 67-701-c, NASA Stennis Space Center (SII stage of Saturn V rocket photo). http://www.ssc.nasa.gov/sirs/photos/history/low/67-701-c.jpg.
[10] Wikipedia, the Free Encyclopedia – SIVB. http://en.wikipedia.org/wiki/S-IVB.
[11] J-2X Pratt and Whitney, Presentation by Tracy Lamm, 26 February 2007. http://www.nasa.gov/pdf/214593main_Bouley(Lamm)2-26-08.pdf.
[12] NASA Image Exchange, ID No. STS062(S)055, NASA Johnson Space Center. http://images.jsc.nasa.gov/lores/STS062(S)055.jpg.
[13] The Internet Encyclopedia of Science – Manned Spaceflight Rocket and Launch Vehicles. http://www.daviddarling.info/encyclopedia/S/Space_Shuttle.html#ME.
[14] National Aeronautics and Space Administration Human Spaceflight-Space Shuttle Basics – Space Shuttle Main Engines. http://spaceflight.nasa.gov/shuttle/reference/basics/ssme/index.html.
[15] NASA Image Exchange, ID No. KSC-04PD-1643, NASA Kennedy Space Center. http://images.ksc.nasa.gov/photos/2004/low/KSC-04PD-1643.gif.
[16] NASA Image Exchange, Photo No. MSFC-7995081. http://mix.msfc.nasa.gov/IMAGES/MEDIUM/7995081.jpg.
[17] Wikipedia, the Free Encyclopedia –Delta (rocket family). http://en.wikipedia.org/wiki/Delta_(rocket_family).
[18] Collins DJ (2006) Evolved expendable launch vehicle: Assuring access to space. *Air Force Space Command High Frontier* 3(1): 47. http://www.afspc.af.mil/shared/media/document/AFD-061128-043.pdf (accessed November 2006).
[19] Pratt and Whitney Rocketdyne RS-68 Propulsion System. http://www.pw.utc.com/StaticFiles/Pratt%20&%20Whitney%20New/Media%20Center/Assets/1%20Static%20Files/Docs/pwr_RS-68.pdf.
[20] Pratt & Whitney Rocketdyne RS-68 propulsion System. http://www.pw.utc.com/vgn-ext-templating/v/index.jsp?vgnextoid=74750eae0846a210VgnVCM1000004f62529fRCRD.
[21] NASA Image Exchange, Photo No. MSFC-0700063. http://www.nasa.gov/images/content/148709main_d4_testing_08.jpg.
[22] Squire JP, Chang-Díaz FR, Carter MD, *et al.* (2007) High power VASIMR experiments using deuterium, neon and argon. In: *30th International Electric Propulsion Conference*, Florence, Italy, 17–20 September. http://www.adastrarocket.com/Jared_IEPC07.pdf.
[23] NASA website. http://www.nasa.gov/vision/space/travelinginspace/future_propulsion.html.
[24] Encyclopedia Astronautica info page on the LE-5. http://www.astronautix.com/engines/le5.htm.
[25] Wikipedia, the Free Encyclopedia File: LE-5.JPG. http://en.wikipedia.org/wiki/File:LE-5.JPG.
[26] Wikipedia, the Free Encyclopedia File: LE-7.JPG. http://en.wikipedia.org/wiki/File:LE-7_rocket_engine.jpg.
[27] Encyclopedia Astronautica info page on the LE-7. http://www.astronautix.com/engines/le7.htm.
[28] Wikipedia, the Free Encyclopedia – Vulcain. http://en.wikipedia.org/wiki/Vulcain.
[29] Space and Tech. http://www.spaceandtech.com/spacedata/engines/vulcain_specs.shtml.
[30] Wikipedia, the Free Encyclopedia – Vulcain. http://en.wikipedia.org/wiki/File:Moteur-Vulcain.jpg.
[31] Dunlop JD and Stockel JF (1982) Nickel hydrogen battery technology – Development and status. *Journal of Energy* 6(1).
[32] Battery Workshop (1993), NASA Technical Reports Server p. 246. http://ntrs.nasa.gov/archive/nasa/casi.ntrs.nasa.gov/19940023606_1994023606.pdf.
[33] R&T 1999 Research & Technology NASA Glenn Research Center. http://www.grc.nasa.gov/WWW/RT/RT1999/5000/5420miller.html.
[34] Designing for Human Presence in Space, An Introduction to Environmental Control and Life Support Systems, NASA RP-1324.
[35] Jet Propulsion Laboratory Photojournal, Photo No. PIA12316. http://photojournal.jpl.nasa.gov/jpeg/PIA12011.jpg.
[36] Jet Propulsion Laboratory Photojournal, Photo No. PIA12316. http://photojournal.jpl.nasa.gov/jpegMod/PIA12316_modest.jpg.
[37] ESA website. http://www.esa.int/esaMI/Planck/SEMBU20YUFF_0.html.
[38] NASA website. http://www.nasa.gov/images/content/323941main_concept.jpg.
[39] Hacker BC and Grimwood JM (1977) On the shoulders of titans: A history of project Gemini. NASA SP-4203, NASA History Series. http://www.hq.nasa.gov/office/pao/History/SP-4203/ch8-4.htm.
[40] Illustration of Gemini Fuel Cell System from 'Fuel Cells – A Survey' by Bernard Crowe, NASA SP-5115 prepared under Contract NASW-2173, p. 21. http://ntrs.nasa.gov/archive/nasa/casi.ntrs.nasa.gov/19730017318_1973017318.pdf.
[41] NASA Photo C-65-3478 from NASA TM X-52149, Swartz, Harvey J., Lewis Research Center. http://ntrs.nasa.gov/archive/nasa/casi.ntrs.nasa.gov/19660005480_1966005480.pdf.

[42] Gemini Mission Report, Gemini V. http://ntrs.nasa.gov/archive/nasa/casi.ntrs.nasa.gov/19750067642_1975067642.pdf (accessed August 1965).
[43] Post Launch Report for Mission AS-202, Manned Space Center. http://ntrs.nasa.gov/archive/nasa/casi.ntrs.nasa.gov/19740075039_1974075039.pdf (accessed 12 October 1966).
[44] Apollo Program Summary Report, JSC-09423, NASA Lyndon B. Johnson Space Center, pp. 4–39. http://history.nasa.gov/apsr/apsr.htm (accessed April 1975).
[45] NASA Apollo Command Module News Reference (1968) North American Aviation, p. 108. http://history.nasa.gov/alsi/CSMNewsRef-Boothman.html.
[46] NASA Apollo Command Module News Reference (1968) North American Aviation, p. 110. http://history.nasa.gov/alsi/CSMNewsRef-Boothman.html.
[47] NASA Apollo Command Module News Reference (1968) North American Aviation, p. 100. http://history.nasa.gov/alsi/CSMNewsRef-Boothman.html.
[48] NASA Apollo Command Module News Reference (1968) North American Aviation, p. 106. http://history.nasa.gov/alsi/CSMNewsRef-Boothman.html.
[49] Ferguson RB (1969) Apollo fuel cell power system. In: *Proceedings of the Twenty-Third Annual Power Sources Conference*, p. 11, 20–22 May.
[50] NASA Apollo Command Module News Reference (1968) North American Aviation p. 109. http://history.nasa.gov/alsi/CSMNewsRef-Boothman.html.
[51] Orbiter Fuel Cell Powerplant Review and Training Course, presented to United Space Alliance, Houston, TX.
[52] NASA Image Exchange, NASA Johnson Space Center, Photo No. S83-28219. http://images.jsc.nasa.gov/lores/S83-28219.jpg.
[53] Kennedy Space Center Multimedia Gallery, Photo No. KSC-06PD-0005. http://mediaarchive.ksc.nasa.gov/detail.cfm?mediaid=27656.
[54] National Aeronautics and Space Administration, NASA History Office. SP-407 http://history.nasa.gov/SP-407/p63.htm.
[55] Independent Orbiter Assessment, prepared by McDonnel Douglas Astronautics Company Houston Division, under NASA contract NAS-9-17650. http://ntrs.nasa.gov/archive/nasa/casi.ntrs.nasa.gov/19900001598_1990001598.pdf.
[56] Spath PL and Mann MK (2001) Life cycle assessment of hydrogen production via natural gas steam reforming. *National Renewable Energy Laboratory*, Revised February 2001. http://www.nrel.gov/docs/fy01osti/27637.pdf.
[57] World Hydrogen – Industry Study with Forecasts for 2013 and 2018, Study #2605, The Freedonia Group. http://www.freedoniagroup.com/brochure/26xx/2605smwe.pdf (accessed February 2010).
[58] U.S. Fuel Cell Council Industry Overview 2010. http://www.usfcc.com/download_a_file/download_a_file/IndustryOverview2010.pdf.
[59] Fuel Cells – US Industry Study with Forecasts for 2012 and 2017, Study #2328, The Freedonia Group. http://www.freedoniagroup.com/brochure/23xx/2328smwe.pdf (accessed April 2008).
[60] Wikipedia, the Free Encyclopedia – Hydrogen Economy. http://en.wikipedia.org/wiki/Hydrogen_economy.
[61] Wikipedia, the Free Encyclopedia – Haber Process. http://en.wikipedia.org/wiki/Haber_process.
[62] Xebec Inc. website information. http://www.xebecinc.com/applications-industrial-hydrogen.php.
[63] Van de Walle CG and Neugebauer J (2006) Hydrogen in semiconductors. *Annual Review of Materials Research* 36: 179–198. http://www.annualreviews.org/doi/pdf/10.1146/annurev.matsci.36.010705.155428.
[64] UTC Power, a United Technologies Company, 'Purecell ® System – How It Works' Datasheet. http://www.utcpower.com/fs/com/Attachments/data_sheets/DS0118_120608.pdf.
[65] Hexis Ltd., Galileo Product Brochure. http://www.hexis.com/downloads/HEXIS_Galileo1000N.jpg.
[66] Plug Power Inc., Gensys High Temperature Fuel Cell System for Residential Applications Brochure. http://www.plugpower.com/userfiles/file/GenSysHT-03-09.pdf.
[67] U.S. Fuel Cell Council Industry Overview 2010, p. 22. http://www.usfcc.com/download_a_file/download_a_file/IndustryOverview2010.pdf.
[68] Horizon Fuel Cell Technologies Pte. Ltd., Minipak Product Brochure. http://www.horizonfuelcell.com/file/MiniPak_brochure.pdf.
[69] Wikipedia, Fuel Cell Bus. http://en.wikipedia.org/wiki/File:Urbanussplussle_busscar.jpg.
[70] Fueleconomy.gov website. http://www.fueleconomy.gov/feg/fuelcell.shtml.
[71] Wikipedia, Honda FCX Clarity. http://en.wikipedia.org/wiki/File:FCX_Clarity.jpg.
[72] U.S. Department of Energy, Energy Efficiency and Renewable Energy website. http://www1.eere.energy.gov/hydrogenandfuelcells/applications.html.
[73] U.S. Fuel Cell Council Industry Overview 2010, p. 16. http://www.usfcc.com/download_a_file/download_a_file/IndustryOverview2010.pdf.

4.03 Hydrogen Economics and Policy

N Hughes and P Agnolucci, Imperial College London, London, UK

© 2012 Elsevier Ltd. All rights reserved.

4.03.1	Introduction	46
4.03.2	The Hydrogen Energy Chain – Technological Characterizations and Economic Challenges	47
4.03.2.1	Production	48
4.03.2.1.1	Electrolysis	48
4.03.2.1.2	Steam methane reforming	49
4.03.2.1.3	Gasification	50
4.03.2.1.4	Biological production	51
4.03.2.1.5	Water splitting through high-temperature heat	51
4.03.2.1.6	Summary of hydrogen production processes	51
4.03.2.2	Infrastructure	52
4.03.2.2.1	Costs of hydrogen delivery infrastructure	52
4.03.2.2.2	Capacity factors and infrastructure design	53
4.03.2.2.3	Costs of hydrogen refueling stations	54
4.03.2.2.4	Introducing hydrogen infrastructure – Incremental or step-change approaches	54
4.03.2.3	Storage	55
4.03.2.3.1	Storage technologies and performance in relation to onboard vehicle requirements	55
4.03.2.3.2	Storage applications	57
4.03.2.4	End-Use Technologies and Applications	58
4.03.2.4.1	End-use technologies – ICEs	58
4.03.2.4.2	End-use technologies – FCs	58
4.03.2.4.3	Applications – Stationary power	59
4.03.2.4.4	Applications – Auxiliary power and 'niche' applications	60
4.03.2.4.5	Applications – Passenger transport	61
4.03.2.4.6	Hydrogen vehicles – The cost to consumers	62
4.03.2.4.7	Hydrogen vehicles – Early prototypes and costs	62
4.03.2.4.8	Wider market opportunities for FCVS, and other low-carbon vehicle drive trains, across the transport sector	63
4.03.2.5	Conclusions on Economics	64
4.03.3	Hydrogen within the Whole-Energy-System Context	65
4.03.3.1	Effects of Transport Decarbonization on Low-Carbon Energy Resources	65
4.03.3.2	Decarbonization of the Electricity Grid – Opportunities for Hydrogen	66
4.03.3.3	Summary on Whole System Interactions	67
4.03.4	Developing Policies to Support Hydrogen	67
4.03.4.1	Policies in the Transport Sector	68
4.03.4.2	Policies in the Electricity Sector	69
4.03.4.3	Policies Relating to Fundamental Scientific Research	70
4.03.5	Conclusion	71
References		72
Further Reading		75
Relevant Websites		75

Glossary

Capacity factor The average consumption, output, or throughput over a period of time of a particular technology or piece of infrastructure divided by its consumption, output, or throughput if it had operated at full (rated) capacity over that time period.

Carbon capture and storage (CCS) The separation of carbon dioxide (CO_2) from fossil fuels during or after electricity generation or other energy-related processes, for subsequent burial in geological strata, to avoid emissions to the atmosphere.

Electrolysis (of water) The decomposition of water into oxygen and hydrogen due to an electric current being passed through the water.

Forward commitment procurement A commitment given, usually by a public sector body, to purchase an as-yet unspecified technology, having stated performance characteristics, in a stated quantity, for a stated price, at a stated future point in time.

Fuel cells Electrochemical cells for the production of electricity from a fuel without combustion.

Higher heating value A measure of energy content of a fuel expressed as the energy released as heat when the fuel

> undergoes complete combustion, including the latent heat of vaporization of water in the combustion products.
> **Lower heating value** A measure of energy content of a fuel expressed as the energy released as heat when the fuel undergoes complete combustion, excluding the latent heat of vaporization of water in the combustion products.
>
> **Market niche** In economics, a subset of users with particular requirements that differentiate them from general consumers, thereby also differentiating the technologies that they require and will purchase.
> **Technological niche** The demonstration, usually by a public sector body, of a technology that has no current market, on the basis of its hoped-for future benefits (also, 'demonstration project').

4.03.1 Introduction

The use of molecular hydrogen to store and carry energy is a concept that has reappeared over many years within scenarios, blueprints, or other imaginings of future energy systems. Hydrogen has been proposed as offering solutions to a range of energy system problems such as air and noise pollution, security of supply, and the potential exhaustion of fossil fuel resources, as well as the reduction of CO_2 emissions associated with the use of such fossil resources. Some authors have gone yet further, arguing that hydrogen could be the fuel that 'democratizes' the energy system, wresting the control of energy resources from the powerful few and literally bringing 'power to the people' [1]. The potential future significance of hydrogen imagined by some commentators is often conveyed within the phrase 'the Hydrogen Economy', though precisely what is implied by that term is the subject of multiple contrasting interpretations [2].

The earliest description of a Hydrogen Economy may well be that given by the character Cyrus Harding in Jules Verne's novel of 1874, 'The Mysterious Island'. Verne expresses through his characters the attraction of a future economy whose primary resource is water, "decomposed into its primitive elements…by electricity, which will then have become a powerful and manageable force… I believe that water will one day be employed as fuel, that hydrogen and oxygen which constitute it, used singly or together, will furnish an inexhaustible source of heat and light, of an intensity of which coal is not capable. Some day the coalrooms of steamers and the tenders of locomotives will, instead of coal, be stored with these two condensed gases, which will burn in the furnaces with enormous calorific power…. Water will be the coal of the future." [3].

Though Cyrus Harding's depiction of a future energy system involves the use of hydrogen as a fuel, he is correct of course in identifying that hydrogen is not in fact the 'primary' energy resource of that future economy. Harding's monologue highlights a fact that is fundamental to understanding hydrogen's potential role within the energy system. Although it is often stated that hydrogen is the most abundant element in the universe, it is almost exclusively to be found bound up with other elements within chemical compounds. Molecular hydrogen does not easily escape from these bonds, and so there are no natural reservoirs of hydrogen waiting to be tapped. If hydrogen is to be used as a means of providing energy for a particular use, energy must first be deployed to separate it from the natural compounds of which it forms a component part. It follows that, although this chapter appears within a volume reviewing various kinds of renewable energy, hydrogen cannot itself be described as a 'source' of renewable energy. It is rather an 'energy carrier' – something in which energy is invested in order to take energy out again at a later stage. Whether the energy hydrogen is carrying can be said to be renewable is entirely dependent on the process by which the hydrogen was liberated from its natural compound-confined state.

Yet more pertinently, the second law of thermodynamics states that the conversion of energy from one form to another inevitably results in a loss of energy to the second form, through entropy. This means that in order to produce hydrogen, it must always be necessary to expend more energy than is available within the hydrogen for use at the end of the process. This fundamental and inescapable fact is recurrently cited as a key objection to the practicality of the hydrogen vision [4, 5] and will be returned to later in this chapter.

However, despite the inevitable entropic losses, there are clearly instances where it is considered advantageous to convert energy from one form to another, because there is a desired benefit associated with the energy being in that particular form. It is through appealing to such benefits that the argument for hydrogen is made – arguments against hydrogen must be made on the grounds that other energy conversion processes offer the same benefits with fewer thermodynamic losses. The potential benefits of energy in the form of hydrogen are the following:

- Hydrogen can be used as a fuel with very low or zero emissions at the point of use. Of course, this may only mean that the polluting part of the energy conversion chain is being pushed away to a different location – the location at which the hydrogen is produced – rather than avoided altogether. However, it may be that a more centralized production of an energy carrier such as hydrogen gives greater opportunity for that production to be low carbon, which would not be possible at the highly distributed locations where the energy is required – for example, it is not possible to fit every car with a wind turbine or a carbon capture and storage (CCS) plant.
- In many ways, a more obvious carrier of low-carbon energy is electricity – many countries already have extensive electricity infrastructures, and most low-carbon technologies (i.e., wind, wave, tidal, and solar power) produce electricity directly. However, hydrogen has different properties compared with electricity. It is a fuel that can be stored in large quantities and can be dispatched

relatively quickly – electricity on the other hand must be stored in batteries that must be charged, a process that currently takes significantly longer per unit of energy than transferring hydrogen from one storage unit to another.

- As hydrogen is present in so many materials, this gives a range of sources and processes from which molecular hydrogen can be produced. It can be released from water through electrolysis, using electrical energy from any power source; 'reformed' from hydrocarbons – fossil fuels or biomass; or generated biologically through the stimulation of algae or bacteria.

The extent to which these characteristics of hydrogen are sufficiently advantageous compared with other means of carrying energy to give hydrogen a valuable role in a future energy system will be discussed in the following pages.

In what follows, some broad assumptions about the key drivers for hydrogen will be made. Important environmental priorities are considered to be air quality and the mitigation of climate change through reducing greenhouse gas emissions. A number of nations have introduced legislation to drive reduction of greenhouse gas emissions, notably the United Kingdom with its Climate Act of 2008, which sets an 80% reduction target below 1990 levels by 2050, with a requirement for interim carbon budgets [6]. At the EU level, there is a target of reducing greenhouse gas emissions across the EU by 20% compared with 1990 levels by 2020 [7]. The Ambient Air Quality Directive in 2008 set legally binding limits for concentrations in outdoor air of pollutants that affect public health [8]. Hydrogen could contribute to these objectives by replacing the use of fossil fuels in transport and other applications. Another important driver is considered by many to be security of supply and reducing the dependence on resource-constrained fossil fuels. Such a desire, however, need not necessarily be equivalent to a desire to reduce dependence on all fossil fuels. In some particular areas of the world, availability of certain fossil fuels, such as coal, may be high, even as supplies of others, such as oil, become constrained, which could conceivably present a rationale for producing a fuel such as hydrogen, in a carbon-intensive manner from a primary fossil fuel such as coal. However, in this chapter, and especially given the context of this volume, it is assumed that the environmental driver of reducing carbon emissions would be the most compelling motivation for hydrogen, as it would for many other 'clean' technologies.

This chapter will therefore not consider in detail carbon-intensive means of producing hydrogen – although these may be considerably less expensive and therefore have, in a narrow sense, better economic prospects. Thus, it is worth noting at the outset that the key drivers for hydrogen, as with most low-carbon technologies, are 'public goods' – benefits which are felt by society as a whole, not by the individual recipient of the energy service. Whether hydrogen can deliver 'private goods' can vary between applications and will be explored in the sections that follow.

4.03.2 The Hydrogen Energy Chain – Technological Characterizations and Economic Challenges

This section outlines the basic technological components that would be necessary to constitute a hydrogen energy system, describing key technical limitations and barriers as well as challenges from an economic perspective.

Figure 1 is a simplified schematic of the hydrogen energy chain. It shows that hydrogen must be produced from other resources or energy carriers; it must be transported and distributed to the point of use, where it must be stored and can be used to provide energy services for a number of different applications, using a number of different conversion technologies.

Each stage in the hydrogen energy chain involves additional costs as well as energy losses. For this reason, distributed production of hydrogen at a smaller scale, close to the point of demand, can be attractive as it avoids the costs and energy losses of the distribution stage. However, smaller scale production often has higher costs than large-scale production due to lack of economies of scale.

The following sections review estimates of performance and cost data found in the literature, drawing on a range of sources. (As with any such review, it is important to emphasize that the performance and economics of hydrogen technologies is an evolving field. It is highly possible that any figures quoted in this section will become outdated rapidly. Moreover, because several of the processes reviewed here are not currently deployed at a large scale, some of the costs that are given in the literature are projections rather than being based on experience. Hence, this section does not intend to offer definitive data, but the results of a review of available sources at a particular point in time. Cost data are presented as given in the sources, that is, they have not been adjusted to a base year currency. Given the uncertainties associated with these figures in any case, such adjustments were considered to be overly precise. Nonetheless, dates of published sources are given to allow the reader to account for the possibilities of such discrepancies; however, in general, these figures should be viewed as indicative, rather than precise.)

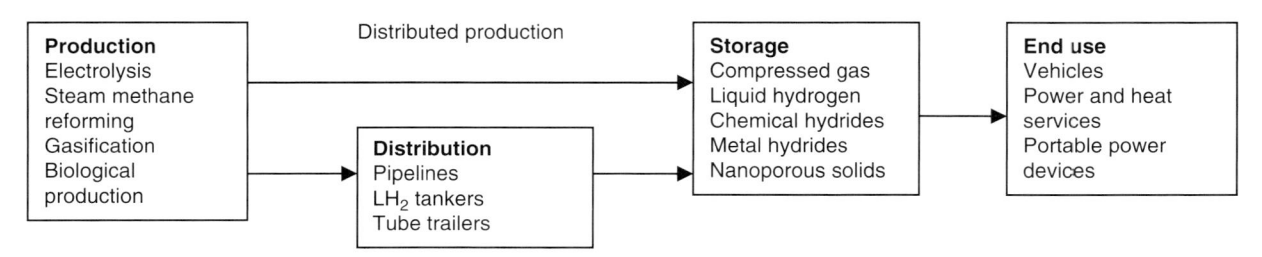

Figure 1 The hydrogen energy chain.

4.03.2.1 Production

Hydrogen production processes are by no means unknown – although the use of hydrogen for applications such as transport is currently insignificant, the International Energy Agency (IEA) reports current hydrogen production of 5 exajoules (EJ) or 100 million tons of oil equivalent (Mtoe), with the vast majority of this used as a feedstock in chemical processes or refineries [9]. (By comparison, the total primary energy supply (TPES) is 11.7 billion toe [10], meaning that current global hydrogen production is equivalent to just under 1% of TPES). Ninety-six percent of this hydrogen was produced directly from fossil fuels, with the remaining 4% from electrolysis [9].

The various methods of hydrogen production are discussed below. As these methods are discussed in greater technical detail in other chapters in this volume, the focus of this discussion will be on the parameters that most influence the overall economics of hydrogen use – the cost of the materials and the efficiency with which hydrogen can be produced from an input energy source.

Broadly, current production methods could deliver hydrogen within a cost range of 2–9 $ kg^{-1} [11]. The US Department of Energy (DOE) has set cost reduction targets for hydrogen production, designed to reduce the cost of hydrogen delivered at the pump to $2.00–3.00 per gallon of gasoline equivalent (gge) (One kilogram of hydrogen is approximately equal to 1 gge.) [12]. This target reflects the long-run expected retail price of gasoline in the United States. However, the situation is of course different depending on the country in question. In the United Kingdom, for example, due to higher fuel taxes, the current retail price of petrol is around £1 litre^{-1}, which is roughly $6 gallon^{-1}. In such a context, hydrogen might seem more competitive as a transport fuel earlier – however, this would of course depend on assumptions about how fuel taxes were being applied to hydrogen. Levels of fuel taxation vary significantly among different countries, as shown in **Figure 2**.

Currently, the United States and several European countries offer tax exemptions or rebates for 'renewable' fuels, aimed at making them cost-competitive with gasoline and diesel – these policies are focused on stimulating biofuel production in the near term but in theory could be extended to 'renewable' hydrogen [14, 15]. However, if in the future such renewable fuels came to account for a substantial percentage of total transport fuel demand, the lost tax earnings of such exemption or rebate policies may encourage their revision.

4.03.2.1.1 Electrolysis

Hydrogen can be produced from the decomposition of water in an electrolysis cell with the addition of an electrical charge. An electrolysis cell requires two electrodes, the anode and the cathode. In the reaction, oxygen (O_2) is produced at the anode (positively charged electrode) and hydrogen (H_2) at the cathode (negatively charged electrode). An electrolyte and catalyst are also required to achieve a workable efficiency in electrolysis cells.

There are two principal electrolyzer technologies. Alkaline electrolyzers use a liquid electrolyte, commonly potassium hydroxide (KOH) solution, whereas proton exchange membrane (or polymer electrolyte membrane) (PEM) electrolyzers operate with a solid polymer electrolyte membrane [16]. PEM electrolyzers in particular are capable of being operated at small scale with no major loss of efficiency [11]. This could provide an attractive option for delivering hydrogen to points of use without the need for a dedicated hydrogen infrastructure – relying instead on the already existing electricity grid for the transmission of energy. At present, state-of-the-art electrolyzer efficiencies are around 67% [17], although future efficiencies of 75% are thought possible [11].

Table 1 compares some recent estimates of costs and efficiencies of hydrogen electrolyzers. The US DOE cost and performance targets are also shown for comparison.

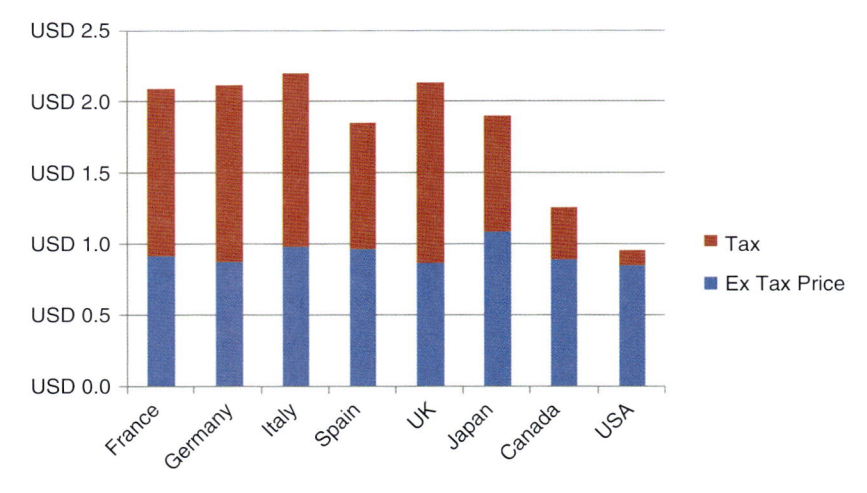

Figure 2 Fuel prices and taxes, September 2011. Source: IEA (2011) End-Use Petroleum Product Prices and Average Crude Oil Import Costs, September 2011. [Online] http://www.iea.org/stats/surveys/mps.pdf [13].

Table 1 Comparison of cost estimates for hydrogen production from electrolysis

Sources	Scale (kg day^{-1})	Electrolyzer capital cost ($ kW^{-1})	Efficiency (%)	Gate cost of hydrogen ($ gge^{-1})
NRC (2004) [11]	480	1000	63.5	6.56
NREL (2009) [17]	Forecourt – 1500	380	67	5.2
NREL (2009) [17]	Central – 50 000	460	67	3
US DOE/EERE targets for 2017				
EERE (2007) [12]	Distributed	125	74	<3
EERE (2007) [12]	Centralized	109	74	<2

Further future cost reductions are considered possible. In current technologies, the catalyst is crucial to achieving acceptable levels of efficiency. For most electrolyzers (as in most fuel cells, FCs), precious metals such as platinum are used for this purpose. It is perhaps unsurprising therefore that the reduction of platinum loading on the catalyst is considered one of the major routes toward reducing the capital cost of electrolyzers and FCs. Efficiency improvements, which would reduce the cost of hydrogen relative to the input electricity, may be achieved through reducing current densities – however, reducing the current density itself can raise the capital costs of the electrolyzer, which can negate any electricity cost savings [18]. Cost reductions would also be expected from mass production of units and simplification of the balance of plant (BOP). However, it should also be noted that the uncertainty that has the greatest impact on the final price of electrolytic hydrogen is the price of electricity [11, 17].

Another development of potential interest is the demonstration at laboratory scale of bioelectrolysis [19–21]. Using similar principles to that of biological FCs, the process uses electrolysis to extract hydrogen from a biological substrate. Using acetic acid – a dead end product of fermentation processes – hydrogen yields of 50–99% of the theoretical maximum of that contained in the substrate have been reported [19]. The electrical charge required to stimulate the process is relatively small – 0.2–0.8 V. Overall efficiencies (accounting for both electrical and biomass inputs) are between 64% and 82%. If the biological substrate were regarded as a waste by-product, and hence discounted as an energy input, the yield of hydrogen compared with the input of electricity alone would be very large – up to 288% of input electricity [19]. The process could be applied to other waste biological matter, including sewage sludge [20].

4.03.2.1.2 Steam methane reforming

The production of hydrogen from natural gas (methane) is currently the cheapest and therefore the most widespread method of production – in 2003, 48% of all hydrogen was produced from natural gas [9].

The process involves the reaction of natural gas with steam over a nickel-based catalyst to produce a syngas comprising hydrogen and carbon monoxide (CO). Carbon monoxide is then converted to carbon dioxide (CO_2) through a water gas shift process, and finally, a pressure swing absorption (PSA) reaction removes high-purity hydrogen [11]. This process of course releases carbon dioxide and therefore the hydrogen cannot be thought of as 'zero carbon'. However, some studies have shown that even hydrogen produced via steam methane reforming (SMR) would have moderate improvements in carbon intensity compared with the use of petroleum fuels in internal combustion engine (ICE) vehicles of current efficiencies [22]. A means of further improving the carbon benefits of SMR hydrogen would be to add CCS to the SMR process. Needless to say, the addition of CCS would add to the cost of hydrogen.

SMR is possible at large and small scales, and some have argued that small-scale reforming at filling station forecourts could be an important step toward facilitating the growth of hydrogen vehicle markets, before a comprehensive hydrogen infrastructure was put in place [9, 11]. However, the loss of economies of scale means that there is a significant cost penalty for small-scale SMR (see **Table 2**). Moreover, small-scale SMR would make CCS virtually impracticable, due to the complexity of the CO_2 transportation

Table 2 Comparison of cost estimates for hydrogen production from SMR

Sources	Scale (kg day^{-1})	Capital cost ($ kW^{-1})[a]	Efficiency (%)	Delivered cost of hydrogen ($ gge^{-1})
NRC (2004) [11]	Distributed – 480	2342	56	3.51
NRC (2004) [11]	Large – 1 200 000	250	72	1.03
NRC (2004) [11]	Large – 1 200 000 with CCS	317	61	1.22
NREL (2006) [23]	Distributed – 1500	1309	64	2.75–3.50
US DOE/EERE targets for 2015				
EERE (2007) [12]	Distributed – 1500	235	75	2

[a] Author calculations from available data in sources.

network that would be required to service many distributed stations. Hence, if hydrogen were ultimately to fulfill its potential as a very low-carbon energy carrier, this would not be a satisfactory long-term option.

Table 2 compares the costs and efficiencies given by different assessments of SMR hydrogen production in the literature. The table is restricted to assessments of current performance and divided into small- and large-scale units. The US DOE hydrogen production cost target is again included for comparison. (The US DOE does not have a target for centralized natural gas production of hydrogen.)

The costs of SMR, as might be expected given the extent to which it is already a widely used and commercialized technology, are in general significantly less than electrolysis. Even the cost of adding CCS to large-scale plants, according to the above estimates [11], would be expected to deliver hydrogen at a cost well within the DOE targets. Distributed production is more expensive; however, the National Renewable Energy Laboratory (NREL) study of current technology suggests a hydrogen price even from distributed SMR that is close to being competitive.

One of the biggest single variable factors on the cost of hydrogen from SMR is the price of the natural gas feedstock. All of the above cost projections are highly sensitive to the natural gas price assumed, as indeed an operational plant would be in reality.

4.03.2.1.3 Gasification

Gasification of solid hydrocarbons is another well-established technology. It is the basis of the now widely deployed integrated gasification combined cycle (IGCC) coal plants. By using heat to gasify coal before combustion, such plants achieve a higher overall combustion efficiency. A new generation of biomass integrated gasification combined cycle (BIGCC) power plants is also being designed and deployed and operate on the same principle [24].

When solid hydrocarbons are gasified, they produce a syngas of hydrogen and carbon monoxide (CO). In order to separate hydrogen from this syngas, a similar process to that described under SMR is required, that is, a water gas shift followed by pressure swing adsorption [11].

It should be remembered that gasification is not purely a hydrogen production method – there are numerous potential ways of using the syngas from gasification apart from producing hydrogen, including direct combustion for heat and power, production of diesel fuels through Fischer–Tropsch synthesis [25], or the synthetic production of methanol [26]. Several commentators have observed that the production of such low-carbon synthetic liquid fuels could contribute to decarbonizing transport without the need for hydrogen and avoiding the complexities associated with storing and transporting hydrogen [4].

Table 3 sets out cost estimates for hydrogen production via gasification, again in comparison with the US DOE hydrogen production target (for biomass gasification).

In this table, the cost of hydrogen from coal appears to be potentially very low. The National Research Council (NRC) notes that for gasification, the delivered cost of hydrogen is much more sensitive to the capital cost of the plant than the coal feedstock cost – the reverse of the case with SMR [11].

Gasification of coal is a well-understood process, occurring as an intermediate stage in most modern coal power plants. IGCC coal plants gasify coal prior to combustion in gas turbines and recovery of waste heat via steam turbines, resulting in increased efficiencies compared with burning solid fuel in conventional boilers. CCS, which can be applied as a postcombustion 'end-of-pipe' separation process on coal plants, can also be included in IGCC-type designs after gasification but before combustion – known as 'precombustion CCS'. In precombustion CCS, CO_2 is separated from the syngas, leaving a hydrogen-rich fuel to be delivered to the turbines. Clearly, this could open up opportunities for the supply of hydrogen as well as electricity. The proposed FutureGen project, a US-based $1 billion public–private partnership to create zero-emission coal-fired power plant, also advertises its potential to coproduce hydrogen [28]. In the United Kingdom, a recent government announcement of the intention to build four CCS demonstration plants indicated that the designs would be a mix of precombustion and postcombustion capture technology [29]. However, so far, the potential for hydrogen to play a role as a separate product in any precombustion plants that are constructed has not been emphasized.

Table 3 Comparison of cost estimates of hydrogen production from gasification

Source	Scale (kg H_2 day^{-1})	Capital cost ($ kW^{-1})[a]	Efficiency (%)	Delivered cost of hydrogen ($ gge^{-1})
NRC (2004) [11] – coal	1 200 000	585	75	0.96
NRC (2004) [11] – coal with CCS	1 200 000	597	75	1.03
NRC (2004) [11] – biomass	24 000	3070	50	4.63
Lau et al. (2002) [27] – switchgrass	148 000	415	64	0.83
Lau et al. (2002) [27] – switchgrass	37 000	601	64	1.13
US DOE/EERE targets for 2017 EERE (2007) [12] – biomass	194 000	345	60	1.1

[a] Author calculations from available data in sources.

Table 4 Summary of hydrogen production options and costs

Process	Inputs	Efficiency (%)	Gate cost of H_2 ($ gge^{-1})	Comments
Electrolysis	Water, electricity	65–75	2–6.5	Other uses compete for electricity
Bioelectrolysis	Biological substrate: acetic acid, sewage sludge, etc.	60–80 overall		Limited by availability of biological substrate
SMR	Methane	50–75	1–3.5	No CCS at small scale
Gasification	Coal	75	0.96–1.03	Could be integrated with precombustion CCS
Gasification	Biomass	50–64	1.1–4.6	Limited by availability of biomass
Biological	Biomass/biological substrate			Limited by availability of biomass
High-temperature water splitting	Water and heat			Not yet demonstrated. Requires high-temperature nuclear plant

4.03.2.1.4 Biological production

Hydrogen can be produced through biological processes, by controlling the photosynthetic behavior of algae or bacteria to encourage these microorganisms to emit hydrogen [30–32]. As with other biological processes, such as the use of algae to produce biofuels, these processes have generated interest due to their avoidance of competition with other resources or energy carriers such as fossil fuels or electricity, as well as their potential to avoid the land-use competition issues that are a problem for most biofuel processes. However, such processes are currently at a very early stage of development [9]. As such, cost data are not available for comparison in Table 4.

4.03.2.1.5 Water splitting through high-temperature heat

In the future, it may be possible to achieve a higher hydrogen yield from decomposition of water through the use of high temperatures, either via electrolysis of steam or by splitting water through thermochemical processes. Such processes would require heat in the range of 700–1000 °C. The use of heat from nuclear power plants has been considered as a potential source of this heat; however, although next generation nuclear plants may operate with such output temperatures, most current generation light water reactors (LWRs) produce heat at only 350 °C [11]. High-temperature processes appear to be considered somewhat speculative; the NRC's 2004 [11] review of hydrogen technologies produced no cost estimates for such processes, and IEA notes that "they are still a long way from being commercially viable" [9].

4.03.2.1.6 Summary of hydrogen production processes

Table 4 summarizes the production processes discussed in this section, showing ranges of costs and efficiencies where available.

Though these cost projections are based on 'current technologies', they are nonetheless uncertain as most have not been demonstrated at any significant scale – key exceptions are coal gasification and SMR. Some options are particularly sensitive to the feedstock costs, in particular SMR and electrolysis. Gasification appears less sensitive to feedstock costs, though the cost ranges associated with biomass gasification reflect the uncertainty of this process that has not been demonstrated at scale. The data suggest that gasification from coal may be one of the cheapest means of producing hydrogen, even including the cost of CCS – although as CCS itself has not yet been demonstrated at scale, additional uncertainties must be admitted here.

All of these production methods involve resources that will be competed for by other processes in the energy system. The fossil fuel resources natural gas and coal may be a core part of a low-carbon electricity system, with CCS. Biomass resources are limited, but could also be used for liquid biofuels, direct heat, or power production. High-temperature heat from nuclear or solar energy could be prioritized for electricity generation. Electricity itself could also be used directly in an increasing range of end uses, including transport and heat.

The gate costs of hydrogen projected by the studies reviewed here are encouragingly within the range of being competitive with oil-based transport fuels. The retail price of petrol in the United Kingdom, as of 2010, is the equivalent of around $6 gge^{-1}, including taxes. However, this is not the only relevant cost comparison – electric vehicles are likely to offer lower running costs. Assuming an electric vehicle with an efficiency of 4 miles kWh^{-1} and an electricity price of 10 pence kWh^{-1} ($0.16), the price of electricity as a transport fuel would be the equivalent of around $1.20 gge.

Further, as the costs indicated are gate costs – the price of the hydrogen as it leaves the production plant – these costs would not reflect the final pump price. For distributed or forecourt production, the pump price may not be significantly greater – however, compression and storage would add additional costs. For centralized plants, greater costs would be accrued as a result of the distribution of hydrogen to end-use points, as shall be discussed in Section 4.03.2.2.

4.03.2.2 Infrastructure

4.03.2.2.1 Costs of hydrogen delivery infrastructure

After production, the next key stage in the hydrogen energy chain is the distribution infrastructure necessary to deliver hydrogen to various possible end uses. The use of hydrogen in the automotive sector raises particular challenges in terms of the infrastructure needed to guarantee the adoption of the energy carrier by consumers. This is due to the highly distributed nature of the energy demand technologies in question – vehicles. As has been noted, decentralized production may offer the potential to 'leapfrog' the infrastructure question; however, small production can lose benefits of economies and scale and therefore have high capital costs. On-site (OS) production also raises challenges for storage (see Section 4.03.2.3).

There are various ways hydrogen could be distributed from centralized production points – as a compressed gas and on board trailers; liquefied and on board trailers; or in pipelines. Table 5 adapted from Hawkins [33] offers a direct cost comparison (in year 2000 US$) between these methods, based on a review of estimates in the literature. The cost ranges vary significantly, between 0.1 and 2 $ kg^{-1} H$_2$ (100 km)$^{-1}$.

Table 5 presents estimated current and target future costs (in year 2005 US$) of key elements of hydrogen distribution infrastructure, from the US DOE's Office of Energy Efficiency and Renewable Energy (EERE)'s Multi-year Research, Development and Demonstration Plan [12]. EERE estimates that transportation via gaseous tube trailers or cryogenic liquid trucks adds between $4 and $9 gge^{-1} to the cost of hydrogen (a kg of hydrogen is approximately equivalent to 1 gge of hydrogen) [12], whereas pipeline distribution costs are typically less than $2 gge^{-1}. The DOE's cost targets for the total contribution of delivery to the cost of hydrogen is <$1 gge^{-1} of hydrogen [12].

Table 5 Costs and characteristics of hydrogen delivery options

	Pipeline	Liquid (road)	Liquid (ship)	Gaseous tube trailer
Total cost added to hydrogen (year 2000 $ kg^{-1}(100 km)$^{-1}$)	0.1–1.0	0.3–0.5	1.8–2.0	0.5–2.0
Comments	Suitable for large volumes	Higher volumes per truck load than compressed gas	Costs uncertain – based on comparison with LNG ships	Small quantities per truck, becomes inefficient at high volumes
	High efficiency	Energy required for liquefaction	Energy required for liquefaction	More suitable for low demands
	Low variable cost but high capital cost	Boil-off losses	Boil-off losses	

Source: Hawkins S (2006) *Technological Characterisation of Hydrogen Storage and Distribution Technologies.* UKSHEC Social Science Working Paper No. 21. London: Policy Studies Institute. www.psi.org.uk/ukshec [33], p. 32, Table 3.2.

Table 6 Current status and EERE technical targets for selected hydrogen delivery chain components

Category	2005 status	2017 target
Pipelines: transmission		
Total capital investment ($k mile^{-1} for a 16-in. pipeline)	700	490
Pipelines: distribution		
Total capital investment ($k mile^{-1} for a 2-in. pipeline)	320	190
Tube trailers		
Delivery capacity (kg of H$_2$)	280	1100
Operating pressure (psi)	2640	<10 000
Purchased capital cost ($)	165 000	<300 000
Liquid hydrogen delivery		
Small-scale liquefaction (30 000 kg H$_2$ day^{-1})		
Installed capital cost ($)	50 million	30 million
Energy efficiency (%)	70	85
Large-scale liquefaction (300 000 kg H$_2$ day^{-1})		
Installed capital cost ($)	170 million	100 million
Energy efficiency (%)	80	87

Source: Adapted from Office of Energy Efficiency and Renewable Energy (EERE) (2007) *Multi Year Research, Development and Demonstration Plan: Planned Program Activities for 2005–2015.* Washington, DC: DOE. http://www1.eere.energy.gov/hydrogenand-fuelcells/mypp/ [12].

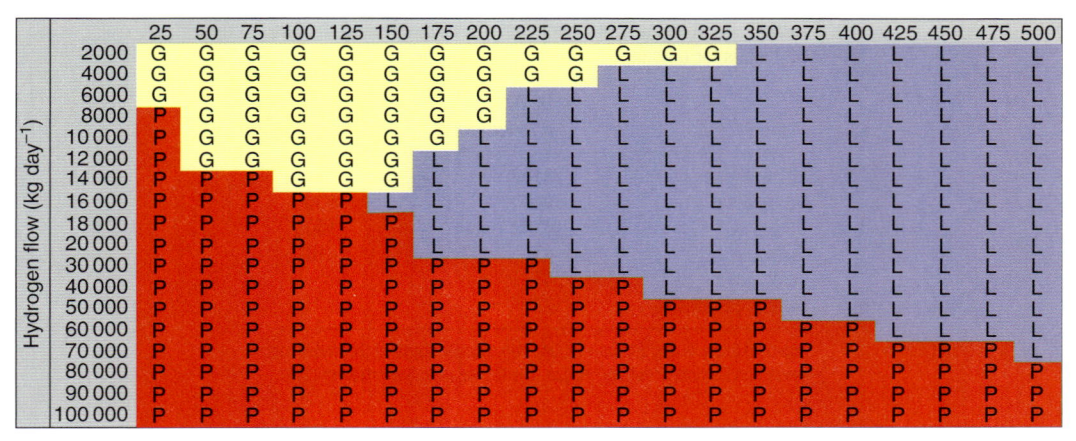

Figure 3 Lowest cost hydrogen delivery options as a function of hydrogen flow (kg day^{-1}) and transport distance (km). G, L, and P indicate compressed gas trucks, liquid trucks, and pipelines, respectively. Reproduced with permission from Yang C and Ogden J (2007) Determining the lowest-cost hydrogen delivery mode. *International Journal of Hydrogen Energy* 32: 268–286 [34]. Copyright (2007) Elsevier.

The potential variability in hydrogen distribution costs is a result of the significant impacts of a number of contextual factors. **Figure 3** illustrates that two of the most significant factors influencing the most cost-effective distribution option are the distance of distribution and the rate of hydrogen supply. The figures on the axes show hydrogen flow rate in kilograms per day (vertical) and delivery distance in kilometers (horizontal). These provide a guide to the regions at which shifts in cost-optimality between delivery options could occur; however, the diagram is not intended as a precise gauge of these points. In reality, the most cost-effective option could also be influenced by topography, planning constraints, road infrastructure, and other location-specific factors.

The broad indication which **Figure 3** is intended to give is that at low levels of demand and short distances, compressed gas trailer distribution is usually most cost-effective – it has low energy density but avoids the upfront costs of liquefaction or pipeline construction. Over longer distances, the costs of liquefaction can be justified, as the greater energy density compared with gaseous hydrogen will reduce the number of trucks required, hence reducing fuel costs, which become a dominant part of the cost over longer distances. Liquefaction could be an important option if hydrogen is imported from other countries, that is, over considerably long distances. At higher levels of demand, pipelines can be the cost-optimal option – pipelines are less sensitive to volume than distance, as the incremental cost of installing a wider pipeline is small compared with the additional cost of building the pipeline for an additional mile (**Table 6**). However, pipelines are an inflexible investment with high upfront costs, and hence would only be built when hydrogen demand was sufficiently high and certain. Thus, a key logistical challenge facing hydrogen infrastructure is the apparent paradox that is hard to stimulate demand for vehicles while no supporting infrastructure exists, and yet at the same time it is not economic to make large infrastructure investments in advance of significant numbers of vehicles being on the roads.

4.03.2.2.2 Capacity factors and infrastructure design

During the introduction of hydrogen in the transport sector, capacity factors will play an important role in the adoption of the fuel. The capacity factor is defined as the average consumption, output, or throughput over a period of time of a particular technology or piece of infrastructure, divided by its consumption, output, or throughput if it had operated at full (rated) capacity over that time period. Capacity factors influence the price of hydrogen needed to obtain a certain rate of return on the investment. However, for some time after introduction, high capacity factors might be extremely challenging to achieve, and low capacity factors achieved in the years after construction could cause financial problems for investors if capital has to be paid back. There is clearly a trade-off between economies of scale and capacity factors. While economies of scale for capital equipment encourage the construction of large-scale high-capacity infrastructure, such larger investments risk lower capacity factors in earlier years due to underutilization, leading to higher hydrogen cost [34].

Due to this interplay between capacity factors and economies of scale, the development of hydrogen infrastructure will be influenced by both the actual and anticipated hydrogen demands. These can be identified on the basis of population size and density, car ownership, and average vehicle use [35]. The optimal location of hydrogen delivery infrastructure can then be determined by minimizing the distance between hydrogen production and consumption centers. In the case of refueling stations in a city, one can determine the number of stations based on the average maximum distance of drivers to the closest hydrogen station. In the case of roads connecting residential centers, some authors have suggested a distance between hydrogen stations of a maximum 50 miles in the early stages of the deployment of the infrastructure. In the second phase, this will be shortened to 20 miles in order to increase the convenience of motorists. Another approach consists in determining the amount of hydrogen that would be required by cars when driving on intercity roads [36]. It should be mentioned that minimizing the average driving time tends to favor siting of stations near populations that would otherwise have to drive a long distance, and that this method does not guarantee that a similar percentage of total demand is allocated to each station [37].

Table 7 Average investment cost of hydrogen filling stations. OS stands for on-site

Station	USD (in thousands)	kg day^{-1}
All nonhome	3400	
OS medium	2400	500
OS big	5700	1000
Home	4.8	<10
Central liquid H$_2$	487	
Central gaseous H$_2$	781	

Source: Mulder F and Girard J (2004) Policy Implications of the Investment Needs and Economic Viability. Hague, The Netherlands: SenterNovem [39].

4.03.2.2.3 Costs of hydrogen refueling stations

Regardless of their location and capacity factors, it is fair to say that hydrogen refueling stations will be more expensive than those needed by other alternative fuels. For example, the cost of converting a current filling station to dispense 50 000 gge month^{-1} is US $1.4 million in the case of hydrogen, US$0.9 million for compressed natural gas (CNG), and US$0.6 million for liquefied natural gas (LNG) [38]. The cost for methanol, ethanol, dimethyl ether (DME), and liquefied petroleum gas (LPG) is reported to be about US$200 000, whereas in the case of biodiesel, no significant conversion costs are implied. An extensive assessment of the cost of hydrogen filling stations has been undertaken by Mulder and Girard [39], whose conclusions are presented in **Table 7**. The much higher cost of filling stations that include OS hydrogen production is due to the fact that they comprise the entire infrastructure needed to introduce hydrogen for the transport system. In the case of central stations, that is, stations dispensing centrally produced hydrogen that is shipped to the station by truck or pipeline, the investment cost of distribution and production should be added to that of the filling station to obtain the total investment costs.

The uncertainty of the costs of building the entire infrastructure needed to produce, deliver, and retail hydrogen in the transport sector is of course even bigger than the uncertainty related to the cost of the single components, such as the filling stations in **Table 7**. In fact, the cost of the single components is only one of the several factors influencing total investment costs of a scenario. When trying to estimate the capital cost of the infrastructure, it is important to assess the entire infrastructure needed to deliver hydrogen to the transport system, that is, including hydrogen production costs (discussed in Section 4.03.2.1) and hydrogen storage costs (discussed in Section 4.03.2.3) alongside questions of utilization and capacity factor. Overall, the infrastructure needed for hydrogen is much more expensive than for methanol and CNG [38].

The estimates of the hydrogen price needed to make this infrastructure financially viable vary greatly in the literature. This is not surprising if one considers the different assumptions used in different studies and the uncertainty related to capital costs. However, there seems to be a wide agreement that the capacity factor of hydrogen infrastructure is the single most important factor influencing the price of hydrogen [39–41]. By influencing hydrogen price, capacity factors also have an effect on the competitiveness of different infrastructures to deliver hydrogen. For example, one study discovered that OS SMR is not competitive with centralized coal production when assuming that the infrastructure is fully utilized and spatially optimized, that is, sited in the best locations, although it becomes much more competitive when these two conditions do not apply [42].

Table 8 shows a summary of the findings from the extensive survey of the literature conducted by Mulder and Girard [39]. Large hydrogen stations (defined by Mulder and Girard as stations with a throughput of 1000 kg day^{-1}) with hydrogen produced OS can deliver very competitively priced hydrogen. Unfortunately, these very low prices can be achieved only when the market becomes well-established and there will be enough customers to warrant filling stations of considerable size [43]. **Table 8** indicates that hydrogen delivered by using electrolysis is much more expensive than hydrogen delivered from other feedstocks. However, the table suggests that small filling stations with hydrogen produced OS are comparatively economic. This reflects that in these cases, the smaller size of the stations avoids underutilization, which compensates for the loss of economies of scale compared with larger stations. Considering a geographically sparse demand in the years after market introduction, low capacity factors are likely to be obtained regardless of station size. However, all things being equal, smaller stations will increase the convenience to customers and therefore may increase the penetration rates of hydrogen.

4.03.2.2.4 Introducing hydrogen infrastructure – Incremental or step-change approaches

The complexity of the issues relating to the codependence of transport technologies with their supporting infrastructure, such that investments in one are inhibited by lack of preceding investments in the other, as well as the complex interactions between capacity factors and economies of scale in decisions about size and siting of new infrastructure leads to contrasting views as to the appropriate strategy for rolling out new technological infrastructure systems, such as hydrogen transportation systems. These strategies can be summarized as 'incremental' or 'step-change' approaches.

Some contributions have advocated the adoption of an incremental approach in the introduction of hydrogen infrastructure [44]. The principle of this is that a large-scale system can eventually be reached by implementing small incremental steps across successive market segments.

Table 8 Hydrogen price from different typologies of stations. Figures are in euros per petrol liter equivalent

	Average	Range	
All nonhome stations	0.93	0.34	0.93
All nonhome stations – nonelectro	0.76	0.34	1.28
All nonhome stations – electro	1.23	0.66	3.09
On-site and small	0.77	0.66	0.88
On-site and medium	1.02		
On-site medium electro	1.6	0.77	3.09
On-site and big	0.61	0.34	0.97
Home stations	1.74	1.5	2.06
Central	1.11	0.51	2.33
Central – electro	1.84	1.24	1.5
Central liquid – nonelectro	0.86	0.59	1.27
Central gaseous – nonelectro	1.05	0.51	2.05

Source: Mulder F and Girard J (2004) Policy Implications of the Investment Needs and Economic Viability. Hague, The Netherlands: SenterNovem [39].

The viability of the incremental approach for hydrogen in the transport sector in particular is based on the underlying assumptions that (1) some economic actors receive higher benefits from early adoption of hydrogen vehicles than others and (2) some actors may be less sensitive to the inconvenience of adopting a technology for which the supporting infrastructure is not yet extensive. Customers who find it convenient to switch to hydrogen earlier allow producers to accrue revenues that can fund further R&D needed to decrease the cost of the new products, thereby increasing the appeal of the technology to a wider pool of potential customers. According to many authors, the first step to initiate this virtuous circle consists of the establishment of demonstration projects, followed by the introduction of hydrogen among fleets. Fleet vehicles have the supposed advantages of being regularly refueled and undergoing maintenance at one location and driving along fixed routes or at least within a certain area.

However, some authors have pointed out that very few fleets refuel and are repaired exclusively at the depot [45]. In addition, infrastructure development at fleet depots may not increase fuel availability for the general public, as many fleet depots are located in restricted or inconvenient locations [46, 47].

In the incremental approach, after hydrogen has penetrated the fleet market, early adopters of hydrogen vehicles are central to the diffusion of the fuel in the passenger market, as they may be more willing to bear the inconvenience of a limited refueling infrastructure [41]. Early adopters will live in urban areas as the first filling stations will be built in such areas due to a higher population density, number of potential customers, and per-capita income. After the early adopters, hydrogen will be adopted by the remaining consumers until it reaches a significant share of the market.

The incremental approach is therefore dependent upon the existence of some early adopters for whom the attractions of the new technologies outweigh the inconvenience of their lack of supporting infrastructure. However, if the existence of such a market segment is in doubt, an alternative strategy would be to advocate a 'step-change approach'. In the case of hydrogen used in the transport sector, growth of the new technology is inhibited because the new fuel will have a higher price than the dominant fuel, and investments are characterized by long lead times [48]. A slow build-up of refueling infrastructure is not attractive to industries focused on mass markets such as the automotive and fuel supply industries [49]. The step-change solution therefore consists of fostering a high degree of coordination of large-scale investments among all involved stakeholders simultaneously, that is, fuel providers, car manufacturers, government, and consumers [41]. A number of authors have identified that 10% of current filling stations would be required to ensure that a large fraction of potential fuel cell vehicle (FCV) buyers have comfortable access to hydrogen fueling [34, 41, 50] and have calculated that this number of filling stations could be converted in about 5 years. While this may be possible, it may be difficult to introduce sufficiently quickly a large enough number of cars to guarantee a decent capacity factor to these stations. A successful vehicle introduction, that is, hybrid vehicles, took about a decade to reach 0.5% share of the market. Thirty percent of the total vehicle fleet in 2050 can be reached only if FCVs expand at an annual growth rate similar to that experienced over 1960–2000 by the semiconductor industry (which faced no competition) [18]. Additional barriers to such a rapid market penetration could be supply chain issues such as the availability of trained mechanics and dealerships and institutional or regulatory issues such as the existence of codified standards and health and safety legislation. The absence of such codes and legislation could inhibit the use of hydrogen technologies in public locations or complicate their qualification for insurance and warranties [51].

4.03.2.3 Storage

4.03.2.3.1 Storage technologies and performance in relation to onboard vehicle requirements

The properties of hydrogen as a lightweight gas are such that although it has a high energy density per unit of weight (gravimetric energy density – 142 MJ kg^{-1} (higher heating value, HHV)), its energy density per unit of volume (volumetric energy density – 12.8 MJ m^{-3}

(HHV)) is very low. In some storage applications, this low volumetric energy density may not present serious problems, for example, where hydrogen is stored in bulk for industrial uses and where space is not a constraint. However, for many applications, low volumetric energy density is a significant disadvantage. Storage capacity at filling stations or refueling points is limited by space (although if hydrogen was distributed through a pipeline network, this infrastructure could reduce the need for OS storage). Perhaps most acutely though, the need for storage on board vehicles that use hydrogen as their fuel is limited by the size of the body of the vehicle and the space it also requires within that body for carrying its engine, passengers, and cargo. It should be remembered, however, that the storage constraints and requirements may vary quite significantly between different kinds of vehicles – the requirements for storage capacity are different for a car, a bus, or a ship, for example.

There are numerous approaches to improve the volumetric energy density of hydrogen in development, which broadly takes the approach of either altering the state of the hydrogen through compression or liquefaction or trapping the hydrogen physically or chemically within a specially designed material. However, as such approaches improve the volumetric energy density, they suffer increasing penalties in other important areas, including the weight of the overall system (gravimetric energy density), the additional input energy required for the system to function, the speed with which the hydrogen can be loaded or discharged, other practical and engineering challenges such as management of nonambient temperatures or pressures required by the system, and, crucially, cost. The following paragraphs briefly discuss a number of the approaches to hydrogen storage currently in development and the extent to which they involve trade-offs in these different parameters. Table 9 then presents a recent comparison of costs, though as several of the systems mentioned are still at the experimental stage, this summary is unlikely to be definitive.

This simplest way to increase the volumetric energy density of hydrogen is to store it as a compressed gas. Gas compression for storage is a common process – compression of hydrogen to around 300–400 bar is common in the refining and chemical industries (by comparison, natural gas is commonly stored at 200–250 bar). However, for vehicles, such pressures would still produce inadequate energy densities. In order to improve energy densities, vehicle manufacturers are now designing onboard vehicle storage tanks designed to hold hydrogen at 700 bar [52]. This would store $0.039\,\mathrm{kg\,H_2\,l^{-1}}$ [53], resulting in an energy density about one-sixth that of petrol. Tanks designed for such high pressures, however, are likely to use heavier materials than more conventional storage tanks, incurring a weight penalty on the system as a whole.

Liquid hydrogen has a considerably higher volumetric energy density than gaseous hydrogen, storing $0.07\,\mathrm{kg\,H_2\,l^{-1}}$ [53], providing a volumetric energy density just under a third of that of petrol. Hence, the liquefaction of hydrogen can have benefits for the convenience of storing and transporting hydrogen, and the process is currently employed in industrial uses of hydrogen. The key disadvantage with liquefaction is the considerable energy input required to liquefy the hydrogen initially – hydrogen must be cooled to $-253\,°C$ to become liquid – and to maintain it at this temperature while in storage. It has been estimated that the energy required for the initial liquefaction of hydrogen is over 30% that of the lower heating value of hydrogen [53]. Another potentially serious issue is that liquid hydrogen has a natural 'boil-off' rate that is unavoidable, no matter how well insulated the storage vessel. Though in larger storage vessels this can be less critical, at around 0.06% day^{-1}, for smaller vessels (such as the fuel tank of a car), the rate could amount to 2–3% day^{-1} [33, 53].

Bulk underground storage is a cheap option for large-scale storage of hydrogen, but is limited to areas with a suitable natural geology. In the United Kingdom, the storage of hydrogen at Teesside for industrial uses is achieved in underground salt caverns [54]. Novel methods of hydrogen storage are currently the subject of exploration at the laboratory scale, as well as to a limited extent in prototype vehicle demonstrations. Chemical hydrides can store hydrogen within a liquid slurry, with high gravimetric and volumetric energy density, which releases hydrogen on being exposed to water, in a highly exothermic reaction. The reaction leaves behind a spent fuel (metal hydroxide) that can be recycled as a hydrogen store – but this regeneration requires high temperatures and must be undertaken at a central processing plant. In the context of vehicle storage then, chemical hydrides are seen as requiring 'off-board' regeneration [53], which would impose a rather different refueling paradigm upon car users.

Metal hydrides are solid materials that can chemically bond with hydrogen, 'storing' it in their molecular framework and releasing it when required. In contrast to chemical hydrides, within a vehicle, these compounds could take up hydrogen and be

Table 9 Status of hydrogen storage technologies relative to targets

	Energy capacity		System cost ($ kWh^{-1})
	Volumetric (kWh l^{-1})	Gravimetric (kWh kg^{-1})	
Chemical hydrides	1.0	1.4	8
Metal hydrides	0.6	0.8	16
Liquid H$_2$	1.2	1.7	6
700 bar gas	0.8	1.6	18
350 bar gas	0.5	1.9	15
2010 target	**1.5**	**2.0**	**4**
2015 target	**2.7**	**3.0**	**2**

Source: Data from National Research Council (NRC) (2005) Review of the Research Program of the Freedom Car and Fuel Partnership. Washington, DC: National Academies Press [56].

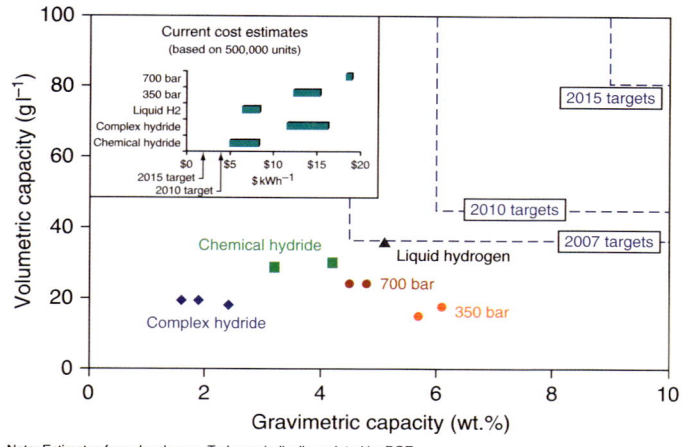

Figure 4 The 2007 status of hydrogen system storage capacity and costs. Reprinted with permission from Satyapal S, Petrovic J, Read C, et al. (2007) The U.S. Department of Energy's National Hydrogen Storage Project: Progress towards meeting hydrogen-powered vehicle requirements. *Catalysis Today* 120: 246–256 [53]. Copyright (2007) Elsevier.

regenerated 'onboard' – a more familiar refueling paradigm for users. Again, high temperatures are involved in the storage processes – hydrogen absorption (uptake) is exothermic, whereas desorption is endothermic, requiring temperatures greater than 250 °C. The management of such temperatures would present challenges on board vehicles. Kinetics, or speed with which hydrogen is absorbed or released, are problematic for metal hydrides and require further research [55].

Nanoporous materials, often produced from carbon-based materials, can deliver storage with good kinetics and good reversibility (i.e., the material can be reused without significant loss of performance). These materials involve physisorption processes – the hydrogen is trapped in physical spaces within the material, rather than held in chemical bonds. In contrast to the chemical and metal hydrides, they require very low temperatures – for example, 77 K – for adsorption, and their level of hydrogen storage by percentage of weight (wt.%) is generally less than the above two categories [53].

The US DOE provides a range of targets for the performance of hydrogen storage systems. These targets represent in material and engineering terms the performance that would be required for the system to deliver comparable performance to a current mainstream vehicle, characterized as at least 300 miles of range, a refueling time of 2.5 min for 5 kg, a system cost of $30 kW^{-1}, and a number of other parameters related to life-cycling ability and toxicity [53]. **Figure 4** indicates the performance of the different categories of hydrogen storage systems in comparison with two of the US DOE system targets for 2007, 2010, and 2015 – those for volumetric and gravimetric energy density. As the diagram shows, all storage methods are currently some way from meeting the 2015 targets, which would be required to achieve 'similar performance to today's gasoline vehicles' [53]. It should also be remembered that other parameters will also be crucial to the practical performance of any storage material, notably kinetics, reversibility, and temperature required for hydrogen uptake/desorption.

Figure 4 also indicates the estimated system costs of the various storage methods in relation to 2010 and 2015 targets. These costs do not include regeneration or processing of materials as part of the storage process, or for liquid hydrogen the cost of liquefaction. **Table 9** outlines another set of cost estimates for the various kinds of storage, with similar ranges. Costs for metal hydride, chemical hydride, and nanoporous solid storage systems are highly uncertain as many of these materials are at the laboratory scale and have not been built to scale.

As indicated by **Figure 4** and **Table 9**, no current technologies are capable of meeting the storage requirements set by US DOE targets for satisfactory performance of hydrogen vehicles. The reviewing committee of the FreedomCar program reported hydrogen storage to be one of the 'greater risks for reaching the program goals in 2015', stressing that the area needs a 'breakthrough discovery as the forerunner of development and innovation [56]'. This perception was confirmed in a more recent review of storage technologies [55]. This latter paper also proposed a number of possible ways in which performance could be improved and suggested that computer simulations could help to guide the development of improved storage materials. However, such developments, and the prospects for hydrogen storage in general, appear not significantly different from how they were at the time of the NRC review [56] – uncertain and dependent on a technological breakthrough that is essentially impossible to anticipate.

4.03.2.3.2 *Storage applications*

Before concluding this section on storage, it is important to mention the various kinds of applications for which hydrogen storage could be required. As has been mentioned, the US DOE storage system targets are based on requirements for onboard hydrogen storage for conventional vehicles, which might be thought of as the average family car. However, other hydrogen storage applications may have different requirements, and these should be considered too.

An important storage application for any widespread use of hydrogen in transport would be at a filling station or refueling point. This would be particularly important if the infrastructure was not served by pipelines. Clearly, volumetric energy density would remain important, but gravimetric energy density would not be such a binding constraint for a stationary hydrogen store.

Hydrogen has been demonstrated as a fuel for marine vessels (see Section 4.03.2.4.8 on applications for further discussion). The storage requirements for marine applications would again be different from those of cars. Volumetric constraints might be less binding, as to a certain extent would gravimetric constraints. Management of nonambient temperatures would also be less challenging on a large marine vessel than on board a car – indeed it is possible that waste heat, for example, released by chemical hydride systems, could be reused to heat water for onboard services.

If hydrogen was used as an energy storage medium to smooth out intermittency on the electricity grid (see Section 4.03.3.2) again gravimetric energy density would not be a concern – as hydrogen used for electricity storage would be a stationary store. Depending on the location, volumetric density might not be such a constraint either. An important parameter would be the kinetics or speed with which hydrogen could be released. The coproduction of hydrogen in IGCC coal CCS plants may see a growing need for storage with similar characteristics.

In the absence of a pipeline infrastructure, a denser way of transporting hydrogen on board trucks, but which avoids the energy penalties of liquefaction, might also be extremely beneficial.

Table 10 sets out a range of possible hydrogen storage applications and compares the different performance requirements that might apply to them.

4.03.2.4 End-Use Technologies and Applications

The final stage of the hydrogen energy chain involves the conversion of the energy present in the hydrogen that is delivered to the point of use to useful energy services – power, heat, or motion. This can be achieved broadly in two ways: combustion or the use of an FC for direct generation of electricity.

4.03.2.4.1 End-use technologies – ICEs

The ICE may be a preferred option for the extraction of energy from hydrogen, as it is a mature and low-cost technology, in contrast to FCs (discussed in Section 4.03.2.4.2) that are currently considerably more expensive than other power trains. However, ICEs in general have a lower efficiency of conversion of hydrogen than FCs. Indeed, because hydrogen has a higher burning velocity than most hydrocarbons, it can cause a larger heat transfer to the combustion chamber walls, causing a cooling loss that can make hydrogen ICEs less efficient than conventional hydrocarbon-fueled engines [57].

For hydrogen vehicles, the main proponent of the ICE approach has for some years been BMW, whose Hydrogen 7 vehicle is a flex-fuel vehicle able to switch between hydrogen and petrol. As the lower efficiency of the engine reduces the potential range of the vehicle, the Hydrogen 7 vehicle is designed with liquid hydrogen storage, to compensate for this with increased fuel storage density. However, a recent announcement by the company claims that hydrogen combustion has been demonstrated with an efficiency of 42%, equaling that of advanced turbodiesel engines [58].

4.03.2.4.2 End-use technologies – FCs

In general, more efficient extraction of energy from hydrogen can be achieved through the use of an FC, which converts fuel directly into electricity. An FC is an electrochemical cell in which a fuel reacts with an oxidant in the presence of an electrolyte to produce electrical power. There are a number of different kinds of FCs, which can be broadly divided into those that operate at high temperatures or at low temperatures. High-temperature FCs, such as solid oxide fuel cells (SOFCs), have the advantage that they are

Table 10 Possible applications for hydrogen storage and associated performance characteristics

	Capacity	Thermodynamics	Kinetics	Reversibility
CCS hydrogen storage	Not space or weight constrained	Could use heat from power plant	Fast	Important
Stand-alone grid intermittency management	Not space or weight constrained	Input heat not available but potential to reuse desorption heat in district heating	Fast	Important
'Island' renewables storage	Not space or weight constrained	Input heat not available but potential to reuse desorption heat in district heating	Fast	Important
Shipping	Some space and weight constraints but less than cars	Excessive desorption heat undesirable, though moderate heat potentially manageable on large craft	Medium-fast	'Spent' fuel can be off-loaded at port
Trailer distribution	Both volumetric and gravimetric density important	High or low temperatures for uptake or desorption could be managed at loading or unloading depots	Less important	Less important

Table 11 Characteristics of different FC types

FC type	Operating temperature (°C)	System output	Electrical efficiency	CHP efficiency	Applications	Advantages
Polymer electrolyte membrane (PEM)	50–100	<1–250 kW	53–58% (transportation) 25–35% (stationary)	70–90%	Backup power Portable power Small distributed generation Transportation	Low temperature Quick start up
Alkaline (AFC)	90–100	10–100 kW	60%	>80%	Military space	Faster cathode reaction gives higher performance
Phosphoric acid (PAFC)	150–200	50 kW–1 MW	>40%	>85%	Distributed generation	High CHP efficiency Tolerant to impurities in hydrogen
Molten carbonate (MCFC	600–700	<1kW–1 MW	45–47%	>80%	Electric utility Large distributed generation	High efficiency Fuel flexibility Heat output suitable for CHP
Solid oxide	600–100	<1 kW–3 MW	35–43%	<90%	Auxiliary power Electric utility Large distributed generation	High efficiency Fuel flexibility Heat output suitable for CHP

Source: Adapted from US DOE (2008) Comparison of fuel cell technologies, fact sheet. http://www1.eere.energy.gov/hydrogenandfuelcells/fuelcells/pdfs/fc_comparison_chart.pdf [61].

able to operate on a range of fuels including methane, as the high temperature 'internally reforms' hydrocarbons into hydrogen and carbon dioxide. Low-temperature FCs, such as the PEM fuel cell (PEMFC), are not capable of internal reforming and so require a pure stream of hydrogen as their fuel. Direct methanol fuel cells (DMFCs) are a type of PEMFC, operating at temperatures of 60–90 °C, designed for specific operation on methanol. These are finding emerging markets in portable power applications as well as in niche vehicles [59, 60]. Table 9 compares the performance of a range of FCs, based on data from the US DOE [61].

It is clear from Table 11 that high-temperature FCs in particular can operate on a range of fuels. For this reason, although there is an overlap between FCs and hydrogen, as FCs are usually the most efficient means of converting hydrogen to energy, the overlap is not total – FCs could quite successfully be employed in a number of applications independently of hydrogen as a fuel.

The usual choice for the conversion of hydrogen in transportation applications is the PEMFC, whereas stationary hydrogen applications would often use phosphoric acid fuel cells (PAFCs). The PEMFC uses the same materials as the PEM electrolyzer described in the previous section, but operating in reverse. However, Table 11 shows a considerably lower electrical efficiency for this reverse reaction than that given for electrolysis in Table 1. This is due to the fact that in an FC some of the energy of the fuel is released as heat.

4.03.2.4.3 Applications – Stationary power

FCs are being increasingly used as a means of providing clean and efficient heat and power at a district scale, driven both by air quality legislation and by the attraction to users such as companies and local authorities of deploying innovative 'clean' technologies. The installation rate for such applications has hovered around 50 yr^{-1} globally for the last few years [62]. However, whether these applications can be said to be bringing about a dedicated hydrogen fuel supply chain is questionable. Forty percent of the units supplied in 2008 were molten carbonate fuel cells (MCFCs), capable of internally reforming fossil fuels; a little less than another 40% of the market share was taken by PAFCs, and it is likely that many of these are constructed with an OS reformer to extract hydrogen from natural gas, as in the combined heat and power (CHP) unit installed by the Woking Council in the United Kingdom [63].

PEMFCs are now the dominant technology for small stationary power, a market segment in which uninterruptible power supplies (UPS) are the major application [64]. This demand is driven by the needs of some users to have backup power, due to the significant costs that accrue to their operations in the case of grid power cuts. Approximately 4000 of such units were shipped in 2008. Only a third of these require direct hydrogen, as the remainder use fossil fuels with an OS reformer [64].

Some commentators have considered a more extensive use of hydrogen for stationary power, involving the distribution of hydrogen through a pipeline network at least as extensive as the current natural gas grid, for direct heat and power production in homes. Such a scenario was included in a set of possible hydrogen futures for the United Kingdom developed by McDowall and Eames [65]. The scenarios were the result of extensive consultation with a wide range of stakeholders holding views about the prospects for hydrogen and were intended to represent the breadth of these views. Though excitement about such 'ubiquitous' hydrogen scenarios has been raised in the past (perhaps most notably in Jeremy Rifkin's book 'The Hydrogen Economy' [1]), views within the emerging hydrogen community have in recent years tended to put less emphasis on them. In such a scenario, hydrogen would be replacing, at vast expense, an energy carrier for which a dedicated infrastructure already exists that is itself a crucial carrier of low-carbon energy – electricity. With energy system modeling studies consistently showing the importance of electricity in a low-carbon economy [66, 67], and bearing in mind the still considerable technical and economic challenges to hydrogen described in the previous sections, the ubiquitous hydrogen option is currently less prominently presented as a practicable and cost-effective route to decarbonization [68].

4.03.2.4.4 Applications – Auxiliary power and 'niche' applications

Recent work within science and technology studies has observed that major technological transitions can sometimes be said to have sprung from particular 'niches', which have provided 'protected spaces' for a certain area of technological novelty that has subsequently been taken up on a large scale within the wider 'landscape', in areas including shipping, aviation, and public health and sanitation [69–71]. Hydrogen and FCs can be said to be operating at present within certain 'niche' markets, which occur due to particular needs of certain consumers [59, 60, 62, 64]. This section explores the drivers behind the current emergent demand for hydrogen and FC technologies within one particular market niche – auxiliary power units (APUs) – and explores whether this niche demand could transfer to the wider markets. A more detailed discussion of this particular application can be found in Agnolucci and McDowall [72].

APUs are often hailed as one of the more promising early applications of FCs [73, 74]. APUs may be desired as a source of power on board vehicles in addition to the main ICE, to provide power and heat for onboard services, such as entertainment, heating, and air-conditioning. As well as the more efficient use of fuel that they can achieve in comparison with drawing power from the main ICE, the potential benefits of FCs in APU applications could also be their clean and silent operation, compared with ICEs. How much these particular benefits are valued depends of course on the user and the application. Two of the competing FC technologies for APU applications are PEMFCs and SOFCs.

The interest in the development of FC APUs is a result of the considerable rise in electric power demands onboard civilian vehicles [75]. Among the different markets for FC APUs, civilian vehicles, luxury passenger vehicles, recreational vehicles, and line-haul heavy-duty trucks are the most promising markets for early adoption. For recreational vehicles (motorized caravans), the attraction of an auxiliary source of power would be to allow users to experience in the wilderness the same comfort that is currently enjoyed only in recreational vehicle parks, while avoiding the intrusive noise of a conventional generator. Adamson [76] reports that an FC APU from Smart Fuel Cell has been integrated as standard equipment in the S-class, that is, the premium line of Hymer vehicles (http://www.hymer.com/eu).

In the luxury passenger vehicle market, the trend for increasing onboard power demands from comfort and entertainment systems might create demands for APUs. However, FC APUs are a competitive alternative to ICEs only for those devices requiring more or less constant power when the primary ICE is off (i.e., when the vehicle is stationary) [77]. Meissner and Richter [78] are skeptical about the need for new power sources as several of the new functions, especially those aiming at improved reliability and comfort, can be satisfied by existing 14 V electrical systems. The appeal of FC APUs would be weakened by the diffusion of hybrid electric vehicles, as these vehicles will have large batteries.

In line-haul trucks, APUs could substitute discretionary idling, that is, the continued running of the engine while the vehicle is stationary to provide heat and power services, especially when drivers sleep overnight in the truck [74, 79, 80]. However, the growing availability of plug-in electric points at truck stops may reduce the comparative attraction of FC APUs in this niche [70, 74, 80]. Military applications may also offer a promising near-term market for FC APUs in 'Silent Watch' settings, that is, a tactical mode of operation demanding full electrical power for all mission activities except mobility, without the acoustic and infrared signature of an ICE [72]. The deployment of technologies in niche applications can in some cases precede a wider penetration in larger markets [72]. Experience gained through manufacturing and producing technologies in niche applications can begin to create economies of scale, which lead to reduced costs of the technology, making it more attractive to wider markets. When a technology becomes successfully established in a niche market, expectations about its future performance are enhanced, and investors gain confidence in the possibilities of the technology in other applications [81]. Internal economies of scale occur at the level of a single firm, where cost per unit of output decreases as the output increases. External economies of scale – benefits which accrue at the level of the industry or local cluster, rather than within the individual firms – can also grow from niche applications. A firm in a cluster or in a bigger industry can benefit from rapid informal dissemination and absorption of innovations and new skills, qualified and easily accessible specialized labor, efficient machinery tailored to the needs of the industry, and larger supplier networks so that transaction costs decrease [72].

Thus, it might be argued that success in niche applications such as APUs could allow the FC industry to grow, which could improve the prospects for hydrogen due to its close association with FCs. However, the increasing technological separation between different FC applications may reduce the potential for such spillover benefits [72, 82]. PEMFCs (the most likely fuel technology for hydrogen vehicles) seem to have a secondary role in these niche markets where SOFCs and DMFCs are the more prominent technologies [82]. The development of tailored machineries and input suppliers for SOFC or DMFC APUs is likely to be of limited importance for PEMFCs used in the vehicle or stationary power markets. This implies that the improvements experienced by firms producing FC APUs might only have a limited role in the diffusion of technologies relevant to the wider 'hydrogen economy' [82].

4.03.2.4.5 Applications – Passenger transport

Transport is generally considered to be one of the hardest sectors within the energy system to decarbonize. However, increasing concerns over the levels by which emissions must be reduced, represented in the United Kingdom by a shift, from 2005 to 2008, from a 60% to an 80% emissions reduction target by mid-century, have increasingly put transport among the sectors considered to require very deep decarbonization [66, 67]. Assuming that incremental efficiency improvements in conventional ICEs would not be sufficient to deliver such deep decarbonization in the transport sector, there are broadly three kinds of technological option: biofuels, electric vehicles, or hydrogen vehicles.

Each option has advantages and disadvantages. Biofuels, as liquid hydrocarbons, would require only relatively modest and incremental changes to vehicle technologies and fuel distribution infrastructure to be widely used. In theory, biofuels could substitute for hydrocarbon fuels across all transport technologies, including aviation. Electricity is a long established transport energy carrier – transport was one of the earliest applications for electrical power in the United Kingdom, through the electrification of metropolitan tramways, and currently around 39% of the UK rail network is electrified [83]. Electric vehicles are broadly speaking viable technologies, but key disadvantages could be their range and ability to carry heavy cargo, and that currently at least they have long recharging times. Hydrogen vehicles could have attractions over electric vehicles due to faster refueling times, the future possibility of longer range capability, and better applicability to larger, heavier transport modes. However, as discussed above, hydrogen energy chains have significant challenges around cost and performance to overcome.

Hydrogen and FC transport end-use technologies also have challenges to overcome with respect to their cost and performance. As with the other components of the hydrogen energy chain, the US DOE has set targets for the costs of PEMFC systems, including BOP, for automotive applications. These are given in **Table 12**.

The US DOE's hydrogen strategy is focused on a commercialization decision on all hydrogen and FC technologies in 2015. This means that DOE targets are designed to deliver cost-competitive vehicles by this point. A series of reports [85, 86] by TIAX and Directed Technologies, Inc. (DTI), which have been undertaken periodically since the targets were set, project the cost of current technologies if they were mass produced – typically at levels of 500 000 yr^{-1}. In 2005, the mass produced cost of current FC systems was projected at \$108 kW^{-1} and was considered to have a 98% probability of being within the US DOE 2005 target of \$125 kW^{-1} [87]. A sensitivity analysis showed that the major contributing factors to the overall cost of the FC stack were power density, price of platinum, and platinum loading. Subsequent TIAX and DTI analyses have indicated substantial reductions in the overall system cost, as a result of both PEM stack cost reductions and BOP cost reductions [85, 86]. **Table 13** summarizes the recent progress (all costs projected to manufacturing volumes of 500 000 units yr^{-1}).

All costs are given in dollars of the year of analysis. In order to compare with the US DOE targets (set out in **Table 12**), the costs for 2008 and 2009 were also rendered in equivalent 2002 dollars, which were \$60 and \$51, respectively. The most important factors in these cost reductions were the reduction in platinum loading and the increase in the power density of the stack. Further improvements of this nature would be important for meeting the 2015 targets; however, the price of platinum remains one of the biggest uncertainties on the system cost. Therefore, the development of nonplatinum catalysts could be an important breakthrough with regard to meeting the 2015 targets.

The IEA in 2005 [18] estimated the cost of manually produced FC stacks to be US\$1826 kW^{-1}. It concluded that the following changes were required to reduce stack cost to \$103 kW^{-1}:

- Mass production of membranes and possibly use of new materials (other than Nafion)
- Mass production of electrodes based on gas diffusion layer technology
- Mass production of either plastic or coated steel bipolar plates

Table 12 US DOE cost targets for PEMFC systems for automobile applications [84]

Year	2005	2010	2015
Cost (\$)	125	45	30

Table 13 Projected costs of automotive FC systems from TIAX/DTI analyses [85, 86]

Cost (\$ kW^{-1})	2007	2008	2009
Stack	50	34	27
BOP	42	37	33
System assembly and testing	2	2	1
Total system	94	73	61

- An increase in power density from 2 to 3 kW m^{-2}
- Production of 100 000 m^2 yr^{-1} of FC stacks, equivalent to 4000 vehicles per year

This production volume is significantly less than that assumed in the TIAX/DTI analyses, and power density assumptions are more conservative. However, other material advances considered are more radical.

4.03.2.4.6 Hydrogen vehicles – The cost to consumers

Notwithstanding the remaining uncertainties around the costs of storage and distribution infrastructure, the discussions on hydrogen production suggested that it may not be unrealistic to consider that hydrogen could be produced at a cost that makes it comparable as a transport fuel with petrol. This could mean that for an owner of a hydrogen vehicle, running costs would not be significantly greater. Nonetheless, the major economic barrier for the typical consumer would be the 'upfront' cost. Individual consumers tend to have a different view of cost to companies and tend to be more sensitive to capital cost [81]. As shown in Table 14, the IEA estimates that the incremental cost of FCVs over conventional vehicles in 2030 could range from US$2500 to US$7625 [18]. The lower figure corresponds to an FC stack cost of US$35 kW^{-1} – close to the US DOE 2015 goal. Hence, even if PEMFC stack costs did begin to approach the US DOE commercialization targets, the incremental cost of FCVs compared with alternatives could still be large enough to deter price-sensitive consumers.

There are two possible ways in which higher capital costs of hydrogen FCVs might be mitigated. One is if they were being purchased as fleet vehicles by companies (i.e., delivery, haulage, or bus companies), which would tend to be less sensitive to capital costs and more interested in the running cost of a vehicle [82]. Another possibility is that new ownership models for private vehicles based on leasing rather than outright purchase could become more popular. Such ownership models are frequently employed by developers of new car models with high capital cost (see below). Consumers in the United Kingdom are becoming increasingly familiar with such alternative models of ownership, through the growth of shared car clubs. Total membership of such schemes is now at least 50 000 in the United Kingdom [88].

4.03.2.4.7 Hydrogen vehicles – Early prototypes and costs

A number of companies have launched early prototypes of FCVs, with a leasing model allowing these vehicles to be driven by individual consumers. In California, where Honda and General Motors (GM) are leasing FCVs, this is no doubt also significantly helped by the existence of the 'Hydrogen Highway' – a state-level initiative to drive forward deployment of both vehicles and filling station infrastructure [89]. Toyota is also leasing a small number of five-seater FCVs in Japan. The cost of these leasing arrangements appears to vary substantially. Honda's FCX Clarity is available in the United States for a 3-year lease at $600 month^{-1} [90], whereas Toyota's vehicle is available in Japan for 840 000 yen [91] (just over $9000) per month. It is hard to infer any indication of commercial readiness from these prices, as such leasing arrangements are not yet commercial activities, being primarily used by companies to gather information on the performance of the vehicles.

Commercialization targets are periodically announced; in 2006, Adamson and Crawley collated a number of announcements that had recently been made by vehicle manufacturers regarding commercialization targets [92], shown in Table 15.

Notably, these focused on a commercialization year of 2015, which may have been influenced by the US DOE cost targets, most of which are also focused on that year. More recently, such targets are no longer being emphasized. In the changed economic climate that now prevails, several of the companies previously developing FCVs have shifted their focus to electric vehicles that are considered a nearer term prospect. However, companies such as Honda, Toyota, and GM are continuing at present to develop FCV prototypes and to emphasize their view of FCVs as the long-term option [91].

Most hydrogen prototypes have a range of 200–250 miles. However, Toyota recently generated some considerable interest by demonstrating an FCV with a range extended to over 400 miles, in part through the use of a hybrid battery system [93].

Table 14 Estimated costs of a hydrogen FC vehicle (80 kW FCV)

	2005	2010	2030 Optimistic reduction	2030 Optimistic but slower	2030 Pessimistic reduction
PEMFC stack (US$ kW^{-1})	1800	500	35	65	75
Gaseous H storage at 700 bar (US$ kg^{-1})	1000	500	225	375	500
PEMFC stack (US$)	144 000	40 000	2800	5200	6000
Gaseous H storage at 700 bar (US$)	4000	2000	900	1500	2000
Electric engine (US$)	1900	1700	1200	1400	2025
Ref: Conventional ICE vehicle (US$)	19 450	19 450	19 450	19 450	19 450
Ref: Conventional vehicle w/o engine (US$)	17 050	17 050	17 050	17 050	17 050
Hydrogen FCV (US$)	**167 000**	**60 750**	**21 950**	**25 150**	**27 075**
H FCV drive system cost (US$ kW^{-1})	**1875**	**545**	**60**	**100**	**125**

Source: Selected data drawn from Gielen D and Simbolotti G (2005) Prospects for Hydrogen and Fuel Cells. Paris: International Energy Agency, Copyright OECD/IEA, table 2.5, p. 101 [18].

Table 15 2006 snapshot of FC vehicle manufacturer's timetable for launch

Manufacturer	Year	Numbers	Notes
Daimler Chrysler (Germany)	2012	10 000	Initial launch
	2015		Mass market
Ford (United States)	2015		'Commercial readiness'
GM (United States)	2010–2015		Commercial viability
	2025		Mass market
Honda (Japan)	2010	12 000 (in United States)	Start production
	2020	50 000 (in United States)	
Hyundai (Korea)	2010		Road tests 2009
Toyota (Japan)	2015		Will cost US$50 000

Source: Various press releases and conference reports available at www.fuelcelltoday.com [92].

4.03.2.4.8 Wider market opportunities for FCVS, and other low-carbon vehicle drive trains, across the transport sector

The above vehicles are aimed at providing a direct replacement for the average family car. Companies such as Mitsubishi, Renault, Tesla, and Nissan [94–97] are also developing electric vehicles aimed at a similar market. The key challenge for both electric vehicles and FCVs if they are to provide a direct replacement for the current mainstream vehicle is that of range – the number of miles that can be traveled by the vehicle before refueling or recharging is required. In the long term, the question of whether either battery electric or hydrogen FC drive trains will deliver a viable option for a long-range 'family' vehicle is still uncertain. However, what is much clearer is that in the short term, battery electric vehicles (BEVs) are some way ahead of FCVs in terms of meeting the more attainable market of specialized short-range vehicles. Limited range electric vehicles are already on the roads. For example, encouraged by exemptions granted from London's congestion charge, manufacturer GoinGreen has put close to 1000 of its electric vehicles on the streets of the UK capital [98]. The first generation of G-Wiz vehicles that use lead acid batteries has a range of 40 miles, while newer lithium ion-based models achieve 75 miles per charge [99]. In 2011, G-Wiz vehicles were on the market from £10 000 to £15 000 [98]. This was reasonably competitive with conventional small cars on the market, for example, the Fiat 500 which was for sale for £9900 [100].

Without venturing too far into speculations clouded by technological uncertainty, on the basis of such recent developments, it is conceivable that electric vehicles with a limited range – for example, up to 100 km – could relatively quickly be a market-ready product if a clear demand for them was forthcoming. Even with such a limitation, the impact of such electric vehicles on decarbonization of transport could be significant – over 90% of all journeys made in the United Kingdom are under 100 km, such journeys accounting for 60% of total car kilometers traveled [101]. Clearly, the extent of the low-carbon benefits of electric vehicles is dependent on the extent to which efforts to decarbonize the electricity grid are successful.

It may be, however, that for technical reasons, the penetration of electric vehicles will be limited to covering such short-range passenger journeys. Views from the industry currently do not suggest that such vehicles will improve their range significantly beyond 100 km, due to limitations imposed by the weight and cost of batteries [101, 102]. While it is still far from clear that hydrogen vehicles will provide a serious long-range alternative, the recent demonstration of a 400 mile range in Toyota's FCV highlights that this is, at least, a possibility [93].

In the nearer term, there is some interest in the potential for FCs and hydrogen in niche transport applications. For example, one application that is considered a promising niche market for hydrogen and FCs is forklift trucks, used for materials handling in warehouses [60]. In comparison with battery-powered forklifts, FC forklifts are considered to offer potential advantages, notably longer running time, a more evenly sustained power output, and shorter refueling time. If successful in this niche, it might be argued that hydrogen FC systems could build up to a transition to wider transportation markets. However, the existence of any demand at all for either battery vehicles or FCVs is due more fundamentally to the characteristics of this particular 'niche', which means that zero-emission vehicles are required for operation in an enclosed warehouse environment. Without this requirement, there would be no driver for either technology, and it is this aspect of this particular niche – a need for zero-emission vehicles – that is not present in wider, mainstream vehicle markets. This means that even if FCVs did become established in this niche, a broader transition from niche to mainstream markets would not be a seamless and logical continuation of the process without policy intervention aimed at 'artificially' creating that need within those wider markets.

Hydrogen FC systems may also exhibit advantages over electric drive trains in the transit of heavier loads. Although in the United Kingdom companies such as Smith Electric Vehicles [103] and Modec have carved out markets in short-range light duty vehicle (LDV) applications (although in 2011 Modec went into administration) [104], it is generally perceived that for longer range and heavier vehicles such as heavy goods vehicles (HGVs), buses, and ships, the increased weight of the required battery packs may mean that electric drive trains will not be able to operate satisfactorily in such applications. On this basis, the Committee on Climate Change (CCC) concluded that "low carbon liquid fuels with a higher energy density, such as biofuels or hydrogen, may therefore be essential" in such modes, if full decarbonization of the transport sector is to be achieved [67].

Hydrogen buses are costly compared with standard buses – their cost has been reported as around US$1 million, around double the cost of a diesel bus [105]. Hydrogen buses have been demonstrated in recent years in a number of cities as part of the EU's Clean Urban Transport for Europe (CUTE) project [106]. These demonstration projects are important testing grounds for new technologies such as hydrogen FCs. However, the prospects for further deployment of such vehicles are currently uncertain due to the lack of clear policy direction at regional or national levels, as will be discussed further below.

Emissions from shipping are at present an underregulated area; however, as emissions targets and ambitions tighten, the sector could come under increasing scrutiny. International shipping currently accounts for roughly 3% of global CO_2 emissions, although if no abatement action is taken, it could account for between 15% and 30% of permitted emissions in 2050, according to the CCC analysis [67]. This could provide a driver for policies aimed at reducing carbon emissions from shipping, which could lead to opportunities for low-carbon vectors such as hydrogen. Demonstration stage applications of hydrogen-powered marine vessels include the University of Birmingham's canal boat, the 'Ross Barlow' [107], and the zero-emission ship, or ZEMShip, produced by Proton Motor, which operates as a pleasure cruiser in Hamburg harbor. It first sailed in 2008 and was scheduled to run for 2 years [108].

Though the US DOE cost and performance targets have a focus on the direct replacement of private family cars, the consideration of different transport applications such as those discussed above can also change the economic prospects of hydrogen FC drive trains. The IEA claims that FC drive trains can be competitive with ICEs in buses at costs of US$200 kW^{-1} and for delivery vans at US$135 kW^{-1} [8]. In contrast to the targets required for cost parity with ICE cars, according to TIAX/DTI reviews [85, 86], this cost level is well within the range of what is currently thought to be an achievable cost for FC stacks, 'assuming mass production'. If this is the case, then the question of the viability of FCVs in these particular applications might not be a question of further technological development, but of how to stimulate sufficient confidence in the industry to move toward manufacturing at high volumes. The characteristics of such vehicles may also exert less pressing requirements for hydrogen storage, as greater space may be available on board. Further, applications such as buses, delivery vans, and ships have vastly fewer complications around the questions of how to provide the necessary infrastructure. The predictable drive cycles of ships, buses, and delivery vehicles, which return to a limited number of ports or depots for refueling, present a significantly simplified infrastructure provision prospect compared with that of trying to meet the needs of private consumers accustomed to huge flexibility in their refueling practices.

Therefore, if there were policies of sufficient strength to drive decarbonization of transport options across the transport sector, including in heavy-loaded or long-distance modes, there could be a crucial role for a low-carbon transport technology other than the BEV, even if BEVs did prove to be dominant in the short-range passenger vehicle segments of transport demand. Moreover, in many cases, such applications have characteristics that imply fewer barriers and more favorable economic prospects for hydrogen vehicles than are generally expected when considering hydrogen drive trains in mainstream private passenger vehicles.

4.03.2.5 Conclusions on Economics

The major economic challenge for hydrogen energy technologies is rooted in the fact that each step in the hydrogen energy chain, depicted in **Figure 1**, involves costs and energy penalties. When each of these steps is taken into account, it seems likely, on the basis of what is currently known about the various potential technological options, that hydrogen would in most cases be a higher cost decarbonization route than, for example, electricity or biofuels.

However, the cost challenges are not equally great at each stage in the hydrogen energy chain. Taken in isolation, the production stage of the chain seems relatively promising from an economic perspective. It seems possible that hydrogen could be produced at a cost that is competitive with petrol at its current pump price – particularly at UK prices. Notably, production of hydrogen from fossil fuels, even including CCS, appears to be possible at comparatively low delivered hydrogen costs. Although FCV drive trains are still expensive, cost reduction progress has been impressive in the last few years, and there appears to be potential for further cost reductions, through continuing to reduce platinum loading and increase stack power density.

The more uncertain and challenging areas of the hydrogen energy chain, particularly in economic terms, are the infrastructure required to deliver hydrogen to end users and the technologies required to store it at adequate density. The former is particularly vulnerable to the costs of low utilization factors, which would be almost unavoidable in the early years of hydrogen diffusion; the latter are beset by economic and technical challenges, in particular with regard to meeting targets for onboard storage for mainstream passenger vehicles. The area appears to remain somewhat dependent on the arrival of a technological breakthrough; whether such a breakthrough will in fact be forthcoming is inherently uncertain.

A potentially attractive way of producing hydrogen and avoiding the costs and complications of infrastructure is through small-scale production methods. For low-carbon hydrogen, this would have to be small-scale electrolysis. However, it is clear that hydrogen produced in such a way could not be lower in cost than the electricity it used, which could also be used as a transport fuel directly. Indeed, it should be remembered that as a low-carbon energy carrier for transport, hydrogen will not be competing with petrol, but with other (potentially) low-carbon energy carriers, such as biofuels and electricity. The well-to-wheels production, distribution, and infrastructure costs of hydrogen, described in Sections 4.03.2.1 and 4.03.2.2, will make it challenging for hydrogen to compete with these other low-carbon fuels.

There is some potential for hydrogen and FCs to be deployed in niche markets, where users with particular needs select them because of certain desirable characteristics. Such niche uses of technologies can be effective in providing protected spaces, allowing companies to build expertise and supply chains. However, it should be acknowledged that the characteristics that may see hydrogen and FCs valued in APU or forklift applications are because of the needs of particular users operating within those niches. The needs of users operating within other vehicle markets are not at present similar, hence a spontaneous spillover would be unlikely. Such a spillover, however, could be brought about through very strong policy, which would be needed to stimulate a desire for FCVs in transport sectors that currently have minimal incentives or drivers to decarbonize. It is also important to recall that the different FC technologies appropriate to niche compared with wider markets means that not all niche FC applications will create benefits for any wider use of hydrogen.

If policies of sufficient strength to bring about radical technological decarbonization in the transport sector were enacted, electric vehicles and biofuels may also be encouraged. However, despite its higher costs and technological uncertainties, hydrogen may have advantages over the above two processes. Electric vehicles may for technical reasons be limited to short-range drive cycles and low-weight cargo; and although biofuels are an attractive direct substitute for petroleum products, the prospects for their large-scale production are currently uncertain due to land-use constraints and the unproven nature of algal biofuel processes.

In some of these long-range, heavier loaded modes, the prospects for hydrogen may be more promising. Hydrogen drive trains appear to be more competitive with incumbent technologies within these applications; onboard storage requirements may be less stringent in certain parameters; and infrastructure needs are significantly less extensive. If hydrogen vehicles remained at a higher capital cost than conventional ICEs, owners of such fleet vehicles would be more likely to absorb such costs given more favourable running costs, than private vehicle owners who tend to be sensitive to higher capital costs. For such private owners, however, leasing ownership models may offer a route to greater penetration of hydrogen vehicles.

4.03.3 Hydrogen within the Whole-Energy-System Context

The previous section considered the economics of the hydrogen energy chain. However, the whole energy system is comprised of numerous energy chains, which sometimes interact and in some cases compete for energy resources. If hydrogen is deployed on a large scale in the energy system, it will have a significant impact on other energy chains, because of the resources that will be used to produce it. This section considers the whole-energy-system interactions of the hydrogen energy chain.

4.03.3.1 Effects of Transport Decarbonization on Low-Carbon Energy Resources

As has been discussed, key options for the significant future decarbonization of the transport sector are biofuels, electric vehicles, and hydrogen. A problem common to all of these options is the question of which resources are used to produce them. They are all energy carriers, not energy resources. For biofuels, the problem is land constraints. It is currently unclear whether large-scale biofuel production can be achieved without creating unacceptable pressure on other important uses of land [109]. However, proponents argue that in the future, lignocellulosic fermentation processes, as well as biodiesel produced from algae, could dramatically improve the yield of biofuel per hectare of land, thereby reducing these competition effects [110, 111].

The full decarbonization of passenger surface transport demand through BEVs would have a significant impact on levels of electricity generation capacity required, perhaps increasing required generation capacity by another third from today's levels [66, 112]. There are already significant challenges associated with building sufficient low-carbon generation capacity to meet electricity demands if they remained at current levels; with such increases in required capacity, the challenge both to the electricity generation sector and to the transmission and distribution networks would be even greater [113, 114]. One of the potential advantages of hydrogen is that it can be produced from a variety of resources. However, it remains important to question whether producing hydrogen is in each case the optimal use of that limited resource. As discussed above, and summarized in **Table 4**, in broad terms, the main potential resources from which hydrogen could be produced are fossil fuels, biomass, electricity (with water), or high-temperature heat (with water).

Biomass may be a potential source of hydrogen, but one that would ultimately have the same land constraints as using the biomass to produce liquid biofuels. In a study of the potential for the United Kingdom to grow bioenergy crops, Aylott *et al.* [115] modeled production of poplar and willow short rotation coppice from an assumed available land area of 1.3 m ha, – a figure that was derived by assuming 100% of set-aside land, 10% of arable land, and 20% of improved grassland – and calculated from this a potential annual yield of 13 million tons of biomass. The conversion rate of hydrogen from biomass (in this case switchgrass) assumed in calculations by Lau *et al.* is 0.08 tons hydrogen per toe biomass [27]. On this basis, Aylott *et al.*'s 13 million tons could yield just over 1 million tons of H_2 per annum, or 155 PJ. Using figures from the Digest of UK Energy Statistics (DUKES, 2009), this would account for around 9% of the total annual UK transport fuel demand [116]. By contrast, according to the German Energy Agency [117], biodiesel yields from biomass-to-liquids processes could be $4000 \, l \, ha^{-1}$, which in the above example would provide 198 PJ. It is therefore not clear that biomass to hydrogen processes would be significantly more efficient than advanced biomass to liquid biofuel route and, therefore, whether hydrogen production would be a better use of limited biomass resource. However, either of these methods would still produce a relatively small proportion of the United Kingdom's transport fuel demand. Ultimately, the constraint on availability of biomass and land is equally constraining on this option as it is for the production of biofuels.

The production of hydrogen from electrolysis has the significant attraction of potentially bypassing the problems of distribution infrastructure, if distributed electrolysis was employed at or close to the point of use or dispensing. It has already been observed that the hydrogen produced in such a fashion would of necessity be more expensive than electricity that was used at the same point as direct energy vector for transport. This economic fact reflects a more fundamental point about thermodynamics that is worth reasserting. **Figure 5**, from Bossel [118], emphasizes the considerable efficiency losses involved in using hydrogen produced from electrolysis as a transport fuel, compared with using electricity directly.

Bossel includes a transmission loss in the distribution of hydrogen from centralized electrolysis. This could be avoided with distributed electrolysis. However, even if this loss was avoided, there would instead be a grid transmission loss. In theory, this could

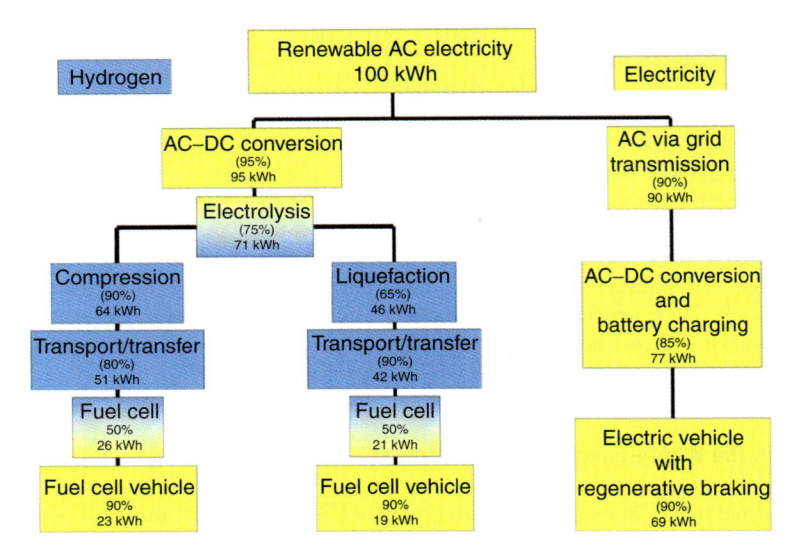

Figure 5 Comparison of conversion efficiency of electricity to transport energy for hydrogen FCVs and electric vehicles. Source: Bossel U (2006) Does a hydrogen economy make sense? In: *Proceedings of the IEEE Conference*, pp. 1826–1836, October 2006. www.efcf.com/reports [118].

raise the overall efficiency of the electricity to FCV chain from Bossel's 23%, up to 26%, but this would still be some way behind the 69% whole chain efficiency of using electricity directly in battery vehicles. The potential impacts upon electricity generation requirements from electrification of transport have already been noted. The implication of these calculations is that electrolysis to produce hydrogen would add an even greater load on to the electricity system.

4.03.3.2 Decarbonization of the Electricity Grid – Opportunities for Hydrogen

It has been suggested that hydrogen could have a role as an 'electricity store', for balancing intermittent or inflexible electricity generation sources that would become more prominent in a low-carbon electricity system. The principle of this idea is that hydrogen would be produced through electrolysis at times of over-supply (e.g., when wind turbines were operating with high output at times of low electricity demand), stored, and then reconverted to electricity in an FC at times of lower supply (when wind output was low at times of higher demand). A key consideration for such an application would be the round-trip efficiency. Assuming a 74% efficient electrolyzer (**Table 1**) and a 50% efficient FC (mid-range of values in **Table 11**), the round-trip efficiency would be 37%. A more optimistic calculation in Sørensen *et al.* [119] suggests a practical maximum of 50%, assuming higher electrical efficiencies of regenerating FCs. Based on experimental data, an 18% round-trip efficiency for a hydrogen-electricity storage system has been reported [120]. Other electricity storage options appear to offer better round-trip efficiencies. Pumped storage currently achieves round-trip efficiencies of 75% [5], and other technologies such as batteries, capacitors, and flywheels are thought to be capable of 80–90% [119]. However, round-trip efficiency may not be the only consideration for electricity storage technologies – total energy storage capacity and speed of discharge are also important parameters, within which, according to the discussions in Sections 4.03.2.3 and 4.03.2.4.2, hydrogen and FC systems might have attractive characteristics.

It has been mentioned that experiments with bioelectrolysis have reported a return of hydrogen equivalent to 288% of the energy content of the electricity alone. The process could use a range of biological substrates, including sewage sludge. Hydrogen extraction has been reported close to 100% of the theoretical maximum [19].

Though the hydrogen return on the input electricity is attractive, the limiting factor for the process is the amount of biological substrate available. For the United Kingdom, the energy content of dry solids arising after sewage treatment, plus available cattle slurries, combines to give a total of around 17 PJ yr^{-1} [121]. This would represent a maximum level for the hydrogen potentially available from this resource via bioelectrolysis. However, given that Cheng and Logan report that close to 100% of the hydrogen present in the biomass is theoretically obtainable [19], the hydrogen resource could in the most optimistic assumptions be close to this amount. According to calculations by MacKay [5], the level of long-term storage required to cope with weather 'lulls' in an electricity system with 33 GW of wind would be around 1200 GWh (or 4.3 PJ) of stored electricity. If this 17 PJ yr^{-1} of hydrogen was converted in a stationary FC at 50% efficiency (mid-range figure from **Table 11**), it would yield 8.5 PJ of electricity per year – more than sufficient to meet MacKay's hypothesized storage requirement.

Bioelectrolysis has been proposed as a future means of managing biodegradable wastes and producing energy in the form of hydrogen from them. The very rough calculations above suggest that the hydrogen potentially available from wastes could be significant within the future electricity system's electricity storage needs. However, it is also the case that such biological wastes can be treated and energy extracted from them through less expensive processes such as anaerobic digestion, which produces biogas.

This gas could then be used in a turbine to generate power, also potentially offering the option of flexible power generation, which could be of benefit in a low-carbon grid.

The discussion on production suggested that the cheapest low-carbon means of producing hydrogen could be from fossil fuels with CCS. If CCS technology was successfully developed and commercialized (a prospect which, it should be noted, as of 2011 remains uncertain, considering continuing delays to the successful demonstration of the technology at scale [122]), it is likely that the technology would be prioritized for electricity production, rather than the available fossil resources and CCS infrastructure being dedicated only to hydrogen production. However, what is more plausible is the coproduction of hydrogen with electricity. This is particularly the case as with IGCC-based precombustion CCS, a hydrogen-rich gas is produced as an interim stage in the process. It would not add huge amounts of complexity to the system to purify and store this as hydrogen gas. The key economic advantage of including hydrogen storage capacity within an IGCC precombustion CCS plant would be to give the plant the ability to be flexible in when it produces electricity, while allowing it to maintain its gasification and gas separation processes at constant load, maximizing efficiency and improving the economics. This stored hydrogen could either be sent to the turbines to produce electricity in a flexible manner, similar to current open cycle gas turbines (OCGTs) or combined cycle gas turbines (CCGTs), or it could potentially be sold as a fuel if a demand from the transport sector did emerge. Clearly, the comparative prices of transport fuel and electricity would have an influence on which of these routes were followed; this flexibility could allow the plant to further improve its economics, by altering its output according to whether hydrogen or electricity had the higher premium.

The benefits of constructing CCS plants in a manner designed for flexibility could be very large for an electricity network that will be losing its highly flexible generation sources and potentially faced with investing in expensive electricity storage systems as a means to balance the system. The potential for designing IGCC plants with CCS for the flexible coproduction of hydrogen and electricity has been identified as a realistic prospect in a number of papers [123–125]. However, the concept has not yet been widely discussed within the context of the United Kingdom's ongoing CCS competition [29].

The concept would require a hydrogen storage system. Reflecting on the kind of parameters for storage systems discussed in the previous section, it is possible to say something in broad terms about the performance characteristics of a storage system used in this context. Good volumetric energy density would probably be desirable, though not necessarily – this would depend on the land space constraints in the area of the plant. Gravimetric energy density need not be a limiting factor, as this would be a stationary store. High temperatures required or expelled either during uptake or release of hydrogen would be less problematic in this context, not least as thermal power plant designs are accustomed to managing and recycling high-temperature heat; a low-temperature storage system could be more challenging. An important characteristic of the system would be fast release of hydrogen, as a key part of the concept would be the ability to ramp up to high-power output within a short space of time.

4.03.3.3 Summary on Whole System Interactions

Where hydrogen competes as a low-carbon energy carrier with electricity, it faces challenges due to the limited nature of the potential sources of hydrogen, and in the case of electrolysis, the significant efficiency losses compared with direct use of electricity. It has therefore been argued that the direct use of electricity is more likely to be a more efficient use of scarce low-carbon energy resources [118]. However, even if this conclusion holds, the previous sections have identified other applications where there could still be a potential role for hydrogen. Within the transport sector, there are particular transport applications for which BEVs may not be suited, such as for long distance or heavy load transport demands. It is for these applications that hydrogen may be able to offer a useful solution, if close to full decarbonization of the transport sector is desired. In these applications, it may be considered worth paying the additional energy penalty of electrolysis, due to the more useful characteristics of having energy in the form of hydrogen. In such applications, which are not suited to BEVs, alternative solutions may also be offered through developments in 'second-generation' biofuel production methods and algal biofuels [126, 127]. Hence, in the transport sector, to the extent that hydrogen may be thought of as having competitors, its long-term competition may not be with electric drive trains, but with biofuels. In the electricity sector, the potentially growing need for electricity storage technologies may create opportunities for hydrogen and FC systems. There may also be important synergies available from the production of electricity from fossil fuels with CCS, with hydrogen potentially available as a coproduct.

4.03.4 Developing Policies to Support Hydrogen

The previous sections have identified some applications and processes in which hydrogen may offer value as an energy carrier within future energy systems.

Drawing on the discussion in the previous section, there are two broad areas of policy in which developments could affect the prospects for hydrogen. First, transport, because hydrogen might have a role in facilitating the decarbonization of certain transport modes, particularly those not easily accessible to electric vehicles. Second, electricity, because hydrogen might have a role in providing flexibility in low-carbon electricity systems, either within a stand-alone FC storage and regeneration system or as a coproduct within fossil fuel CCS processes. This section discusses each of these two policy areas, primarily from the UK perspective, though broader observations can be applied more generally. Following this, some observations about fundamental R&D processes are made, before finally some conclusions are drawn.

4.03.4.1 Policies in the Transport Sector

UK CO_2 emissions from transport are currently 130 $MtCO_2$ per annum, or around 24% of all UK CO_2 emissions [67]. Current policies in the United Kingdom in the area of transport are largely focused on pushing incremental improvements in the efficiency of ICE vehicles and in encouraging 'smarter choices' to bring about a more efficient use or higher load factor in current transport modes. In line with EU targets, by 2020, all new cars sold must achieve 95 $g CO_2 km^{-1}$ [128].

There is an EU-wide target that 10% of transport fuel by energy must be 'renewable' by 2020 [129]. However, the Gallagher Review has questioned whether this can be achieved sustainably. The review advised that the UK's Renewable Transport Fuels Obligation (RTFO) [130] that currently mandates 2.5% of transport fuels by volume are renewable should be allowed to rise to 5% by volume by 2013–14. Beyond this point, any further increases in the RTFO should only be implemented if biofuels have been shown to be sustainable [109].

The Department for Transport (DfT) estimates that the current suite of policies in transport could result in CO_2 emissions around 32 $MtCO_2$ lower in 2020 than would have occurred with no intervention [128]. The CCC's 'current ambition' scenario for the transport sector delivers reductions from current levels of 5 $MtCO_2$ by 2020. These gains are achieved from efficiency and with 5% biofuels by volume [67]. This would be equivalent to a sectoral reduction of around 4% from the present emissions level. The United Kingdom's overall legislated carbon budget for 2020 is 34% below 1990 levels, or 21% below 2005 levels [67, 131].

Making a judgment about whether such an emissions trajectory for transport would be 'sufficient' is complex, as the question of which sectors should lead in emissions reduction activity is contested. However, energy system studies are clear about the long-term need for significant transport sector decarbonization if CO_2 reductions of 80% or more are to be met [66, 67]. To achieve such trajectories, major technology shifts would need to occur.

Significant decarbonization of the transport sector through major technology shift would require transport technology manufacturers to transform their manufacturing processes and scale up production. The deployment scenarios developed for the Hyways project [132], illustrated in **Figure 6**, indicate possible rates at which new vehicle technologies (in this case FCVs) could be deployed. These deployment curves indicate different levels of policy support and technological learning. Perhaps more crucially, they all implicitly assume that manufacturers are aware of a clear and growing market demand for the new technology.

Clearly then, such deployment rates represent something close to an upper bound for the speed with which the transport fleet could be transformed. However, on the basis of the current suite of low-carbon transport policies, the much more immediate binding constraint is the distinct absence of an important assumption under which the deployment curves in **Figure 6** were imagined – the confidence in the industry that a serious demand for low-carbon vehicles will be forthcoming.

The congestion charge in London allows exemptions for low-carbon vehicles. This combined with car parking exemptions has created a potential market for low-carbon vehicles, one which niche manufacturer Goingreen has capitalized on with its G-Wiz cars, designed for short-distance commuting [98]. This simple measure has created a limited, but nonetheless significant demand for a technology; and the confidence in this demand being present has enabled a company to send a new technology into production.

The importance of creating certainty of future demand to give manufacturers the confidence to develop supply chains has been emphasized by Jack Frost, Director of Johnson Matthey Fuel Cells and Chairman of the Government's Environmental Innovation Advisory Group (EIAG) from 2003 to 2008. When innovation is slow, it is because of the lack of confidence that a genuine market will exist for a product at the end of the innovation process. The prospect of developing a product, setting up supply chains, and scaling up production only to find that no demand exists for it is a serious and ultimately paralyzing risk. On the other hand, Frost maintains that if a public sector procurer can provide a 'credible, articulated demand' for a particular kind of product by a certain

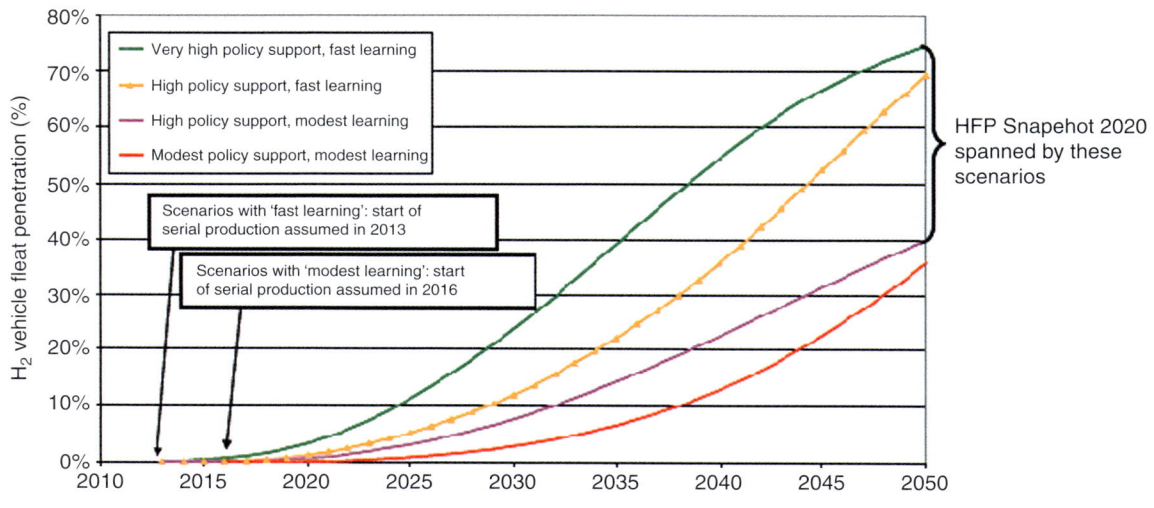

Figure 6 Scenarios of penetration rates of hydrogen vehicles for passenger transport. Reprinted with permission from European Commission (EC), HyWays – The European Hydrogen Energy Roadmap. www.hyways.de [132]. Copyright (2008) HyWays.

date, this will create the certainty needed for manufacturers to scale up their production of such products. The basic principle is that "a public sector body offers to buy in the future a product or service that delivers specified performance levels including environmental benefits at a defined volume and at a cost it can afford" [133]. Such a 'Forward Commitment Procurement' process, Frost argues, is crucial for creating the credible articulated demand manufacturers need in order to innovate. Frost has also cited the state of California's progressive emissions reductions targets as a mechanism that had the effect of creating a clear future demand for low-emission vehicles and that stimulated major improvements over 20 years in vehicle technologies in California. Forward procurement has also had a number of successes in the UK prison and hospital services [133]. In principle, a similar approach could be used as a means to accelerate innovation and deployment of new low-carbon technologies [133, 134].

It is this level of certainty about future demand for technologies that manufacturers require in order to have the confidence to scale up production of a new technology. However, this level of certainty is by no means present around the prospect of scaling up production of zero-carbon vehicles, because the current policy trajectory only specifies incremental improvements.

One of the ways in which future demand for low-carbon vehicles could be made more clear would be to use the Forward Commitment Procurement model to specify ambitious low-carbon transport demands in areas controlled by public procurement – for example, a forward commitment to procure zero-carbon buses in a future specified year.

In the area of privately owned vehicles, the procurement model is less easily transferrable. However, the likely existence of a future demand could nevertheless be made clearer through forward commitment to legislation that would penalize carbon-intensive vehicles and benefit by comparison low-carbon vehicles. A commitment to roll out and scale up measures of the nature of London's congestion charge, and to give a clear timeline for when this will happen, would create a much greater certainty of demand for potential manufacturers of low- and zero-carbon vehicles, just as the current London congestion charge has opened up an emergent demand for manufacturers of niche electric vehicles. However, public acceptance of congestion charge proposals in other areas are low, showing that there may be challenges to rolling out such policies more widely [135]. Indeed, it is important to note that the challenges in terms of public acceptability of such a policy trajectory should not be underestimated, as transport is an area in which the UK public have traditionally been highly resistant to policy intervention for environmental reasons. In fact, "transport appears to be the least acceptable area of policy for the public with respect to tackling climate change" [136]. This is why a transparent and relatively long-term timeframe for the measures would be important to allow the industry time to provide options that would not be penalized. However, the effective communication of the importance of such policies to a diverse range of public and transport user groups, as well as their potential benefits to UK industry, would also be a crucial part of their successful implementation.

The kinds of policies described above are in essence technology neutral – the procurer simply specifies a need, and it is up to the industry to decide on the most appropriate technology to meet that need. It has already been observed that electric vehicles are significantly closer to market than hydrogen vehicles, and the immediate effect of such policies designed to establish a clear future demand for low-carbon transport could be a scale up in production of various models of electric vehicle. At the start of 2011, the market prospects for electric vehicles in the United Kingdom were further enhanced by the launch of a £5000-per-vehicle purchase grant fund [137]. However, it has also been observed that electric vehicles may be limited in the number of applications for which they are applicable, notably long distances and heavy loads. It is for these applications that hydrogen vehicles may potentially offer an attractive solution in the future. It has also been noted that in heavy loading vehicle applications such as delivery vans and buses, hydrogen technologies are closer to being cost-effective in comparison with incumbent technologies. However, as has also been observed, breakthroughs in biofuel productions could again postpone the need for hydrogen in these applications.

These things may come about as a natural effect of a technology-neutral policy trajectory. However, for technologies like hydrogen, new relationships and supply chains are required to bring them into being, between FC manufacturers, fuel suppliers, and vehicle manufacturers. In order to give the technology a chance of success, it may be important for the public sector to take a role in building and coordinating such actor-networks and supply chains.

An important way in which the public sector can act to bring such actors together is by funding demonstration projects, such as the hydrogen bus demonstrations in cities across Europe through EU's CUTE project [106]. While isolated projects involving very small numbers of vehicles may not be of very great interest to large-scale manufacturers, greater interest generated through joint procurement arrangements can help to address this, where a number of procurers (such as city or regional authorities) join forces to bulk order vehicles. This was indeed the principle behind the CUTE project, through which nine European cities commissioned a total of 33 Citaro FC buses.

Such demonstration projects have in general been regarded as successes; however, they are currently limited to being bounded experiments, with no clear sense of how these will progress into a large-scale rollout of the technology [138]. The presence of a longer term, forward procurement commitment is a crucial accompaniment to such early demonstration projects, in order to stimulate the required long-term certainty and continuity.

If hydrogen vehicles are to have any role as passenger transport vehicles for longer range journeys (assuming that electric vehicles will not be able to meet such range requirements), it is likely that due to their high capital costs, they would be most successfully rolled out on a leasing model, rather than requiring outright purchase. Policies that aim to support and encourage leasing-based models of car ownership would possibly benefit new vehicle technologies for this reason.

4.03.4.2 Policies in the Electricity Sector

The decarbonization of electricity supply is considered in the United Kingdom to be a critical component of both near-term (2020) [139] and long-term (2050) [67, 113] carbon reduction targets. There are a number of policies driving decarbonization in the power sector, most significantly the Renewables Obligation [140] that places an obligation on electricity suppliers to source a rising percentage of their electricity from renewable sources. A feed-in-tariff has also been introduced that provides an incentive for the installation of small-scale renewable technologies available for small-scale generation, by buying back the electricity at higher than market rates [141]. The EU emissions trading scheme provides an additional framework, though its low-carbon prices have failed to have a significant impact upon low-carbon investment [142]. In 2010, the Department for Energy and Climate Change launched a consultation on reform of the electricity markets, which included proposals to set a floor price for carbon (to bolster the relatively weak price signal given by the EU ETS) and to extend a form of feed-in-tariff to large-scale power generation [143].

If such policies are successful in stimulating investment and deployment of low-carbon and renewable energy technologies within the electricity sector, an additional effect of this could be to create an indirect demand for hydrogen technologies. The prospects of an electricity supply system dominated by nuclear and wind raise considerable challenges for grid management and could create a need for energy storage technologies. As discussed in Section 4.03.3.2, hydrogen may be able to compete with other storage technologies, as despite possibly having lower round-trip efficiencies, it could offer fast response and possibly a large and cost-effective storage reservoir, depending on the location. The prospects for all electricity storage technologies are, however, dependent on careful market design, to ensure that the system-wide benefits of the service they provide can be reflected in the price received for these services by the storage operators [144–147].

As has also been discussed in Section 4.03.3.2, hydrogen could become a useful component within IGCC precombustion CCS designs, where it could be viewed either as a coproduct from this process or as a storable fuel to enable the power plant to operate in a flexible load-following mode. In order to encourage potential builders and operators of such plant to use hydrogen storage to increase the flexibility of the plant, policy signals should be designed to indicate that in the long term, plant flexibility is a characteristic that will be valued and rewarded. It is currently uncertain whether a plant would receive sufficient reward if it was required to operate at very low load factors, designed to be called into action at short notice, particularly if significantly greater quantities of such backup plant were required on a system dominated by variable renewables, than is the case today. A possible alternative approach could be to develop electricity market signals that incentivize capacity, not generation. In the longer term, the existence of other demands for hydrogen, for example, from certain transport modes, could provide alternative revenue streams, transforming the economics of such a plant. It could use the hydrogen to generate electricity only when the price was highest, and at all other times sell hydrogen as a fuel.

The key role for policy in facilitating the use of hydrogen in grid interactions is first to provide this long-term framework for companies and technology developers to understand that the product being developed will be rewarded through financial mechanisms in future electricity market regimes. However, in addition to this, in a manner comparable with that emphasized for vehicles, policy should act to bring together the various actors – electricity generation companies, regulators, hydrogen technology developers, and researchers – who would need to work together to bring such applications into being. This is particularly the case as many of these actors would have no history of working together.

4.03.4.3 Policies Relating to Fundamental Scientific Research

Policies that provide the framework under which demand for technologies with particular characteristics can be made more certain, to encourage and support the activities of technology developers, and that act to coordinate and bring together the various actors who will constitute the necessary supply chains are clearly important to provide the necessary pull-through from the demonstration stage to wider deployment. However, innovative technology development is also made possible by ongoing research of a fundamental scientific nature.

The extent to which new technologies have been developed and have potential to be used in sustainable energy systems is ultimately thanks to basic scientific research at laboratory scale. This research is of an autonomous nature, often driven by questions of purely scientific interest rather than direct commercial application, only rarely translating into a discreet 'invention' that can bring a direct revenue as reward for the endeavors. Nonetheless, without this ever-evolving basis of scientific research, commercial and engineering technology deployments would not be possible. The privatization and liberalization of the energy industries in the United Kingdom appear to have resulted in some increased efficiencies and lowered costs for consumers [148]. However, coincidentally or not, it has also been accompanied by a significant fall in basic R&D funding (Figure 7).

This is problematic, as with a much narrower basic science research base, it will be harder to find effective solutions to the various challenges of the next decades. The difficulty in public funding of speculative research of any kind is that investment that fails to yield a technological application that 'works' will be perceived as wasted. The opportunity costs of pouring money into unsuccessful technological research at the expense of other areas of public policy are significant. Hydrogen is a case in point – a technology that remains beset by economic and technical challenges and therefore whose potential useful contribution to energy systems remains highly uncertain.

The process of funding speculative research in energy technologies must almost of necessity involve following some blind alleys, as some materials or processes that are researched for many years may not yield a result that 'works'. Conversely, successful 'inventions' can spin out of primary research that was intended for a completely different application. To a certain extent then, the funding of scientific research cannot become overly constrained by deterministic expectations of what it should deliver and indeed must expect the possibility of some technological failures.

However, this is not to say that fundamental research should take place in a vacuum, completely removed from the changing needs, developments, and interests of the technology area for which it is intended. In the case of hydrogen, one of the most

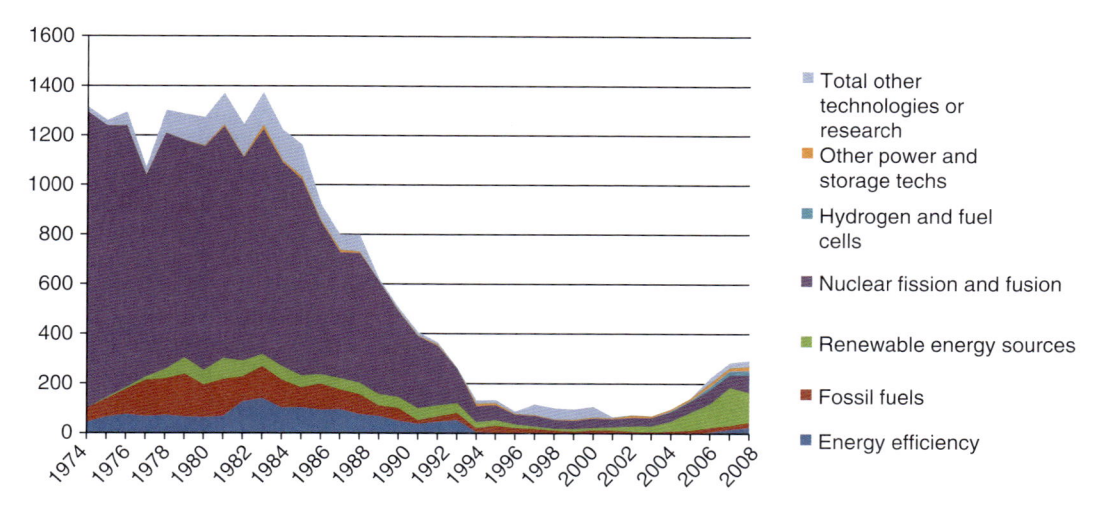

Figure 7 UK RD&D spend, 1974–2008. Source: IEA (2011) RD&D Statistics. [Online] http://www.iea.org/stats/rd.asp [149].

influential links between fundamental scientific research and technology deployment and applications has been the series of targets set by the US DOE by which to judge the performance of hydrogen materials, processes, and technologies from their performance at laboratory scale right through to demonstration. These targets have been widely adopted as benchmarks across the scientific community, in demonstrating how close their research has come to produce something with commercial potential, as well as providing a guide for terminating particular research directions if they do not appear to be approaching these benchmarks [53].

The universality of these targets is interesting, particularly as they are in most cases heavily influenced by the representation in measurable terms of 'equivalent performance' to the equivalent component of current mainstream ICE vehicles, and its associated infrastructure. However, a conclusion of this chapter is that the mainstream 'family car' may not be the application for which hydrogen technologies have the highest chance of success or in which they would deliver the greatest value, particularly in the context of the whole energy system and considering what may be delivered by other low-carbon technologies and fuels. If this is the case, then many of the DOE targets are giving misleading guidelines to scientists – they are testing their materials against specifications that may not be the only appropriate or useful ones for future applications.

This suggests that improving the communication between the work being carried out in basic scientific research and the developments and needs of applications within an evolving dynamic energy system can have important benefits in guiding the characteristics that experimental scientists search for, as well as ensuring that potentially valuable research effort is not discarded because it fails to meet specifications influenced by a too-narrow conception of the potential end-use technology applications.

4.03.5 Conclusion

The vision of an energy economy powered by sustainably produced and freely available supplies of hydrogen remains in many ways as alluring as it was when first articulated by Jules Verne through his character Cyrus Harding in 1874. However, in reality many of the technologies required to produce, distribute, and convert hydrogen to useful energy services are still beset by technical and economic challenges in comparison with other equivalent technologies. Moreover, the energy costs of producing hydrogen from a particular energy resource are in many cases hard to justify compared with using that resource in a more direct fashion, which can be cheaper, involve fewer energy losses, and in many cases involve no more pollution than the hydrogen route.

In a previous report, the use of hydrogen for most stationary heat and power applications was found not to be a cost-effective decarbonization route, compared with other options [68]. Indeed, the review of hydrogen economics in this chapter suggested that in general, and even if strong low-carbon policies are assumed, in the absence of significant cost breakthroughs in the hydrogen and FC technologies, hydrogen may struggle to establish itself in applications where viable and less expensive low-carbon technologies – in particular biofuels and direct use of electricity – are available.

However, this chapter has identified a number of specific applications in which hydrogen may play a useful role in future low-carbon energy systems, even without major step changes in cost and performance. First is the provision of transport services in modes in which electric drive trains are unlikely to be suitable due to their technical limitations. These may particularly include vehicles with long-range requirements, or heavier loads, such as buses, HGVs, or boats. Second, hydrogen could have an important role as an energy storage medium for balancing a low-carbon electricity system. This could include as part of a stand-alone electrolysis–FC regeneration system or within an IGCC precombustion CCS coal power plant, as a means of increasing the flexibility of the plant.

Due to the economic challenges facing hydrogen technologies, the policy landscape will be critical to the question of whether hydrogen technologies have a major role to play in a future energy system. Low-carbon technologies require long-term, consistent, and sustained policy signals in order to generate sufficient confidence to stimulate investment. Long-term frameworks such as the UK's Climate Change Act [6] provide a positive signal; however, more specific and sectoral intervention is required. Hydrogen technologies are particularly challenging in that they are costly and complicated even compared with other viable low-carbon options. However, it is possible that they could play a useful role in certain applications within a future low-carbon system. First, if hydrogen technologies, as well as any other low-carbon technologies, are to be deployed in a serious way in the kinds of applications discussed in this chapter, of paramount importance is a policy framework with a long view and a clear articulation of a future demand for low-carbon technologies, within specific sectors and applications. This is crucial to generate the confidence manufacturers need to scale up their investment in such products. If, as modeling suggests, the successful implementation of an 80% reduction of emissions from the energy system requires radical decarbonization of the transport sector, this need should be made explicit within particular sectors of the transport sector, such as car passenger transport, public bus transport, domestic shipping, and vehicle freight transport. Clear emissions reductions targets pertaining to each of these sectors, leading to an advance commitment to future policies that clearly incentivize low-carbon options within each sector, would create confidence in the manufacturing sector in a future demand for currently emergent low-carbon technologies. The approaches for generating this confidence would vary between sectors. For example, in the realm of public transport, the Forward Commitment Procurement approach would be relevant. In private transport, advance commitment to policies, such as London's congestion charge being rolled out on a larger scale, would give both industries and consumers time to react. In the electricity sector, advance consideration must be given as to how electricity storage devices, as well as low-carbon generation plants capable of providing much needed flexibility on a low-carbon grid, can be sufficiently rewarded for this service, as designs of very long-lived power system assets are finalized over the next few years.

These technology-neutral processes are important to give an overall direction, but for emerging technologies such as hydrogen, another important policy activity will be the building of actor-networks and supply chains. A key means for doing this is through demonstration projects, which should focus on the kinds of applications for which hydrogen is considered to be a more viable option. Coordination between the national-level policy trajectories of the kind described in the previous paragraphs and such demonstration projects that are frequently coordinated at the local level, is therefore clearly important. Coordination is also important between demonstration projects of similar size in different locations, as joint procurement can make the involvement of large-scale technology manufacturers more viable. If CCS technology demonstration plants are constructed, governments could play a role to coordinate the necessary actors to ensure that the potentially beneficial role that hydrogen could play within pre-combustion CCS is being considered, as a coproduct to increase plant flexibility.

At the same time as these interventions, continued investment in fundamental scientific research and development is crucial to provide a fertile soil from which innovation can flourish. Although such investment must be made in the understanding that scientific innovation is an uncertain process, nonetheless maintaining good lines of communication between developments at the market, industry, and policy level and the research priorities of scientists is essential to ensure that all parties are more alive to the emerging opportunities. In the case of hydrogen, fundamental science research remains dominated by US DOE targets that primarily pertain to a direct substitution-based comparison with the corresponding part of the fossil fuel-based automotive energy chain, with a strong focus on the private passenger car. This chapter contends that other applications could constitute more beneficial uses of hydrogen and may have somewhat different performance requirements. Research efforts should therefore not be restricted to meeting a narrow range of performance requirements, but should be conducted in the light of the performance requirements of the full range of applications in which the technology could play a beneficial role.

References

[1] Rifkin J (2002) *The Hydrogen Economy: The Creation of the Worldwide Energy Web and the Redistribution of Power on Earth*. New York: Jeremy P. Tarcher.
[2] McDowall E and Eames M (2006) Forecasts, scenarios, visions, backcasts and roadmaps to the hydrogen economy: A review of the hydrogen futures literature. *Energy Policy* 34: 1236–1250.
[3] Verne J (1986) *The Mysterious Island*. New York: Signet Classics.
[4] Bossel U, Eliasson B, and Taylor G (2005) The future of the hydrogen economy: Bright or bleak? *European Fuel Cell Forum*, Switzerland. www.efcf.com/reports/E08.pdf (last accessed 21 December 2011).
[5] MacKay DJC (2009) *Sustainable Energy – Without the Hot Air*. Cambridge: UIT Cambridge Ltd.
[6] HM Stationery Office (2008) Climate Change Act 2008. London. [Online] http://www.legislation.gov.uk/ukpga/2008/27/pdfs/ukpga_20080027_en.pdf (last accessed 21 December 2011).
[7] EU (2010) The EU Climate and Energy Package – Useful Documents. [Online] http://ec.europa.eu/clima/policies/package/documentation_en.htm (last accessed 21 December 2011).
[8] EC (2008) Directive 2008/50/EC of the European Parliament and of the Council of 21 May 2008 on Ambient Air Quality and Cleaner Air for Europe. [Online] http://eur-lex.europa.eu/LexUriServ/LexUriServ.do?uri=OJ:L:2008:152:0001:0044:EN:PDF (last accessed 21 December 2011).
[9] IEA (2006) *Energy Technology Perspectives*. Paris: IEA.
[10] IEA Energy Statistics. [Online] www.iea.org/stats/balancetable.asp?COUNTRY_CODE=29 (last accessed 21 December 2011).
[11] National Research Council (NRC) and National Academy of Engineering (NAE) (2004) *The Hydrogen Economy: Opportunities, Costs, Barriers, and R&D Needs*. Washington, DC: The National Academies Press.
[12] Office of Energy Efficiency and Renewable Energy (EERE) (2007) *Multi Year Research, Development and Demonstration Plan: Planned Program Activities for 2005–2015*. Washington, DC: DOE. http://www1.eere.energy.gov/hydrogenandfuelcells/mypp/ (last accessed 21 December 2011).
[13] IEA (2011) End-Use Petroleum Product Prices and Average Crude Oil Import Costs, September 2011. [Online] http://www.iea.org/stats/surveys/mps.pdf (last accessed 21 December 2011).

[14] van Thuijl E and Deurwaarder EP (2006) *European Biofuel Policies in Retrospect*. The Netherlands: ECN. [Online] http://www.ecn.nl/docs/library/report/2006/c06016.pdf (last accessed 21 December 2011).
[15] DOE (2011) Biomass Program – Federal Biomass Policy. [Online] http://www1.eere.energy.gov/biomass/federal_biomass.html (last accessed 21 December 2011).
[16] Hawkins S and Joffe D (2006) *Technological Characterisation of Hydrogen Production Technologies*. UKSHEC Social Science Working Paper No. 25. London: Policy Studies Institute. www.psi.org.uk/ukshec (last accessed 21 December 2011).
[17] National Renewable Energy Laboratory (NREL) (2007) *Current (2009) State-of-the Art Hydrogen Production Cost Estimate Using Water Electrolysis*. Golden, CO: NREL. www.hydrogen.energy.gov/peer_reviews.html (last accessed 21 December 2011).
[18] Gielen D and Simbolotti G (2005) *Prospects for Hydrogen and Fuel Cells*. Paris: International Energy Agency (IEA).
[19] Cheng S and Logan B (2007) Sustainable and efficient biohydrogen production via electrohydrogenesis. *Proceedings of the National Academy of Sciences* 104(47): 18871–18873.
[20] Logan B, Call D, Cheng S, *et al*. (2008) Microbial electrolysis cells for high yield hydrogen gas production from organic matter. *Environmental Science & Technology* 42(23): 8630–8640.
[21] Cheng S and Logan B (2011) High hydrogen production rate of microbial electrolysis cell (MEC) with reduced electrode spacing. *Bioresource Technology* 102: 3571–3574.
[22] Wietschel M, Hasenauer U, and de Groot A (2006) Development of European hydrogen infrastructure scenarios – CO_2 reduction potential and infrastructure investment. *Energy Policy* 34(11): 1284–1298.
[23] National Renewable Energy Laboratory (NREL) (2006) *Distributed Hydrogen Production from Natural Gas*. Golden, CO: NREL. [Online] www.hydrogen.energy.gov/peer_reviews.html (last accessed 21 December 2011).
[24] IEA (2008) *Energy Technology Perspectives*. Paris: IEA.
[25] Vliet OPR, Faaij A, and Turkenburg WC (2009) Fischer-Tropsch diesel production in a well-to-wheel perspective: A carbon, energy flow and cost analysis. *Energy Conversion and Management* 50(4): 855–876.
[26] Li K and Jiang D (1999) Methanol synthesis from syngas in the homogeneous system. *Journal of Molecular Catalysis A: Chemical* 147(1–2): 125–130.
[27] Lau F, Bowen D, Dihu R, *et al*. (2002) Techno-economic analysis of hydrogen production by gasification of biomass. *Report for US Department of Energy*. Work performed under DOE Contact Number: DE-FC36-01G011089. www.osti.gov/bridge/ (last accessed 21 December 2011).
[28] FutureGen (2009) FutureGen Alliance. [Online] www.futuregenalliance.org/alliance.stm (last accessed 21 December 2011).
[29] Miliband E (2009) Statement – Coal and carbon capture and storage. Statement by Ed Miliband to the House of Commons, 23 April 2009. http://www.publications.parliament.uk/pa/cm200809/cmhansrd/cm090423/debtext/90423-0006.htm (last accessed 21 December 2011).
[30] Beer L, Boyd E, Peters J, and Posewitz M (2009) Engineering algae for biohydrogen and biofuel production. *Current Opinion in Biotechnology* 20: 264–271.
[31] Hawkes F, Forsey H, Premier G, *et al*. (2008) Fermentative production of hydrogen from a wheat flour industry co-product. *Bioresource Technology* 99(11): 5020–5029.
[32] Prakasham R, Brahmaiah P, Sathish T, and Sambasiva Rao K (2009) Fermentative biohydrogen production by mixed anaerobic consortia: Impact of glucose to xylose ratio. *International Journal of Hydrogen Energy* 34(23): 9354–9361.
[33] Hawkins S (2006) *Technological Characterisation of Hydrogen Storage and Distribution Technologies*. UKSHEC Social Science Working Paper No. 21. London: Policy Studies Institute. www.psi.org.uk/ukshec (last accessed 21 December 2011).
[34] Yang C and Ogden J (2007) Determining the lowest-cost hydrogen delivery mode. *International Journal of Hydrogen Energy* 32: 268–286.
[35] Ni J, Nils J, Ogden JM, *et al*. (2005) Estimating hydrogen demand distribution using geographic information systems (GIS). In: *Paper Presented at the National Hydrogen Association Conference*. Washington, DC, 29 March–1 April.
[36] Ogden JM, Yang C, Johnson N, *et al*. (2005) *Technical and Economic Assessment of Transition Strategies Toward Widespread Use of Hydrogen as an Energy Carrier*. Davis: Institute of Transportation Studies, University of California.
[37] Nicholas M (2004) Hydrogen Station Siting and Refueling Analysis Using Geographic Information Systems: A Case Study of Sacramento County. Master's Thesis, University of California Davis, Davis, CA.
[38] Wang M, Mintz M, Singh M, *et al*. (1998) *Assessment of PNGV Fuels Infrastructure, Phase 2 – Final Report: Additional Capital Needs and Fuel Cycle Energy and Emissions Impacts*. Argonne, IL: Argonne National Laboratory, Center for Transportation Research and Decision and Information Sciences Division. Available online from: www.osti.gov/bridge (last accessed 21 December 2011).
[39] Mulder F and Girard J (2004) *Policy Implications of the Investment Needs and Economic Viability*. Hague, The Netherlands: SenterNovem.
[40] California Hydrogen Highway Network (CHHN) (2005) *Economic Team Report*. West Sacramento: California 2010 Hydrogen Highway Network. www.hydrogenhighway.ca.gov/plan/reports/econreport.pdf (last accessed 21 December 2011).
[41] Melaina M (2003) Initiating hydrogen infrastructures: Preliminary analysis of a sufficient number of initial hydrogen stations in the US. *International Journal of Hydrogen Energy* 28: 743–755.
[42] Johnson N, Yang C, Ni J, *et al*. (2005) Optimal design of a fossil fuel-based hydrogen infrastructure with carbon capture and sequestration: Case study in Ohio. In: *Paper Presented at the National Hydrogen Association Conference*. Washington, DC, 29 March–1 April 2005.
[43] Moore RB and Raman V (1998) Hydrogen infrastructure for fuel cell transportation. *International Journal of Hydrogen Energy* 23: 617–620.
[44] US DOE (2002) *A National Vision of America's Transition to a Hydrogen Economy to 2030 and Beyond*. Washington, DC: United States Department of Energy.
[45] Nesbitt K and Sperling D (1998) Myths regarding alternative fuel vehicle demand by light-duty vehicle fleets. *Transportation Research Part D* 3: 259–269.
[46] Leiby P and Rubin J (2004) Understanding the transition to new fuels and vehicles: Lessons learned from experience of alternative fuel and hybrid vehicles. In: Sperling D and Cannon J (eds.) *The Hydrogen Energy Transition – Moving Toward the Post Petroleum Age in Transportation*. Burlington, MA: Elsevier.
[47] Zhao J and Melaina MW (2006) Transition to hydrogen-based transportation in China: Lessons learned from alternative fuel vehicle programs in the United States and China. *Energy Policy* 34: 1299–1309.
[48] Sperling D (1988) *New Transportation Fuels. A Strategic Approach to Technological Change*. Berkeley: University of California Press.
[49] Wurster R (2002) *Pathways to a Hydrogen Refueling Infrastructure Between Today and 2020*. Ottobrunn, Germany: L-B-Systemtechnik GmbH. www.hyweb.de/Knowledge/article/LBST_H2-Roadmap_27MAY2002.pdf (last accessed 21 December 2011).
[50] Jensen MW and Ross M (2000) The ultimate challenge: Developing an infrastructure for fuel cell vehicles. *Environment* 42: 10–22.
[51] AEA (2007) Removing the economic and institutional barriers to a hydrogen future. *AEA Energy & Environment and Air Products, Report to DfT Horizons Programme*. [Online] http://www.hydrogen-infrastructures.co.uk/projectdocuments.php (last accessed 21 December 2011).
[52] Mori D and Hirose K (2009) Recent challenges of hydrogen storage technologies for fuel cell vehicles. *International Journal of Hydrogen Energy* 34(10): 4569–4574.
[53] Satyapal S, Petrovic J, Read C, *et al*. (2007) The U.S. Department of Energy's National Hydrogen Storage Project: Progress towards meeting hydrogen-powered vehicle requirements. *Catalysis Today* 120: 246–256.
[54] Hoffheinz G, Kelly N, and Ete A (2007) Evaluation of hydrogen demonstration systems & United Kingdom hydrogen infrastructure. *Report to UK Department of Trade and Industry*. [Online] http://webarchive.nationalarchives.gov.uk/+/http://www.berr.gov.uk/files/file38314.pdf (last accessed 21 December 2011).
[55] Guo Z, Shang C, and Aguey-Zinsou K (2008) Materials challenges for hydrogen storage. *Journal of the European Ceramic Society* 28: 1467–1473.
[56] National Research Council (NRC) (2005) *Review of the Research Program of the Freedom Car and Fuel Partnership*. Washington, DC: National Academies Press.
[57] Shudo T (2007) Improving thermal efficiency by reducing cooling losses in hydrogen combustion engines. *International Journal of Hydrogen Energy* 32(17): 4285–4293.
[58] BMW (2009) BMW Hydrogen Engine Reaches Top Level Efficiency. *BMW*, Munich, Press Release, 3 March 2009. [Online] https://www.press.bmwgroup.com/pressclub/p/pcgl/startpage.htm (last accessed 21 December 2011).
[59] Butler J (2009) Portable fuel cell survey. *Fuel Cell Today*, London. www.fuelcelltoday.com (last accessed 21 December 2011).

[60] Adamson K and Callaghan Jerram L (2009) Niche transport survey. *Fuel Cell Today*, London. www.fuelcelltoday.com (last accessed 21 December 2011).
[61] US DOE (2008) Comparison of fuel cell technologies. *Fact Sheet.* http://www1.eere.energy.gov/hydrogenandfuelcells/fuelcells/pdfs/fc_comparison_chart.pdf (last accessed 21 December 2011).
[62] Adamson K (2008) Large stationary survey. *Fuel Cell Today*, London. www.fuelcelltoday.com (last accessed 21 December 2011).
[63] Woking Council. Woking Park Fuel Cell CHP. [Online] www.woking.gov.uk/environment/climate/Greeninitiatives/sustainablewoking/fuelcell (last accessed 21 December 2011).
[64] Adamson K (2009) Small stationary survey. *Fuel Cell Today*, London. www.fuelcelltoday.com (last accessed 21 December 2011).
[65] McDowall W and Eames M (2007) Towards a sustainable hydrogen economy: A multi-criteria sustainability appraisal of competing hydrogen futures. *International Journal of Hydrogen Energy* 32(18): 4611–4626.
[66] UK Energy Research Centre (UKERC) (2009) *UKERC Energy 2050 Project: Making the Transition to a Secure and Low Carbon Energy System, Synthesis Report.* London: UKERC. www.ukerc.ac.uk (last accessed 21 December 2011).
[67] The Committee on Climate Change (CCC) (2008) *Building a Low-Carbon Economy – The UK's Contribution to Tackling Climate Change.* London: CCC. www.theccc.org.uk/reports (last accessed 21 December 2011).
[68] E4 Tech (2004) Element energy, Eoin Lees energy, A strategic framework for hydrogen energy in the UK. *Final Report for DTI, E4 Tech*, London.
[69] Geels F (2002) Technological transitions as evolutionary reconfiguration processes: A multi-level perspective and a case-study. *Research Policy* 31: 1257–1274.
[70] Geels F (2005) Co-evolution of technology and society: The transition in water supply and personal hygiene in the Netherlands (1850–1930) – A case study in multi-level perspective. *Technology in Society* 27: 363–397.
[71] Geels F (2006) Co-evolutionary and multi-level dynamics in transitions: The transformation of aviation systems and the shift from propeller to turbojet (1930–1970). *Technovation* 26: 999–1016.
[72] Agnolucci P and McDowall W (2007) Technological change in niches: Auxiliary power units and the hydrogen economy. *Technological Forecasting and Social Change* 74(8): 1394–1410.
[73] HFP Secretariat (2005) *European Hydrogen and Fuel Cell Technology Platform: Deployment Strategy.* Brussels, Belgium: HFP Secretariat.
[74] Brodrick C-J, Lipman TE, Farshchi M, et al. (2002) Evaluation of fuel cell auxiliary power units for heavy-duty diesel trucks. *Transportation Research – Part D: Transport and Environment* 7(4): 303–316.
[75] Lamp P, Tachtler J, Finkenwirth O, et al. (2003) Development of an auxiliary power unit with solid oxide fuel cells for automotive applications. *Fuel Cells* 3(3): 146–152.
[76] Adamson K-A (2005) Calculating the price trajectory of adoption of fuel cell vehicles. *International Journal of Hydrogen Energy* 30: 341–350.
[77] Lutsey N, Brodrick C-J, Sperling D, and Dwyer HA (2003) Markets for fuel-cell auxiliary power units in vehicles: Preliminary assessment. *Transportation Research Record* 1842: 118–127.
[78] Meissner E and Richter G (2001) Vehicle electric power systems are under change! Implications for design, monitoring and management of automotive batteries. *Journal of Power Sources* 95: 13–23.
[79] Arthur D. Little (ADL) (2001) Conceptual design of POX SOFC 5 kW Net System. *Final Report to the Department of Energy National Energy Technology Laboratory*, 8 January 2001.
[80] Stodolsky F, Gaines L, and Vyas A (2000) *Analysis of Technology Options to Reduce the Fuel Consumption of Idling Trucks Report ANL/ESD-43.* Argonne, IL: Argonne National Laboratory.
[81] Russell S and Williams R (2002) Concepts, spaces and tools for action? Exploring the policy potential of the social shaping perspective. In: Srensen KH and Williams R (eds.) *Shaping Technology, Guiding Policy: Concepts, Spaces and Tools.* Cheltenham: Edward Elgar.
[82] Hughes N (2006) Summary of Discussions from Expert Stakeholder Workshops on the Economics of Hydrogen Technologies. UKSHEC Social Science Working Paper No. 27. London: Policy Studies Institute. www.psi.org.uk/ukshec (last accessed 21 December 2011).
[83] Railway Forum (2009) [Online] www.railwayforum.com/electrification.php (last accessed 21 December 2011).
[84] US DOE (2006) *Hydrogen Posture Plan: An Integrated Research, Development and Demonstration Plan.* Washington, DC: US DOE.
[85] DOE (2008) Hydrogen Program Record No. 8019. *Fuel Cell System Cost.* www.hydrogen.energy.gov/program_records.html (last accessed 21 December 2011).
[86] DOE (2009) Hydrogen Program Record No. 9012. *Fuel Cell System Cost.* www.hydrogen.energy.gov/program_records.html (last accessed 21 December 2011).
[87] NREL (2006) *Fuel Cell System for Transportation – 2005 Cost Estimate. Independent Review.* Golden, CO: NREL. www.hydrogen.energy.gov/peer_reviews.html (last accessed 21 December 2011).
[88] BBC (2008) Car club members on the increase. *BBC News.* [Online] http://news.bbc.co.uk/1/hi/programmes/moneybox/7601102.stm (last accessed 21 December 2011).
[89] State of California, California Hydrogen Highway. *Homepage.* [Online] www.hydrogenhighway.ca.gov (last accessed 21 December 2011).
[90] Honda, FCX Clarity. *Official Website.* [Online] http://automobiles.honda.com/fcx-clarity/ (last accessed 21 December 2011).
[91] Callaghan Jerram L (2009) Light duty vehicle survey. *Fuel Cell Today*, London. www.fuelcelltoday.com (last accessed 21 December 2011).
[92] Adamson K and Crawley G (2006) Light duty vehicle survey. *Fuel Cell Today*, London. www.fuelcelltoday.com (last accessed 21 December 2011).
[93] Wipke K, Anton D, and Sprik S (2009) Evaluation of Range Estimates for Toyota FCHV-adv Under Open Road Driving Conditions, SRNL/NREL. www.osti.gov/bridge (last accessed 21 December 2011).
[94] IMIEV – Mitsubishi [Online] http://www.mitsubishi-cars.co.uk/imiev/ (last accessed 21 December 2011).
[95] Renault Z.E. [Online] http://www.renault-ze.com/en-gb/renault-z.e-electric-vehicles-kangoo-fluence-zoe-twizy-1931.html (last accessed 21 December 2011).
[96] Tesla Motors [Online] http://www.teslamotors.com/ (last accessed 21 December 2011).
[97] Nissan Leaf [Online] Available at www.nissan.co.uk/leaf (last accessed 21 December 2011).
[98] GoinGreen, *Homepage.* [Online] www.goingreen.co.uk (last accessed 21 December 2011).
[99] Green Car Site, 75 miles with the G-Wiz L-ion. [Online] www.greencarsite.co.uk/econews/g-wiz-l-ion.htm (last accessed 21 December 2011).
[100] Fiat 500 [Online] www.fiat.co.uk/500 (last accessed 21 December 2011).
[101] Element Energy (2009) Strategies for the uptake of electric vehicles and associated infrastructure implications. *Report for Committee on Climate Change.* Cambridge: Element Energy. http://www.theccc.org.uk/reports/1st-progress-report/supporting-research- (last accessed 21 December 2011).
[102] AEA (2009) *Market Outlook to 2022 for Battery Electric Vehicles and Plug-in Hybrid Electric Vehicles, Report for Committee on Climate Change.* Didcot, UK: AEA. http://www.theccc.org.uk/reports/1st progress-report/supporting-research- (last accessed 21 December 2011).
[103] Smith Electric Vehicles [Online] http://www.smithelectricvehicles.com/ (last accessed 21 December 2011).
[104] Guardian (2011) Could Modec Crash Kill off UK's Commercial Electric Vehicle Market, guardian.co.uk, 8 March 2011.
[105] Haraldsson K, Folkesson A, and Alvfors P (2005) Fuel cell buses in the Stockholm CUTE project – First experiences from a climate perspective. *Journal of Power Sources* 145(2): 620–631.
[106] EU (2011) HyFLEET:CUTE, Homepage [online] Available at: http://www.global-hydrogen-bus-platform.com/ (last accessed 21 December 2011).
[107] University of Birmingham (2009) Hydrogen Hybrid Canal Boat: Clean and Silent Propulsion for the Inland Waterways, Birmingham. [Online] www.original.bham.ac.uk/energy/news/hydrogen-canal-boat.shtml (last accessed 21 December 2011).
[108] Proton Motor (2008) *First Fuel Cell Ship Goes into Service.* Puchheim, Germany: Proton Motor. [Online] www.proton-motor.de/zem-ship-zero-emission-ship.html (last accessed 21 December 2011).
[109] Renewable Fuels Agency (RFA) (2008) *The Gallagher Review of the Indirect Effects of Biofuels Production.* St. Leonards-on-Sea, UK: RFA. www.renewablefuelsagency.gov.uk (last accessed 21 December 2011).
[110] Naik S, Goud V, Rout P, and Dalai A (2010) Production of first and second generation biofuels: A comprehensive review. *Renewable and Sustainable Energy Reviews* 14(2): 557–577.

[111] Brennan L and Owende P (2010) Biofuels from microalgae – A review of technologies for production, processing and extractions of biofuels and co-products. *Renewable and Sustainable Energy Reviews* 14(2): 557–577.
[112] Ault G, Frame D, Hughes N, and Strachan N (2008) Electricity network scenarios for Great Britain in 2050. *Final Report for Ofgem's LENS Project*, Glasgow/London. www.ofgem.gov.uk/Networks/Trans/ElecTransPolicy/lens/Pages/lens.aspx (last accessed 21 December 2011).
[113] DECC (2010) 2050 Pathways Analysis. [Online] http://www.decc.gov.uk/en/content/cms/tackling/2050/2050.aspx (last accessed 21 December 2011).
[114] Strbac G, Gan CK, Aunedi M, et al. (2010) Benefits of Advanced Smart Metering for Demand Response based Control of Distribution Networks. *Summary Report. Imperial College London/Energy Networks Association*. [Online] www.energynetworks.org (last accessed 21 December 2011).
[115] Aylott M, Casella E, Tubby I, et al. (2008) Yield and spatial supply of bioenergy poplar and willow short rotation coppice in the UK. *New Phytologist* 178: 358–370.
[116] Department of Energy and Climate Change (DECC) (2011) *Digest of UK Energy Statistics (DUKES)*. London: TSO. www.decc.gov.uk (last accessed 21 December 2011).
[117] Deutsche Energie-Agentur GmbH (dena) (2006) *Biomass to Liquid – BtL – Implementation Report, Summary*. Berlin: dena. www.dena.de (last accessed 21 December 2011).
[118] Bossel U (2006) Does a hydrogen economy make sense? In: *Proceedings of the IEEE* 94(10): 1826–1837.
[119] Sørensen B, Breeze P, Da Rosa A, et al. (2009) *Renewable Energy Focus Handbook*. Oxford: Elsevier.
[120] Bernier E, Hamelin J, Agbossou K, and Bose T (2005) Electric round-trip efficiency of hydrogen and oxygen-based energy storage. *International Journal of Hydrogen Energy* 30(2): 105–111.
[121] Defra/DTI/DfT (2007) *UK Biomass Strategy*. London: Defra. www.decc.gov.uk (last accessed 21 December 2011).
[122] BBC (2011) Longannet carbon capture scheme scrapped, *bbc.co.uk*, 19 October 2011. [Online] http://www.bbc.co.uk/news/uk-scotland-north-east-orkney-shetland-15371258 (last accessed 21 December 2011).
[123] Starr F, Tzimas E, and Peteves S (2007) Critical factors in the design, operation and economics of coal gasification plants: The case of flexible co-production of hydrogen and electricity. *International Journal of Hydrogen Energy* 32: 1477–1485.
[124] Tzimas E, Cornos C, Starr F, and Garcia-Cortes C (2009) The design of carbon capture IGCC-based plants with hydrogen co-production. *Energy Procedia* 1(1): 591–598.
[125] Davison J, Arienti S, Cotone P, and Mancuso L (2009) Co-production of hydrogen and electricity with CO_2 capture. *Energy Procedia* 1(1): 4063–4070.
[126] Sims REH, Mabee W, Saddler JN, and Taylor M (2010) An overview of second generation biofuel technologies. *Bioresource Technology* 101(6): 1570–1580.
[127] Demirbas MF (2011) Biofuels from algae for sustainable development. *Applied Energy* 88(10): 3473–3480.
[128] Department for Transport (DfT) (2009) *Low Carbon Transport: A Greener Future. A Carbon Reduction Strategy for Transport*. London: TSO.
[129] EC (2011) Renewable Energy: Biofuels and Other Renewable Energy in the Transport Sector. [Online] http://ec.europa.eu/energy/renewables/biofuels/biofuels_en.htm (last accessed 21 December 2011).
[130] DfT (2011) Renewable Transport Fuels Obligation. [Online] http://www.dft.gov.uk/topics/sustainable/biofuels/rtfo/ (last accessed 21 December 2011).
[131] Department of Energy and Climate Change (DECC) (2008) Climate Change Act 2008. [Online] www.decc.gov.uk/en/content/cms/legislation/cc_act_08/cc_act_08.aspx (last accessed 21 December 2011).
[132] European Commission (EC) (2008) HyWays – The European Hydrogen Energy Roadmap. www.hyways.de (last accessed 21 December 2011).
[133] Environmental Innovations Advisory Group (EIAG) (2006) *Bridging the Gap Between Environmental Necessity and Economic Opportunity. First Report of the Environmental Innovations Advisory Group*. London: DTI.
[134] Green Futures (2006) Take me to the future. *Forum for the Future*, London. www.forumforthefuture.org.uk/greenfutures/articles/602532 (last accessed 21 December 2011).
[135] BBC (2005) Edinburgh rejects congestion plan, *bbc.co.uk*, 25 February 2005. [Online] http://news.bbc.co.uk/1/hi/scotland/4287145.stm (last accessed 21 December 2011).
[136] Anable J, Lane B, and Kelay T (2006) Evidence base review of public attitudes to climate change and travel behaviour. *Report to Department for Transport*.
[137] Guardian (2011) UK Government Launches £5,000 Electric Car Grant Scheme. *Guardian.co.uk*, 1 January 2011. [Online] http://www.guardian.co.uk/environment/2011/jan/01/electric-car-grant-uk (last accessed 21 December 2011).
[138] Hodson M, Marvin S, and Hewitson A (2008) Constructing a typology of H_2 in cities and regions: An international review. *International Journal of Hydrogen Energy* 33(6): 1619–1629.
[139] DECC (2009) *The UK Low Carbon Transition Plan – National Strategy for Climate and Energy*. London: UK Department for Energy and Climate Change. [Online] http://www.decc.gov.uk (last accessed 21 December 2011).
[140] DECC (2011) Renewables Obligation. [Online] http://www.decc.gov.uk/en/content/cms/meeting_energy/renewable_ener/renew_obs/renew_obs.aspx (last accessed 21 December 2011).
[141] DECC (2011) Feed-in Tariffs. [Online] http://www.decc.gov.uk/en/content/cms/meeting_energy/Renewable_ener/feedin_tariff/feedin_tariff.aspx (last accessed 21 December 2011).
[142] Pollitt M (2010) *UK Renewable Energy Policy since Privatisation*. EPRG Working Paper No. 1002. Cambridge, UK: University of Cambridge.
[143] DECC (2010) Electricity Market Reform – Consultation document. [Online] http://www.decc.gov.uk/en/content/cms/consultations/emr/emr.aspx (last accessed 21 December 2011).
[144] He L, Delarue E, D'haeseleer W, and Glachant J (2011) A novel business model for aggregating the values of electricity storage. *Energy Policy* 39(3): 1575–1585.
[145] Connolly D, Lund H, Finn P, et al. (2011) Practical operation strategies for pumped hydroelectric energy storage (PHES) utilizing electricity price arbitrage. *Energy Policy* 39(7): 4189–4196.
[146] Loisel R, Mercier A, Gatzen C, et al. (2010) Valuation framework for large scale electricity storage in a case with wind curtailment. *Energy Policy* 38(11): 7323–7337.
[147] Ekman CK and Jensen SH (2010) Prospects for large scale electricity storage in Denmark. *Energy Conversion and Management* 51(6): 1140–1147.
[148] Branston JR (2000) A counterfactual price analysis of British electricity privatisation. *Utilities Policy* 9: 31–46.
[149] IEA (2011) RD&D Statistics. [Online] http://www.iea.org/stats/rd.asp (last accessed 21 December 2011).

Further Reading

Ekins P (ed.) (2010) *Hydrogen Energy – Economic and Social Challenges*. London: Earthscan.
Walker G (ed.) (2008) *Solid-state Hydrogen Storage: Materials and Chemistry*. London: Taylor & Francis.

Relevant Websites

http://www.fuelcelltoday.com – Fuel Cell Today.
http://www.hydrogen.energy.gov – US DOE Hydrogen Program.

4.04 Hydrogen Safety Engineering: The State-of-the-Art and Future Progress

V Molkov, University of Ulster, Newtownabbey, Northern Ireland, UK

© 2012 V Molkov. Published by Elsevier Ltd. All rights reserved.

4.04.1	Introduction	78
4.04.2	Hazards Related to Hydrogen Properties	81
4.04.3	Regulations, Codes, and Standards and Hydrogen Safety Engineering	82
4.04.4	Unignited Releases of Hydrogen	86
4.04.4.1	Momentum-Controlled Jets	86
4.04.4.2	The Underexpanded Jet Theory	89
4.04.4.3	Transition from Momentum- to Buoyancy-Controlled Flow within a Jet	90
4.04.5	Hydrogen Fires	91
4.04.5.1	Dimensional Flame Length Correlation	91
4.04.5.2	The Nomogram for Flame Length Calculation	92
4.04.5.3	Dimensionless Flame Length Correlation	92
4.04.5.4	Separation Distance: Jet Flame Tip Location Compared to Lower Flammability Limit Location	94
4.04.6	Pressure Effects of Hydrogen Unscheduled Releases	95
4.04.6.1	Unignited Release in a Garage-Like Enclosure	95
4.04.6.2	Delayed Ignition of Nonpremixed Turbulent Jets	97
4.04.7	Deflagrations and Detonations	99
4.04.8	Safety Strategies and Accident Mitigation Techniques	101
4.04.8.1	Inherently Safer Design of Fuel Cell Systems	101
4.04.8.2	Mitigation of Release Consequences	102
4.04.8.3	Reduction of Separation Distances Informed by the Hydrogen Safety Engineering	102
4.04.8.4	Mitigation by Barriers	102
4.04.8.5	Mitigation of Deflagration-to-Detonation Transition	103
4.04.8.6	Prevention of Deflagration-to-Detonation Transition within a Fuel Cell	103
4.04.8.7	Detection and Hydrogen Sensors	103
4.04.9	Future Progress and Development	104
4.04.9.1	Release Phenomena	104
4.04.9.2	Ignition Phenomena	104
4.04.9.3	Hydrogen Fires	104
4.04.9.4	Deflagrations and Detonations	105
4.04.9.5	Storage	105
4.04.9.6	High-Pressure Electrolyzers	105
4.04.9.7	Hazard and Risk Identification and Analysis for Early Markets	105
4.04.10	Conclusions	105
Acknowledgments		107
References		107

Glossary

Deflagration and detonation Propagation of a combustion zone at a velocity that is less than (deflagration) and greater than (detonation) the speed of sound in the unreacted mixture.

Equivalence ratio – The ratio of fuel-to-oxidizer ratio to stoichiometric fuel-to-oxidizer ratio.

Fire-resistance rating A measure of time for which a passive fire protection system can withstand a standard fire-resistance test.

Flammability range The range of concentrations between the lower and the upper flammability limits. The lower flammability limit (LFL) is the lowest concentration of a combustible substance in a gaseous oxidizer that will propagate a flame. The upper flammability limit (UFL) is the highest concentration of a combustible substance in a gaseous oxidizer that will propagate a flame.

Hazard A chemical or physical condition that has the potential for causing damage to people, property, and the environment.

Hydrogen safety engineering (HSE) An application of scientific and engineering principles to the protection of life, property, and environment from the adverse effects of incidents/accidents involving hydrogen.

Laminar burning velocity The rate of flame propagation relative to the velocity of the unburned gas that is ahead of it, under stated conditions of composition, temperature, and pressure of the unburned gas.

Mach disk A strong shock normal to the underexpanded jet flow direction.
Reynolds number A dimensionless number that gives a measure of the ratio of inertial to viscous forces.
Risk The combination of the probability of an event and its consequence.
Separation distance The minimum separation between a hazard source and an object (human, equipment, or environment) that will mitigate the effect of a likely foreseeable incident and prevent a minor incident escalating into a larger incident.
Underexpanded jet A jet with a pressure at the nozzle exit that is above atmospheric pressure.

4.04.1 Introduction

The scarcity of fossil fuel reserves, geopolitical fears associated with fossil fuel depletion, and issues of environment pollution and climate change as well as the need to ensure independence of energy supply make the low-carbon economy with an essential hydrogen vector inevitable in the coming decades. Today, the first series of hydrogen-fueled buses and cars are already on the road and refueling stations are operating in different countries around the world. High priority research directions for the hydrogen economy include safety as not only a technological issue but also as a psychological and sociological issue [1]. This chapter provides an overview of the state-of-the-art in hydrogen safety as a technological issue only. Global fuel cell demand is expected to reach $8.5 billion in 2016 [2].

Public perception of hydrogen technologies is still affected by the 1937 'Hindenburg' disaster. It is often associated with hydrogen as a reason; even there is an opinion that the difference in electrical potential between the Zeppelin's 'landing' rope and the ground during descending had generated electrical current and ignited the dirigible canopy made of extremely combustible material. This was followed by diffusive combustion of hydrogen in air, without the generation of a significant blast wave able to injure people. **Figure 1** shows a photo of the burning Hindenburg dirigible fire demonstrating that there was no 'explosion' [3].

Contrary to popular misunderstanding, hydrogen helped to save 62 lives in the Hindenburg disaster. The NASA research has demonstrated [4] that the disaster would have been essentially unchanged even if the airship was lifted not by hydrogen but by nonflammable helium, and that probably nobody aboard was killed by a hydrogen fire. The 35% who died were killed by jumping out, or by the burning diesel oil, canopy, and debris (the cloth canopy was coated with what nowadays would be called rocket fuel). The other 65% survived by riding the flaming dirigible to earth as the clear hydrogen flames swirled harmlessly above them.

There is a clear understanding of the importance of hydrogen safety engineering (HSE) in emerging hydrogen and fuel cell (HFC) technologies, applications, and infrastructure. Hydrogen safety studies were initiated decades ago as a result of accidents in the process industries, and were supported by safety research for nuclear power plants and the aerospace sector. However, the Challenger Space Shuttle disaster (2007) and more recently the Fukushima nuclear tragedy (2011) demonstrated that our knowledge and engineering skills to deal with hydrogen even within these industries require more investment, from both intellectual and financial perspectives. Nowadays, dealing with hydrogen is getting out of the hands of highly trained professionals in industry and has become an everyday

Figure 1 Photo of the Hindenburg dirigible fire demonstrating that there was no explosion (deflagration) [3].

activity for the public. This implies a need for the establishment of a new safety culture, innovative safety strategies, and breakthrough engineering solutions. It is expected that the level of safety at the consumer interface with hydrogen must be similar to or exceed that present with fossil fuel usage. Safety parameters of HFC products will directly define their competitiveness in the market.

Safety engineers, designers, technical staff at maintenance workshops and refueling stations, and first responders should be professionally educated to deal with hydrogen systems at pressures up to 100 MPa and temperatures down to −253 °C (liquefied hydrogen) in open and confined spaces. Regulators and public officials should be provided with state-of-the-art knowledge and guidance to professionally support the safe introduction of HFC systems to everyday life of public. Engineers and technicians, including those who have handled hydrogen in different industries for several decades, need to undergo periodic retraining through continuous professional development courses to acquire the latest knowledge and engineering skills for using hydrogen in the public domain. Indeed, emerging hydrogen systems and infrastructure will create in the near future an entirely new environment of hydrogen usage, which is not covered by industrial experience or by existing codes and recommended practice [5].

Hydrogen-powered vehicles are one of the main applications of HFC technologies. Hazards and associated risks for hydrogen-fueled cars should be understood and interpreted in a professional way with full comprehension of consequences by all stakeholders starting from system designers through regulators to users. Probably the first comparison of the 'severity' of a hydrogen and gasoline fuel leak and ignition was performed by Swain [6]. **Figure** 2 shows snapshots of hydrogen jet fire and gasoline fire at 3 s (left) and 60 s (right) after car fire initiation.

The scenario presented in **Figure** 2 is rare; for example, it can be realized at a false self-initiation of a pressure relief device (PRD). Indeed, the release of hydrogen through the PRD from the onboard storage would be in the majority of cases initiated by an external fire. Such a scenario drastically changes hazards and associated risks compared to the scenario shown in **Figure** 2.

Figures 3 and 4 demonstrate some results of a study on hydrogen-powered car fires performed in Japan by Tamura *et al.* [7]. The hydrogen fuel cell vehicle (HFCV) was equipped with a thermal pressure relief device (TPRD) with a vent pipe of internal diameter 4.2 mm. In the test shown in **Figure** 3, the compressed hydrogen gas tank was installed exactly at the position of the removed gasoline tank. By this reason, there was no chance to install a larger storage vessel, and a small tank of 36 l volume at pressure 70 MPa was used. The spread of fire from a gasoline vehicle to HFCV was investigated to address scenarios where different types of vehicles are catching fire in car collisions or in natural disasters like earthquake. The experiment revealed that when the TPRD of HFCV is activated by gasoline fire, a fireball of more than 10 m diameter is formed (**Figure** 3, right).

In another test by Tamura *et al.* [7], two vehicles were parked approximately 0.85 m apart and the spread of fire from HFCV to the gasoline vehicle was investigated. **Figure** 4 shows two vehicles after TPRD initiation in the HFCV. It can be concluded that evacuation from cars with such a design of hydrogen release system is impossible and original equipment manufacturers (OEMs) have to address this customer safety issue.

Figure 2 Hydrogen jet fire and gasoline fire: 3 s (left) and 60 s (right) after car fire initiation [6].

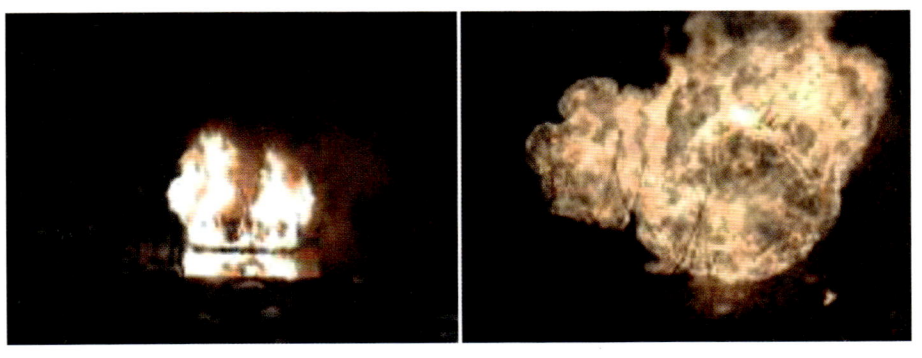

Figure 3 An HFCV gasoline pool fire test: (left) gasoline fire just before the initiation of TPRD; (right) gasoline fire 1 s after TPRD initiation [7].

Figure 4 The HFCV with initiated TPRD (left) and the gasoline car (right) [7].

Under the test conditions of Reference 7, the cause of spread of fire from the HFCV to the adjacent gasoline vehicle, in the authors' opinion, is flame spreading from the interior and exterior fittings of the HFCV but not the hydrogen flame from the TPRD (it is worth noting that a small storage tank of only 36 l with a shorter hydrogen release time was used in this study instead of a 120 l tank that is needed to provide competitive driving range). However, the authors concluded that in car carrier ships and other similar situations with closely parked HFCVs, the test results point to the possibilities of a fire in an HFCV to activate its TPRD and thereby generate hydrogen flames, which in turn may activate the underfloor TPRD in the adjoining HFCV. Therefore, to minimize damage by HFCV fire, the authors suggested that it is important to detect and extinguish fire at an early stage before the TPRD activation. Unfortunately, they did not give a solution how to do it. Hopefully, OEMs do not plan that this issue has to be tackled by first responders only and have appropriate safety engineering solutions. The experiments by Tamura *et al.* [7] have clearly demonstrated that the consequences of hydrogen-powered vehicle fire can be very 'challenging' from the point of view of both life safety and property loss.

Risk is by definition the combination of the probability of an event and its consequence. The general requirement is that the risk associated with hydrogen-fueled vehicles should be the same or below the risk associated with today's vehicles using fossil fuels. Currently, this requirement is not yet achieved, as the consequences of hydrogen-powered car fire on life safety and property loss in confined spaces such as garages are more 'costly' compared to the consequences of fossil fuel vehicle fire. Indeed, the probability of external influences causing a vehicle fire, for example, at home garages and general vehicle parking garages, will be the same independent of the vehicle type. The garage fires statistics from the National Fire Protection Association (NFPA) is as follows. During the 4-year period from 2003 to 2006, an estimated average of 8120 fires per year that started in the vehicle storage areas, garages, or carports of one- or two-family homes were reported [8]. These fires caused an average of 35 civilian deaths, 367 civilian injuries, and $425 million in direct property damage. Further to this, NFPA [9] estimated that during 1999–2002, an average of 660 structure fires and 1100 vehicle fires in or at general vehicle parking garages were reported per year (including bus, fleet, or commercial parking structures). A total of 60% of the vehicle fires and 29% of the structure fires in these properties resulted from failures of equipment or heat source. Vehicles were involved in the ignition of 13% of these structure fires. Exposure to another fire was a causal factor in roughly one-quarter of both structure and vehicle fires. The data do not distinguish between open and enclosed garages.

This statistics makes it clear that safety strategies and solutions, including those developed by OEMs, have to be improved to rely on a firm engineering design rather than a general risk assessment the uncertainties of which are impossible to define for emerging technologies.

The European Network of Excellence (NoE) HySafe (Safety of Hydrogen as an Energy Carrier; 2004–09), an EU-funded project totaling €12 million, paved the way for defragmentation of hydrogen safety research in Europe and beyond and closing knowledge gaps in the field. Since 2009, when the HySafe project was formally finished, the coordination of international hydrogen safety activities worldwide is led by the International Association for Hydrogen Safety [10], which brings together experts in hydrogen safety science and engineering from industry, research organizations, and academia from Europe, Americas, and Asia. The International Energy Agency's Hydrogen Implementing Agreement Task 31 'Hydrogen Safety' is also contributing to the prioritization of problems to be solved and to the cross-fertilization of safety strategies and engineering solutions developed in different countries around the globe.

The main sources of published knowledge in hydrogen safety include currently the *Biennial Report on Hydrogen Safety* initiated by NoE HySafe [10], *Proceedings of the International Conference on Hydrogen Safety*, and the *International Journal of Hydrogen Energy*. The main educational/training activities in the area of hydrogen safety include so far the European Summer School on Hydrogen Safety, the International Short Course and Advanced Research Workshop (ISCARW) series 'Progress in Hydrogen Safety', and the world's first postgraduate course in hydrogen safety, that is, MSc in Hydrogen Safety Engineering at the University of Ulster. However, the need for an increasing stream of highly qualified university graduates to underpin the emerging industry and early markets is obvious.

Unfortunately, it is impossible to describe in one chapter all recent progress made by the international hydrogen safety community in the field of hydrogen safety science and engineering. The materials presented here are mainly the results of the studies performed at the HySAFER Centre as a seeding research and within the projects funded by the European Commission and the Fuel Cells and Hydrogen Joint Undertaking.

4.04.2 Hazards Related to Hydrogen Properties

Hydrogen is neither more dangerous nor safer than other fuels [5]. Hydrogen safety fully depends on how professionally it is handled at the design stage and afterward. On the one hand, it is known that a hydrogen leak is difficult to detect as hydrogen is a colorless, odorless, and tasteless gas; it will burn in a clean atmosphere with an invisible flame and it is more prone to deflagration-to-detonation transition (DDT) than most other flammable gases. Safety measures to exclude the potential of DDT are very important. Indeed, while the deflagration of quiescent stoichiometric hydrogen–air cloud in the open atmosphere generates a pressure wave of only 0.01 MPa (below the level of eardrum injury threshold), the detonation of the same mixture at some conditions would generate a shock of more than 2 orders of magnitude higher of about 1.5 MPa (far above the fatal pressure of about 0.1 MPa). In addition to this, hydrogen has the smallest minimum ignition energy (MIE) of 0.019 mJ [10] and the narrowest minimum experimental safety gap (MESG) of 0.08 mm [10] to prevent flame propagation out of a shell, composed of two parts, through the gap between two flanges. For comparison, MIE of petrol is in the range 0.23–0.46 mJ and MESG for petrol is 0.96–1.02 mm [11]. On the other hand, the main hydrogen safety asset, that is, its buoyancy is the highest on Earth, confers the ability to rapidly flow out of an incident scene, and mix with the ambient air to a safe level below the lower flammability limit (4% by volume of hydrogen in air). This safety asset can 'self-manage' a hazardous hydrogen accumulation if the safety system is properly designed by a professional.

The energy density of hydrogen per unit mass is approximately 2.5 times larger than that of natural gas. On the other hand, for the same volumetric leak rate, the energy content of a hydrogen leak is smaller than that of hydrocarbons. The lower heating value of hydrogen is 241.7 kJ mol^{-1} and the higher heating value is 286.1 kJ mol^{-1} [10]. The difference of about 16% is due to the heat of condensation of water vapor, and this value is larger compared to other gases. The specific heat ratio of hydrogen at NTP (normal temperature and pressure: 293.15 K and 101.325 kPa) is 1.405. Hydrogen has a somewhat higher adiabatic flame temperature for a stoichiometric mixture in air of 2403 K [10]. The laminar burning velocity of a stoichiometric hydrogen–air mixture can be calculated as an experimental propagation velocity, observed by a schlieren photography – a method to register the flow of fluids of varying density [12], divided by the expansion coefficient of combustion products $E_i = 7.2$, and is accepted in HySAFER numerical studies as 1.91 m s^{-1} [13]. This laminar burning velocity is far greater than that of most hydrocarbons when velocities are in the range of 0.30–0.45 m s^{-1}.

It is worth noting that the maximum burning velocity for a hydrogen–air mixture is reached not in a stoichiometric mixture of 29.5% (by volume) hydrogen but in a mixture with hydrogen concentration in air of 40.1% [10], where it is 2.44 m s^{-1} [13]. This is due to the high molecular diffusivity of hydrogen, with the diffusion coefficient equal to 6.1E−05 m^2 s^{-1} [14]. Thus, the maximum burning velocity for a hydrogen–air premixed flame occurs at an equivalence ratio of 1.8, while for hydrocarbon–air flames it occurs at around 1.1.

The flammability range of hydrogen, on the one hand, is wider than that of most hydrocarbons, that is, 4–75% by volume in air at NTP. For comparison, the flammability range of methane in air is 5.28–14.1% by volume [11]. The flammability range of hydrogen expands with temperature, for example, the lower flammability limit (for an upward propagating flame) drops from 4% at NTP to 3% at 100 °C. The lower flammability limit of hydrogen depends on the direction of flame propagation. In an initially quiescent mixture, the lower flammable limit (LFL) is 4% by volume (NTP) for upward propagation, and it increases to 7.2% for horizontally propagating flames; for downward and spherically propagating flames, LEL is 8.5–9.5% as stated in a classical study [15]. Upward flame propagation at an LFL of 4% is in the form of separate 'bubbles' with unburned mixture in between. This explains why the burning of a quiescent 4% hydrogen–air mixture in a closed vessel can generate negligible, in a practical sense, overpressure. It is worth noting that a quiescent hydrogen–air mixture in the range of concentration 4–7.1% could burn practically without overpressure in a number of scenarios, for example, if ignited at the top of an enclosure, as in such conditions it cannot propagate flame in any direction and thus no heat release accompanied by pressure buildup can be observed. On the other hand, the lower flammability limit of hydrogen is high compared to most hydrocarbons. The near-stoichiometric concentration of hydrogen in air (29.5% by volume) is very much higher than that of hydrocarbons (only a few percent). Moreover, at the lower flammability limit, the ignition energy requirement of hydrogen is similar to that of methane, and weak ignition sources such as electrical equipment sparks, electrostatic sparks, or sparks from striking objects typically involve more energy than is required to ignite these flammable mixtures [16].

Compared to other fuels, hydrogen is most prone to spontaneous ignition during sudden releases into air by the so-called diffusion mechanism, where high-temperature air, heated by a shock, mixes with cold hydrogen at the contact surface between the two gases and chemical reactions can be initiated when critical conditions are reached. Indeed, sudden hydrogen releases into piping filled with air, after a safety burst disk ruptures, can be spontaneously ignited at pressures as low as about 2 MPa [16]. On the other hand, the standard autoignition temperature of hydrogen in air is above 520 °C, which is higher than for hydrocarbons.

Hydrogen is essentially an electrical insulator in both gaseous and liquid phases. Only above some critical 'breakdown' voltage, where ionization occurs, does it become an electrical conductor [10]. When high-velocity hydrogen flow accompanies high-pressure vessel blowdown, this property can potentially be responsible for the generation of static electrical charge present in piping particulates by triboelectricity, which is a type of contact electrification in which certain materials become electrically charged after they come into contact with a different material and are then separated [12]. The probability of hydrogen ignition by this mechanism increases with the increase of the blowdown time (time to empty a storage tank) with other conditions remaining the same.

Detonation is the worst-case scenario for hydrogen accident. The detonability range of hydrogen in air is 11–59% by volume [14]. This is narrower and within the flammability range of 4–75%. The detonability limits are not fundamental characteristics of the mixture as they strongly depend on the size of the experimental setup where they are measured. Indeed, the diameter of the tube, where detonation can propagate, should be of the order of detonation cell size. The detonation cell size increases as the detonability limits are approached (see Section 4.04.7 for further details). Thus, the larger is the scale of an experimental apparatus, the smaller is the lower detonability limit (the larger is the upper detonability limit). The detonability limits of a hydrogen–air mixture of the same concentration expand with the scale of a flammable cloud. This explains the difference between the lower detonability limit of hydrogen (11% by volume) reported in Reference 14 and the underestimated value of 18% published in standard ISO/TR 15916:2004 [17]. Experimental values of detonation cell size for a stoichiometric hydrogen–air mixture are 1.1–2.1 cm [18].

The experimentally observed run-up distance for transition from deflagration to detonation (DDT) in a stoichiometric hydrogen–air mixture in a tube has a typical length-to-diameter ratio of approximately 100. The DDT phenomenon is still one of the challenging subjects for combustion research. Different mechanisms are responsible for a flame front acceleration to a velocity close to the speed of sound in an unburned mixture, including but not limited to turbulence in an unburned mixture, turbulence generated by flame front itself, and various instabilities such as hydrodynamic, Rayleigh–Taylor, Richtmyer–Meshkov, and Kelvin–Helmholtz instabilities. Then, there is a jump from the sonic flame propagation velocity to the detonation velocity, which is about twice the speed of sound at least for a near-stoichiometric hydrogen–air mixture. The detonation wave is a complex of precursor shock and combustion wave; it propagates with the speed of von Neumann spike and its description can be found elsewhere [19]. Detonation front thickness is the distance from the precursor shock to the end of reaction zone where the Chapman–Jouguet (CJ) condition (sonic plane) is reached.

The presence of obstacles in a tube can essentially reduce run-up distance for DDT. This is thought to be due to significant contribution of the Richtmyer–Meshkov instability just before the DDT. Indeed, the Richtmyer–Meshkov instability increases the flame front area in both directions of a shock passage through the flame front as opposed to the Rayleigh–Taylor instability, where only one direction is unstable to the pressure gradient (acceleration of flow in the direction from lighter combustion products to heavier unburned mixture). The initiation of detonation during DDT is thought to happen in the so-called hot spot(s), which potentially could be located within the turbulent flame brush or ahead of it, for example, in the focus of a strong shock reflection. The peculiarities of DDT mechanisms do not affect the steady-state detonation wave following DDT.

The main safety asset of hydrogen is its buoyancy as underlined above. Indeed, hydrogen has a density of $0.0838 \, \text{kg m}^{-3}$ (NTP), which is far lower than that of air, which has a density of $1.205 \, \text{kg m}^{-3}$. The unwanted consequences of hydrogen releases into the open atmosphere, and in partially confined geometries, where conditions that allow hydrogen to accumulate do not exist, are drastically reduced by buoyancy. In the contrary, heavier hydrocarbons are able to form a huge combustible cloud, as in the case of disastrous Flixborough explosion in 1974 [20] and Buncefield explosion in 2005 [21]. In many practical situations, hydrocarbons may pose stronger fire and explosion hazards than hydrogen.

Thus, a conclusion can be drawn that hydrogen is neither more dangerous nor safer compared to other fuels. Hydrogen is different and has to be professionally handled with knowledge of underpinning science and HSE to provide public safety.

4.04.3 Regulations, Codes, and Standards and Hydrogen Safety Engineering

The quality of hydrogen safety provisions will directly depend on the availability of an overall performance-based HSE methodology rather than a group of codes and standards, which are often prescriptive in nature. The HSE methodology must be in compliance with regulations and with standards and codes where applicable (when explicitly mentioned in the regulations). A highly educated workforce and contemporary tools such as computational fluid dynamics (CFD) are needed for HSE.

There is an overestimation to some extent of expectations from the role of regulations, codes, and standards (RCS) in the safety design of HFC systems from the author's point of view. Standards are at least 3 years old compared to the current level of knowledge in the field due to the procedure of their development and approval. They can be quite narrowed by a particular topic or include only general statements without concrete information for engineering. Standards cannot account for all possible situations to be resolved, especially for new and developing technologies. They are written from the perspective of the industry and reflect mainly the interests of the industry rather than all stakeholders. Safety information in standards relevant to HFC systems is 'naturally' fragmented throughout a growing number of standards with time in this area. An overarching safety-oriented standard for HSE, which gives a methodology to carry out HSE, and that systemizes and maintains the knowledge in this field, is needed.

Some standards can include information derived from risk assessment methods. Risk-informed methodology and quantitative risk assessment require statistical data. In the author's opinion, they can complement but not substitute innovative safety engineering design of HFC systems. Indeed, emerging technologies can hardly be characterized by the availability of statistical data. This, at the moment, makes the use of probabilistic methods in hydrogen safety less valuable. The public is keen to know that everything possible has been done by engineers to make hydrogen-powered systems safe, rather than be satisfied by information that the probability of personal fatality is 10^{-4} or 10^{-6} or 10^{-8}. The same is valid for court proceedings as presented at the 2003 AIChE Loss Prevention Symposium in New Orleans (USA). There is another implication that potential risk assessment methods 'oversell', that is, resources are diverted away from a creative engineering, including HSE, and practical problem solving to everlasting discussions on acceptable risk level, the uncertainty of which is often unacceptably high and questionable. Unfortunately, the Fukushima disaster proved the author's doubts once again [22].

Table 1 International regulations relevant to hydrogen safety

Commission Regulation (EU) No 406/2010 of 26 April 2010 implementing Regulation (EC) No 79/2009 of the European Parliament and of the Council on type-approval of hydrogen-powered motor vehicles: http://eur-lex.europa.eu/JOHtml.do?uri=OJ:L:2010:122:SOM:EN:HTML
IMO International Code for the Construction and Equipment of Ships Carrying Liquefied Gases in Bulk (IGC Code): http://www.imo.org/environment/mainframe.asp?topic_id=995
ADR UN ECE Agreement concerning the International Carriage of Dangerous Goods by Road: http://www.unece.org/trans/danger/publi/adr/adr_e.html
RID is the European Agreement on the International Carriage of Dangerous Goods by Rail. The regulations appear as Appendix C to the Convention concerning International Carriage by Rail (COTIF) concluded at Vilnius on 3 June 1999: http://www.otif.org/en/law.html
ADN is the European Agreement concerning the International Carriage of Dangerous Goods by Inland Waterways concluded at Geneva on 26 May 2000: http://www.unece.org/trans/danger/publi/adn/adn_e.html
The rules related to transport of dangerous goods, regulated in Europe by the international agreements, mentioned in the three items above, that is, the ADR, RID, and ADN, have also been extended to national transport in the EU under the Inland transport of dangerous goods Directive 2008/68/EC: http://europa.eu/legislation_summaries/transport/rail_transport/tr0006_en.htm
The International Maritime Dangerous Goods (IMDG) Code covers the transport of dangerous goods by sea: http://www.imo.org/safety/mainframe.asp?topic_id=158
UN Recommendations on the Transport of Dangerous Goods, Model Regulations. These are updated every 2 years. Recommendations relevant to hydrogen are UN 1049 (Hydrogen, Compressed), UN 1066 (Hydrogen, refrigerated liquid), and UN 3468 (hydrogen in a metal hydride storage system): http://www.unece.org/trans/danger/publi/unrec/12_e.html
Dangerous Substances Directive 67/548/EEC: http://ec.europa.eu/environment/chemicals/dansub/home_en.htm; http://eur-lex.europa.eu/JOHtml.do?uri=OJ:L:2009:011:SOM:EN:HTML
Low Voltage Directive (LVD) 2006/95/EC: http://ec.europa.eu/enterprise/sectors/electrical/lvd/; http://ec.europa.eu/enterprise/sectors/electrical/files/lvdgen_en.pdf
Electromagnetic Compatibility Directive (EMC) 2004/108/EC: http://ec.europa.eu/enterprise/sectors/electrical/emc/; http://ec.europa.eu/enterprise/sectors/electrical/files/emc_guide__updated_20100208_v3_en.pdf
Pressure Equipment Directive (PED) 97/23/EC: http://ec.europa.eu/enterprise/sectors/pressure-and-gas/documents/ped/index_en.htm; http://www.bsigroup.com/en/ProductServices/About-CE-Marking/EU-directives/Pressure-Equipment-Directive-PED/
Simple Pressure Vessels Directive (SPVD) 2009/105/EC: http://ec.europa.eu/enterprise/sectors/pressure-and-gas/documents/spvd/index_en.htm
Transportable Pressure Equipment Directive (TPED) 1999/36/EC: http://ec.europa.eu/transport/tpe/index_en.html
Gas Appliances Directive 2009/142/EC includes fuel cells (where the primary function is heating): http://ec.europa.eu/enterprise/sectors/pressure-and-gas/gas_appliances/index_en.htm
Equipment and protective systems for potentially explosive atmosphere Directive (ATEX 95) 94/9/EC: http://ec.europa.eu/enterprise/sectors/mechanical/atex/index_en.htm
Directive on minimum requirements for improving the safety and health protection of workers potentially at risk from explosive atmospheres (ATEX 137) 99/92/EC: http://eur-lex.europa.eu/LexUriServ/LexUriServ.do?uri=CELEX:31999L0092:en:NOT
Machinery Directive (MD) 2006/42/EC: http://ec.europa.eu/enterprise/sectors/mechanical/files/machinery/guide_application_directie_2006-42-ec-2nd_edit_6-2010_en.pdf; http://ec.europa.eu/enterprise/sectors/mechanical/machinery/
Seveso II Directive: http://ec.europa.eu/environment/seveso/index.htm
The integrated pollution prevention and control Directive (IPPC) 2008/1/EC: http://ec.europa.eu/environment/air/pollutants/stationary/ippc/summary.htm
Measures to encourage improvements in the safety and health of workers 89/391/EEC: http://europa.eu/legislation_summaries/employment_and_social_policy/health_hygiene_safety_at_work/c11113_en.htm
Personal protective equipment Directive 89/686/EEC: http://ec.europa.eu/enterprise/sectors/mechanical/documents/legislation/personalprotectiveequipment/

Note: Japan has a national regulation in force covering fuel cell passenger cars with compressed hydrogen storage. An unofficial English version is available (http://www.unece.org/trans/main/wp29/wp29wgs/wp29grsp/sgs_legislation.html). The International Fire Code (IFC) and the International Building Code (IBC), both produced by the International Code Council (ICC) in the United States, are likely to be used in other countries.

A list of international regulations, which are international laws to be complied with, relevant to hydrogen safety is presented in Table 1. Currently, hydrogen is not yet considered as a fuel but still as one of the 'dangerous goods' and it will take time to update regulations for the emerging HFC systems and infrastructure.

Four technical committees (TCs) of the International Organization for Standardization (ISO) produce standards relevant to HFC technologies, systems, and infrastructure. Technical Committee 197 'Hydrogen Technologies' published a number of documents including

- ISO/TR 15916:2004 Basic considerations for the safety of hydrogen systems;
- ISO 14687 Hydrogen fuel – Product specification;
- ISO 16110-1:2007 Hydrogen generators using fuel processing technologies – Part 1: Safety;
- ISO/TS 20100:2008 Gaseous hydrogen – Fuelling stations;
- ISO 17268:2006 Compressed hydrogen surface vehicle refuelling connection devices;
- ISO 22734-1:2008 Hydrogen generators using water electrolysis process – Part 1: Industrial and commercial applications;
- ISO 26142:2010 Hydrogen detection apparatus – Stationary applications.

Technical Committee 22 SC21 on electric road vehicles issued standards with safety specifications: ISO 23273-2:2006 Fuel cell road vehicles – Safety specifications – Part 2: Protection against hydrogen hazards for vehicles fuelled with compressed hydrogen; ISO 23273-3:2006 Fuel cell road vehicles – Safety specifications – Part 3: Protection of persons against electric shock; and so on.

Technical Committee 58 on gas cylinders published several parts of standard ISO 11114 Transportable gas cylinders – Compatibility of cylinder and valve materials with gas contents, etc. Technical Committee 220 on cryogenic vessels published a number of standards related to large transportable vacuum-insulated vessels, gas/materials compatibility, valves for cryogenic service, and so on.

The International Electrotechnical Commission (IEC) publishes standards relevant to fuel cell (FC) technologies.

The US NFPA has a number of relevant standards: NFPA 2 Hydrogen Technologies Code; NFPA 52 Vehicular Gaseous Fuel Systems Code; NFPA 55 Compressed Gases and Cryogenic Fluids Code; NFPA 50A Standard for Gaseous Hydrogen Systems at Consumer Sites; NFPA 50B Standard for Liquefied Hydrogen Systems at Consumer Sites; NFPA 221 Standard for High Challenge Fire Walls, Fire Walls, and Fire Barrier Walls; NFPA 853 Standard for the Installation of Stationary Fuel Cell Power Systems.

The US Society of Automotive Engineers (SAE) relevant standards include J2578 Recommended Practice for General Fuel Cell Vehicle Safety; J2601 Fuelling Protocols for Light Duty Gaseous Hydrogen Surface Vehicles; J2719 Information Report on the Development of a Hydrogen Quality Guideline for Fuel Cell Vehicles; J2799 70 MPa Compressed Hydrogen Surface Vehicle Fuelling Connection Device and Optional Vehicle to Station Communications; etc.

The European Industrial Gas Association (EIGA) produced the following documents among others: IGC Document 122/04 Environmental impacts of hydrogen plants; IGC Document 15/06 Gaseous hydrogen stations; IGC Document 121/04 Hydrogen transportation pipelines; IGC Document 6/02 Safety in storage, handling and distribution of liquid hydrogen; IGC Document 23/00 Safety training of employees; IGC Document 75/07 Determination of safety distances; IGC Document 134/05 Potentially explosive atmosphere – EU Directive 1999/92/EC; etc.

The Compressed Gas Association (CGA) documents include G-5.3 Commodity Specification for Hydrogen; G-5.4 Standard for Hydrogen Piping Systems at User Locations; G-5.5 Hydrogen Vent Systems; G-5.8 High Pressure Hydrogen Piping Systems at Consumer Locations; C-6.4 Methods for External Visual Inspection of Natural Gas Vehicle (NGV) and Hydrogen Vehicle (HV) Fuel Containers and Their Installations; etc.

The American Society of Mechanical Engineers (ASME) standards include ASME B31.12: Hydrogen piping and pipelines; ASME PTC 50: Performance Test Code for Fuel Cell Power Systems Performance; ASME BPVC Boiler and Pressure Vessel Code; etc.

The Canadian Standards Association (CSA) published standards: Stationary Fuel Cell Power Requirements: ANSI/CSA America FC 1-2004; Portable Fuel Cell Power Systems ANSI/CSA America FC 3-2004; CSA America HPRD1 Basic Requirements for Pressure Relief Devices for Compressed Hydrogen Vehicle Fuel Containers.

There are also a number of useful guidelines in the field listed in **Table 2**.

HSE is defined as an application of scientific and engineering principles to the protection of life, property, and environment from the adverse effects of incidents/accidents involving hydrogen.

Despite the progress in hydrogen safety science and engineering during the last decade, especially through the HySafe partnership [10], an overarching performance-based methodology to carry out HSE is still absent.

HSE comprises a design framework and technical subsystems (TSSs). A design framework for HSE, developed at the University of Ulster, is similar to British standard BS7974 for application of fire safety engineering to the design of buildings [23] and is expanded to reflect specific hydrogen safety-related phenomena, including but not limited to high-pressure underexpanded leaks and dispersion, spontaneous ignition of sudden hydrogen releases into air, high-momentum jet fires, deflagrations and detonations, and specific mitigation techniques.

The HSE process includes three main steps. First, a qualitative design review (QDR) is undertaken by a team that can incorporate owner, hydrogen safety engineer, architect, representative of authorities having jurisdiction, for example, emergency services, and other stakeholders. The team defines accident scenarios, suggests trial safety designs, and formulates acceptance criteria. Second, a quantitative safety analysis of selected scenarios and trial designs is carried out by qualified hydrogen safety engineer(s) using the state-of-the-art knowledge in hydrogen safety science and engineering and validated models and tools. Third, the performance of a hydrogen and/or fuel cell system under the trial safety designs is assessed against predefined acceptance criteria.

QDR is a qualitative process based on the team's experience and knowledge. It allows its members to establish a range of safety strategies. Ideally, QDR has to be carried out early in the design process and in a systematic way, so that any substantial findings and relevant items can be incorporated into the design of HFC application or infrastructure before the working drawings are developed. In practice, however, the QDR process is likely to involve some iterations as the design process moves from a broad concept to

Table 2 Guidelines relevant to hydrogen safety

Installation permitting guidance for small stationary hydrogen and fuel cell systems (HYPER) interactive handbook and PDF document: http://www.hyperproject.eu/
US installation guidelines for refuelling stations and stationary applications: http://www.pnl.gov/fuelcells/permit_guide.stm
HyApproval handbook: European handbook for the approval of hydrogen refuelling stations: http://www.hyapproval.org/
NASA: Safety standard for hydrogen and hydrogen systems: Guidelines for Hydrogen System Design, Materials Selection, Operations, Storage, and Transportation: http://www.hq.nasa.gov/office/codeq/doctree/canceled/871916.pdf
NASA/TM–2003–212059 Guide for Hydrogen Hazards Analysis on Components and Systems: http://ston.jsc.nasa.gov/collections/TRS/_techrep/TM-2003-212059.pdf
American Institute of Aeronautics and Astronautics (AIAA) guide to Safety of Hydrogen and Hydrogen Systems (G-095-2004e): http://www.AIAA.org

greater detail. Safety objectives should be defined during the QDR. They should be appropriate to the particular aspects of the system design, as HSE may be used either to develop a complete hydrogen safety strategy or to consider only one aspect of the design. The main hydrogen safety objectives are safety of life, loss control, and environmental protection.

The QDR team should establish one or more trial safety designs taking into consideration selected accident scenario(s). The different designs could satisfy the same safety objectives and should be compared with each other in terms of cost-effectiveness and practicability. At first glance, it is essential that trial designs should limit hazards by implementing prevention measures and ensuring the reduction of severity and frequency of consequences. Although HSE provides a degree of freedom, it is mandatory to fully respect relevant regulations when defining trial designs.

The QDR team has to establish the criteria against which the performance of a design can be judged. Three main methods can be used: deterministic, comparative, and probabilistic. The QDR team can, depending on trial designs, define acceptance criteria following all three methods.

The QDR team should provide a set of qualitative outputs to be used in the quantitative analysis: results of the architectural review; hydrogen safety objectives; significant hazards and associated phenomena; specifications of the scenarios for analysis; one or more trial designs; acceptance criteria; and suggested methods of analysis. Following QDR, the team should decide which trial design(s) is likely to be optimum. The team should then decide whether quantitative analysis is necessary to demonstrate that the design meets the hydrogen safety objective(s).

Following the QDR, a quantitative analysis may be carried out using TSSs where various aspects of the analysis can be quantified by a deterministic study or a probabilistic study. The quantification process is preceded by the QDR for two main reasons: to ensure that the problem is fully understood and that the analysis addresses the relevant aspects of the hydrogen safety system; and to simplify the problem and minimize the calculation effort required. In addition, the QDR team should identify appropriate methods of analysis among simple engineering calculations, CFD simulations, simple probabilistic study, and full probabilistic study. A deterministic study using comparative criteria will generally require fewer data and resources than a probabilistic approach and is likely to be the simplest method of achieving an acceptable design. A full probabilistic study is likely to be justified only when a substantially new approach to hydrogen system design or hydrogen safety practice is being adopted. The analysis may be a combination of some deterministic and some probabilistic elements.

Following the quantitative analysis, the results should be compared with the acceptance criteria identified during the QDR exercise. Three basic types of approach can be considered:

- Deterministic approach shows that on the basis of the initial assumptions a defined set of conditions will not occur.
- Comparative approach shows that the design provides a level of safety equivalent to that in similar systems and/or conforms to prescriptive codes (as an alternative to performance-based HSE).
- Probabilistic approach shows that the risk of a given event occurring is acceptably low, for example, equal to or below the established risk for similar existing systems.

If none of the trial designs developed by the QDR team satisfies the specified acceptance criteria, QDR and quantification process should be repeated until a hydrogen safety strategy satisfies acceptance criteria and other design requirements. Several options can be considered when reconducting QDR following recommendations of standard BS7974 [23]: development of additional trial designs; adoption of more discriminating design approach, for example, using deterministic techniques instead of a comparative study or probabilistic instead of deterministic procedures; and reevaluation of design objectives, for example, if the cost of hydrogen safety measures for property loss prevention outweighs the potential benefits. When a satisfactory solution has been identified, the resulting HSE strategy should be fully documented.

Depending on particularities and scope of the HSE study, the reporting of the results and findings could contain the following information [23]: (1) objectives of the study; (2) full description of the HFC system/infrastructure; (3) results of the QDR; (4) quantitative analysis (assumptions, engineering judgments, calculation procedures, validation of methodologies, sensitivity analysis); (5) assessment of analysis results against criteria; (6) conclusions (hydrogen safety strategy, management requirements, any limitations on use); and (7) references (e.g., drawings, design documentation, technical literature).

To simplify the evaluation of an HSE design, the quantification process is broken down into several TSSs. The following requirements should be accounted for development of individual TSS:

- TSS should together, as reasonably as possible, cover all possible aspects of hydrogen safety.
- TSSs should be balanced between their uniqueness or capacity to be used individually and their complementarities and synergies with other TSSs.
- TSS should be a selection of the state-of-the-art in the particular field of hydrogen safety, validated engineering tools, including empirical and semiempirical correlations, and contemporary tools such as CFD models and codes.
- TSS should be flexible to allow the update of existing or use of new appropriate and validated methods, reflecting recent progress in hydrogen safety science and engineering.

The following TSSs are currently suggested and under development for HSE: TSS1: Initiation of release and dispersion; TSS2: Ignitions; TSS3: Deflagrations and detonations; TSS4: Fires; TSS5: Impact on people, structures, and environment; TSS6: Mitigation techniques; TSS7: Emergency services intervention.

HSE is a key to the success of the hydrogen economy. It is a powerful tool for providing hydrogen safety by qualified specialists in the growing market of HFC systems and infrastructure. Last but not least, the HSE can secure a high level of competitiveness for HFC products.

4.04.4 Unignited Releases of Hydrogen

Hydrogen-powered vehicles have onboard storage at pressures up to 70 MPa, and refueling infrastructure currently operates at pressures up to 100 MPa [24]. Unscheduled release at such pressures creates a highly underexpanded (pressure at the nozzle exit is above atmospheric pressure) turbulent jet that behaves differently from expanded jets (pressure at the nozzle exit is equal to atmospheric pressure) extensively studied previously. For underexpanded jets, the flow expansion occurs near the nozzle exit and is characterized by a complex shock structure, which is well documented and published elsewhere [25]. The schematic representation of an underexpanded shock structure is given in **Figure 5** (left) [25], and the distribution of the Mach number (a dimensionless number equal to the ratio of the local flow velocity to the local speed of sound) in the simulated underexpanded jet (initial stage of release) for a pressure ratio in the storage tank and the atmosphere of 160 is shown in **Figure 5** (right).

Figure 5 shows that local sonic velocity is established at the nozzle exit with Mach number $M=1$. Then, the outflowing gas undergoes rapid expansion and quickly accelerates to high Mach numbers (up to $M=8$ for 70 MPa storage pressure) with the decrease in pressure and density. A series of expansion waves are formed at the nozzle exit edge. These expansion waves are reflected as compression waves from the free surface at the jet flow boundary, which coalesce and form a barrel shock and a Mach disk. As gas with very high Mach number crosses the Mach disk, it undergoes an abrupt decrease in velocity to subsonic speeds and increases in pressure (to the atmospheric pressure) and density. The resulting flow structure after the Mach disk comprises a subsonic core ($M<1$) surrounded by a supersonic shell ($M>1$) with a turbulent eddy producing a shear layer called slip line dividing these regions. For high ratios of nozzle exit to atmospheric pressure above 40, the barrel shock culminates in a single strong Mach disk, and below this critical pressure ratio of 40 multiple barrel shocks and Mach disks appear. This observation is based on simulations of hydrogen underexpanded jets carried out at the HySAFER Centre.

An unignited release leads to the formation of a flammable envelope (mixture within the flammability range). The flammable envelope size, that is, the distance from a leak source to LFL of 4% by volume of hydrogen in air, is used to determine the separation distance. For example, if the flammable envelope reaches the location of an air intake into a high-rise building, then the consequences can be catastrophic. The presence of an ignition source within the flammable envelope could initiate severe jet fire, deflagration, and in the worst case the DDT. Thus, knowledge of hydrogen concentration decay in jets with arbitrary initial parameters is essential for HSE.

In this section, a brief overview of research on unignited hydrogen jets emerging into stagnant air is given. The similarity law for axial concentration decay in momentum-controlled jets, based on the previous research by Ricou and Spalding [26] and Chen and Rodi [27], is presented and validated for both expanded and underexpanded hydrogen jets in the widest known range of conditions. This forms a basis for simple engineering calculation of concentration decay in a momentum-controlled jet, and thus determination of separation distance informed by a flammable envelope size. The nonideal behavior of hydrogen and underexpansion of flow in the nozzle exit at high pressures are accounted for through the original underexpanded jet theory. A methodology to define where a jet transition from momentum- to buoyancy-controlled regime takes place is described. This knowledge is of practical importance as it allows essential reduction of separation distance, for example, for high-debit horizontal jets.

4.04.4.1 Momentum-Controlled Jets

In 1961, Ricou and Spalding [26] demonstrated by a dimensional analysis that when the fluid density is uniform, the Reynolds number is high, and the distance x (m) from the nozzle is much larger than the diameter of the nozzle orifice D (m), then the total

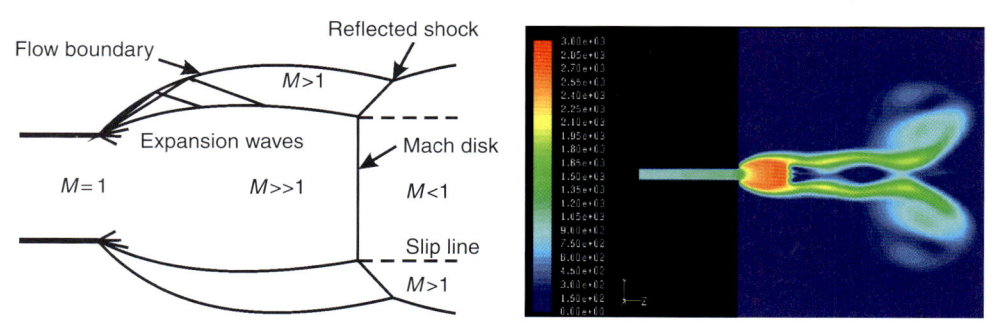

Figure 5 The schematic representation of an underexpanded jet structure (left) [25], and an initial stage of underexpanded jet release at 16.1 MPa through a channel of 0.25 mm (mass flow rate 0.46 g s^{-1}) (right).

mass flow rate, including that of entrained air, across a section at right angle to the jet axis $m(x)$, measured in kg s^{-1}, is proportional to x

$$m(x) = K_1 M_0^{1/2} \rho_S^{1/2} x \qquad [1]$$

where the momentum flux of the jet (kg m s^{-2}) at the orifice is

$$M_0 = \frac{\rho_N U^2 \pi D^2}{4} \qquad [2]$$

and ρ_S is the density of the surrounding fluid (kg m^{-3}); ρ_N is the density of gas at the nozzle exit (kg m^{-3}) and U is the velocity in the nozzle orifice (m s^{-1}). It was found experimentally that the equation for mass flow rate [1] for expanded jets holds, without modification, for nonuniform density provided that buoyancy effects are negligible; the numerical constant K_1 has the value 0.282 irrespective of the density ratio of nozzle gas and surrounding gas, and the presence of combustion reduces K_1. The experimental data for isothermal injection of different gases such as hydrogen, air, propane, and carbon dioxide into stagnant air can be held to obey the same equation rewritten in the form [26]

$$\frac{m(x)}{m_N} = 0.32 \frac{x}{D} \sqrt{\frac{\rho_S}{\rho_N}} \qquad [3]$$

where m_N is the gas mass flow rate (kg s^{-1}) in the nozzle. The mass fraction of nozzle gas in a mixture with the surrounding gas, when averaged through the jet cross-section area at distance x from the nozzle, can be written as a dimensionless value $C_{av} = m_N/m(x)$ and thus can be calculated as the reciprocal of the left-hand side of eqn [3]

$$C_{av} = 3.1 \sqrt{\frac{\rho_N}{\rho_S}} \frac{D}{x} \qquad [4]$$

The mass fraction (C_M) can be calculated from the volumetric (mole) fraction (C_V) as

$$\frac{1}{C_M} = 1 + \left(\frac{1}{C_V} - 1\right) \frac{M_S}{M_N} \qquad [5]$$

where M_S and M_N are the molecular masses (g mol^{-1}) of the surrounding gas and nozzle gas, respectively. For example, mass fraction 0.0288 corresponds to 30% by volume of hydrogen in air, 0.006 39 – 8.5%, 0.002 88 – 4%, 0.001 41 – 2%, and 0.0007 – 1%.

The mean axial mass fraction of fuel in a jet, C_{ax}, is higher than the mass fraction of fuel averaged through the jet cross section, C_{av}, and can be calculated by similarity laws in the form suggested by Chen and Rodi [27] for expanded round (originating from a circular orifice) and plane (originating from a slot) jets respectively

$$\frac{C_{ax}}{C_N} = 5.4 \sqrt{\frac{\rho_N}{\rho_S}} \frac{D}{x} \text{ (round jet)}, \quad \frac{C_{ax}}{C_N} = 2.13 \sqrt{\frac{\rho_N}{\rho_S}} \sqrt{\frac{D}{x}} \text{ (plane jet)} \qquad [6]$$

where C_N is the mass fraction of fuel (hydrogen) in the nozzle gas ($C_N = 1$ for pure hydrogen release).

The two key conclusions that can be drawn from these similarity laws are (1) the distance (x) to a particular concentration expressed in mass fraction (C_{ax}) for jets emerging into stagnant air changes linearly with the nozzle diameter D (square root of nozzle width, D, for a plane jet); and (2) a plane jet decays slower than a round jet.

However, the applicability of the correlations [6] is not clear for underexpanded jets as well as for plane jets with a finite aspect ratio of nozzle length to width. It is worth noting that the original correlations [6] published by Chen and Rodi [27] were validated by concentration measurements in vertical expanded jets only and up to the maximum ratio of distance to diameter of $x/D = 50$ only. Their applicability beyond this range still requires to be validated.

The ratio of distance to diameter (distance to width for a plane jet) calculated by eqn [6] for a round (plane) jet is equal for a number of hydrogen concentrations (with density ratio $\rho_S/\rho_N = 14.45$ in the case of fully expanded flow in a real nozzle): $(x/D)_{30\%} = 49.3$ (379); $(x/D)_{8.5\%} = 222$ (7689); $(x/D)_{4\%} = 493$ (37 854); $(x/D)_{2\%} = 1008$ (157 926); $(x/D)_{1\%} = 2029$ (640 760). Once again, these estimates are valid for expanded jets only. Indeed, for a round expanded jet, with the assumption of pure hydrogen ($C_N = 1$) release into air ($\rho_S/\rho_N = 14.45$), the ratio of the distance to 4% by volume of hydrogen (corresponding to mass fraction $C_{ax} = 0.002\,88$) to orifice diameter, $(x/D)_{4\%}$, can be calculated by eqn [6] as

$$\left(\frac{x}{D}\right)_{4\%} = 5.4 \sqrt{\frac{\rho_N}{\rho_S}} \frac{1}{C_{ax}} = \frac{5.4}{0.002\,88} \sqrt{\frac{1}{14.45}} = 493 \qquad [7]$$

From eqn [7] it follows that for an expanded momentum-controlled round jet with orifice diameter 0.1 mm, the size of flammable envelope, that is, axial distance to 4% of hydrogen in air, will be only 49.3 mm, but for 10 mm diameter leak this distance increases proportionally with the diameter and becomes 4930 mm or about 5 m. This explains why it is so important to have the internal diameter of the piping system as low as possible to reduce the size of flammable envelope in an accident.

The majority of leaks from hydrogen storage and equipment will be in the form of an underexpanded jet at least at the beginning. A jet is called underexpanded if the pressure at the exit from a nozzle has not fully dropped to atmospheric pressure. At high pressures, the nozzle exit velocity remains locally sonic, but the exit pressure rises above ambient. As a result, an expansion down to ambient pressure takes place outside the nozzle. The theoretical critical pressure ratio for a choked flow in the nozzle exit (local sonic flow is established) is about 1.9 according to the well-known equation

$$\frac{p_N}{p_R} = \left(\frac{2}{\gamma+1}\right)^{\gamma/(\gamma-1)} \qquad [8]$$

where γ is the ratio of specific heats of hydrogen (1.405) and p_N and p_R are pressure (Pa) in the nozzle exit and the reservoir, respectively. There are data from Japanese researchers [28] stating that jets exhausted from the open end of the test tube tend to be subsonic jets for pressure ratios in the high-pressure and the low-pressure chambers (the only parameter controlling the jet strength) between 1 and 4.1 (if pressure in the nozzle is roughly half of the storage pressure, that is, $p_R/p_N = 2$, then it is close to the theoretical critical pressure ratio of 1.9), sonic underexpanded jets for pressure ratios between 4.1 and 41.2, and supersonic underexpanded jets for pressure ratios above 41.2. An interesting observation that could affect the convergence of experimental data on concentration decay in jets is the phenomenon of repeating barrel shock and Mach disk structure downstream of the first Mach disk mentioned previously. The phenomenon of multiple barrel shock and Mach disk structure is characteristic of nozzle exit to atmospheric pressure ratios below 40 as has been shown by simulations performed at the University of Ulster.

In 1984, Birch *et al.* [29] suggested that the similarity law for concentration decay in expanded jets suggested by Chen and Rodi [27] works also for underexpanded jets if the real nozzle diameter is substituted by the so-called notional nozzle exit diameter. The study by Thring and Newby [30] was probably the first where the pseudo-diameter (or notional nozzle diameter) concept was introduced. They suggested that pseudo-diameter is calculated by the equation $D_{nn} = D_N\sqrt{\rho_N/\rho_{nn}}$, where subscript 'N' denotes actual nozzle diameter and 'nn' stands for notional nozzle diameter. So, D_{nn} is the aperture of a jet through which the same mass flow rate of nozzle fluid would have resulted with the same jet momentum but with density ρ_{nn} instead of ρ_N. The notional nozzle exit diameter is larger than the real nozzle diameter due to the decrease of density during expansion. However, it is obvious that this simple relationship is valid only if an assumption of equal flow velocity at real and notional nozzles exists, which is not trivial, to satisfy the law of conservation of mass. Moreover, flow velocity in the underexpanded jet after the Mach disk is extremely nonuniform, as will be shown later in this chapter, and all underexpanded jet theories assume that the flow velocity throughout the notional nozzle exit is uniform. One of the first and the most cited notional nozzle theories was published in 1984 by Birch *et al.* [29]. In 1987, Birch *et al.* [31] published an incorrect, from the point of view of the author of this chapter, form of the similarity law, which, in three aspects, contradicts the original form of the similarity law [6] published by Chen and Rodi. First, the volumetric fraction was used in the equation by Birch *et al.* instead of the mass fraction as in the original correlation by Chen and Rodi. Second, the density ratio applied by Birch *et al.* is reciprocal to the original one. Third, the notional nozzle or effective diameter is introduced into the equation instead of the real nozzle diameter. These three essential deviations from the original form of the similarity law have generated inconsistencies in the following publications by different research groups trying to use the correlation by Birch *et al.* in the form published in Reference 31. It is worth noting that Birch *et al.* did not validate the form of the correlation they published, instead only the correlation between volumetric concentration and effective diameter was presented in the paper. It is known that mass and volumetric fractions change practically linearly at their low values, where measurements of concentrations in jets are usually performed, and this gives an impression of data 'correlation' even without right coefficients of proportionality in the similarity law.

Thus, the suggestion of Birch *et al.* about the universal character of the similarity law by Chen and Rodi [27] and its validity to underexpanded jets still has to be confirmed. There is another reason why the approaches of Birch *et al.* [31] and similar theories, developed for systems with moderate storage pressures, cannot be applied to jets issuing from storage pressures above a few hundreds of atmospheres. This is because of the limitation to apply the ideal gas law at high pressures above 10–20 MPa. Indeed, the ideal gas law overestimates the hydrogen mass released from a 70 MPa storage by about 45% as can be concluded from a comparison of calculations by the Abel–Noble equation [32] and the ideal gas law equation [12]. There is no need to say that this is a serious overestimate of a released hydrogen inventory that can make hydrogen safety systems more costly.

In 2007, the calculation of notional nozzle parameters by taking into account the nonideal behavior of hydrogen at high pressures was carried out for the first time by Schefer *et al.* [33]. This approach is analogous to that used by Birch *et al.* and is based on the conservation of mass and momentum; it assumes no viscous forces but ambient pressure and a uniform velocity profile across the notional nozzle cross section, sonic flow (choked flow with Mach number $M = 1$) at the jet exit from the nozzle, and isentropic flow relations. Similar to other underexpanded jet theories, it allows calculation of jet conditions both at the actual (physical) nozzle exit and at the notional nozzle exit (where jet expands to atmospheric pressure).

The validity of extension of the similarity law [6] by Chen and Rodi [27] from expanded jets to underexpanded jets has been proven through the application of the original underexpanded jet theory [34] and a hypothesis that only the density at the exit from a real nozzle ρ_N is the unknown parameter in the similarity law [6]. This makes the use of eqn [6] for underexpanded jets 'a bit more complicated' as compared to that for expanded jets, where the application of eqn [6] is straightforward with hydrogen density at the nozzle $\rho_N = 0.0838$ kg m^{-3} (NTP). Indeed, for underexpanded jets, there is a need to calculate the density of gas in the nozzle exit, ρ_N, for different storage pressures and account for minor and friction losses when they are essential.

4.04.4.2 The Underexpanded Jet Theory

In 2009, the underexpanded theory [34] was developed, which is similar to the notional nozzle theory by Schefer et al. [33]. However, the underexpanded theory is based on mass and energy conservation equations rather than mass and momentum, and an assumption of the speed of sound at the notional nozzle. The underexpanded jet scheme is shown in **Figure 6**.

It is assumed that flow velocity in the reservoir, 1, is zero. For high-pressure storage, the parameters at the nozzle exit, 3, are those for choked flow and therefore the nozzle exit velocity is equal to the local speed of sound ($M = 1$). The notional nozzle, 4, parameters correspond to a fully expanded jet with pressure equal to ambient. The uniform local sonic velocity is assumed at the notional nozzle similar to Birch et al. [29] and other underexpanded jet models. Expansion of the Abel–Noble gas from the reservoir, 1, to the nozzle exit, 3, is isentropic, without losses in the flow in this particular model. The ideal gas equation is not applicable to hydrogen storage pressures above 10–20 MPa where the effects of nonideal gas have to be accounted for. Indeed, the Abel–Noble equation of state can be represented as

$$p = Z\rho R_{H_2} T \qquad [9]$$

where p is the pressure (Pa), ρ is the gas density (kg m^{-3}), R_{H_2} is the hydrogen gas constant (4124.18 J kg^{-1} K^{-1}), T is the temperature (K), and the compressibility factor Z is

$$Z = \frac{1}{1 - b\rho} \qquad [10]$$

in which $b = 7.69\text{E}{-}03$ m^3 kg^{-1} is the co-volume constant for the Abel–Noble equation. The compressibility factor (multiplier of the density if the ideal gas state equation form is assumed) is equal to $Z = 1.01$ at 1.57 MPa, 1.1 at 15.7 MPa, and 1.5 at 78.6 MPa (temperature 293.15 K). There is no air entrainment to an expanding jet between the nozzle exit 3 and the notional nozzle exit 4 (similar to a barrel shock area in underexpanded jet where there is no air entrainment). The system of nine equations with nine unknown parameters ($\rho_1, \rho_3, u_3, T_3, \rho_3, \rho_4, u_4, T_4, A_4$) is as follows (the known parameters are p_1, T_1, A_3, p_4 and constants c_p, R_{H_2}, b, γ). Here ρ is the density (kg m^{-3}), u is the gas velocity (m s^{-1}), A is the cross-section area (m^2), and c_p is the specific heat capacity at constant pressure (J kg^{-1} K^{-1}). Subscripts '1–4' denote gas parameters at locations '1–4' shown in **Figure 6**.

Three equations of state for gas parameters at the reservoir, 1, the real nozzle exit, 3, and the notional nozzle exit, 4, are

$$\rho_1 = \frac{p_1}{bp_1 + R_{H_2} T_1}, \quad \rho_3 = \frac{p_3}{bp_3 + R_{H_2} T_3}, \quad \rho_4 = \frac{p_4}{R_{H_2} T_4} \qquad [11]$$

Two equations of energy conservation, one between the reservoir, 1, and the nozzle exit, 3, and another between the real nozzle exit, 3, and the notional nozzle exit, 4, are

$$c_p T_1 = c_p T_3 + \frac{u_3^2}{2}, \quad c_p T_3 + \frac{u_3^2}{2} = c_p T_4 + \frac{u_4^2}{2} \qquad [12]$$

Two equations for the speed of sound, one for choked flow in the nozzle exit, 3, and another for the assumption of the speed of sound at the notional nozzle exit, 4, are

$$u_3^2 = a_3^2 = \frac{\gamma p_3}{\rho_3 (1 - b\rho_3)}, \quad u_4 = a_4 = \sqrt{\gamma R_{H_2} T_4} \qquad [13]$$

The mass conservation equation between the real nozzle exit, 3, and the notional nozzle exit, 4, and isentropic expansion equation between the reservoir, 1, and the nozzle exit, 3, are

$$\rho_3 u_3 A_3 = \rho_4 u_4 A_4, \quad p_1 \left(\left(\frac{1}{\rho_1} \right) - b \right)^\gamma = p_3 \left(\left(\frac{1}{\rho_3} \right) - b \right)^\gamma \qquad [14]$$

The system of equations for the underexpanded jet (eqns [11]–[14]) after a reduction are solved numerically. The underexpanded jet theory [34] was used to build and validate the universal similarity law that is valid for both expanded and underexpanded jets in the momentum-controlled regime (see **Figure 7**).

The similarity law is validated against 53 experimental data sets in a wide range of pressures up to 40 MPa and leak diameters from 0.25 to 25 mm. Axial hydrogen concentration in air was measured in experiments in a wide range from 1% to 86.6% by volume. The approach is validated for ratios of distance from the nozzle, x, to the nozzle diameter, D, in the extremely wide range

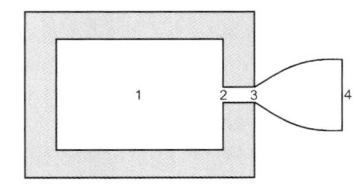

Figure 6 The underexpanded jet scheme: 1, storage vessel; 2, nozzle entrance; 3, nozzle exit; 4, notional nozzle exit.

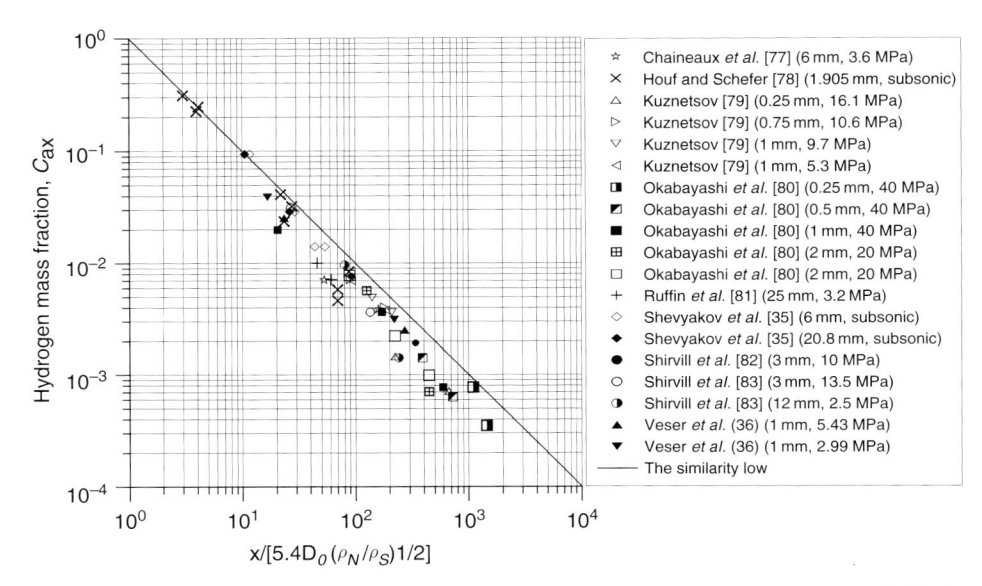

Figure 7 The similarity law (line) for hydrogen concentration decay in expanded and underexpanded momentum-controlled hydrogen jets and experimental data (x, distance from the nozzle (m); D_0, actual nozzle diameter (m)).

$x/D=4-28\,580$, which is far beyond the maximum validation limit in previous studies, that is, $x/D=170$ in the studies of Birch et al. Both laminar and turbulent momentum-controlled flows were used for validation with Reynolds numbers in the range from $Re=927$ to $Re=7.1\times10^6$.

It is worth noting that all experimental points in **Figure 7** are on or shifted to the left of the similarity law line. This corresponds to our physical understanding of the phenomenon. Indeed, the presence of friction and minor losses in real nozzles reduces the hydrogen density in the nozzle, ρ_N. This has to be 'matched' by a reduction of distance x to a particular measured concentration. Thus, an experimental point is shifted to the left of the similarity law line.

The similarity law is an important tool for HSE. An example of its application in the design of a PRD for a forklift used in a warehouse is presented in Section 4.04.8. One of the important results to be mentioned is the applicability of the similarity law to cryo-compressed jets. The validation includes cold jets with an initial storage gas temperature down to 80 K based on experiments by Veser et al. [36]. Sunavala et al. [37] suggested introducing into the equation of concentration decay a multiplier in the form of square root of the ratio of surrounding temperature to gas temperature in the nozzle. This temperature ratio does not appear to be necessary for introduction to the similarity law [6] as it fairly predicts concentration decay in a jet if all parameters are calculated by the underexpanded jet theory [34].

4.04.4.3 Transition from Momentum- to Buoyancy-Controlled Flow within a Jet

It is important for HSE to know whether a leak is momentum-dominated or buoyancy-controlled immediately downstream of the nozzle, as well as at which concentration of hydrogen on a jet axis the momentum flow regime changes to buoyant. Indeed, this knowledge could be then applied to reduce separation distances for a horizontal jet as it can be 'redirected' by buoyancy from horizontal to vertical. The engineering technique to qualify the underexpanded jet or its part as momentum-controlled, and the rest of the jet as buoyancy-controlled, is presented here and is based on the work of Shevyakov et al. [35] for expanded jets.

Figure 8 shows in logarithmic coordinates the dependence of the distance to nozzle diameter (notional nozzle exit diameter for underexpanded jets) ratio x/D (ordinate) on the Froude number (abscissa) in its classical form [35]

$$Fr = \frac{u^2}{gD} \qquad [15]$$

where u is the velocity at the nozzle exit (notional nozzle exit for underexpanded jets) in m s^{-1}, g is the gravitational acceleration (m s^{-2}), and D is the nozzle diameter (notional nozzle exit diameter for underexpanded jets) in meters. For an underexpanded jet, the notional nozzle exit diameter and the velocity at the notional nozzle exit were calculated by the underexpanded jet theory [34]. The five theoretical curves by Schevyakov et al. [35], experimental data for expanded jets [35], and data of other researchers for underexpanded jets are presented in **Figure 8**. Both expanded and underexpanded jets obey the same functional dependence with an accuracy of 20%, which is acceptable for engineering applications. There are four curves for hydrogen concentrations 4%, 17%, 30%, and 60% by volume, respectively. Each of these four curves has an ascending buoyant part and a momentum 'plateau' part. The Froude number at transition from the buoyant part of the curve to the momentum part depends on the concentration of hydrogen under consideration. The fifth curve gives for jets directed vertically downward a dimensionless distance from the nozzle

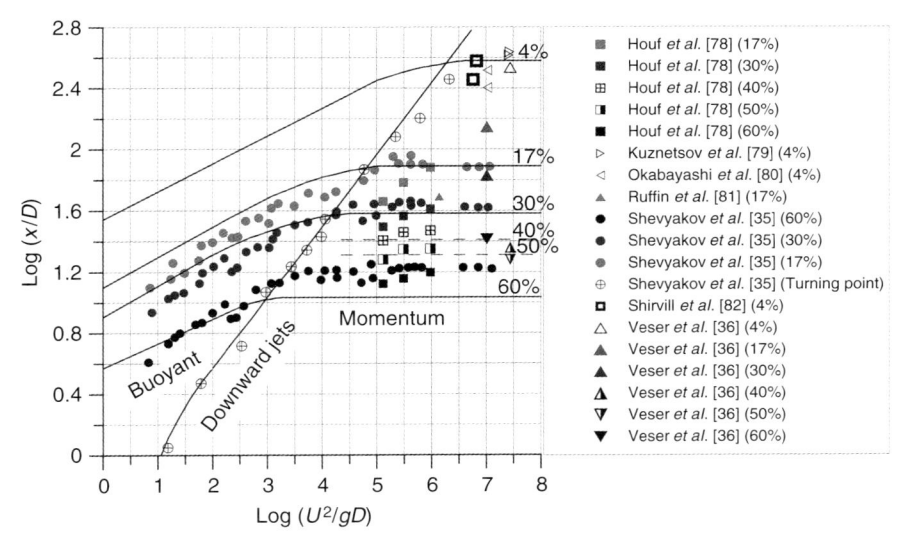

Figure 8 The dependence of distance to nozzle diameter (notional nozzle exit diameter for underexpanded jets) ratio x/D on the Froude number [35].

to the turning point, where the jet changes the direction of flow from downward to upward, as a function of the Froude number. As could be expected, the fifth curve intersects each of the four curves in the region of transition from momentum-dominated to buoyancy-controlled jet.

The following sequence of actions is applied to use **Figure 8**. First, the nozzle Froude number is calculated. The underexpanded theory [34] is applied to calculate the notional nozzle exit diameter and the velocity in the notional nozzle exit when applicable. Then, a vertical line is drawn from a point on the abscissa axis equal to the calculated Froude number. The intersection of this vertical line with the line marked 'downward jets' on the graph indicates the concentration above which the jet is momentum-dominated and below which the jet is buoyancy-controlled. For example, if $\log(Fr) = 4.25$, a jet is momentum-dominated when the concentration in the jet is above 30% by volume and it becomes buoyant when the concentration on the jet axis is below 30%. If a jet is characterized by $\log(Fr) = 6.5$, then the jet is momentum-dominated up to a concentration of 4% by volume (LFL).

This engineering technique is very simple and useful to develop cost-effective hydrogen safety systems. Indeed, for a horizontal jet, only the length of the momentum part could be taken as an indication of separation distance rather than virtual distance to LFL (4% by volume) under the assumption of fully momentum-controlled jet.

4.04.5 Hydrogen Fires

A jet fire is another typical scenario of an accident with hydrogen along with an unignited release. A source of hydrogen jet fire could be a small crack or full-bore rupture of a piping system. To tackle hydrogen jet flames, including those arising from high-pressure storage, it is important for hydrogen safety engineers to know how the jet flame length depends on storage pressure and leak diameter. Separation distance for an unignited jet is determined by the flammable envelope size, which can be calculated as the distance equal to 4% by volume (LFL). In this section, we will discuss correlations for hydrogen jet flames, present a simple engineering nomogram for calculation of the flame length, and clarify contradictory statements about the location of a turbulent nonpremixed flame tip.

4.04.5.1 Dimensional Flame Length Correlation

Figure 9 presents the correlation for hydrogen jet flame length derived by means of similitude analysis and validated against experimental data for the widest known range of parameters [38]. The correlation relates the flame length to both the diameter and the mass flow rate of a leak. This expands previous knowledge linking the flame length to only the diameter as in the seminal work of Hawthorne et al. [39] or only the mass flow rate as in the correlation by Mogi et al. [40].

The dimensional flame length, L_F, of subsonic, sonic, and supersonic jets (in meters) obeys the same functional dependence

$$L_F = 76(\dot{m}D)^{0.347} \qquad [16]$$

where $\dot{m}$ is the mass flow rate of hydrogen (kg s^{-1}) and D is the real nozzle diameter (m). This is a best-fit curve equation for 95 experimental points obtained by different authors. The conservative estimate for the flame length in the whole range of processed experimental data, that is, the dashed line in **Figure 9**, gives 50% longer flame and can be calculated by the equation

$$L_F = 116(\dot{m}D)^{0.347} \qquad [17]$$

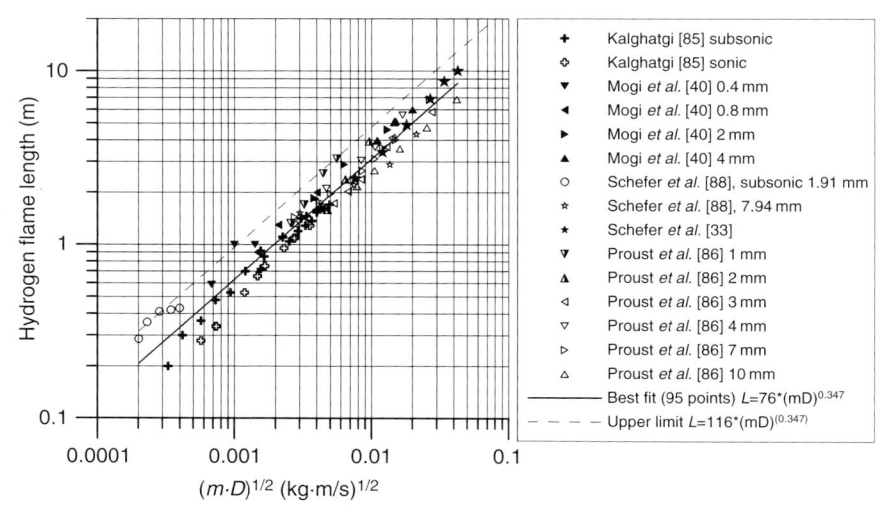

Figure 9 The dimensional flame length correlation ($\dot{m}$, mass flow rate (kg s^{-1}); D, actual nozzle diameter (m)) [38].

The accuracy of prediction is higher, that is, about 20%, for underexpanded jets with a large flame length. The mass flow rate is needed to define the flame length. This can be done by means of the underexpanded jet theory [34].

4.04.5.2 The Nomogram for Flame Length Calculation

To simplify the use of the dimensional correlation, a nomogram is designed for graphical calculation of jet flame length using two parameters of a leak, i.e., storage pressure and actual diameter of the leak [38] (see **Figure 10**).

The nomogram is derived from the best-fit line of the dimensional flame length correlation shown in **Figure 9**. The use of the nomogram for calculation of flame length is demonstrated in **Figure 10** by thick lines with arrows. First, the diameter of a leak nozzle, for example, $D = 3$ mm in this case, and the storage pressure, for example, $p = 35$ MPa, are chosen. Second, a horizontal line is drawn from the diameter axis at a point 3 mm to the right until it intersects with the pressure line denoted as 35 MPa. Third, a vertical line is drawn from the first intersection point upward until it intersects with the only line available in coordinates (L_F, $(\dot{m}D)^{1/2}$). Finally, to get the flame length, a horizontal line is drawn from this intersection to the left until it intersects with the axis 'Hydrogen flame length L_F (m)'. In the example considered, a leak of hydrogen at pressure 35 MPa through an orifice of 3 mm diameter will result in a flame length of 5 m. The conservative estimate of the flame length, as derived from eqns [16] and [17], is 50% longer, that is, 7.5 m. The use of this engineering nomogram is simple and does not require any additional knowledge other than leak diameter and storage pressure.

The nomogram incorporates a special feature based on the results of Mogi *et al.* [40], Okabayashi *et al.* [41], and other researchers, that is, no stable flame was observed for nozzle diameters 0.1–0.2 mm as the flame blew off although the spouting pressures were as high as 40 MPa (denoted as 'No flame area' in **Figure 10**). For example, a stable jet flame cannot exist at pressures equal to or below 35 MPa if the leak orifice diameter is below 0.3 mm. It should be noted that the nomogram does not account for conditions when flow losses in a leakage pathway cannot be ignored. In such cases, a straightforward use of the nomogram gives a conservative result. A more accurate prediction of the flame length in equipment with essential friction and minor losses can be obtained if a method is available that allows calculation of the density in the nozzle exit affected by the losses.

4.04.5.3 Dimensionless Flame Length Correlation

There have been previous attempts to build a dimensionless correlation for the flame length. Practically, all dimensionless flame length correlations suggested so far are based on the use of only Froude number, Fr, in one form or another. Unfortunately, the predictive capability of these correlations for underexpanded jets is very poor in the traditional momentum-controlled part, that is, ±50%.

Some recent correlations for underexpanded jets are also constructed based on a modified Fr that incorporates notional nozzle exit parameters. However, a notional nozzle exit diameter depends on an applied theory and its assumptions, which sometimes are quite far from reality. For example, a constant flow velocity is assumed through a notional nozzle exit cross section in all theories, while in fact at high pressures there is a strong supersonic flow on the periphery immediately downstream of the Mach disk and sometimes practically a stagnant flow downstream of the Mach disk as has been demonstrated above (see **Figure 5**).

Experimental data and theoretical studies indicate that a jet flame length has to be a function of not only Fr number but also Reynolds (Re) and Mach (M) numbers. It is impossible to build a universal correlation based on only one of these dimensionless numbers.

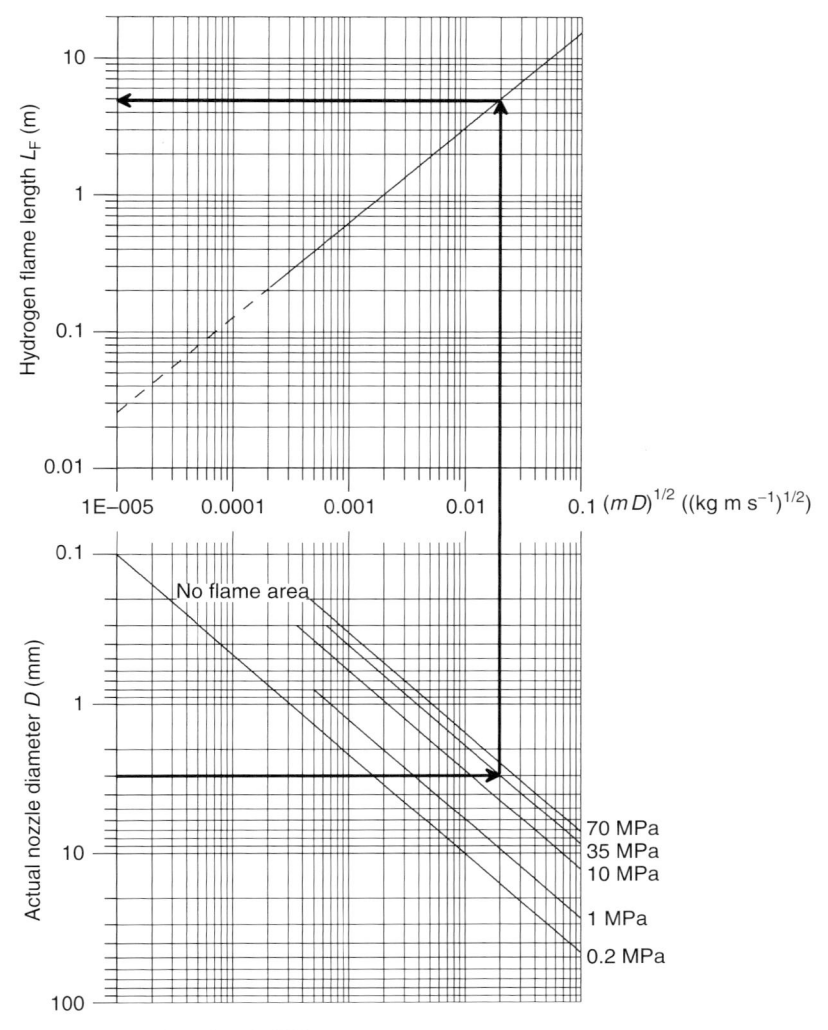

Figure 10 The nomogram for hydrogen jet flame length [38].

The dimensionless correlation for a jet flame length accounting for dependence on Fr, Re, and M numbers and covering the full spectrum of hydrogen releases including laminar and turbulent flows, buoyancy- and momentum-controlled leaks, and expanded and underexpanded jets has been developed recently [42] and is shown in **Figure 11**.

The dimensional correlation $L_F = 76(\dot{m}D)^{0.347}$ shows that the dimensionless flame length L_F/D is practically independent of the real nozzle diameter D but depends on the density ρ_N and the velocity U_N of hydrogen in the nozzle exit. Based on this analysis, the following dimensionless group is suggested to correlate with the dimensionless flame length L_F/D (see **Figure 11**), in which the density in the nozzle exit, ρ_N, is normalized by the density of the surrounding gas, ρ_S, and the flow velocity at the nozzle exit, U_N, is normalized by the speed of sound in hydrogen at thermodynamic parameters in the nozzle exit, C_N,

$$\frac{\rho_N}{\rho_S}\left(\frac{U_N}{C_N}\right)^3 = \frac{g\mu_N}{\rho_S C_N^3} Re\, Fr \qquad [18]$$

where the speed of sound for nonideal gas was calculated as a function of temperature in the nozzle exit using the equation

$$C_N = \frac{\sqrt{\gamma R_{H_2} T_N}}{1 - b\rho_N} \qquad [19]$$

in which R_{H_2} is the hydrogen gas constant (4124 J kg^{-1} K^{-1}); Re and Fr are determined through parameters of hydrogen flow in the nozzle exit $Re = (\rho_N U_N D)/\mu_N$ and $Fr = U_N^2/(gD)$, where μ_N is the dynamic viscosity in the nozzle exit (kg m^{-1} s^{-1}).

For subsonic flows ($M < 1$), the form of the dimensionless group [18] assumes dependence of the dimensionless flame length L_F/D on the nozzle Mach number $M = U_N/C_N$ only. Indeed, the density in the nozzle ρ_N is a constant for

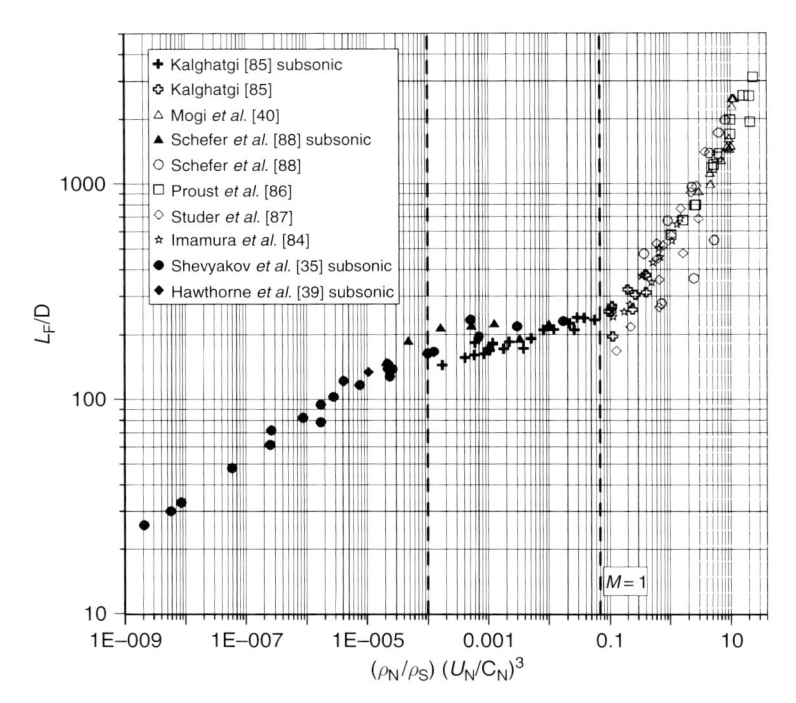

Figure 11 The dimensionless hydrogen jet flame length correlation [42].

subsonic flows with the assumption of constant temperature, and thus the ratio of densities ρ_N/ρ_S is also a constant. For choked flows ($M = U_N/C_N = 1$), the dimensionless flame length L_F/D is expected to depend on only hydrogen density in the nozzle ρ_N.

There are only a few validation experiments in **Figure 11** performed with laminar jets when $Re < 2000$ [43], and the majority of the experiments were carried out for turbulent jets. About 20% of the experimental points correspond to buoyancy-controlled jets (by the criterion $Fr < 10^6$) and 80% to momentum-dominated jets. One-half of 125 tests were done at the subsonic outflow regime and the other half with choked flow in a nozzle.

There are three distinguishable parts in the dimensionless correlation shown in **Figure 11**. These are 'traditional' buoyancy-controlled, 'saturated' momentum-dominated (where dimensionless flame length is essentially a constant), and the third new part that represents choked and underexpanded jet fires. The correlation clearly demonstrates that there is no saturation of the dimensionless flame length at value $L_F/D = 230$ observed in previous studies with expanded jets. Recently reported experiments with high-pressure hydrogen releases exhibit more than an order of magnitude higher values up to $L_F/D = 3000$.

For underexpanded jets, the dimensionless flame length depends only on the Re number, as the M number is constant (flow is choked, $M = 1$) and the Fr number is constant too as the actual nozzle diameter is applied in the Froude number. This is done to exclude the notional nozzle exit diameter, which depends on an underexpanded jet theory adopted.

4.04.5.4 Separation Distance: Jet Flame Tip Location Compared to Lower Flammability Limit Location

To design robust hydrogen safety systems, it is important to know the distance from the nozzle to the location of the jet flame tip (characterized by an intermittency of 50% of the visible flame). In 1957 Sunavala et al. [37] suggested, and later in 1976 Bilger [44] reinforced, the widespread view that the jet flame length may be obtained by substitution of the concentration corresponding to the stoichiometric mixture in the equation of axial concentration decay for a nonreacting jet. However, this point of view was not confirmed in our analysis performed in 2009 [38] when it was shown that the hydrogen nonpremixed jet tip is located far above the location of the axial stoichiometric hydrogen concentration in air. This result has an important safety implication and was confirmed in 2010 [45]. Indeed, **Figure 12** shows the dimensionless flame length L_F/D (experimental points) and the dimensionless distance x/D (lines) corresponding to three concentrations of hydrogen in an unignited jet (8%, 11%, and 16% by volume) from the same leak source.

The important conclusion from **Figure 12** is that for momentum-controlled jets the flame tip is located at the distance from the leak source where the axial concentration of hydrogen in an unignited jet is in the range of 8–16%, that is, far below the stoichiometric concentration of 29.5% as was thought previously [37, 44]. The best-fit line of the dimensionless experimental flame lengths L_F/D is close to the line of dimensionless distances x/D to concentration of 11% by volume in unignited jets.

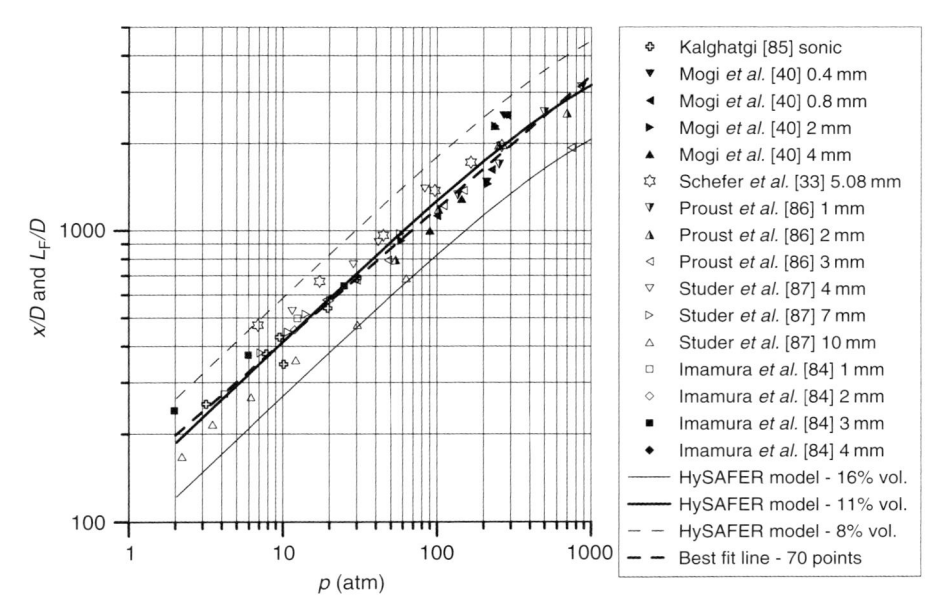

Figure 12 The dimensionless flame length L_F/D (experimental points) and the dimensionless distance x/D (lines) corresponding to three concentrations of hydrogen in an unignited jet (8%, 11%, and 16% by volume) from the same leak source as a function of storage pressure [45].

4.04.6 Pressure Effects of Hydrogen Unscheduled Releases

Pressure effects during an accident with hydrogen can be caused by an unignited release in a confined space such as garage-like enclosures, or a turbulent jet combustion after delayed ignition of the jet (followed by jet fire), or a premixed cloud combustion (deflagrations and detonations).

4.04.6.1 Unignited Release in a Garage-Like Enclosure

It has been found recently that the dynamics of pressure buildup during high mass flow hydrogen release in a vented enclosure is different from that for other gases [45]. The phenomenon is called the pressure-peaking effect. The hypothetical worst-case scenario considered involves a release from an onboard hydrogen storage tank at 35 MPa through a 5.08 mm diameter orifice in a 'typical' PRD (mass flow rate 390 g s^{-1}), in a small garage of $L \times W \times H = 4.5 \times 2.6 \times 2.6$ m (volume 30.4 m^3) with a single vent equivalent in area to a typical brick of $L \times H = 25 \times 5$ cm located flush with the ceiling.

The results indicate that the overpressure transient within the enclosure has a characteristic maximum, which is essentially higher than an estimate of overpressure by the orifice equation [20] with the assumption of 100% by volume of hydrogen in the garage.

At steady-state conditions, when hydrogen fully occupies the enclosure, the mass flow rate into the enclosure from the PRD equals the mass flow rate out of the enclosure vent. The orifice equation for a subsonic regime can be used to estimate the steady-state overpressure within the enclosure [46]

$$\dot{m}_{vent} = CA \left\{ \frac{2\gamma p \rho}{\gamma - 1} \left[\left(\frac{p_S}{p}\right)^{2/\gamma} - \left(\frac{p_S}{p}\right)^{(\gamma+1)/\gamma} \right] \right\}^{1/2} \quad [20]$$

where C is the dimensionless discharge coefficient, A is the vent area (m^2), p_S is the pressure in the surrounding medium (Pa), p (Pa) and ρ (kg m^{-3}) are the pressure and density in the enclosure, respectively, and γ is the specific heat ratio. The Bernoulli's equation [12] with the assumption of no velocity in the reservoir gives a simple formula for the outflow velocity

$$u = \sqrt{\frac{2\Delta p}{\rho}} \quad [21]$$

and can be used instead of eqn [20]. Here Δp is the pressure drop from the reservoir to the atmosphere (Pa).

Equation [20] predicts a steady-state overpressure in an enclosure of 17.9 kPa ($C = 0.6$, $\gamma = 1.4$, $p_S = 10^5$ Pa, $\dot{m} = 390$ g s^{-1}) for the conditions chosen. This corresponds to a moderate level of damage to structures by overpressure according to the following classification [47]: overpressures below 3.5 kPa, light damage; above 17 kPa, moderate damage; above 35 kPa, severe damage; above 83 kPa, total structure destruction.

Unfortunately, this 'straightforward' engineering estimate of maximum overpressure (17.9 kPa) is wrong as it does not account for the injection of a lighter gas (hydrogen) into a heavier gas (air). The system of ordinary differential

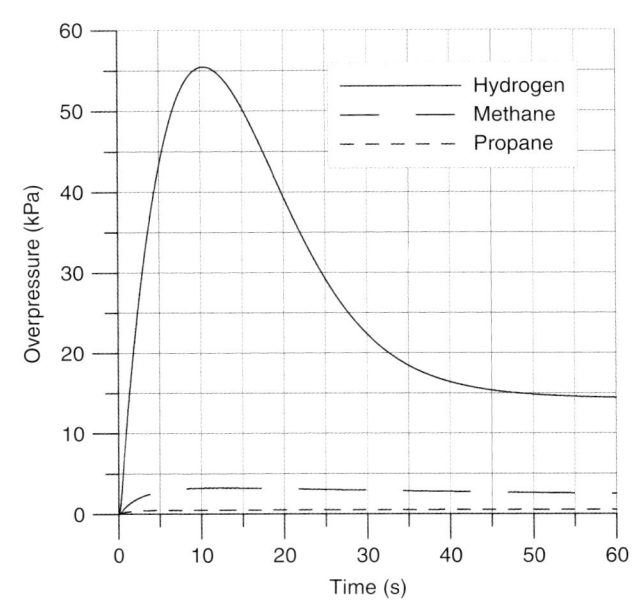

Figure 13 The pressure-peaking phenomenon for the release of hydrogen from an onboard storage in the vented garage (the same mass flow rate of 390 g s^{-1} is applied for the release of hydrogen, methane, and propane).

equations (ODEs) of the process with the assumption of perfect mixing of hydrogen and residual air is used to predict the development of the overpressure within the enclosure with time to calculate the dynamics of the so-called pressure-peaking phenomenon in a vented enclosure, which is characteristic of only one flammable gas – hydrogen [45]. The actual maximum pressure peak obtained by solving the ODE system is of an order of magnitude higher than 17.9 kPa and is in the region of 56 kPa. The results of the ODE model prediction of the pressure-peaking effect were reproduced by CFD simulations also.

Figure 13 demonstrates that the pressure-peaking phenomenon is unique for hydrogen only. The 'standard' engineering overpressure in the enclosure by solution of ODE is about 14 kPa, which is slightly below 17.9 kPa calculated by eqn [20]. The difference can be attributed to the choice of C = 0.6 in the calculation using eqn [20]. Indeed, a methane (the closest fuel to hydrogen by molecular mass) release with the same mass flow rate of 390 g s^{-1} has a practically undistinguished peak (see **Figure 13**). The propane release produces no peaking effect at all as its molecular mass is larger than air. It is clearly seen how the maximum overpressure for steady-state condition in the case of heavier than air gas drops with increasing molecular mass. This finding is of importance for HSE. The phenomenon of pressure peaking excludes the use of orifice equations by engineers to estimate overpressure in a vented enclosure at comparatively high mass flow rates.

Unfortunately, in this scenario, the garage as a typical civil structure will be destroyed by overpressure generated by the unignited release in a few seconds when the overpressure exceeds 10–20 kPa. RCS have to include the requirement to account for the pressure-peaking phenomenon when designing HFC systems. Safety engineering design of HFC systems for indoor use must also take this into account.

The explanation of the pressure-peaking phenomenon is quite straightforward. The volumetric mass flow rate through an enclosure vent is inversely proportional to the square root of the density of a gas flowing out of the enclosure and proportional to the square root of overpressure in the enclosure for subsonic flows. Thus, at the initial stages of the release, with the assumption of uniform mixing of hydrogen with air, the density of the mixture within the enclosure is quite high and close to the air density. To compensate the volumetric inflow of pure hydrogen, a higher pressure within the enclosure is required to provide the same volumetric flow rate for higher molecular mass gas escaping the enclosure through the vent.

The dynamics of flammable hydrogen–air mixture development in the same garage-like enclosure was studied as well using CFD technique in Reference 48. It was found that almost 50% of the garage was engulfed by a flammable atmosphere in less than 1 s. The presence of a small vent means that a mixture with a potential to deflagrate exists in most part of the garage, with the exception of a small rich region, even after 10 s of the release. Numerical simulations demonstrated another hazard from this scenario, that is, formation of a flammable jet from the vent outside the enclosure. At 5.6 s after the start of release, a concentration of 8% by volume of hydrogen can already be found at 5 m from the vent. At this point in time, the jet is momentum-controlled, that is, horizontal.

Overall, a conclusion can be drawn that the currently available PRDs for hydrogen-powered vehicles should be redesigned. RCS should include relevant requirements if vehicles are intended for garage parking, which is an obvious customers' requirement.

4.04.6.2 Delayed Ignition of Nonpremixed Turbulent Jets

The Health and Safety Laboratory (HSL) performed a series of experiments with high-pressure releases of hydrogen as a part of the HYPER project [49]. These experiments were carried out to simulate a leak from two 0.05 m^3 hydrogen cylinders at 20.5 MPa through a 9.5 mm nozzle. The ignition delay was 0.8 s. Pressure generated in the near field of the free jet was 16.5 kPa. It is worth noting that there is a wall in the experiments behind the nozzle. In the case of a vertical 90° barrier, the pressure peak of combustion after delayed ignition of the turbulent jet increases to 42 kPa. **Figure 14** shows a sequence of snapshots (from top to bottom) after the delayed ignition of hydrogen jet impinging a 90° barrier. In fact, before a jet flame reaches quasi-steady-state conditions (bottom snapshot in **Figure 14**), there is obviously a deflagration of the nonuniform mixture in the confined space between the barrier and the ground (see top and middle snapshots in **Figure 14**).

A barrier inclined at 60° increases pressure further to 57 kPa. **Figure 15** shows a sequence of two snapshots after the delayed ignition of hydrogen jet impinging a 60° barrier.

Some of the conclusions from this experimental study by HSL are as follows:

- The inclusion of flow restrictors in hydrogen supply lines reduces the flame lengths observed, therefore reducing safety distances required. This is thought to be due to pressure losses on the restrictor and thus lower pressure at the jet exit from the pipe.

Figure 14 The delayed (0.8 s) ignition of hydrogen jet (20.5 MPa pressure storage, 9.5 mm diameter nozzle) impinging a 90° barrier: deflagration stage (top and middle snapshot), steady-state impinging jet fire stage (bottom snapshot); HSL test [49].

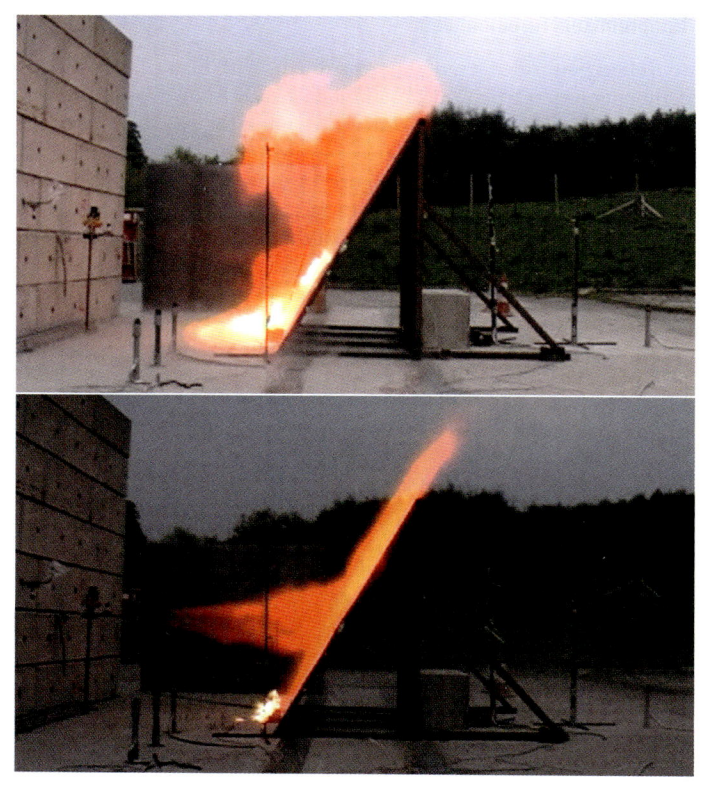

Figure 15 The delayed (0.8 s) ignition of hydrogen jet (20.5 MPa pressure storage, 9.5 mm diameter nozzle) impinging a 60° barrier: deflagration stage (top snapshot), steady-state impinging jet fire stage (bottom snapshot); HSL test [49].

- Jets from hydrogen storage at 20.5 MPa are predominantly momentum-controlled, that is, the cloud is relatively nonbuoyant up to the lower flammability limit.
- When a release is oriented such that attachment to a surface can occur, the jet length may be enhanced. The flame length of a free unattached horizontal jet with a nozzle 1.2 m above the ground is 3 m (nozzle diameter $D = 1.5$ mm), 6 m ($D = 3.2$ mm), 9 m ($D = 6.4$ mm), and 11 m ($D = 9.5$ mm). For an attached jet from a nozzle located only 0.11 m above the ground, the flame length increases from 3 to 5.5 m (nozzle diameter $D = 1.5$ mm), from 6 to 9 m ($D = 3.2$ mm), from 9 to 11 m ($D = 6.4$ mm), and from 11 to 13 m ($D = 9.5$ mm).
- Ignition in a close to the flammability limits region of the jet cloud results in a relatively slow burn and hence a small overpressure.
- Maximum overpressures were observed when the jet was ignited at a time that coincided with the area of maximum turbulence within the front portion of the jet, reaching the ignition point.
- The effect of release nozzle diameter on the maximum overpressure in a free jet without impingement is as follows (800 ms ignition delay): $D = 1.5$ mm – overpressure is not registered, $D = 3.2$ mm – overpressure is 3.5 kPa, $D = 6.4$ mm – 15.2 kPa, $D = 9.5$ mm – 16.5 kPa. From these results, it can be concluded that to reduce overpressure following ignition the nozzle diameter (diameter of piping system) should be reduced as low as reasonably possible by the use of technology.
- The effect of ignition delay on the maximum overpressure in a free jet is as follows ($D = 6.4$ mm, ignition is 2 m from the nozzle): 400 ms – 3.7 kPa; 500 ms – 18.4 kPa; 600 ms – 19.4 kPa; 800 ms – 15.2 kPa; 1000 ms – 11.7 kPa; 1200 ms – 12.5 kPa; 2000 ms – 9.5 kPa. Based on these results, it could be assumed that the spontaneous ignition of a sudden hydrogen release should reduce overpressure of self-ignited release compared to delayed ignition.
- The effect of ignition location on the maximum overpressure in a free jet is as follows ($D = 6.4$ mm, fixed ignition delay 800 ms): 2 m from the nozzle – 15.2 kPa; 3 m – 5 kPa; 4–5 m – 2.1 kPa; 5–10 m – overpressure is not recordable; beyond 10 m – no ignition is possible.

The highest overpressures registered in experiments by HSL [49] for larger nozzle diameters can be a reason for serious injuries. Indeed, peak values of overpressure and the associated level of injury to people outdoor [50] are as follows: 8 kPa – no serious injury to people; 6.9–13.8 kPa – threshold of skin lacerations by missiles; 10.3–20 kPa – people are knocked down by pressure wave;

13.8 kPa – possible fatality by being projected against obstacles; 34 kPa – eardrum rupture; 35 kPa – 15% probability of fatality; 54 kPa – fatal head injury; 62 kPa – severe lung damage; 83 kPa – severe injury or death.

The jet turbulence and size had a greater effect on the deflagration pressure than the total amount of hydrogen leaked. The total amount of hydrogen released is not always important, especially in the open atmosphere, as buoyancy continues to drive dilution of hydrogen by entrained air until it reaches the LFL of 4% by volume and beyond. Thus, portions of hydrogen released in the beginning in many practical scenarios will not contribute to combustion as they form a part of cloud which is below the LFL.

Takeno et al. [51] studied the effects of an ignition delay and location of ignition source on deflagration pressure following the release of hydrogen from the storage at pressures between 40 and 65 MPa through a 10 mm diameter nozzle (pressure in the nozzle was 40 MPa). In the open atmosphere, the flame propagation velocity was assessed to be over 300 m s^{-1} at a distance of approximately 4 m. The increase of ignition delay from 0.85 to 5.2 s, when an ignition source was located at a distance of 4 m from the nozzle, led to a decrease in the maximum deflagration overpressure in the near field (about 2 m from the nozzle) from 90 to 15 kPa. It was concluded that the shorter is the ignition delay, the greater is the overpressure. It was also concluded that the turbulence has a greater effect on the 'explosiveness' than the total amount of leakage or the premixed volume.

Tanaka et al. [52] also investigated the ignition of jets from a refueling dispenser in the open. The horizontal jet from an 8 mm diameter nozzle was ignited at a distance of 4 m. It was found that the logarithm of the peak overpressure decreases linearly with increased logarithm of time to ignition. The largest overpressure was found for a 1.2 s ignition delay. This conclusion is supported by HySAFER blind simulations of the HSL blowdown experiment. The simulations demonstrated that the maximum volume of near-stoichiometric mixture is formed at about 1 s after the release start.

4.04.7 Deflagrations and Detonations

There are two types of 'combustion explosions', that is, deflagrations and detonations. Deflagration propagates with a velocity below the speed of sound in the mixture. The flame propagation velocity of a stoichiometric hydrogen–air mixture in the open atmosphere in a 20 m diameter hemispherical cloud increases up to 84 m s^{-1}, and the explosion overpressure is on the order of 10 kPa in the near field. Then, the pressure in a blast wave decays inversely proportional to the radius, while for high explosives the pressure decays inversely proportional to the radius squared. The ratio of maximum deflagration pressure to initial pressure in a closed vessel is 8.15 [10].

A detonation front is in principle different from a deflagration front. It is a complex of leading shock and following the shock reaction zone as was for the first time suggested by Chapman [53] and Jouguet [54]. Detonation propagates faster than the speed of sound with the CJ velocity and the CJ pressure, which for a stoichiometric hydrogen–air mixture are 1968 m s^{-1} and 1.56 MPa, respectively [10]. Once initiated, detonation will propagate as long as the mixture is within the detonability limits (cloud size should be sufficient to support detonation). The detonation wave is led by a von Neumann pressure spike [55], which has a short spatial scale on the order of one intermolecular distance, and is about double the CJ pressure. The detonation front has a complicated three-dimensional structure. An example of the hydrodynamic structure of detonation with characteristic cells is shown in **Figure 16** [56].

The detonation cell size is a function of mixture composition. **Figure 17** shows the results of the classical work by Lee [57] on dependence of detonation cell size on concentration of hydrogen in air.

The ability of a hydrogen–air mixture to directly initiate detonation is greater than that of hydrocarbons. The direct initiation of hydrogen–air mixture detonation is possible by 1.1 g of tetryl (high explosive) [10]. Only 1.86 g of TNT is needed to initiate detonation in a 34.7% hydrogen–air mixture in the open atmosphere. However, for a 20% hydrogen–air mixture, the critical TNT charge increases significantly to 190 g. For comparison, the release of energy during the explosive reaction of 1 g of TNT is arbitrarily standardized as 4.184 kJ (1 g of TNT releases 4.1–4.602 kJ upon explosion [12]), and the lower heat of combustion of 1 g of hydrogen is $(241.7 \text{ kJ mol}^{-1})/(2.016 \text{ g mol}^{-1}) = 119.89$ kJ. Thus, the TNT equivalent of hydrogen is high: 28.65, that is, 28.65 g of TNT is energetic equivalent of 1 g of hydrogen.

Hydrogen is prone to DDT. DDT was observed during mitigation of deflagration in enclosure by the explosion venting technique. Venting of a 30% hydrogen–air deflagration in a room-like enclosure with an internal jet camera and initially closed venting panels resulted in DDT with overpressures up to 3.5 MPa in experiments performed in the Kurchatov Institute by Dorofeev et al. [58]. DDT was initiated a few milliseconds after the destruction of the venting panels. The photographs show the formation of an outflow followed by a localized explosion inside the enclosure near the panel. No effect of the igniting jet size, emerging from the jet camera, on the onset of detonation was observed. The volume size of the jet camera also had no effect, indicating the local character of the detonation onset. The authors suggested that the onset of detonation was not directly connected with jet ignition, but was specifically linked to the sudden venting. Indeed, a needle-like structured flame front can be induced by the venting as observed in the experiments of Tsuruda and Hirano [59]. Flame front instabilities, in particular Rayleigh–Taylor instability, and rarefaction waves propagating into the enclosure after the destruction of the venting panel increase the mixing of the unburned mixture and combustion products. In partially reacted mixtures, this may create an induction time gradient, thereby establishing the conditions for DDT, for example, by pressure wave amplification by the shock wave amplification by coherent energy release (SWACER) [60] mechanism theoretically predicted by Zeldovich et al. [61].

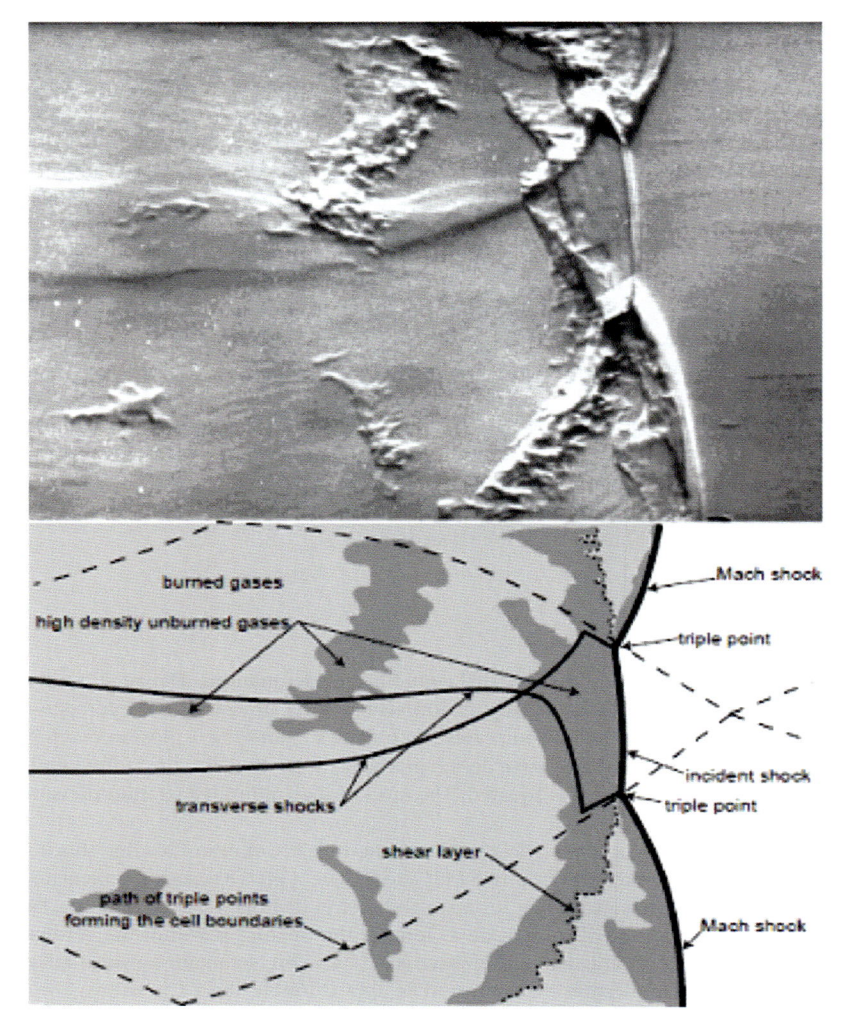

Figure 16 Schlieren photograph of the hydrodynamic structure of detonation [56].

DDT was observed in a large-scale test carried out at Fraunhofer ICT (Germany). The experimental setup included a 'lane' (two parallel walls 3 m apart with height 3 m and length 12 m) and an enclosure (driver section) of size $L \times W \times H = 3.0 \times 1.5 \times 1.5$ m (6.75 m^3 volume) with a vent of 0.82×0.82 m that was initially open to the 'lane'. The 'lane' and the enclosure were filled with the same 22.5% hydrogen–air mixture kept under a plastic film. Venting of 22.5% hydrogen–air deflagration initiated at the rear wall of the enclosure by five ignitors into the partially confined space simulating a 'lane' resulted in DDT. At 54.61 ms after ignition, the DDT occurred in the 'lane' at the ground level, after the accelerated flame emerged from the driver section.

The onset of detonation in a 17% hydrogen–air deflagration was experimentally observed in a laboratory-scale study by Ferrara et al. [62]. The experimental rig was a cylindrical vessel with a volume of 0.2 m^3 ($L \times D = 1.0 \times 0.5$ m) connected to a dump vessel of a volume of approximately 50 m^3 through a gate valve of diameter 16.2 cm and vent pipe ($L = 1$ m, $D = 16.2$ cm). The mixture was prepared by partial pressures in the primary vessel only. Ignition was initiated immediately after opening of the gate valve at the rear wall by a 16 J combustion engine sparkplug. A sudden detonation spike of 1.5 MPa appeared in the pressure transients in the vessel only, well after the leading edge of the flame had left the vessel–duct assembly. Supposedly, the short backflow of products from the duct to the vessel led to turbulization of combustion inside the vessel as was demonstrated in the current author's previous research dating back to 1984 [63]. The entrainment of unburned mixture pockets by the high-velocity hot gases can lead to violent ignition and, under certain circumstances, detonation as demonstrated by Lee and Guirao [64]. For a 17% hydrogen–air mixture at 0.1 MPa and 300 K, the detonation cell size is about 15–16 cm and reduces to 4 cm at 400 K based on the data by Breitung et al. [65] in the State-of-the-art report. This could be a possible explanation for the lack of detonation onset in a 16.2 cm diameter pipe and the presence of detonation onset in a 50 cm diameter vessel, where unburned mixture was preheated by explosion pressure compression to at least 400 K [62]. The occurrence of a detonation wave in the main vessel with similar venting configurations was reported

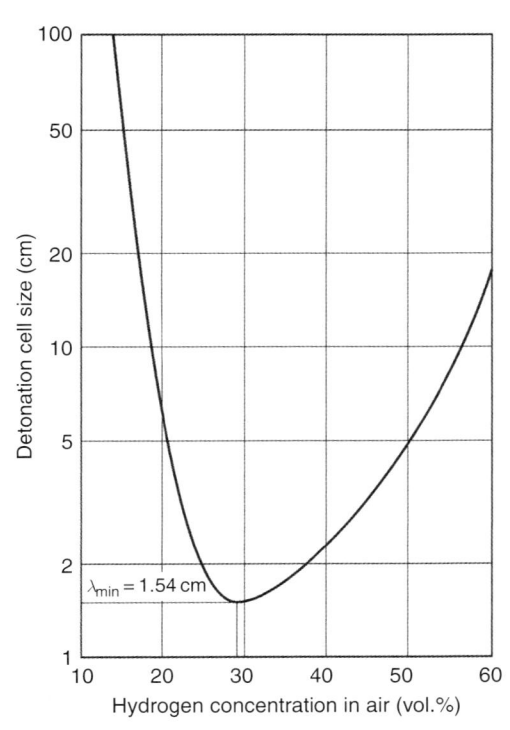

Figure 17 Detonation cell size as a function of hydrogen concentration in air [57].

by Medvedev *et al.* in 1994 [66] at even a smaller scale for highly reactive mixtures with initial pressures higher than ambient.

4.04.8 Safety Strategies and Accident Mitigation Techniques

The standard ISO/TR 15916:2004 'Basic considerations for the safety of hydrogen systems' gives some general recommendations to minimize the severity of the consequences of a potential mishap [17]:

- minimize the quantity of hydrogen that is stored and involved in an operation;
- isolate hydrogen from oxidizers, hazardous materials, and dangerous equipment;
- identify and, if possible, separate or eliminate potential ignition sources;
- separate people and facilities from the potential effects of fire, deflagration, or detonation originating from the failure of hydrogen equipment or storage systems;
- elevate hydrogen systems or vent them above other facilities;
- prevent hydrogen–oxidizer mixtures from accumulating in confined spaces (under the eaves of roofs, in equipment shacks or cabinets, or within equipment covers or cowlings);
- minimize personnel exposure by limiting the number of people exposed and the time that the personnel are exposed;
- use personal protective equipment;
- use alarms and warning devices (including hydrogen and fire detectors), and area control around a hydrogen system;
- practice good housekeeping, such as keeping access and evacuation routes clear and keeping weeds and other debris away from hydrogen systems; and
- observe safe operational requirements, such as working in pairs when operating in a hazardous situation.

The main general safety strategy to deal with hydrogen leaks is to minimize its mass flow rate and diameter, and 'let it go' to prevent its accumulation to a hazardous level when a flammable hydrogen–air mixture represents unacceptable hazards and risks.

4.04.8.1 Inherently Safer Design of Fuel Cell Systems

Inherently safer design is an approach that focuses on reducing or eliminating hazards associated with the product or the process. Consider how an FC safety system could be improved by reducing hazards without interfering with the technology itself. Unfortunately, the current FC systems are often designed using piping diameters of 5–15 mm and pressures of 0.5–1.5 MPa. The mass flow rate through a 5 mm diameter orifice at a storage pressure of 0.5 MPa can be calculated using the underexpanded jet theory [34], and is about 6 g s^{-1}. For a pipe of 15 mm diameter and pressure 1.5 MPa, the mass flow rate is 170 g s^{-1}.

Now estimate the mass flow rate for a 50 kW FC system for providing energy for large facilities such as hotels, hospitals, office buildings, and multifamily dwellings. Assuming that the electrical efficiency of FC is 45% and the upper heat of reaction (combustion) of hydrogen with air is (286.1 kJ mol^{-1})/(2.016 g mol^{-1}) = 141.92 kJ g^{-1}, the mass flow rate for correct functioning of the FC can be calculated as (50 kW)/0.45/(141.92 kJ g^{-1}) = 0.78 g s^{-1}. For example, this mass flow rate can be provided at pressure 0.5 MPa through a restrictor in the storage or piping system with an orifice diameter of only about 1.8 mm, or at pressure 0.2 MPa through an orifice of diameter of about 2.9 mm.

The separation distance for unignited release can be estimated as proportional to the nozzle diameter and the square root of pressure in the nozzle. Thus, a decrease of pipe diameter from 15 to 2.9 mm and pressure from 1.5 to 0.2 MPa could decrease separation distance by more than 14 times. Further analysis can be performed to compare separation distances for the following two options: option 1 – 0.5 MPa and 1.8 mm; option 2 – 0.2 MPa and 2.9 mm. The ratio of separation distances for unignited releases in options 1 and 2 with the assumption of full-bore rupture can be estimated as 0.98, that is, the separation distances are practically the same. These examples clearly demonstrate the advantages of the science-informed safety design of HFC systems to essentially reduce separation distances.

4.04.8.2 Mitigation of Release Consequences

The similarity law [6] with substitution of hydrogen density in the real nozzle exit is an efficient tool for HSE for both expanded and underexpanded round jets. For example, calculate the diameter of a PRD for storage on board the forklift to obey the following safety strategy. In the case of an upward release from the onboard storage at 35 MPa, we would like to exclude the formation of a flammable layer under a ceiling which is 10 m above the PRD. To realize this strategy, the concentration on the jet axis at distance 10 m should be equal to or below 4% by volume (the corresponding mass fraction of hydrogen is C_{ax} = 0.002 88). The density of hydrogen in the nozzle exit, calculated by the underexpanded jet theory [34] for a storage pressure of 35 MPa, is ρ_N = 14.6 kg m^{-3}. Thus, the diameter of the PRD can be calculated in a straightforward manner from the similarity law [6] as equal to or less than 1.5 mm

$$D = \frac{C_{ax}}{5.4}\sqrt{\frac{\rho_S}{\rho_N}}x = \frac{0.00288}{5.4}\sqrt{\frac{1.204}{14.6}}10 = 0.0015 \text{ m} \quad [22]$$

To finalize this safety strategy for use of forklifts in the warehouse, a requirement for fire-resistance rating of the onboard storage tank must be formulated and testing carried out. Indeed, the fire-resistance rating should be greater than the blowdown time (the time to empty the storage vessel) of the storage tank to exclude its catastrophic failure in the case of external fire. It is clear that the use of a PRD with a larger diameter would create a flammable cloud or a jet flame with higher hazards and associated risks.

4.04.8.3 Reduction of Separation Distances Informed by the Hydrogen Safety Engineering

Since 1969, Air Products operates in Houston (Texas, USA) 232 km of hydrogen pipelines of diameter 11.4–22 cm at a pressure of 5.8 MPa. For these parameters, the underexpanded jet theory [34] gives the maximum notional nozzle exit diameter 120 cm and mass flow rate 133.2 kg s^{-1} (for a scenario of full-bore rupture of pipe with 22 cm ID at 5.8 MPa).

Distance to 4% by volume of hydrogen in the jet, if it is assumed to be in momentum-controlled regime, can be calculated graphically directly from the similarity law line (**Figure 7**) or by the following simple equation (assuming for air ρ_S = 1.204 kg m^{-3}):

$$x_{4\%} = 1574\sqrt{\rho_N}D \quad [23]$$

where D is the maximum actual diameter of the release (0.22 m). The density in the nozzle at a storage pressure of 5.8 MPa can be calculated by the underexpanded jet theory [34] and is equal to ρ_N = 2.87 kg m^{-3}. Thus, the distance to 4% by volume calculated by eqn [23], that is, under the assumption of momentum-dominated jet, is 587 m!

Fortunately, the jet is not momentum-controlled at the range of concentration of interest. Indeed, the Froude number calculated by flow parameters at the notional nozzle exit is Fr = 5.1. Analysis of **Figure 8** with Fr = 5.1 shows that the jet becomes buoyancy-controlled (intersection of vertical line from Fr = 5.1 with the curve denoted 'Downward' jets) at log(x/D) = 2 (notional nozzle is applied to use **Figure 8**), that is, at distance x = 100D = 120 m! This distance is 4.9 times shorter than the safety distance determined without accounting for the effect of buoyancy.

4.04.8.4 Mitigation by Barriers

Sandia National Laboratories performed a series of experimental and numerical studies in order to assess the effectiveness of barriers to reduce the hazard from unintended releases of hydrogen, including within the international collaboration project HYPER [49]. For the conditions investigated, that is, 13.79 MPa source pressure and 3.175 mm diameter round leak, the barrier configurations studied were found to reduce horizontal jet flame impingement hazard by deflecting the jet flame, reduce radiation hazard distances for horizontal jet flames, and reduce horizontal unignited jet flammability hazard distances. For the one-wall vertical barrier and three-wall barrier configurations, the simulations of the peak overpressures from ignition were found to be approximately 40 kPa on the release side of the barrier while approximately 3–5 kPa on downstream backside of the barrier.

4.04.8.5 Mitigation of Deflagration-to-Detonation Transition

Strategies to minimize the potential for flame acceleration or detonation include the following [17]:

- Avoid confinement and congestion where flammable hydrogen–air mixtures might form.
- Use flame arrestors, small orifices, or channels to prevent deflagration and detonation from propagating within a system.
- Use diluents, like steam or carbon dioxide, or oxygen depletion techniques where possible and water spray or mist systems to retard flame acceleration. This recommendation of the standard [17] should be taken with care as hydrogen–air flames are difficult to quench and they can burn or even accelerate around the droplets in heavy sprays of water [67].
- Reduce the size of a system where possible to narrow detonability limits.

A low-carbon economy will more and more exploit fuels with addition of hydrogen. Knowing that hydrogen combustion is prone to DDT, especially at large scales, there are serious concerns on how technologies could be made safer. For such kind of applications, the safety strategy can be, in the author's opinion, to organize and control the process of combustion of a hydrogen-contained mixture in a way that the mixture supplied to the burner is between the lower flammability limit and the lower detonability limit.

4.04.8.6 Prevention of Deflagration-to-Detonation Transition within a Fuel Cell

In the experiments of Pro-Science [68], carried out within the HYPER project [49] in a mock-up of FC, a significant flame acceleration was recorded leading to a high overpressure, for the total injected mass of 15 and 25 g, sufficient for complete demolition of the experimental rig. Both experimental and numerical studies of the FC mock-up suggest that the total injected mass should be less than 6 g for the configuration studied in order to keep overpressures below 10–20 kPa. Missile effects could be still possible for this 6 g inventory [50]. So, an inventory of 1 g seems a good target for safety for accidental release within this FC mock-up. This result can be used to formulate requirements to a shutdown safety system for FCs.

The feed line pressure and diameter of the pipe and restrictor orifice should, by design, limit the mass flow rate of hydrogen to a level that is required for the FC to function. The release duration, due to the time required to detect the leak and operate the valve, should be reduced as much as possible to exclude release of more than 1 g of hydrogen. An estimate shows that for a 50 kW FC, which needs a consumption rate of hydrogen just below 1 g s^{-1}, the leak detection time and time of shutting down supply line should be together less than 1 s. Any reduction of this time would have a positive impact on safety. This requirement is difficult to achieve for currently available sensors. Innovative systems of leak detection, for example, based on supply pressure fluctuation analysis, have to be developed and implemented to provide acceptable level of safety. The grid obstacle, used in the Pro-Science experiments to mimic the congestion within a real FC, led to strong flame acceleration [68]. The congestion of internal space of the FC enclosure should be avoided as much as possible by a careful design.

4.04.8.7 Detection and Hydrogen Sensors

The addition of an odorant to hydrogen would ease the detection of small leaks. However, this is not practicable in most situations; for example, this would poison an expensive catalyst in FCs. Moreover, this is not feasible for liquefied hydrogen as any added substance would be in a solid state at the temperature of liquefied hydrogen of 20 K. Hydrogen fire detection can be based on registration of infrared radiation of flames which are not seen during daylight. **Figure 18** shows a typical picture of hydrogen jet flame and hot current in the infrared spectrum registered in HSL experiments [49].

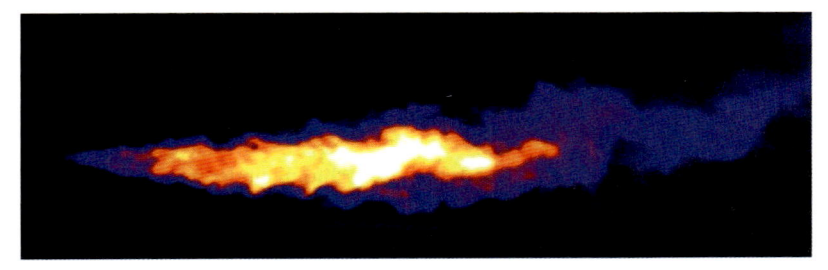

Figure 18 Hydrogen jet flame and hot current in the infrared spectrum [49].

In 2009, the French National Institute for Industrial Environment and Risks (INERIS) conducted a test program within the HYPER project [49] based on the international standard parts IEC 61779-1&4 [69] and aimed at assessing the performance of commercially available hydrogen detectors. These devices were of electrochemical and catalytic types, that is, the two types most often used in industry. The catalytic sensor was 5 times faster than the electrochemical sensor in responding to a sudden exposure of hydrogen. However, the response time was approximately 10 s for the catalytic sensor and 50 s for the electrochemical sensor. These figures also apply for the recovery time. In many practical scenarios, this long time is hardly acceptable.

Catalytic detectors studied within the HYPER project [49] were also prone to loss of sensitivity and drift of zero after a prolonged exposure to hydrogen. This emphasizes the need to regularly calibrate these devices. Higher humidity tended to increase the reading of the catalytic detector for a constant hydrogen content. The catalytic detector was very sensitive to the presence of carbon monoxide, but the interfering was only temporary, that is, when the CO exposure ceases the detector behaves in an ordinary way.

Research by the Joint Research Centre (JRC) within the HYPER project [49] demonstrated that the time required by the electrochemical sensor to respond to hydrogen exposure of known concentration becomes longer when the gas flow rate is reduced, that is, it could be twice longer when the flow rate is reduced from 100 to 30 ml min^{-1}. This finding is particularly important when the sensor is intended to control the formation of an explosive atmosphere within an FC cabinet.

There is another issue related to faster catalytic sensors that is not yet addressed: the potential to ignite hydrogen–air mixture with high concentrations by the sensor. The ignition of hydrogen–air mixtures with high content of hydrogen by recombiners was observed previously [70].

A variety of methods and sensor types are commercially available to detect the presence of hydrogen [17]. Many of these detectors are suitable for use in automatic warning and operating systems (see ISO 26142:2010 [71] for details concerning stationary systems).

4.04.9 Future Progress and Development

In Europe, the priorities in hydrogen safety research are formulated by industry through calls of the Fuel Cells and Hydrogen Joint Undertaking (FCH JU) [72] mainly as a part of cross-cutting issues. The international hydrogen safety community contributes to the prioritization of research through different activities of the International Association for Hydrogen Safety [10]. The International Energy Agency Hydrogen Implementation Agreement Task 31 'Hydrogen Safety' [73] is also actively involved in the process. A gap analysis of CFD modeling of accidental hydrogen release and combustion has been performed recently by an expert group led by JRC, Institute for Energy, European Commission [74].

In spite of indubitable progress in hydrogen safety in the last decade, there are still numerous knowledge gaps and a need for science-intensive tools, based on contemporary theories and thorough validation against a series of experiments carried out at different conditions. The nonexhaustive list has been prioritized by the hydrogen safety community and broken down into research topics, including but not limited to the following items grouped by phenomena or application.

4.04.9.1 Release Phenomena

Hydrogen leak source characterization and modeling; shape of leak source; dispersion in enclosed areas and ventilation; surface effects on jet release; liquid hydrogen release behavior; releases in real-complex configurations; dispersion of hydrogen releases in enclosures with natural or forced ventilation; effect of wind on outdoor releases in areas with complex surroundings; behavior of plane jets; interaction of multiple jets; transient effects in high-momentum jets; dynamics of transition from momentum- to buoyancy-controlled flow; flammable envelope for downward free and impinging jets; dynamics of unsteady releases (blowdowns and hydrogen puff, etc.); behavior of cold jets released in humid air; and so on.

4.04.9.2 Ignition Phenomena

Mechanisms of hydrogen release ignition; CFD modeling and validation of the membrane rupture and the associated transient processes; CFD modeling of transition from spontaneous ignition to jet fires and/or the quenching of the spontaneous ignition; development and validation of subgrid-scale models accounting for interaction of turbulence and chemistry; jet ignition delay time and position of ignition source for simulations of deflagration overpressure; ignition in complex geometries like PRDs; and so on.

4.04.9.3 Hydrogen Fires

Behavior of jet flames, for example, thermal radiation issues in the presence of a crosswind and surface effects on flame jet propagation; validation of CFD tools for large-scale hydrogen jet fires, including under transient conditions of decreasing notional nozzle diameter and temperature during a blowdown; pressure effects of indoor hydrogen fires; underventilated fires and reignition phenomenon; impinging jet fires and heat transfer to structural elements, storage vessels, and so on; predictive simulations of blow-off, lift-off, and blow-out phenomena; plane jet flames effect of microflames on materials; and so on.

4.04.9.4 Deflagrations and Detonations

Flammability and detonability limits of gaseous mixtures containing hydrogen; coherent deflagration during explosion venting in low-strength equipment accounting for Rayleigh–Taylor instability; effect of inertia of vent cover on explosion dynamics, including DDT; partially premixed flames, in particular triple flames in hydrogen–air layers and their pressure effects in enclosed space; development of SGS models of DDT at large industrial scales accounting for Richtmyer–Meshkov instability; and so on.

4.04.9.5 Storage

Fire resistance of onboard storage vessels and effect of PRD; metal hydride dust cloud explosion tests; engineering solutions to reduce heat transfer during external fire scenarios (localized and engulfing fires); and so on.

4.04.9.6 High-Pressure Electrolyzers

An explosion of a pressurized electrolyzer at an operational pressure of 40 MPa occurred on 7 December 2005 at a demonstration hydrogen stand at Kyushu University [75]. Possibly after the membrane leak, an internal hydrogen–oxygen jet fire resulted in metal (titanium) fire and explosion or rupture of the electrolyzer shell. Internal fluid and combustion products were released into the surrounding including parking area around the laboratory building. Several vehicle glass damages occurred due to the exposure to hydrogen fluoride which formed by the decomposition of polymer materials. A French–Russian study [76] reports the analysis of the failure mechanisms of proton exchange membrane (PEM) water electrolysis cells which can ultimately lead to the destruction of the electrolyzer. A two-step process involving the local perforation of the solid polymer electrolyte followed by the catalytic recombination of hydrogen and oxygen stored in the electrolysis compartments has been evidenced. Experimental evidence (photographs) of a stainless-steel fitting and nut drilled by a hydrogen–oxygen flame formed inside the PEM stack is presented. According to Millet et al. [76], the internal hydrogen–oxygen combustion prevails over explosion.

4.04.9.7 Hazard and Risk Identification and Analysis for Early Markets

Data collection from new hydrogen-based operating devices, systems, and facilities; failure statistics of new hydrogen applications; systems safety analysis of hydrogen applications; engineering correlations; and so on. Since new technologies are penetrating densely populated urban environment, special attention should be paid to hazards and risk mitigation technologies and methods such as sensors, barriers/walls. and separation distances.

4.04.10 Conclusions

We tend to treat our current fuels, notably petrol and natural gas, quite 'casually' due to familiarity with them, whereas hydrogen is viewed with some trepidation as it is 'unknown' and wrongly linked as a reason to past 'catastrophic' events like the Hindenburg dirigible.

The inevitability of the hydrogen economy and the important role of hydrogen safety, especially the HSE, in its underpinning are introduced in this chapter. HSE is defined as an application of scientific and engineering principles to the protection of life, property, and environment from the adverse effects of incidents/accidents involving hydrogen.

Hazards related to hydrogen properties are discussed and compared to other fuels. It is concluded that hydrogen is neither more dangerous nor safer than other energy carriers. Hydrogen is different and requires professional safety knowledge and skills at all stages starting from the design of HFC systems through their certification and permitting to new safety culture in use by public.

The safety of HFC systems and infrastructure is paramount for their commercial competitiveness and public acceptance. The activities of the European NoE HySafe (2004–09) and currently of the International Association for Hydrogen Safety (IA HySafe) along with national and international programs funded, for example, by the European FCH JU and US Department of Energy provide a firm guarantee of the progress in closing numerous knowledge gaps and development of innovative safety strategies and breakthrough engineering solutions. The progress achieved is far to be interpreted as a closure of safety issues. New processes of hydrogen production, storage, transportation, and use in HFC systems will appear that will require both basic and applied research.

Hazards and associated risks have to be fully understood and addressed. The role of risk assessment methods should not be overestimated in the absence of reliable statistics on probable potential benefits of the business and in no way at the cost of public safety. OEMs carrying out competitive research on hydrogen-powered vehicles should be more open and cooperative in solving common safety problems. The opinion 'there are no safety issues' with HFC technologies should be considered as not professional and misleading public. The examples of innovative safety strategies and inherently safer engineered systems should be disseminated as wide as possible instead. The test results of safety performance of hydrogen-fueled vehicles should be publicly available and activities on improvement of safety characteristics should be continuously reported to public to prevent rumors and nonprofessional misinterpretations. Conclusion is drawn that onboard storage and PRDs currently available for hydrogen-powered vehicles should be redesigned to mitigate potential accidents especially in confined spaces such as garages, car parks, maintenance shops, and tunnels. This requires at least reduction of mass flow rate during release through the PRD and increase of fire-resistance rating of the onboard storage from current 1–6 min by an order of magnitude.

The underestimation of the role of safety for HFC products and following accidents, which will happen as for any other technology, would have catastrophic consequences and thus imply further delays for the commercialization. That is what no one working in the field of HFC technologies wants to happen.

Inherently safer design of HFC systems has to be the primary goal of developers. For example, parameters of piping system, that is, pressure and internal diameter, have to be minimized to provide technological requirements on mass flow rate but not more. It is demonstrated that separation distances could be reduced by more than an order of magnitude if system designers are educated in carrying out HSE. Another example of inherently safer design is as follows. The safety strategy for burners and turbines using mixtures of hydrogen with other gases could be a provision that the mixture supplied to the combustion device is between the lower flammability limit and the lower detonability limit to sustain combustion yet to prevent detonation.

There is a clear need for the development of an overarching standard for performing HSE of HFC applications and infrastructure that is scientifically informed. Indeed, current RCS in the field are fragmented, are far from being complete, have grown in number, are prepared mainly by the industry and for the industry, are difficult to interpret, and are sometimes contradicting available knowledge being by definition at least 3 years old. This standard should have organizational and technical frameworks on how to carry out HSE and gather together in one place description of TSSs, for example, through the so-called 'published documents' similar to standard BS 7974 approach for fire safety engineering [23]. The concept of the standard and the structure of TSSs allow for their continuous update by research results and are convenient for new people to get quickly into the emerging profession of HSE. Professional workforce having a higher education degree to lead hydrogen safety activities in industry, regulatory bodies, research organizations, and academia is another important element in securing the safe introduction of HFC technologies to the market.

The progress in closing knowledge gaps in hydrogen safety science and engineering can be briefly summarized, based on the research results presented in this chapter, as follows.

For nonreacting hydrogen releases:

- The underexpanded jet theory is developed for prediction of flow parameters at the actual nozzle and notional nozzle exits. The theory accounts for nonideal behavior of hydrogen at high pressures by the Abel–Noble equation. For example, the use of the ideal gas law will overestimate the hydrogen mass released from a 70 MPa storage tank by about 45% as can be concluded from a comparison with the Abel–Noble equation.
- At high ratios of nozzle exit to atmospheric pressure above 40, the barrel shock culminates in a single strong Mach disk, and below this critical pressure ratio in multiple Mach disks.
- The similarity law for hydrogen concentration decay in both expanded and underexpanded momentum-controlled jets is proposed and validated. This can be applied for HSE for arbitrary initial parameters. An example of the application of similarity law in the design of a PRD for a forklift used in a warehouse is given as part of the safety strategy to exclude formation of flammable layer.
- A methodology to define where a jet transition from momentum- to buoyancy-controlled regime takes place is developed. This is of importance to essentially reduce separation distance, for example, for high-debit jets from pipelines. For example, for a hydrogen pipeline of internal diameter 22 cm at pressure 5.8 MPa, the separation distance for the most dangerous horizontal release can be reduced by about 5 times from unrealistic 587 m, when you apply the similarity law valid only for momentum-controlled jets, to 120 m (still a challenging distance).

For ignitions and hydrogen fires:

- The dimensional correlation for hydrogen jet flame length is developed. The conservative estimate of the flame length is 50% longer than the best-fit curve. A simple engineering nomogram for graphical calculation of the flame length based on the dimensional correlation is available.
- The universal dimensionless correlation for a jet flame length accounting for dependence on Fr, Re, and M numbers and covering the full spectrum of hydrogen releases, including laminar and turbulent flows, buoyancy- and momentum-controlled leaks, and expanded and underexpanded jets, is developed. There are three distinguishable parts in this innovative correlation: traditional ascending buoyancy-controlled and traditional momentum-dominated plateau for expanded jets and a new third ascending part that represents underexpanded jet fires, where dimensionless flame length depends on Reynolds rather than on Froude number. There is no saturation of the dimensionless flame length at value $L_F/D = 230$ observed in previous studies with expanded jets, instead reported experiments demonstrate values up to $L_F/D = 3000$.
- The contradictory statements available in combustion literature about the location of a turbulent nonpremixed flame tip are clarified. It is established that the flame tip is located for momentum-controlled jets (both expanded and underexpanded) at a distance from the leak source where the axial concentration of hydrogen in an unignited jet is 11% by volume (in the range from 8% to 16%). This is far below the stoichiometric concentration of 29.5% by volume as was thought previously.
- The potential of sensors to ignite mixtures with high concentrations of hydrogen has to be addressed from the beginning of hydrogen detector development. Relevant testing methods have to be developed and included in RCS.

For hydrogen deflagrations and detonations:

- Delayed ignition of hydrogen releases produces highly turbulent deflagration. It has been demonstrated in experiments by HSL that with an ignition delay of 0.8 s a release from a 20.5 MPa storage through a 9.5 mm orifice generates an overpressure of 16.5 kPa for free jet, 42 kPa if a 90° barrier wall is installed, and 57 kPa if a 60° barrier is applied. This is comparable with the moderate level of damage to structures by overpressure according to the following classification: 17 kPa, moderate damage; above 35 kPa, severe damage; and above 83 kPa, total structure destruction. It is concluded that the piping system diameter has to be as small as possible to provide sufficient amount of hydrogen to the system yet not more than that to reduce potential hazards and associated risks. Indeed, in the same series of experiments carried out by HSL, no overpressure was observed for a nozzle diameter of 1.5 mm.
- Experimental and numerical studies show that turbulence of the mixture during the sudden release of high-pressure hydrogen to the atmosphere has a greater effect on the deflagration overpressure than the total amount of released gas or the volume of flammable mixture.
- Mitigation by barriers study performed by Sandia National Laboratories for 13.79 MPa release through 3.175 mm diameter round leak demonstrated that for different barrier configurations the peak overpressure to be approximately 40 kPa on the release side of the barrier and only 3–5 kPa on downstream backside of the barrier.
- The DDT phenomenon is not yet extensively studied to have predictive contemporary models and tools for solving large-scale engineering applications. In particular, the mechanism of DDT during mitigation of hydrogen–air deflagration by the venting technique is not clear. Detonation is the worst-case scenario for an accident involving hydrogen and all measures should be undertaken to prevent it. Indeed, the energetic equivalent of 1 g of hydrogen is quite high – 28.65 g of TNT.
- The results of the HYPER project (Pro-Science) indicate that the accidental release of no more than 1 g of hydrogen inside the FC is a good target for hydrogen safety engineers to prevent DDT. This is difficult to achieve with the response time of currently available sensors and research on innovative systems of leak detection, for example, by analysis of pressure dynamics in the piping system, should be continued.

Acknowledgments

The author is grateful to colleagues from the HySAFER Centre at the University of Ulster for their collaboration and devotion to hydrogen safety research. Financial support of the European Commission and the Fuel Cell and Hydrogen Joint Undertaken to hydrogen safety research at HySAFER is highly appreciated.

References

[1] Office of Science, US Department of Energy (2004) Basic research needs for the hydrogen economy. http://www.science.energy.gov/~/media/bes/pdf/reports/files/nhe_rpt.pdf (accessed February 2004).
[2] PennWell Corporation. Fuel cell demand to reach $8.5 billion in 2016. http://www.militaryaerospace.com/ (last accessed 14 December 2011).
[3] Environmental graffiti alpha. The Hindenburg Disaster in Pictures. http://www.environmentalgraffiti.com/anthropology-and-history/news-hindenberg-disaster-accident-waiting-happen (last accessed 14 December 2011).
[4] Bain A and Van Vorst WD (1999) The *Hindenburg* tragedy revisited: The fatal flaw found. *International Journal of Hydrogen Energy* 24: 399–403.
[5] Ricci M, Newsholme G, Bellaby P, and Flynn R (2006) Hydrogen: Too dangerous to base our future upon? *Proceedings of the IChemE Symposium Hazards XIX*, pp. 42–60. 27–30 March 2006, University of Manchester, UK: IChemE.
[6] Swain MR Fuel leak simulation. http://evworld.com/library/swainh2vgasVideo.pdf (last accessed 14 December 2011).
[7] Tamura Y, Takabayashi M, Takeuchi M, and Mitsuishi H (2011) The spread of fire from adjoining vehicles to a hydrogen fuel cell vehicle. *Proceedings of the Fourth International Conference on Hydrogen Safety*. San Francisco, CA, 12–14 September.
[8] Ahrens M (2009) Structure fires originating in vehicle storage areas, garages or carports of one- or two-family homes excluding fires in properties coded as detached garages. September. Quincy, MA: National Fire Protection Association, Index No. 1457, 26 pages.
[9] Ahrens M (2006) Structure and vehicle fires in general vehicle parking garages. January. Quincy, MA: National Fire Protection Association, 34 pages.
[10] The EC Network of Excellence for Hydrogen Safety 'Hysafe'. Biennial Report on Hydrogen Safety. www.hysafe.org (last accessed 14 December 2011).
[11] Baratov AN, Korolchenko AYa, and Kravchuk GN (eds.) (1990) *Fire and Explosion Hazards of Substances and Materials*, 496pp. Moscow, Russia: Khimiya. ISBN 5-7245-0603-3 part 1, ISBN 5-7245-0408-1 part 2.
[12] Wikimedia Foundation Inc. The Free Encyclopedia. http://en.wikipedia.org/ (last accessed 14 December 2011).
[13] Lamoureux N, Djebaili-Chaumeix N, and Paillard C-E (2003) Laminar flame velocity determination for H_2–air–He–CO_2 mixtures using the spherical bomb. *Experimental Thermal and Fluid Science* 27: 385–393.
[14] Alcock JL, Shirvill LC, and Cracknell RF (2001) Compilation of existing safety data on hydrogen and comparative fuels. Deliverable Report of European FP5 project EIHP2. http://www.eihp.org/public/documents/CompilationExistingSafetyData_on_H2_and_ComparativeFuels_S.pdf (accessed May 2001).
[15] Coward HF and Jones GW (1952) Limits of flammability of gases and vapors. Bulletin 503, Bureau of Mines. http://www.galcit.caltech.edu/EDL/public/flammability/USBM-503.pdf (last accessed 14 December 2011).
[16] Dryer FL, Chaos M, Zhao Z, *et al.* (2007) Spontaneous ignition of pressurized releases of hydrogen and natural gas into air. *Combustion Science and Technology* 179: 663–694.
[17] International Organization for Standardization (2010) Standard ISO/TR 15916:2004. Basic considerations for the safety of hydrogen systems. ISO Technical Committee 197 Hydrogen Technologies, Geneva, Switzerland.

[18] Gavrikov AI, Efimenko AA, and Dorofeev SB (2000) A model for detonation cell size prediction from chemical kinetics. *Combustion and Flame* 120: 19–33.
[19] Zbikowski M, Makarov D, and Molkov V (2008) LES model of large scale hydrogen–air planar detonations: Verification by the ZND theory. *International Journal of Hydrogen Energy* 33: 4884–4892.
[20] Health and Safety Executive. Flixborough (Nypro UK) Explosion 1st June 1974. http://www.hse.gov.uk/comah/sragtech/caseflixboroug74.htm (last accessed 14 December 2011).
[21] The Buncefield Major Incident Investigation Board. Buncefield Investigation. http://www.buncefieldinvestigation.gov.uk/index.htm (last accessed 14 December 2011).
[22] Website of Prof Joseph Shepherd. Crisis at Fukushima Dai-ichi Nuclear Power Plant. http://www.galcit.caltech.edu/~jeshep/fukushima/ (last accessed 14 December 2011).
[23] BSI (2001) British Standard BS7974:2001 Application of fire safety engineering to the design of buildings – Code of practice. London, UK.
[24] Haskel International. High pressure gas and liquid engineering. http://www.haskel.com/corp/details/0,,CLI1_DIV139_ETI10610,00.html (last accessed 14 December 2011).
[25] Dulov VG and Luk'yanov GA (1984) *Gas Dynamics of the Outflow Processes*. Novosibirsk, Russia: Nauka.
[26] Ricou FP and Spalding DB (1961) Measurements of entrainment by axisymmetrical turbulent jets. *Journal of Fluid Mechanics* 8: 21–32.
[27] Chen C and Rodi W (1980) *Vertical Turbulent Buoyant Jets – A Review of Experimental Data*. Oxford, UK: Pergamon Press. ISBN 0-08-024772-5.
[28] Ishii R, Fujimoto H, Hatta N, and Umeda Y (1999) Experimental and numerical analysis of circular pulse jets. *Journal of Fluid Mechanics* 392: 129–153.
[29] Birch AD, Brown DR, Dodson MG, and Swaffield F (1984) The structure and concentration decay of high pressure jets of natural gas. *Combustion Science and Technology* 36: 249–261.
[30] Thring MW and Newby MP (1953) Combustion length of enclosed turbulent jet flames. In: Lewis B, Hottel HC, and Nerad AJ (eds.) *Fourth International Symposium on Combustion*, pp. 789–796. Baltimore, MD: Williams & Wilkins Co.
[31] Birch AD, Hughes DJ, and Swaffield F (1987) Velocity decay of high pressure jets. *Combustion Science and Technology* 52: 161–171.
[32] Noble RA and Abel FA (1985) Researches on explosives. Fired gunpowder. *Philosophical Transactions of the Royal Society of London* 165: 49–155. doi: 10.1098/rstl.1875.0002.
[33] Schefer RW, Houf WG, Williams TC, et al. (2007) Characterization of high-pressure, underexpanded hydrogen-jet flames. *International Journal of Hydrogen Energy* 32(12): 2081–2093.
[34] Molkov V, Makarov D, and Bragin M (2009) Physics and modelling of under-expanded jets and hydrogen dispersion in atmosphere. In: Fortov VE, Karamurzov BS, Temrokov AI, et al. (eds.) *Physics of Extreme State of Matter 2009*, pp. 143–145. Chernogolovka, Russia. ISBN 978-5-901675-89-2. Institute of Problems of Chemical Physics of Russian Academy of Sciences.
[35] Shevyakov GG, Tomilin VP, and Kondrashkov YuA (1980) *Engineering Physical Journal*, deposit with VINITI, N3671-80 (in Russian). [Reproduced in Schevyakov GG and Savelieva NI (2004) Dispersion and combustion of hydrogen jet in the open atmosphere. *International Scientific Journal for Alternative Energy and Ecology* 1(9), 23–27 (in Russian).
[36] Veser A, Kuznetsov M, Fast G, et al. (2009) The structure and flame propagation regimes in turbulent hydrogen jets. In: Lewis B, Hottel HC, and Nerad AJ (eds.) *Third International Conference on Hydrogen Safety*. Ajaccio, France, 16–18 September.
[37] Sunavala PD, Hulse C, and Thring MW (1957) Mixing and combustion in free and enclosed turbulent jet diffusion flames. *Combustion and Flame* 1: 179–193.
[38] Molkov V (2009) Hydrogen non-reacting and reacting jets in stagnant air: Overview and state-of-the-art. *Proceedings of the 10th International Conference on Fluid Control, Measurements, and Visualization (FLUCOM 2009)*. Moscow, Russia, 17–21 August.
[39] Hawthorne WR, Weddell DS, and Hottel HC (1949) Mixing and combustion in turbulent gas jets. In: Lewis B, Hottel HC, and Nerad AJ (eds.) *Third International Symposium on Combustion, Flame and Explosion Phenomena*, pp. 266–288. Baltimore, MD: Williams & Wilkins Co.
[40] Mogi T, Nishida H, and Horiguchi S (2005) Flame characteristics of high-pressure hydrogen gas jet. *Proceedings of the First International Conference on Hydrogen Safety*. Pisa, Italy, 8–10 September.
[41] Okabayashi K, Hirashima H, Nonaka T, et al. (2007) Introduction of technology for assessment on hydrogen safety. *Mitsubishi Heavy Industries Ltd. Technical Review* 44(1): 1–3.
[42] Molkov V and Saffers J-B (2011) The correlation for non-premixed hydrogen jet flame length in still air. *Proceedings of the 10th International Symposium on Fire Safety Science*. University of Maryland, College Park, MD, USA, June, pp. 933–943. ISNN 1817-4299.
[43] Shevyakov GG and Komov VF (1977) Effect of non-combustible admixtures on length of an axisymmetric on-port turbulent diffusion flame. *Combustion, Explosion and Shock Waves* 13: 563–566.
[44] Bilger RW (1976) Turbulent jet diffusion flames. *Progress in Energy and Combustion Science* 1: 87–109.
[45] Molkov V, Bragin M, Brennan S, et al. (2010) Hydrogen safety engineering: Overview of recent progress and unresolved issues. *Proceedings of the International Congress on Combustion and Fire Dynamics*. Santander, Spain, 20–23 October.
[46] Molkov VV and Nekrasov VP (1982) Dynamics of gas combustion in a constant volume in the presence of exhaust. *Combustion, Explosion and Shock Waves* 17(4): 363–369.
[47] Stephens MM (1970) Minimizing damage to refineries from nuclear attack, natural or other disasters. Office of Oil and Gas, US Department of the Interior(AD-773 048, Distributed by NTIS). Washington, USA.
[48] Brennan S, Makarov D, and Molkov V (2011) Dynamics of flammable hydrogen–air mixture formation in an enclosure with a single vent. In: Bradley D, Makhviladze G, and Molkov V (eds.) *Proceedings of the Sixth International Seminar on Fire and Explosion Hazards*, pp. 493–503. Leeds, UK, 11–16 April. ISBN-13: 978-981-08-7724-8, ISBN-10: 981-08-7724-8.
[49] EU FP6 project HYPER. Installation Permitting Guidance for Hydrogen and Fuel Cells Stationary Applications. www.hyperproject.eu/ (last accessed 14 December 2011).
[50] Barry TF (2003) *Risk-Informed, Performance-based Industrial Fire Protection*. Knoxville, USA: Tennessee Valley Publishing. ISBN 1-882194-09-8.
[51] Takeno K, Okabayashi K, Kouchi A, et al. (2007) Dispersion and explosion field tests for 40 MPa pressurized hydrogen. *International Journal of Hydrogen Energy* 32: 2144–2153.
[52] Tanaka T, Azuma T, Evans JA, et al. (2007) Experimental study on hydrogen explosions in a full-scale hydrogen filling station model. *International Journal of Hydrogen Energy* 32: 2162–2170.
[53] Chapman DL (1899) On the rate of explosion in gases. *Philosophical Magazine* 47: 90–104.
[54] Jouguet JCE (1905) On the propagation of chemical reactions in gases. *Journal des Mathématiques Pures et Appliquées* 1: 347–425. [Continued 2: 5–85, 1906].
[55] Neumann Von J (1942) Theory of detonation waves. In: Taub AJ (ed.) *John Von Neumann, Collected Works*, vol. 6, pp. 203–218. New York: Macmillan.
[56] Radulescu MI, Sharpe GJ, and Law CK (2005) The hydrodynamic structure of detonations. *Proceedings of the 20th ICDERS*, 31 July–5 August. Montreal, Canada.
[57] Lee JHS (1982) Hydrogen air detonations. *2nd International Workshop on the Impact of Hydrogen on Water Reactor Safety*, 3–7 October. Albuquerque, NM.
[58] Dorofeev SB, Bezmelnitsin AV, and Sidorov VP (1995) Transition to detonation in vented hydrogen–air explosions. *Combustion and Flame* 103: 243–246.
[59] Tsuruda T and Hirano T (1987) Growth of flame front turbulence during flame propagation across an obstacle. *Combustion Science and Technology* 51: 323–328.
[60] Lee JHS, Knystautas R, and Yoshikawa N (1978) Photochemical initiation and gaseous detonations. *Acta Astronautica* 5: 971–972.
[61] Zeldovich B, Librovich VB, Makhviladze GM, and Sivashinsky GI (1970) On development of detonation in a non-uniformly preheated gas. *Astronautica Acta* 15: 313–320.
[62] Ferrara G, Willacy SK, Phylaktou HN, et al. (2005) Venting of premixed gas explosions with a relief pipe of the same area as the vent. *Proceedings of the European Combustion Meeting*, 3–6 April, Louvain-la-Neuve, Belgium.
[63] Molkov VV, Nekrasov VP, Baratov AN, and Lesnyak SA (1984) Turbulent gas combustion in a vented vessel, combustion. *Explosion and Shock Waves* 20: 149–153.
[64] Lee JHS and Guirao CM (1982) Pressure development in closed and vented vessels. *Plant/Operations Progress* 1(2): 75–85.
[65] Breitung W, Chan CK, Dorofeev SB, et al. (2000) Flame acceleration and deflagration-to-detonation transition in nuclear safety. Sate-of-the-art report Nea/CSNI/R(2000)7. Paris, France: OECD Nuclear Energy Agency.

[66] Medvedev SP, Polenov AN, Khomik SV, and Gelfand BE (1994) *25th Symposium (International) on Combustion*, pp. 73–78. The Combustion Institute, Pittsburgh, PA.
[67] Shebeko YuN, Tsarichenko SG, Eremenko OYa, *et al.* (1990) Combustion of lean hydrogen–air mixtures in an atomized water stream. *Combustion Explosion and Shock Waves* 26(4): 426–428.
[68] Friedrich A, Kotchourko N, Stern G, and Veser A (2009) HYPER experiments on catastrophic hydrogen releases inside a fuel cell enclosure. *Proceedings of the Third International Conference on Hydrogen Safety*, Paper ID 118. Ajaccio, Corsica, France, 16–18 September.
[69] International Electrotechnical Commission (IEC) (1998) Standard IEC 61779-1: Electrical apparatus for the detection and measurement of flammable gases – Part 1: General requirements and test methods. Standard IEC 61779-4: Performance requirements for group II apparatus indicating up to a volume fraction of 100% lower explosive limit. Geneva, Switzerland.
[70] Blanchat TK and Malliakos A (1998) Performance testing of passive autocatalytic recombiners. NUREG/CR-6580, SAND97-2632. Division of Systems Technology, Office of Nuclear Regulatory Research, US Nuclear Regulatory Commission, Washington, DC.
[71] International Organization for Standardization (2010) Standard ISO 26142:2010. Hydrogen detection apparatus – Stationary applications. ISO Technical Committee 197 Hydrogen Technologies. Geneva, Switzerland.
[72] Fuel Cells and Hydrogen Joint Undertaking. http://www.fch-ju.eu/ (last accessed 14 December 2011).
[73] International Energy Agency, Hydrogen Implementing Agreement, Task 19 – Hydrogen Safety. http://www.ieah2safety.com/ (last accessed 14 December 2011).
[74] Baraldi D, Papanikolaou E, Heitsch M, *et al.* (2010) Gap analysis of CFD modelling of accidental hydrogen release and combustion, 60pp. Petten, The Netherlands: JRC, Institute for Energy, European Commission. EUR 24399 EN, ISBN 978-92-79-15992-3, ISSN 1018-5593, doi: 10.2790/2090.
[75] Accident of hydrogen stand at Kyushu University investigation committee (2007) Report on the accident of hydrogen stand at Kyushu University, 3rd edn. http://www.kyushu-u.ac.jp/news/hydrogen/hydrogensummary0330.pdf; http://www.nsc.go.jp/senmon/shidai/kasai/kasai004/ssiryo4-1.pdf (last accessed 14 December 2011).
[76] Millet P, Ranjbari A, de Guglielmo F, *et al.* (2011) Cell failure mechanism in PEM water electrolyzers. *Proceedings of the Fourth International Conference on Hydrogen Safety*, paper ID 254. San Francisco, CA, 12–14 September.
[77] Chaineaux J, Mavrothalassitis G, and Pineau J (1991) Modelization and validation of the discharge in air of a vessel pressurized by flammable gas. *Progress in Astronautics and Aeronautics* 134: 104–137.
[78] Houf W and Schefer R (2008) Analytical and experimental investigation of small-scale unintended releases of hydrogen. *International Journal of Hydrogen Energy* 33: 1435–1444.
[79] Kuznetsov M (2006) Hydrogen distribution tests in free turbulent jet. FZK. SBEP V4. Report No.: SBEP V4.
[80] Okabayashi K, Nonaka T, Sakata N, Takeno K, Hirashima H, and Chitose K (2005) Characteristics of dispersion for leakage of high-pressurized hydrogen gas. *Japan Society for Safety Engineering* 44: 391–397.
[81] Ruffin E, Mouilleau Y, and Chaineaux J, Large scale characterization of the concentration field of supercritical jets of hydrogen and methane. *J Loss Prev Process Ind.* 9: 279–284.
[82] Shirvill LC, Roberts PT, Roberts TA, Butler CJ, and Royle M (2006) Dispersion of hydrogen from high-pressure sources. *Proceedings of the IChemE Symposium Hazards XIX*, Manchester, UK, 27–30 March 2006.
[83] Shirvill LC, Roberts PT, Butler CJ, Roberts TA, and Royle M (2005) Characterisation of the hazards from jet releases of hydrogen. *First International Conference on Hydrogen Safety*, Pisa, Italy, 8–10 September 2005.
[84] Imamura T, Hamada S, Mogi T, Wada Y, Horiguchi S, Miyake A, and Ogawa T (2008) Experimental investigation on the thermal properties of hydrogen jet flame and hot currents in the downstream region. *International Journal of Hydrogen Energy* 33: 3426–3435.
[85] Kalghatgi GT (1984) Lift-off heights and visible lengths of vertical turbulent jet diffusion flames in still air. *Combustion Science and Technology* 41: 17–29.
[86] Proust C, Jamois D, and Studer E (2009) High pressure hydrogen fires. *Proceedings of the Third International Conference on Hydrogen Safety*. 16–18 September 2009, Ajaccio, France, paper 214.
[87] Studer E, Jamois D, Jallais S, Leroy G, Hebrard J, and Blanchetière V (2009) Properties of large-scale methane/hydrogen jet fires. *International Journal of Hydrogen Energy* 34: 9611–9619.
[88] Schefer RW, Houf WG, Bourne B, and Colton J (2006) Spatial and radiative properties of an open-flame hydrogen plume. *International Journal of Hydrogen Energy* 31: 1332–1340.

4.05 Hydrogen Storage: Compressed Gas

D Nash, University of Strathclyde, Glasgow, UK
D Aklil, E Johnson, R Gazey, and V Ortisi, Pure Energy Center, Unst, Shetland Isles, UK

© 2012 Elsevier Ltd. All rights reserved.

4.05.1	Introduction	111
4.05.2	Containment Vessels	111
4.05.3	Theory and Principles of Design	112
4.05.3.1	Steel Vessels	112
4.05.3.1.1	Materials	112
4.05.3.1.2	Design for pressure loading	113
4.05.3.1.3	Dished ends	115
4.05.3.1.4	Nozzles and openings	115
4.05.3.2	Composite Vessels	116
4.05.3.2.1	Composite vessels for hydrogen storage	116
4.05.4	Codes and Standards and Best Practices	116
4.05.4.1	Storage Tanks	117
4.05.4.1.1	Gas storage systems and cylinders best practice	117
4.05.4.2	Connectors – Joints and Fittings for Hydrogen	120
4.05.4.3	Auxiliary Equipment	123
4.05.4.4	Basic Safety Requirements When Installing Hydrogen Systems	124
4.05.4.4.1	Training	125
4.05.4.4.2	Local authorities	125
4.05.4.4.3	Electrical grounding	125
4.05.4.4.4	Gas contamination monitoring	127
4.05.4.5	Codes and Standards	127
4.05.4.6	Case Studies	128
4.05.4.6.1	Designing a hydrogen storage tank	128
4.05.4.6.2	The Pure Project case study	131
References		135

4.05.1 Introduction

Storage of compressed gas presents significant challenges over the storage of liquids due to the compressible nature of the medium.

Hydrogen storage, in particular, presents a number of technical challenges for hydrogen generation and production, stationary storage sites, transportable storage, and hydrogen refueling stations. Compressed hydrogen gas can be stored in high-pressure tanks with pressures up to 700 bar (70 MPa). In addition, hydrogen can be cryogenically cooled to −253 °C in insulated tanks within a pressure range of between 6 and 350 bar (35 MPa). It can also be stored in advanced materials, either within the structure or on the surface of the material or in a chemical compound form which will generate hydrogen when undergoing some release reaction.

Hydrogen has a very high energy content by weight (about 3 times that of gasoline fuel), but it has a very low energy content by volume (liquid hydrogen is about 4 times less energy dense than gasoline). This makes hydrogen a challenge to store, especially when transportable storage is required for use in a vehicle situation.

Hydrogen is colorless, odorless, tasteless, nontoxic, and nonpoisonous. Although it is noncorrosive, it has the potential to affect the metallurgy of some materials especially when welded. This can result in hydrogen embrittlement and lead to inherent weaknesses in some storage systems. Although natural gas and propane are also odorless, industrial manufacturers incorporate sulfur-based additives to enhance their detection on leakage. Currently, such additives are not used with hydrogen because of separation and dispersion issues. These additives have been known to contaminate fuel cells and other storage systems and can lead to compromised structural integrity.

Hydrogen is over 50 times lighter than gasoline vapor and 14 times lighter than air. The impact of this is that if it is released in an open environment, it will typically rise and disperse rapidly. This is a significant safety advantage in an outside environment.

While there are risks associated with the storage of dangerous mediums, hydrogen, like petroleum, gasoline, or natural gas, is a fuel that must be handled properly. It can be used as safely as other common fuels when simple guidelines are followed.

4.05.2 Containment Vessels

Hydrogen storage usually is made by the use of some form of pressure vessel or piping system. Pressure vessel design codes normally cover interpretation, responsibilities, certification, selection of materials, evaluation of nominal design stresses, design, manufacture and workmanship, inspection, quality control, and testing. 'ISO 16528 Part 1' defines a pressure vessel as a housing designed and built to contain gases or liquids under pressure, and the Pressure Equipment Directive (PED) defines a pressure vessel as a housing, and its direct attachments, designed and built to contain fluids or gases under pressure. Storage vessels for compressed hydrogen gas are usually designed, constructed, and maintained in accordance with applicable codes and standards, for example, the ASME VIII Boiler and Pressure Vessel Code for structural design and the NFPA2 Code for Hydrogen Storage for testing and operation.

4.05.3 Theory and Principles of Design

A pressure vessel consists of various elements welded together. Certain elements (such as flat ends) may be attached by bolting. These could, in theory, be of any shape. In practice, they are nearly always cylindrical. This is because a cylinder is a very efficient shape for the containment of pressure. Cylinders with relatively thin walls are subject only to tensile stresses when under internal pressure. A spherical shape is even more efficient than a cylinder in terms of the thickness required to withstand a particular pressure, but spherical vessels are difficult to make and provide an awkward shape for purposes other than storage. They are used mostly for storing liquefied gases under pressure. To complete the enclosure, the cylindrical shell must be fitted with ends or heads.

Nozzles are used for getting the fluid or gas into and out of the vessel, for instruments and valves, and for venting and draining the vessel. A typical nozzle would consist of a short length of pipe with a flange welded to one end and the other end welded into a hole cut in the vessel. This is called a set-in nozzle. A set-on nozzle would be welded onto the outside of the vessel. This type would normally be used for small nozzles on thick-walled vessels.

Horizontal vessels are nearly always supported on two saddles. Typical dimensions of saddles for vessels of various sizes are given in 'BS 5276: Part 2 – Specification for saddle supports for horizontal cylindrical pressure vessels'. Wrapper plates are often used to reduce the local stresses in the shell at the support. Small, vertical vessels are often supported on legs – usually three or four, but sometimes more. Larger vessels are usually supported on skirts. Conical skirts are used for tall, slender vessels to give a larger base ring diameter. Sometimes, it is necessary for the supports to be attached part way up the shell – such as for vessels supported in a structure. In this case, brackets are used – typically two or four brackets will be fitted. In the case of heavy vessels, a continuous ring would be used.

'ISO 16528-1 clause 7.3.1' states that pressure vessels shall be designed for loadings appropriate to their intended use, including loadings induced by reasonably foreseeable operating conditions and external events. 'ISO 16528-1 clause 6.2' lists the common failure modes that are generally considered in the design codes, and they are classified as short-term, long-term, and cyclic-type failures. 'ISO 16528-1 Annex A' gives a brief description of these failure modes for guidance.

'Short-term failure modes' are those due to the application of noncyclic loads that lead to immediate failure:

- brittle fracture;
- ductile failures – crack formation, ductile tearing due to excessive local strains, gross plastic deformation, and plastic instability (bursting);
- excessive deformations leading to leakage at joints or other loss of function;
- elastic or elastic–plastic instability (buckling).

'Long-term failure modes' are those due to the application of noncyclic loads that lead to delayed failure:

- creep rupture;
- creep – excessive deformations at mechanical joints or excessive deformations resulting in unacceptable transfer of load;
- creep instability;
- erosion, corrosion;
- environmentally assisted cracking, for example, stress corrosion cracking, hydrogen-induced cracking, and so on.

'Cyclic failure modes' are those due to the application of cyclic loads that lead to delayed failure:

- progressive plastic deformation;
- alternating plasticity;
- fatigue under elastic strains (medium- and high-cycle fatigue) or under elastic–plastic strains (low-cycle fatigue);
- environmentally assisted fatigue, for example, stress corrosion cracking or hydrogen-induced cracking.

4.05.3.1 Steel Vessels

4.05.3.1.1 Materials

When considering the most appropriate material for construction, be it the main pressure-retaining shell or valves and seals, consideration must be given to the possible deterioration of properties when exposed to hydrogen at the intended operating conditions. The mechanical properties of metals, including steels, aluminum and aluminum alloys, titanium and titanium alloys, and nickel and nickel alloys, are detrimentally affected by hydrogen. Exposure of metals to hydrogen can lead to embrittlement, cracking, and/or significant losses in tensile strength, ductility, and fracture toughness. This can result in premature failure in load-carrying components.

4.05.3.1.2 Design for pressure loading

The main loading, which all vessels will be subjected to in their lifetime, is that of 'internal pressure'. Thin shells under this loading are normally analyzed by membrane stress analysis. Thick-walled pressure vessels are normally analyzed by using the Lamé equations. Design equations based on this analysis are given in 'ASME VIII Division 1, Appendix 1'.

The cylindrical shell is the most frequently used geometrical shape in pressure vessel design. The stresses in a closed-end cylindrical shell under internal pressure can be found from the conditions of static equilibrium and by evaluating the governing hoop stress. The design equations are based on thin shell theory.

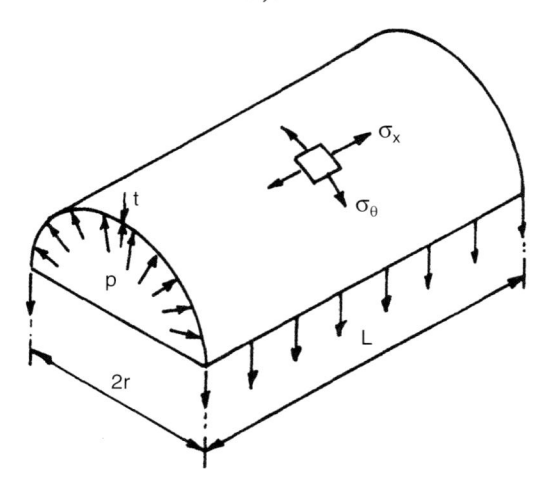

For a thin cylinder of mean radius r and thickness t under internal pressure p, the forces must be in equilibrium:

$$2\sigma_\theta tL = p2rL$$

Hence, the circumferential stress in a thin cylinder is given by

$$\sigma_\theta = \frac{pr}{t}$$

Rearranging this equation to give the required thickness e for a shell of inside diameter D_i and with design stress f gives the following equation as used in British Code PD 5500:

$$e = \frac{pD_i}{2f - p}$$

In practice, the chosen minimum wall thickness for the design must take into account mill tolerance and corrosion allowance.

The American ASME VIII Division 1 code suggests the following approach. For vessels with a known inside radius R, the minimum required thickness t for pressure loading is the 'greater' of the thicknesses obtained from clause UG-27(c)(1) or UG-27(c)(2). These relate to the circumferential and longitudinal stresses, respectively. For vessels with a known outside radius R_o, the minimum required thickness t is obtained from Appendix 1, clauses 1-1(a)(1).

The allowable stress S is obtained from ASME II, Part D, Table 1A or 1B at the design temperature. The joint efficiency, which introduces additional thickness to compensate for differences in weld configuration, E, must be the appropriate value from clause UW-12 for the joint being considered.

For 'circumferential stress' (longitudinal joints), when the thickness does not exceed half the inside radius or P does not exceed $0.385SE$

$$t = \frac{PR}{SE - 0.6P} \quad \text{or} \quad t = \frac{PR_o}{SE + 0.4P}$$

For longitudinal joints, the maximum allowable working pressure (MAWP) is given by

$$P = \frac{SEt}{R + 0.6t} \quad \text{or} \quad P = \frac{SEt}{R_o - 0.4t}$$

For 'longitudinal stress' (circumferential joints), when the thickness does not exceed half the inside radius or P does not exceed $1.25SE$

$$t = \frac{PR}{2SE + 0.4P}$$

For circumferential joints, the MAWP is given by

$$P = \frac{2SEt}{R - 0.4t}$$

Note that the circumferential stress formulae will govern unless the circumferential joint efficiency is less than half the longitudinal joint efficiency, or if there are other loadings that increase the longitudinal stress.

For 'thick cylindrical shells', where the limitations on thickness or pressure given in clause UG–27(c)(1) or UG–27(c)(2) are exceeded, the equations in Appendixes 1 and 2 must be used. The results are very close to those obtained using the Lamé equations (see any standard text on Mechanics of Materials).

For 'circumferential stress' (longitudinal joints), when the thickness exceeds half the inside radius or P exceeds $0.385SE$

$$t = R\left(\exp\left[\frac{P}{SE}\right] - 1\right) \quad \text{or} \quad t = R_o\left(1 - \exp\left[\frac{-P}{SE}\right]\right)$$

For longitudinal joints, the MAWP is given by

$$P = SE \log_e\left(\frac{R+t}{R}\right) \quad \text{or} \quad P = SE \log_e\left(\frac{R_o}{R_o - t}\right)$$

Note that the above equations for t and P may be used *in lieu* of those given in UG–27(c).

For 'longitudinal stress' (circumferential joints), when the thickness exceeds half the inside radius or P exceeds $1.25SE$

$$Z = \left(\frac{P}{SE} + 1\right)$$

$$t = R(Z^{1/2} - 1) \quad \text{or} \quad t = R_o \frac{(Z^{1/2} - 1)}{Z^{1/2}}$$

For circumferential joints, the MAWP is given by

$$Z = \left(\frac{R+t}{R}\right)^2 \quad \text{or} \quad Z = \left(\frac{R_o}{R_o - t}\right)^2$$

$$P = SE(Z - 1)$$

In practice, the chosen minimum wall thickness for the design must take into account the minimum thickness specified in clause UG–16(b), 1/16 inch (1.5 mm) in most cases, as well as mill tolerance and corrosion allowance. Plate specifications such as ASTM A-516 do not usually permit under tolerance on thickness.

Once the basic cylindrical shell is defined, heads must be added to close the pressure envelope. Heads can be spherical, elliptical, or torispherical in form. They can be designed using a spherical shell calculation with suitable modifications to allow for changes in geometry from the true sphere. The design equations are again based on thin shell theory.

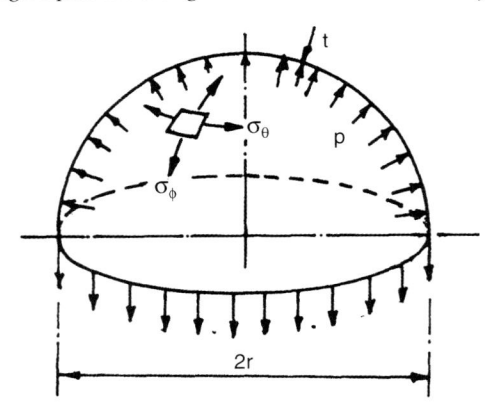

The stress in a thin sphere of mean radius r and thickness t under internal pressure p is given by

$$\sigma_\theta = \frac{pr}{2t}$$

Rearranging this equation to give the required thickness e for a shell of 'inside' diameter D_i with design stress f gives the following equation in PD 5500 format:

$$e = \frac{pD_i}{4f - p}$$

In PD 5500, the equations are approximately based on Lamé equations and incorporate a safety factor, which means that the pressure term has a multiplier. These equations have the following form:

$$e = \frac{pD_i}{4f - 1.2p} \quad \text{or} \quad e = \frac{pD_o}{4f + 0.8p}$$

The equations in ASME VIII Division 1 are given in clause UG-27 and Appendix 1-1. When the thickness does not exceed $0.356R$ or P does not exceed $0.665SE$, the minimum required thickness t for pressure loading is obtained from clause UG-27(d) for vessels with a known inside radius R or from Appendix 1, clauses 1-1(a)(2) for vessels with a known outside radius R_o.

$$t = \frac{PR}{2SE - 0.2P} \quad \text{or} \quad t = \frac{PR_o}{2SE + 0.8P}$$

The MAWP is given by

$$P = \frac{2SE\,t}{R + 0.2t} \quad \text{or} \quad P = \frac{2SE\,t}{R_o - 0.8t}$$

For 'thick spherical shells', where the limitations on thickness or pressure given in clause UG–27(d) are exceeded, the equations in Appendixes 1–3 must be used. The results are very close to those obtained using the Lamé equations.

When the thickness exceeds $0.356R$ or P exceeds $0.665SE$

$$t = R\left(\exp\left[\frac{0.5P}{SE}\right] - 1\right) \quad \text{or} \quad t = R_o\left(1 - \exp\left[\frac{-0.5P}{SE}\right]\right)$$

The MAWP is given by

$$P = 2SE \log_e\left(\frac{R + t}{R}\right) \quad \text{or} \quad P = 2SE \log_e\left(\frac{R_o}{R_o - t}\right)$$

Note that the above equations for t and P may be used *in lieu* of those given in UG-27(d).

4.05.3.1.3 Dished ends

When considering pressure containment, the ideal shape or form for the shell is spherical. Therefore, when designing end closures, a hemisphere would be the obvious choice, especially if the vessels were subjected to a high internal pressure. However, fabrication of hemispherical ends (and indeed, spherical vessels) is expensive, normally using a labor-intensive cap and petal method. The most commonly used closures for pressure vessels are torispherical and ellipsoidal dished ends. Ellipsoidal ends are usually specified as 2:1 (the ratio of major to minor axes), but other ratios may also be used (1.8:1 is commonly used in some European countries).

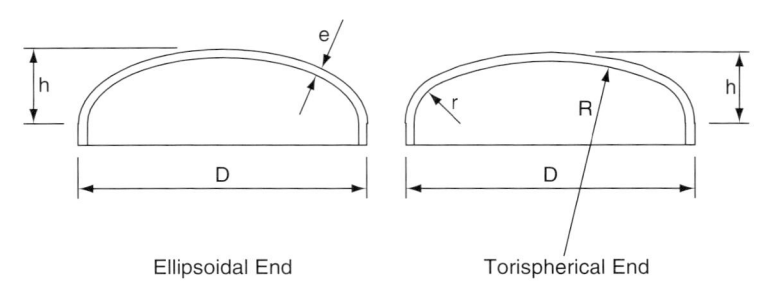

Ellipsoidal End   Torispherical End

A torispherical end consists of a spherical portion (the crown) and a toroidal portion (the knuckle). This type of end is normally made from a disk, which is held at the center and spun and cold-formed into the desired shape. Torispherical ends generally have a crown radius of between 80% and 100% of the shell diameter and a knuckle radius of between 6% and 15% of the diameter. These ratios vary depending on the individual requirement. In PD 5500, torispherical ends are designed as equivalent ellipsoidal ends. In ASME VIII Division 1, separate equations are given for torispherical and ellipsoidal ends.

4.05.3.1.4 Nozzles and openings

Openings are required in pressure vessels to provide access to the vessel shell. Although most openings provide a means for the contents to enter and exit the shell, access can also be required as part of the process or service inspection. Openings can take the form of nozzles, sight glasses, handholes, and manways as well as even larger openings such as entry holes for large mechanical devices. Openings are normally circular or partially elliptical, although some sight glasses can produce rectangular openings.

When an opening is present in a vessel, it produces enhanced stresses around the hole due to the discontinuity and it is therefore a potential weakness. Material can be added around the hole to recover the strength of the vessel. When performing nozzle calculations, the basic objective is to select and provide suitable reinforcing to ensure adequate strength for the design loadings, which may comprise the pressure loading plus some additional mechanical loading.

The traditional way of performing nozzle reinforcing calculations for an opening or nozzle is to provide material near the hole in excess of the required thickness for pressure loading. It has been found from experience that for a section through the shell at the center of the opening, the cross-sectional area of the additional material must be at least equal to the area removed by cutting the hole in a shell of minimum thickness required for pressure. This design approach, known as the 'area-replacement method', is used by ASME VIII Division 1 and by a number of European codes.

In the area-replacement method, a section of the shell within a specified 'limit of reinforcement' is considered. The increased stress due to the opening is assumed to be uniformly distributed across the area of the shell plus the area of any additional reinforcing element within the limit of reinforcement, including the nozzle neck up to a specified distance from the outside of the shell. To prevent this increased stress from exceeding the allowable limits, the total cross-sectional area available must not be less than the cross-sectional area of the 'unpierced' shell within the limits of reinforcement, multiplied by the ratio of the stress in the unpierced shell to the allowable stress. The area available is the cross-sectional area of the shell (excluding the area of the opening) plus the nozzle and additional reinforcing element (such as a pad) within the limits of reinforcement.

4.05.3.2 Composite Vessels

Composite materials have characteristics that are often very different from those of more conventional engineering materials. As such, composite materials are becoming useful in a great number of industrial applications. For example, they are used in the chemical industry, where pipes, tanks, pressure vessels, and storage vessels are being manufactured from fiber-reinforced composites. Often, it has been the case that these materials offer direct replacement of traditional metallic materials.

Composite materials commonly used within the hydrogen industry are carbon or glass fiber-reinforced plastic (CFRP or GRP), where both weight and corrosion resistance are influential factors. Composite pressure vessels are generally lightweight, being one-fifth the weight of steel and half the weight of aluminum.

Composite vessels (GRP) having near-isotropic properties can be constructed by suspending a chopped strand mat (CSM) fiber matrix in a suitable polymer resin. Orthotropic properties are normal for a laminated construction. (An orthotropic material has properties that are different in three mutually perpendicular directions at a point in the body and it has three mutually perpendicular planes of symmetry. Thus, the properties are a function of orientation at a point in the body.) When considering glass reinforcement, the matrix constituents can also comprise directional filament winding (FW) or woven roving (WR) produced from a weave of long fibers. The properties of a composite material can thus be tailored to suit the intended application, by varying laminate thickness and the orientation and constituents of the individual lamina.

Although vertical GRP vessels are widely used, the vessels considered here for hydrogen are principally designed for horizontal application. Generally, horizontal vessels are employed where there is a restriction in height or when there is modest operating pressure. Traditionally, horizontal, cylindrical vessels are supported by two supports located symmetrically about the mid-span of the vessel. These systems have proved to be very efficient in the support of the traditional metallic vessels. However, when the vessel is fabricated from GRP, the manufacturing processes often produce outer surface irregularities. For large GRP vessels, twin supports, symmetrically placed, are also preferred, thus avoiding the transference of load, which occurs if differential settlement takes place in a multiple-support system.

Composite vessels are designed based on the allowable failure strain rather than the stress-based limitation as found in metallic vessels, which is typically two-thirds of the elastic yield strength of the material. For GRP systems, a 2000 microstrain limit is applied, which is increased to 2500 for exceptional loads and test conditions. For CFRP systems, this is much higher, set at 4000 microstrain and usually in the compressive failure mode.

4.05.3.2.1 Composite vessels for hydrogen storage

Modern high-pressure hydrogen storage tanks can be significantly more complex in their design. Tanks can be made up of several layers, each performing a specific function in the overall integrity of the system. A multilayer sandwich style vessel may have an impact-resistant outer shell that provides resistance to damage and impact. In addition, the domed end of the vessel can have a foam covering, again for impact protection. Thereafter, a carbon fiber composite shell supports the main structural pressure loading, and a high-molecular-weight polymer lining can be added to serve as a gas permeation barrier. The system is completed with the addition of a nozzle, providing access for an in-tank regulator which measures the pressure and temperature via a sensor.

Although these vessels can be and are being made at present, there remain a number of technical challenges that need to be addressed before large volumes of low-cost equipment can be employed in the industry. From a cost basis, the carbon fiber accounts for 40–80% of the total cost of a CFRP tank. Development of a low-cost carbon fiber will facilitate greater use and deployability. The use of improved sensor technology to provide 'intelligent' structures will lead to improved weight efficiency and costs. The design burst criteria can therefore be reduced by 25% by reducing the burst ratio factor from 2.35 to 1.8. In addition, reducing the temperature even further can increase the energy density of the fuel.

4.05.4 Codes and Standards and Best Practices

All hydrogen pressurized vessels, components, devices, apparatus, and/or systems should always be designed, manufactured, installed, commissioned, operated, and maintained (at regular intervals) as certified in accordance with local and international applicable codes and standards. This section provides a short review of a number of codes and standards for compressed hydrogen tanks and connectors including joints and fittings, as well as a discussion on some of the best practices. After reading this section, the reader shall be able to define some of the most common codes and standards for hydrogen storage, connectors, and piping as well as the most frequent practices including some basic safety requirements.

4.05.4.1 Storage Tanks

There are many issues that need particular attention when designing a hydrogen storage system. One of the most common and well-recognized issues is 'hydrogen embrittlement'. Hydrogen embrittlement is the process by which various metals become brittle and fracture following exposure to hydrogen. Nowadays, many codes and standards exist to reduce the embrittlement issue and other well-documented problems when storing hydrogen. These codes and standards can be divided into the following three categories:

- stationary storage systems codes and standards based on PED;
- mobile storage systems codes and standards based on Transport Pressure Equipment Directive (TPED);
- liquid hydrogen codes and standards.

The above three categories of codes and standards agree that the selection of appropriate materials is key to the successful design and manufacture of long-lasting hydrogen storage tanks (with sometimes low to no embrittlement potential). To select the most appropriate material for use, the designer of a pressurized hydrogen storage tank, and associated piping systems, must focus on hydrogen interaction with materials used. It is also important to understand that certain techniques used for finalizing the surface of a hydrogen tank can result in hydrogen moving into the crystalline structure of the materials. Hence, these techniques can accelerate deterioration of the material through the phenomenon of hydrogen embrittlement.

The most common materials used for designing and manufacturing hydrogen storage tanks include copper, copper alloys, aluminum alloys, and the well-known stainless steels (the 316 type). A combination of aluminum and carbon fiber has recently been used. It is important to note that nickel and nickel alloys must not be utilized due to their high hydrogen embrittlement potentials. Similarly, cast iron-type piping and storage mechanism must not be used with hydrogen.

4.05.4.1.1 Gas storage systems and cylinders best practice

Good engineering practice dictates that a good project is one that has been well documented. This is also true for hydrogen storage mechanisms whereby documentation for each cylinder installed in the field should consist of a short description of the cylinder, the main list of drawings, and, most importantly, the most recent inspection results with the responsible person's name and a contact phone number for emergency.

It is of critical importance that any hydrogen system must have a naming plate displaying 'hydrogen gas pressure cylinders in use' or a similar inscription such as 'pure hydrogen' to

1. allow anyone not involved in the installed hydrogen storage system to know that there is high-pressure gas available in the vicinity,
2. promote safety,
3. remove any potential confusion during operation and an emergency.

Figure 1 illustrates a set of hydrogen cylinders with a printed inscription on the cylinder.

The display of the nameplate is very significant during any emergency situation where the firemen or any other emergency services will be able to define the risks and dangers by seeing the plate. A common best practice is to display on-site a set of signs showing the following:

- No Smoking
- No Naked Flames
- High-Pressure Cylinders
- Hydrogen Gas
- Keep Out
- A clear emergency phone number

Figure 2 shows a typical example of a sign that needs to be displayed on a hydrogen site.

Any container that is designed and manufactured to contain pressurized gas must be marked with its corresponding code and standard. In other words, when you want to manufacture a pressurized container, you must first select your code and standard. Then you manufacture the container strictly following the code and standard. Finally you must display the code and standard on the container. There are two common methods to display the code and standard; either by stamping the code and standard on the cylinder itself or a nameplate is attached to it. Figure 3 illustrates a sample of a cylinder nameplate summarizing its corresponding code and standard with other information. The cylinders must be tagged with their certificate(s) for use and any special instruction. Documentation should also be understood by the end user, and if necessary, the end user shall be appropriately trained. To avoid any confusion, cylinders must have permanent stamped inscriptions (stamped into the cylinder or tank body) or plates

Figure 1 An example of an inscription on cylinders.

Figure 2 An example of a sign displayed on a hydrogen site.

permanently fastened. In addition, when the cylinders are empty, they should be labeled so. **Figure 4** shows a cylinder with its permanent inscription. The cylinder is used for calibration purposes and its content is hydrogen in air.

Stationary storage systems must be installed on noncombustible supports, and if paint is used, this should comply with fire-retardant requirements. Any hydrogen cylinders and associated storage system must be located outside in a well-ventilated area at a safe distance from any structures. Country-tailored authorized safe distance should be checked, as this will be dependent on storage pressures, volumes, and nearby building and structure types.

If hydrogen cylinders are used indoors (not recommended under normal circumstances), then one must follow a full risk assessment procedure and ensure that implementation is in accordance with local applicable standards. For example, one shall use the Dangerous Substances & Explosive Atmospheres Regulations 2002 in the United Kingdom.

When using compressed gas cylinders (such as the B-type or K-type hydrogen cylinders), these cylinders must be secured and stored vertically (using a restraint to avoid the cylinders being knocked over) in a well-ventilated area, preferably outdoors. The area should be cool (say in a shaded location). A shaded and cool area will avoid an increase in the internal pressure of the cylinder under excessive heat exposure. It is commonly known that when hydrogen cylinders are exposed to heat, such as with direct exposure to sunshine rays, the hydrogen gas will expand and the internal pressure of the cylinder will increase. **Figure 5** illustrates cylinders being secured vertically.

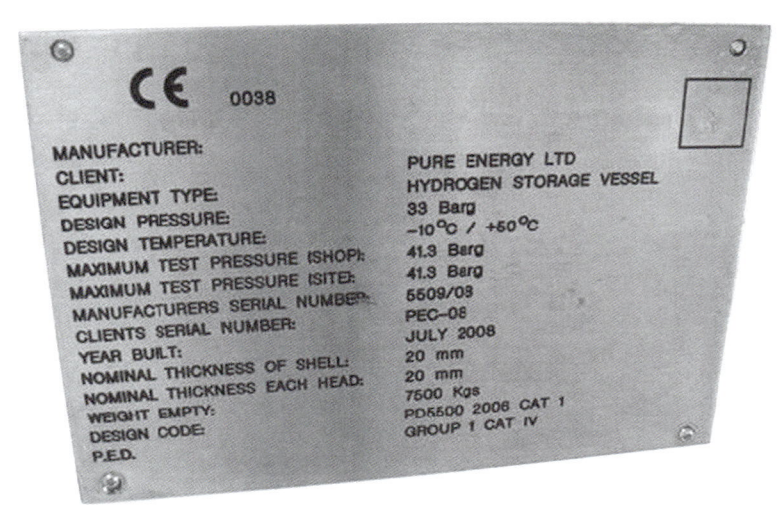

Figure 3 A hydrogen cylinder marked with its code and standard.

Figure 4 A permanent stamped inscription on a cylinder.

Figure 5 Cylinders secured vertically and an example of cylinders not secured.

Figure 6 A fencing system for storage of cylinders.

One should aim to locate the cylinders in a restricted access area (using appropriate fencing and security systems) far away from any emergency or normal exits. **Figure 6** shows an example of a fencing system used for hydrogen (red tank) and nitrogen storage (gray bottle).

The area where the cylinders are located must be free of any combustible materials. One should also avoid installing hydrogen cylinders nearby corrosive substances, highly salted environments (if at all possible), or highly wet surroundings to maintain the integrity of the cylinder to its maximum. Installing cylinders in a dry area without corrosive substance will reduce early corrosion and premature rust. Cylinders must be protected from rolling, dragging, and/or dropping. The preferred method for moving single cylinders is to use two-wheeler hand-type trailers (**Figure 7**).

4.05.4.2 Connectors – Joints and Fittings for Hydrogen

There are many different standards for joints and fittings for hydrogen. In essence, these standards together highlight the following best practices:

1. All joints and fittings must be checked for suitability for hydrogen usage prior to installation in the field and specifically dimensioned and selected for the particular operating conditions. Hydrogen fittings mostly used by the industry are the stainless steel typ. 316. **Figure 8** illustrates a compression fitting.
2. Joints and fittings have inherent hydrogen leaking potentials if not fixed appropriately. Thus, codes and standards always prefer to highlight welding pipes at joints point as the favored option instead of using mechanical compression joints. Properly welded joints can provide a superior safety margin to prevent hydrogen leaks when compared with other mechanical joints. **Figure 9** illustrates a welded joint, whereas **Figure 10** shows hydrogen fitting joints.
3. Joints and fittings (such as compression/flange/screw type and others) other than welded-type joints are generally accepted by codes and standards. In the case that nonwelded joints and fittings are used, then appropriate and demonstrable procedures must be put in place to ascertain and guarantee that leak testing is performed regularly. When nonwelded joints are used, one must ensure that at installation time each individual joint and fitting has been installed accurately. Means such as regular training should also be provided for correct hydrogen leak testing. Supervised inspection must be performed prior to an installation being launched. **Figure 11** illustrates two bad joints after leak testing. This is shown by the bubble. The leak testing was carried out

Figure 7 A two-wheeler trailer for moving cylinders.

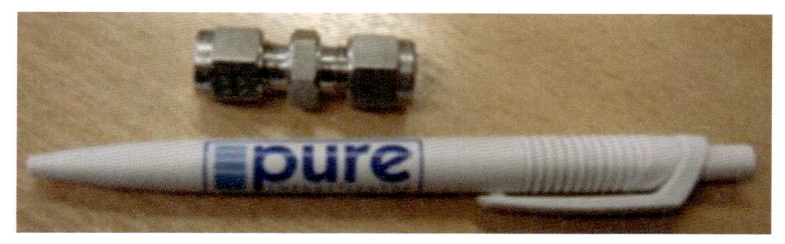

Figure 8 A 316 SS compression fitting.

Figure 9 A hydrogen welded joint.

using a soapy substance, hence the bubble. The joints are of threaded type, which have a higher incidence of hydrogen leakage as described below.

4. For more than obvious reasons, the fewer the mechanical fittings and joints, the better the hydrogen system. The fundamental nature of hydrogen, being the lightest gas, means that the fewer the joints, the less potential leakage will be available. Also, the fewer the joints, the lower the maintenance cost for testing.

Figure 10 Hydrogen threaded fitting joints.

Figure 11 An example of bad joints.

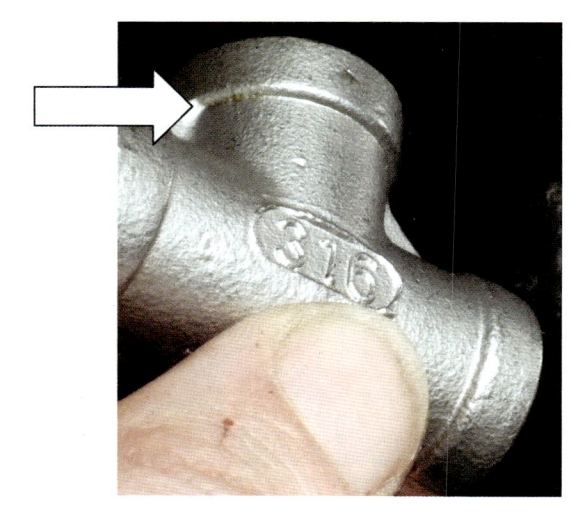

Figure 12 A crack on a hydrogen fitting.

5. One shall not wrongly assume that a joint or fitting is tight. Each individual joint or fitting shall be treated suspiciously as loose during installation and testing, reducing considerably the risk of failure. This is a common error when one becomes acquainted with a system; hence, the level of vigilance drops. Continuous training and warning of potential bad practice as well as good procedure shall be put in place to reduce the likelihood of leaks. Overtightening is also a common issue with installations and can be the cause of cracks on joints and fittings. **Figure 12** illustrates such a crack on a fitting. The cracking is very minor and can

hardly be seen in the figure. However, hydrogen can leak from this cracking and therefore the threaded joint fitting must be replaced.
6. Leaks, even the smallest leak, shall be avoided at all cost. If a small leak is lit at a given fitting or joint, it could lead to a snowball effect. The small leak will become larger, hence releasing more hydrogen with potential for significant damage. Therefore, a strong preventive action and procedural system is preferable when using hydrogen gas.
7. The well-known 'soft' soldering methods used by plumbers and others shall not be permitted for hydrogen fittings and joints. The low melting point of the soft soldering technique can lead to an earlier embrittlement under compression and with cryogenic applications.

In summary, there are a large number of joints and fittings that can be used with hydrogen gas. Some of the most common are brazing fittings, socket welding fittings, and butt welding fittings such as elbow, reducer, tee, and cross and caps tee. Compression equipment are some of the most commonly used fittings by the industry. One should not use compression fittings when installing a highly cyclical compression system. A hydrogen system subjected to high compression cycles will lead to high stresses on each compression fitting. This will lead to expansion and contraction cycles of the fittings, hence leading to premature potential leakages.

There are mainly two common removable joints. These are flanged and unions. When using flanged or unions, gaskets must be selected with a fire-resistant property. Leaks in unions are higher than when using flanged. Therefore, one shall try and avoid using unions if at all possible. Threaded fittings are also widely used by the hydrogen industry. It is known that the frequency of leaks when using threaded joints is higher than when using other fittings. Therefore, threaded fittings should not be used when leaks are not tolerable (most of the cases with hydrogen systems).

4.05.4.3 Auxiliary Equipment

There are many different standards that support the design, manufacture, and installation of auxiliary hydrogen equipment such as relief valves, gauges, and others. These standards highlight the following best practices:

- All auxiliary equipment must be checked for suitability for hydrogen use. **Figure 13** illustrates a hydrogen valve and **Figure 14** shows a hydrogen gauge.
- All auxiliary equipment shall also be checked for the specific operating conditions such as for outside use (all weather-type gauges and relief valves) or inside use only.
- One must be careful when selecting valves as they often use internal/external components made from materials that are different from those used to make the body of the valve. A good example is a valve made of SS316 externally but uses martensitic SS internally. Martensitic SS is known to be incompatible with hydrogen and therefore must not be used in association with hydrogen. Careful attention should always be given when opting for a valve, with the selected product clearly identifying the type of material used inside, commonly referred to as the 'wetted parts'.
- Of importance, one shall understand the different types of end fittings available for each valve and gauge. When selecting a valve or gauge, careful consideration shall be given to any seal to be used at the end of the device (compression fitting or screw-type fitting, etc.).

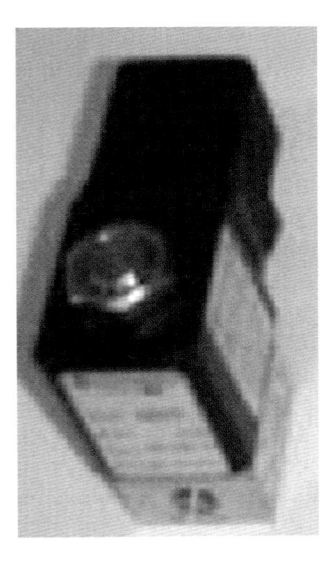

Figure 13 A hydrogen valve.

Figure 14 Two hydrogen gauges.

Figure 15 A pneumatic valve.

- One of the most important best practices used by the hydrogen industry is to use pneumatic control valves. Pneumatically controlled valves can provide an intrinsic safety ensuring that there are no potential ignition sources created by the valve actuator. **Figure 15** illustrates a pneumatic valve.
- The most commonly used valves are known as ball valves. They are preferred due to high tightness against hydrogen leaks. Also the vast majority of ball valves are available and manufactured using fire-resistant sealing materials. **Figure 16** illustrates a ball valve.

4.05.4.4 Basic Safety Requirements When Installing Hydrogen Systems

When installing hydrogen production, compression, storage, transportation, distribution, piping, consuming, and other hydrogen equipment, designers and operators should always adhere to or exceed local codes and standards of the country. If these are not

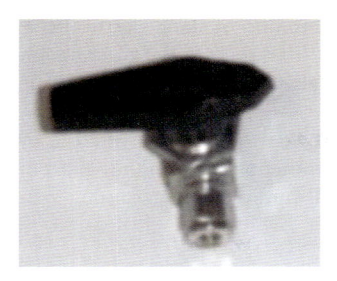

Figure 16 An example of a ball valve.

available, then one should use well-recognized standards such as ISO, CENELEC, IEC, CEN, TUV, EN, BSi, European Industrial Gas Association (EIGA), CGA, NFPA, ASME, and others. In addition to conformance to these codes and standards including local guidelines, a number of additional measures must be followed and implemented to minimize the risk of operator injury and plant failure. Some of the additional measures that can be undertaken when installing/using hydrogen piping and storage systems are described below.

4.05.4.4.1 Training
Of critical importance is the requirement for training the workforce on the safe use of hydrogen storage/piping and training the staff on the design and materials to be used with hydrogen system as well as hydrogen installation issues. **Figure 17** illustrates a group of trainees attending a hydrogen training course.

4.05.4.4.2 Local authorities
In case one designs and installs hydrogen storage/piping, it is important to inform local authorities/municipality/council or other form of public authority of the respective area. At the outmost significance, one shall inform the fire brigade, the police, and rescue services of the installation. One should also aim at providing the rescue services with a leaflet informing them of the dangers/risks with hydrogen technologies. Of importance, one shall provide the authorities with the properties of hydrogen that inherently make it somehow safe. The most important property of hydrogen is that it is extremely light and goes up if leaked. Therefore, one should design and install hydrogen storage and piping systems with this property in mind.

4.05.4.4.3 Electrical grounding
One subject, if designed and implemented incorrectly, that could cause major damage to an installation is the issue of grounding and bonding. As hydrogen is usually stored in steel-based cylinders and all piping, valves, and others are manufactured using a derivative of steel, it is critical that all devices are equipotentially bonded together.

Figure 17 A group of trainees attending a hydrogen training course.

Bonding alone is not enough to prevent the buildup of static electrical charges. The complete bonded hydrogen equipment system must also be connected to zero potential with respect to the ground. This removes the potential for gas ignition from stray static electricity within the hydrogen system. It is also important to regularly check the integrity of the bonding and grounding by using approved process and procedures.

Only a single point of system earthing must exist on any site where a hydrogen production and storage system is to be installed (multiple earthing points without equipotential cross bond, and bond service access is unacceptable). If an earthing system consists of multiple earth electrodes and multiple storage/piping systems, the following should be implemented as a minimum:

- Connection between different earth spikes, within the same building area, should be done directly using an appropriately specified copper conductor installed underground and in contact with ground.
- Connection between spikes should be done using a circular ring so that the failure of one connection does not significantly affect the overall earth connection continuity.
- Any test links should be connected directly to the spikes as above.
- To avoid potential misunderstanding, the cross-sectional area of the wire should be indicated in square millimeters.
- All equipotential earth bonds must be directly connected between points of termination and must not be 'daisy-chained'.
- All new or additional equipment to the system must be fitted with equipotential bonds directly to the same single point of system earth.
- All equipotential bonds must have a measured impedance of less than 1 Ω between points of termination on equipment and main system earth.
- Full equipotential bonding and earthing test certificates must be provided by the customer prior to any on-site installation and commissioning works can begin. Installers of hydrogen storage and piping systems must not allow the usage of their installations till proper, verified earthing test certificates are provided. Of most importance, any hydrogen storage and piping system installer shall be given the chance to visualize the ohmic resistance of the system installed prior to allowing the system to operate.
- All equipotential bonding and electrical supply installation must be compliant with the latest edition, for instance, of the BS7671 wiring regulations (or equivalent).

Figure 18 illustrates the equipotential bond of a hydrogen system which shall be less than 1 Ω between all equipment. Piping and other equipment are not shown in the figure, but shall similarly be bonded and earthed. **Figure 19** illustrates what can happen when a hydrogen installation has two different earthing systems without cross-bonding between each system. From **Figure 19**, one can clearly see the potential damages that a badly bonded system could be subjected to. A sparking event between a joint and a pipe has led the pipe to completely fracture and a joint to melt. The result of a bad bonding shown in **Figure 19** has been performed under a safe laboratory test and it is advisable not to perform such test.

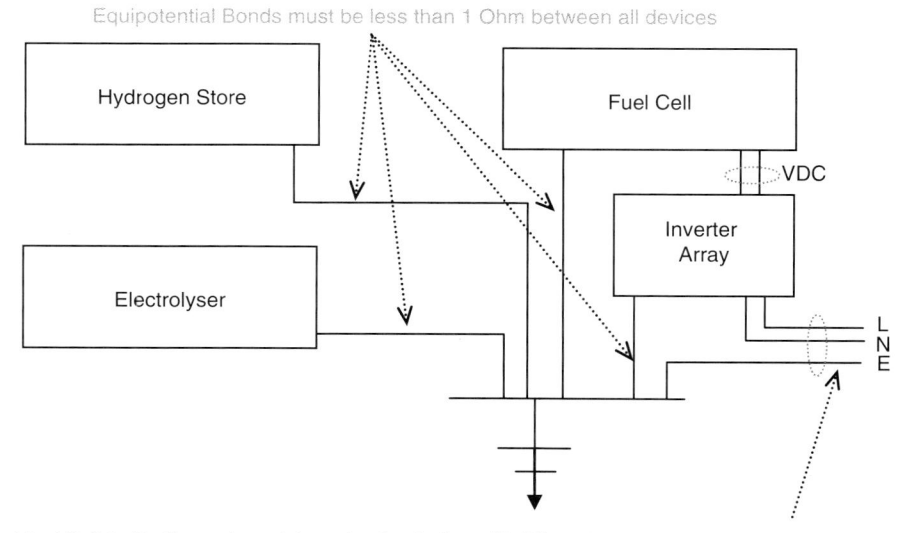

Figure 18 Example of an equipotential bonds system.

Figure 19 Laboratory test result illustrating the outcome of a badly bonded system.

4.05.4.4.4 Gas contamination monitoring

To increase the safety margin, one should consider the use of analytical instrumentation when producing or using hydrogen. Instrumentation devices are, in essence, used to monitor the content of oxygen (O_2) in hydrogen (H_2) in parts per million (ppm). The monitoring measurement output, that is, how much O_2 is in H_2, operates in conjunction with a safety control circuitry to avoid the presence of O_2 in H_2.

If the presence of O_2 in H_2 is detected by the control circuitry and reaches a preset safety level, the complete hydrogen system must be shut down. In addition, it is common to purge all pipe work and the system with an inert gas such as nitrogen prior to operation. The purging allows the removal of air (which includes oxygen), hence avoiding any potential for explosion, ignition, and other actions. **Figure 20** illustrates a gas monitoring device as found in an electrolysis system.

4.05.4.5 Codes and Standards

A large number of standards exist for the design, manufacture, installation, and operation of piping, storage systems, and other hydrogen auxiliary equipment. Some of the most used standards are given below with their main use and application remit.

Figure 20 A gas monitoring device.

Reference number	Description/title
Api Recommended Practice Seventh Edition, January 2008	Protection against ignitions arising out of static, lightning, and stray currents
CP-33	BCGA Code of Practice CP33 – The bulk storage of gaseous hydrogen at users' premises
L138	Dangerous Substances & Explosive Atmospheres Regulations 2002, Approved Code of Practice & Guidance
ISO 13984	1999 Liquid hydrogen – Land vehicle fuelling system interface
ISO 13985-1	Liquid Hydrogen – Land vehicle fuel tanks – Part 1: Design, fabrication, inspection and testing
ISO 13985-2	Liquid Hydrogen – Land vehicle fuel tanks – Part 2: Installation and maintenance
ISO 15869-3	Gaseous hydrogen and hydrogen blends – Land vehicle fuel tanks – Part 3: Particular requirements for hoop wrapped composite tanks with a metal liner
ISO 15869-4	Gaseous hydrogen and hydrogen blends – Land vehicle fuel tanks – Part 4: Particular requirements for fully wrapped composite tanks with a metal liner
ISO 15869-5	Gaseous hydrogen and hydrogen blends – Land vehicle fuel tanks – Part 5: Particular requirements for fully wrapped composite tanks with a non-metal liner
ISO/WD TR 15916	Basic considerations for the safety of hydrogen systems
ISO 11119-1	Gas cylinders of composite construction – Specification and test methods – Part 1: Hoop wrapped composite cylinders
ISO 11119-2	Gas cylinders of composite construction – Specification and test methods – Part 2: Fully wrapped fibre reinforced gas cylinders with load-sharing metal liners
ISO 11119-3	Gas cylinders of composite construction – Specification and test methods – Part 2: Fully wrapped fibre reinforced gas cylinders with non-load-sharing metal liners or non-metallic liners
EN 13445	European Standard, harmonized with the Pressure Equipment Directive (97/23/EC)
BS 5500	Former British Standard, replaced in the United Kingdom by BS EN 13445 but retained under the name PD 5500 for the design and construction of export equipment
AD-Merkblätter	German Standard, harmonized with the Pressure Equipment Directive
EN 286 (Parts 1–4)	European Standard for simple pressure vessels (air tanks), harmonized with Council Directive 87/404/EEC
BS 4994	Specification for design and construction of vessels and tanks in reinforced plastics
IS 2825-1969 (RE1977)	code_unfired_Pressure_vessels
FRP	Tanks and vessels
AIAA S-080-1998	AIAA Standard for Space Systems – Metallic pressure vessels, pressurized structures, and pressure components
AIAA S-081A-2006	AIAA Standard for Space Systems – Composite overwrapped pressure vessels (COPVs)
B51-09	Canadian Boiler, pressure vessel, and pressure piping code
NFPA 50	Standard for Gaseous Hydrogen Systems at Consumer Sites, 1999 edn – This standard is used when gaseous hydrogen is delivered to a consumer site and the hydrogen is produced outside the consumer site
NFPA 50 B	Standard for Liquefied Hydrogen Systems at Consumer Sites, 1999 edn – This standard is used when liquid hydrogen is delivered to a consumer site and the hydrogen is produced outside the consumer site

4.05.4.6 Case Studies

Two case studies are summarized in this section. The first case study describes some of the different steps taken to build a safe hydrogen storage system. The second case study illustrates the minimum requirements for a safe hydrogen system. Although there are many standards for the design and construction of hydrogen storage tanks and hydrogen systems, there are a couple of issues that the designer needs to attend to during the different stages of construction of a hydrogen storage system. The text below provides a snapshot of some of the stages involved in the design of a hydrogen tank and hydrogen installation.

4.05.4.6.1 Designing a hydrogen storage tank

A hydrogen storage tank was designed and built for the Hydrogen Office project. Some of the stages of the design process are described below, showing the most significant issues that the hydrogen tank designer has taken into account during the development process.

4.05.4.6.1(i) The hydrogen storage tank

A hydrogen storage tank was designed for the Hydrogen Office project. This tank has the following parameters:

- Storage size: 340 Nm^3
- Dimensions: 1.5 m diameter × 6 m long × 20 mm wall thickness
- Fixations: Two saddles

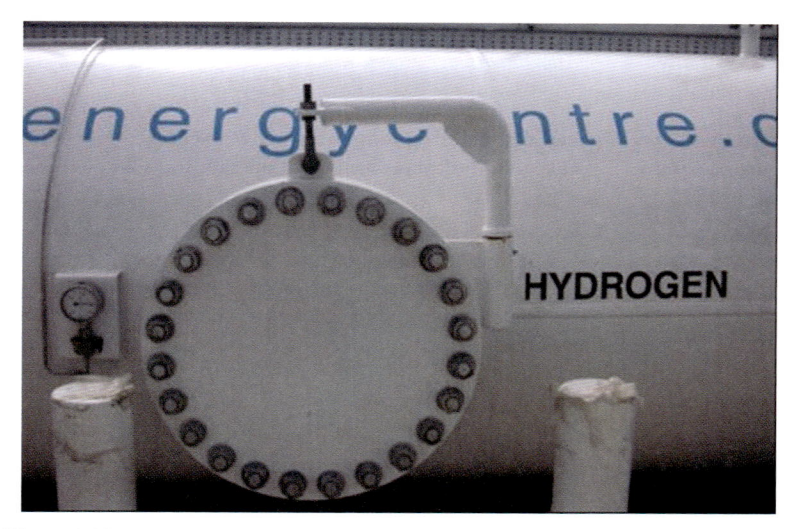

Figure 21 The Hydrogen Office tank 20″ manway.

A 20″ manway has been added for maintenance purposes with two pressure testing nozzles, two padeyes mounted on top of the tank (appropriately load tested), a vent outlet, a safety valve, and a pressure gauge to identify current pressure inside the tank. **Figure 21** illustrates the 20″ manway.

4.05.4.6.1(ii) Selection of the material
Many different types of materials were investigated for this project, from steel to aluminum-based materials. After looking at several options, the BS1501 224 490B LT50 was selected as appropriate.

4.05.4.6.1(iii) Welding integrity
The tank was designed using PED 5500 Cat 1 standard and manufactured using full penetration welds on all joints. These welds have all been 100% radiographic tested using appropriate processes and procedures.

4.05.4.6.1(iv) Internal embrittlement
As the issues with embrittlement are not yet resolved and how embrittlement happens is not yet well known and documented, substantial amount of time was taken to identify a method to reduce the effect of hydrogen on the BS1501 224 490B LT50 material. Some of the factors that can have an influence on the rate of embrittlement are hydrogen pressure, temperature of tank and hydrogen, metal composition, and moisture content of hydrogen. Other parameters were taken into account, although the most important are the ones highlighted above.

In terms of the hydrogen pressure, the hydrogen tank was designed and manufactured for sustaining a pressure of 1.5 times the rated used pressure. In other words, the tank has been manufactured to withstand almost 45 bar of pressure, and will only operate at 30 bar. The lower operating pressure allowed a strong safety margin for the tank and reduced the embrittlement effect from hydrogen pressurized gas.

Hydrogen temperature and the swing in temperature (between day and night) can have an effect on embrittlement. As the tank is installed in a cool country, the swing in temperature between high and low occurs very few times a year. Therefore, it was considered that swings in hydrogen temperature may not have a major effect on tank embrittlement.

The metal composition can lead to high embrittlement as described in Section 4.05.4.1. As such, nickel and nickel alloys were not considered for this project, and the selected metal is the BS1501 224 490B LT50. In addition to this, a stress-relieved manufacture of the tank was selected to comply with the UK Code of Practice, the CP33, the EIGA AISBL, and IGC Doc 15/06/E.

The moisture content of hydrogen can affect the tank in many different ways. It can increase the speed of rust formation inside the tank, reduce the integrity of the tank, and amplify the embrittlement factor. To reduce these issues, a specific internal paint coating can be applied to the tank, but this coating would require substantial amount of maintenance. Another solution is to reduce the moisture content of hydrogen to a maximum before the hydrogen is injected into the vessel. This is achieved using hydrogen driers, which dramatically limit the moisture content of hydrogen.

4.05.4.6.1(v) Warranty
Although the tank was manufactured by one single supplier, several different warranties have had to be deemed acceptable. The most important warranties that need to be identified and checked when designing and manufacturing a hydrogen tank are as follows:

- The vessel structure warranty
- The vessel external coating warranty
- The vessel internal coating warranty

In addition, the standard terms and conditions of the manufacturing company were checked for specific out of warranty clauses, which could have affected the use of the tank in certain locations or mode of operations.

4.05.4.6.1(vi)   Exterior painting

Although painting is thought as a trivial process for any tank manufacture, when used for hydrogen storage, it is important to understand how this phase will be performed. In this case, a fire-retardant painting was selected and a shot-blast painting method based on SA 2.5 standard was used. Two different paint coatings were applied to the tank: one of 150 µm thickness (primer-type coating) and the other of 50 µm thickness (finish-type coating).

4.05.4.6.1(vii)   Material thickness

Computational modeling tool is used as the main method for defining the thickness of a tank. In the present case, a 20 mm wall thickness of the tank was simulated and proven to withstand the hydrogen pressure. Proof of such computational operation must be requested from the computational team to complete the internal documentation.

4.05.4.6.1(viii)   Transportation

As the vessel was quite heavy, it was important to check how it will be transported and installed. The transportation of the tank took into account how to secure the tank on an articulated wagon, how to reduce stresses on the tank during its transport, how to unload the tank at site, and how to finally secure the tank when the vessel was unloaded from the truck. Specific procedures were produced to perform all of these actions.

4.05.4.6.1(ix)   Inspection and documentation

Several inspections must be performed during the manufacturing of the vessels. Radiographic testing must be performed, making sure that all of the welds have been checked. The tank shall also be inspected during internal and external coating and during compression testings. When inspections are finalized, the tank must be signed off by an authorized company signatory. At sign-off time, all certificates and manufacturing documentation as well as nameplates must be obtained.

4.05.4.6.1(x)   Retesting the tank

Under the PED 5500 standard, the hydrogen tank must be tested every 5 years for insurance purposes. One shall look into getting a prequotation for performing this test and the material and workmanship required for the test. This will allow the client to prepare a budget for such test, to keep the equipment operational for another 5 years. It is important to note that in a number of instances, stationary tanks are only tested once in every 10 years. **Figure 22** illustrates the Hydrogen Office tank as installed.

Figure 22   The Hydrogen Office tank as installed.

4.05.4.6.2 The Pure Project case study

In this case study, we will look into the proposed design of a hydrogen system. The system selected has been installed at the Pure Project site. The Pure Project design was specifically created to optimize the generation of hydrogen from wind and solar power using an electrolysis process. The design proposed during the development of the Pure Project took into account a number of unique technologies and codes and standards including

- A method to safely produce hydrogen
- The usage of some of the key hydrogen codes and standards
- A technique to directly and safely connect wind generation and a hydrogen production system, with no grid availability
- A piping and safety system that allows a safe shutdown of the hydrogen system in case of emergency
- A method to achieve high purity of hydrogen to reduce hydrogen embrittlement and rust inside hydrogen cylinders
- The safe integration of a water treatment for supplying a hydrogen electrolyzer
- The safe integration of a purging system to safely shut down the hydrogen process
- The safe integration of a cooling system

Figure 23 provides a graphical representation of the aims and objectives of the Pure Project. The Pure Project was developed in several stages and this is illustrated using a scheme of colors. The different stages of the project are as follows:

- *Stage 1*. Installation of wind generation, shown in orange color in **Figure 23**. The system was also designed with a solar system to be integrated at a later stage of the project.
- *Stage 2*. Hydrogen production system (Hypod®), which includes a high-pressure electrolysis unit (removing the need for a compression stage), a storage and fuel cell system, H_2 Genset, and control and monitoring system. This is shown in blue color in **Figure 23**. The Hypod® and compression unit have been surrounded by a blue dashed line to show that these two systems are in fact a single system at the Pure® project. Compressors are usually separated from the hydrogen production system.
- *Stage 3*. Development of a hydrogen internal combustion engine (H_2ICE) vehicle with a refueler. This is shown in green color in **Figure 23**.
- *Stage 4*. Development of a hydrogen fuel cell vehicle. This is shown in green color in **Figure 23**.
- *Stage 5*. Installation of a hydrogen cooking facility at the Pure Project building. This is shown in green color in **Figure 23**.

Some of the key design stages of the Pure Project are explained below. The selected stages are hydrogen system arrangement, safe enclosure, fuel cell vehicle, and fuel cell installation.

4.05.4.6.2(i) Hydrogen system arrangement

In the hydrogen system arrangement, all pipe work used for the safe delivery and transfer of hydrogen gas has been installed using high-grade 316 stainless steel (see Section 4.05.4.2). All terminations, valve bodies, fittings, and safety vents are also made of

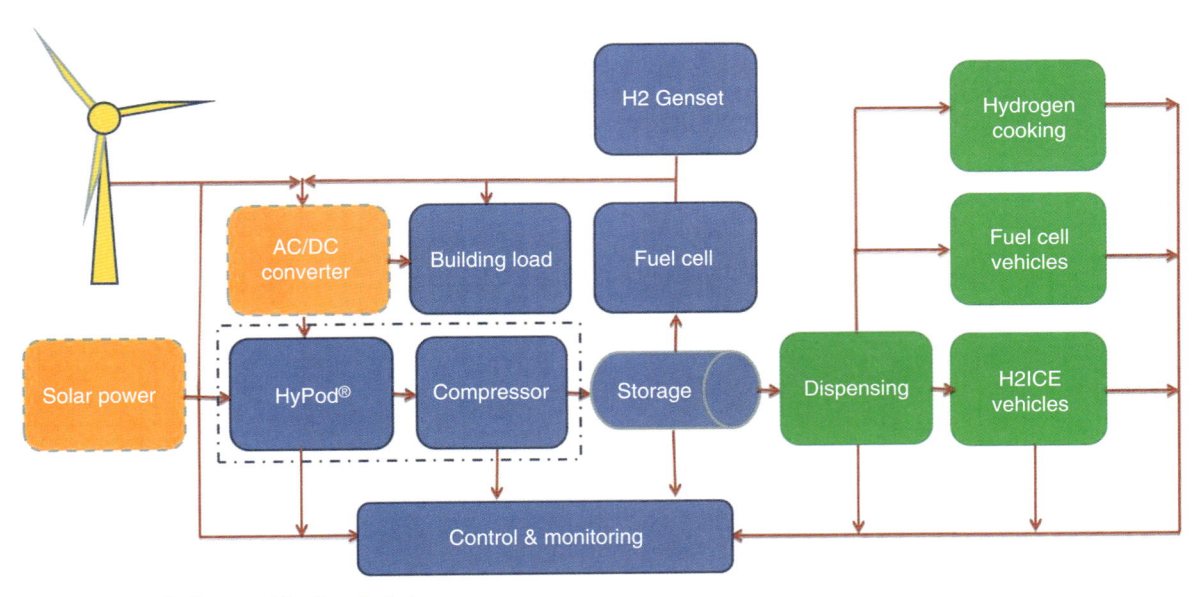

Figure 23 A schematic diagram of the Pure Project.

Figure 24 The H2SEED venting system as installed.

high-grade stainless steel and carry relevant certificates of conformity (as per section 1.3). The internal materials of the valves have been checked for material compliance, where specific attention was given to martensitic SS (see Section 4.05.4.3 – item 3).

As per the UK codes and standards, as much as guidelines, such as the HSE guidelines, all vent lines have been routed to a high level and away from any potential sources of ignition. An example of vent lines developed for the H2SEED project [xxx] can be seen in **Figure 24**.

Many sensors have been installed to provide monitoring information to the control systems. The aim is to detect any out-of-tolerance situation, to record this situation, and to ensure that a safe system shutdown is executed. **Figure 25** illustrates one such sensor installed and in operation at the Pure Project, which complies with all hydrogen safety requirements. The lighting system, which is compliant with ATEX, is also shown in **Figure 25**.

A site layout was designed for the Pure Project in line with the EIGA guidance. The design incorporated the required separation distances between air intakes and devices containing hydrogen. The layout proposed did make most efficient use of cabling and pipe works while providing the lowest risk distribution of gas around the site. This was achieved by localizing high-pressure gas compression and storage to one area of the layout for access by a forklift truck at a later date.

The proposed layout also enabled all electrical services to be distributed via a single subfloor/subground duct in line with the UK hydrogen guidelines. All gas services have been distributed at high level maintaining required separation from potential sources of ignition. **Figures 26** and **27** illustrate the subfloor duct and a distribution of hydrogen at high level.

To provide an additional layer of protection to the system, the design took into account the installation of a fencing system around the hydrogen tanks to protect them from any accidental impacts from vehicles or maintenance equipment. **Figure 28** illustrates the Hydrogen Yorkshire Forward project, where a fence was installed for holding the nitrogen tanks, and **Figure 29** shows a number of removable bollards at the same site.

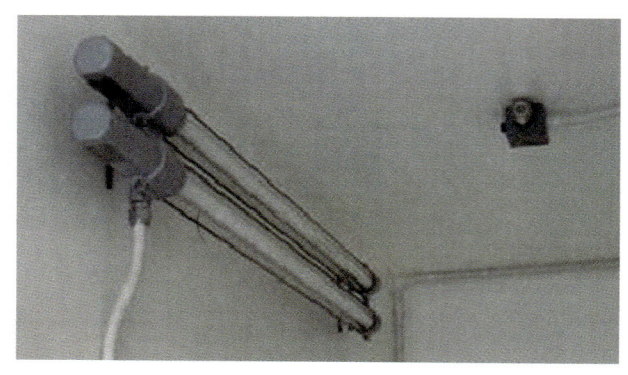

Figure 25 A sensor installed at the Pure Project.

Hydrogen Storage: Compressed Gas 133

Figure 26 Subfloor ducts.

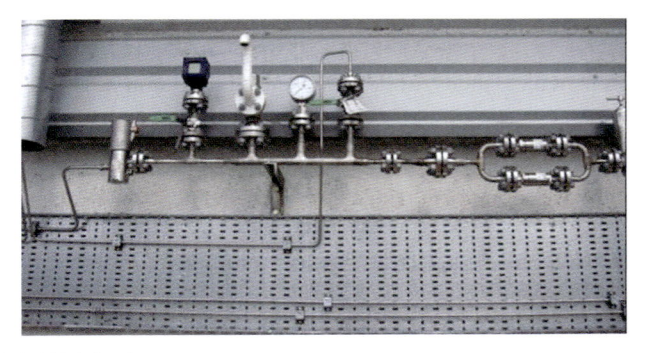

Figure 27 Hydrogen pipes distributed at high level.

Figure 28 Fencing system at the Yorkshire Forward hydrogen project.

Figure 29 Bollard system at the Yorkshire Forward hydrogen project.

4.05.4.6.2(ii) HyPOD® enclosure

A HyPod®, a Hydrogen Pod system, was designed and developed for the Pure Project. The HyPod® was divided into two parts: the process area and the control area. In the process area, a hydrogen electrolyzer and its process unit were installed. As per the UK standard and codes and guidelines, the process area has been developed to be compliant with ATEX (when required to be) to reduce risks associated with the production of hydrogen in an enclosed area. All interconnecting cabling between electrolyzer process and control have been designed with a floor/subfloor level philosophy (see Section 4.05.4.6.2(i)). **Figure 30** illustrates the process unit at Pure Project, with the Knoydart community representative attending a hydrogen training course standing in front.

The rationale for putting cablings at floor (or subfloor) level takes into account the properties of hydrogen, that is, hydrogen is lighter than air. Therefore, locating cables on the floor/subfloor allows reduction in ignition potentials as if there is a hydrogen leak, the hydrogen will move at a high point of the Hypod®, while the potential for ignition will be situated at the floor level. Hence, this design permits a substantial reduction in potential ignition sources coming into contact with hydrogen gas and reduces dramatically dangerous situations. During designing, it was also decided not to install any cable or service trays or ducts and others at high level within the container.

The plant room is designed with active and passive ventilation systems to dilute hydrogen in the event of a hydrogen leakage. Again, by providing this venting facility, a substantial reduction in the likelihood of any leak is achieved, a leak that could create an explosive atmosphere. **Figure 31** illustrates a passive ventilation available at the Hydrogen Office.

Figure 30 The process unit at the Pure Project.

Figure 31 Passive ventilation system.

Figure 32 Pure Energy® Centre Hypod® operating in extreme conditions.

A number of active hydrogen detection devices have been installed in all 'contained' areas to shut down production in the event of leak detection. These devices allow to audibly alert personnel and staff should a high hydrogen concentration atmosphere be detected. **Figure 32** shows the Hypod® operating in extreme conditions. One can visualize the passive ventilation on top of the Hypod®.

4.05.4.6.2(iii) Planning, HSE and SEPA

For the Pure Project and any other hydrogen projects, the installation was designed to comply with the CP33 from the British Compressed Gas Association. In relation to this standard, there were no real planning requirements apart from standard building requirements. Unless installation goes above the COMAH levels, which for hydrogen is 5 tonnes in stored mass, all installations have to comply with local planning permission for buildings and HSE guidelines as well as CP33. It is also important to disclose to SEPA any drainage and potential emissions with a hydrogen system.

In addition to the above, one shall contact the fire brigade and the police. Both entities have provided a number of improvements to the system.

References

[1] Warner MJ (2005) *Low Cost High Efficiency High Pressure Hydrogen Storage, DOE Review*. Irvine, CA: Quantum Technologies.
[2] H_2 Best Safety Practices. http://h2bestpractices.org (last accessed 12 December 2011).
[3] NFPA2, Hydrogen Technologies Code, 2011 Edition. National Fire Protection Association. http://www.nfpa.org/about the codes/ (last accessed 12 December 2011).
[4] Energy Efficiency and Renewable Energy. Fuel Cells Technology Program – Hydrogen Storage. US Department of Energy. http://www.hydrogenandfuelcells.energy.gov (January 2011).
[5] Introduction to Hydrogen for Code Officials. US Department of Energy Hydrogen Program. http://www.hydrogen.energy.gov/ (September 2011).
[6] Wilson JR and Burgh G (2008) *Energising our Future: Rational Choices for the 21st Century*. John Wiley and Sons Inc., Hoboken, New Jersey. ISBN: 978-0-471-79053-2.
[7] Spence J and Tooth AS (2001) *Pressure Vessel Design: Concepts and Principles*. E&F Spon, Boundary Row, London.
[8] Earland SW, Nash DH, and Garden W (2003, March) *Guide to European Pressure Equipment*. Hoboken, NJ: John Wiley and Sons Inc. ISBN: 1-86058-345-8.
[9] Rao KR (2008, Fall) *The Companion Guide to ASME Boiler and Pressure Vessel Code – Third Edition*. ASME Press, Three Park Avenue, New York.
[10] Aklil D, Johnson E, Gazey R, and Ortisi V (2011) The Hydrogen Office. http://www.pureenergycentre.com/pureenergycentre/Hydrogenofficecasestudy.pdf (last accessed 21 December 2011).
[11] Gazey R, Ali D, and Aklil D (2011) Evaluation of Hydrogen Office Wind/Hydrogen demonstration system using operational data and simulation tools. World Hydrogen Technology Convention, 14–16 September 2011.
[12] Aklil D, Johnson E, Gazey R, and Ortisi V (2011) Promoting Unst Renewable Energy (PURE) Project. From wind to green fuel. http://www.pureenergycentre.com/pureenergycentre/Pureprojectcasestudy.pdf (last accessed 21 December 2011).
[13] Gazey R, Salman SK, and Aklil-D'Halluin DD (2006) A field application experience of integrating hydrogen technology with wind power in a remote island location. Elsevier Power Sources Journal, POWER-D05-01096, February 2006.
[14] Angelis Y, Aklil D, Angelis D, Gazey R, and Johnson E (2007) The PURE Project. Fuel Cell Seminar, San Antonio, Texas.
[15] Fuel cells – Understand the Hazards, Control the Risks, 2004, ISBN 9780717627660. http://books.hse.gov.uk/hse/public/saleproduct.jsf?catalogueCode=9780717627660 (last accessed 21 December 2011).
[16] Aklil D, Johnson E, Gazey R, and Ortisi V (2011) The Creed Waste Treatment Plant and the H2SEED Project: from community household waste to green transport. http://www.pureenergycentre.com/pureenergycentre/H2SEEDcasestudy.pdf (last accessed 21 December 2011).
[17] MacIver RD, Goodhand R, Aklil-D'Halluin DD, and Monter M (2008) The H2SEED Project – early commercialization of H2 technologies for remote communities, Sacramento.

4.06 Hydrogen Storage: Liquid and Chemical

P Chen, Dalian Institute of Chemical Physics, Dalian, China

© 2012 Elsevier Ltd. All rights reserved.

4.06.1	Introduction	137
4.06.2	Physical Hydrogen Storage	137
4.06.3	Metal Hydrides	139
4.06.4	Chemical Hydrides	139
4.06.4.1	Ammonia Borane	140
4.06.4.1.1	Homogeneous catalytic dehydrogenation of AB	142
4.06.4.1.2	Solid-state dehydrogenation of AB	143
4.06.4.2	Amidoboranes and Derivatives	144
4.06.4.2.1	Alkali and alkaline earth amidoboranes	144
4.06.4.2.2	Derivatives	145
4.06.5	Complex Hydrides	147
4.06.5.1	Borohydrides	147
4.06.5.2	Amide–Hydride Systems	149
4.06.6	Pending Issues	153
References		154

4.06.1 Introduction

Hydrogen-based energy systems offer a potential solution to the ever-increasing demand for sustainable energy systems. Although over the long term, the ultimate technological challenge is large-scale hydrogen production from renewable sources, a critical practical issue is how to store hydrogen efficiently and safely, particularly for onboard hydrogen fuel cell vehicles [1]. Tremendous efforts have been devoted to the research and development of systems that can hold sufficient hydrogen in terms of gravimetric and volumetric densities to allow fuel cell vehicles to achieve a satisfactory driving range and in the meantime exhibit acceptable charging/discharging kinetics, safety, and cost (see Table 1) [2, 3].

Hydrogen can be stored by either physical or chemical means. For physical storage, the conventional options are compressed hydrogen gas and cryogenic adsorption, that is, liquid hydrogen. For chemical storage, the hydrogen molecule can be dissociated either homolytically or heterolytically and bonds with other elements to form hydrides. The hydrogen uptake and release can be either reversible or irreversible depending on the thermodynamic parameters of the corresponding starting and final materials. During the last decade of exploration and study, the scope of candidate hydrogen storage materials has expanded considerably, from conventional metal hydrides, such as $LaNi_5$ and MgH_2, to complex and chemical hydrides [3–7] and from activated carbon to carbon nanotubes and to metal organic frameworks (MOFs) [8–18]. The employment of advanced synthetic routes has also allowed the physical state of the storage materials to change from being bulk crystalline to amorphous and to nano structures [16, 19, 20]. Advanced theoretical simulations also have an increasing impact not only on the description of the physical properties of known materials but also on the prediction of novel structures and reaction paths [21–23]. A variety of promising storage systems are under intensive investigations. Systems of high hydrogen content are the focus of ongoing studies because they allow more space for material modification and optimization. A comprehensive survey by Thomas, Sandrock, and Bowman, as shown in **Figure 1**, lists over 40 material candidates that are being actively investigated. Among them, high surface area porous materials and nitrogen- and boron-containing hydrides are the most studied systems [24, 25]. In this chapter, a short survey on existing hydrogen storage techniques will be presented. Emphasis will be given to chemical and complex hydrides that have been under intensive research since 2005.

4.06.2 Physical Hydrogen Storage

Physical storage of hydrogen is normally achieved either under high pressure or at cryogenic temperatures. To store high-pressure hydrogen, a compressed hydrogen gas tank made of aluminum or composite materials wrapped with carbon or glass fiber to ensure light weight and high strength is used. The hydrogen energy stored in the compressed gas tank increases with an increase in pressure, but not in a directly proportional manner. Compressed hydrogen at 350–700 bar has been well developed and adopted in prototype fuel cell vehicles. The compression of H_2 will consume ~10–15% of the energy stored, and the size of the tank holding ~4 kg of H_2 is still too large to directly compare with a gasoline tank. There have been considerable efforts in the development of lightweight tanks to store hydrogen up to 1000 bar in recent years. Even with considerable progress, the tanks are somewhat too expensive (~$15 kWh^{-1}) to be practically viable [26]. A recent demonstration on storing compressed hydrogen at 77 K suggested an alternative method with improved characteristics especially in gravimetric and volumetric storage densities. It is, however, of practical importance to take a step forward in reducing the system cost and increasing the energy efficiency (**Table 2**).

Table 1 The vehicle performance targets

Storage parameter	Units	2010	2015	Ultimate
System gravimetric capacity	kWh kg^{-1}	1.5	1.8	2.5
	(kg H$_2$ kg^{-1})	(0.045)	(0.055)	(0.075)
System volumetric capacity	kWh l^{-1}	0.9	1.3	2.3
	(kg H$_2$ l^{-1})	(0.028)	(0.040)	(0.070)
Storage system cost	$ kWh^{-1}	4	2	TBD
	($ kg H$_2^{-1}$)	(133)	(67)	
Fuel cost	$ gge^{-1} at pump	2–3	2–3	2–3
Durability/operability				
Operating ambient temperature	°C	−30/50	−40/60	−40/60
Min/max delivery temperature	°C	−30/80	−40/85	−40/85
Cycle life (1/4 tank to full)	cycles	1000	1500	1500
Cycle life variation	% of mean at % confidence	90/90	99/90	99/90
Min H$_2$ delivery pressure	atm	4 FC/35 ICE	4 FC/35 ICE	2 FC/35 ICE
Max delivery pressure	atm	100	100	100
Charging/discharging rates				
System fill time (for 5 kg H$_2$)	min	4.2	3.3	2.5
	kg H$_2$ min^{-1}	(1.2)	(1.5)	(2.0)
Minimum full-flow rate	(g s^{-1}) kW^{-1}	0.02	0.02	0.02
Start time to full flow	s	5	5	5
Transient response (10% to 90%)	s	0.75	0.75	0.75
Fuel purity	%H$_2$	99.99 (dry basis)		
Environmental health and safety				
Permeation and leakage	scc h^{-1}	Meets or exceeds applicable standards		
Toxicity				
Safety				
Loss of usable H$_2$	(g h^{-1}) kg H$_2^{-1}$	0.1	0.05	0.05

Source: http://www.hydrogen.energy.gov/annual_review11_report.html

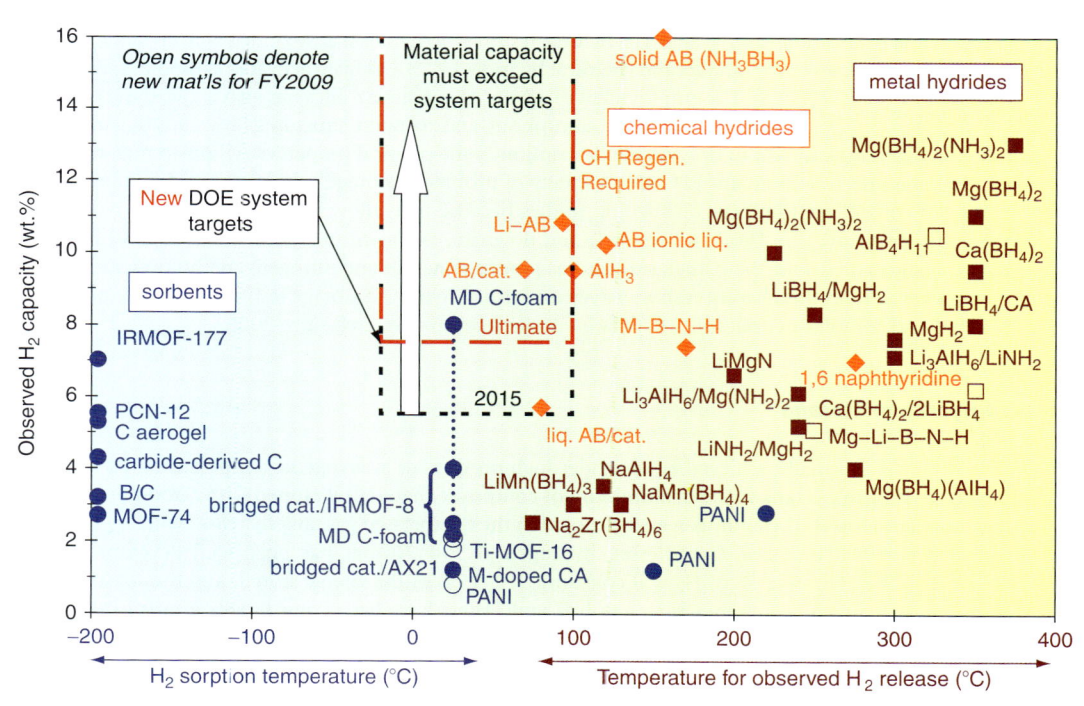

Figure 1 A survey of hydrogen storage materials. http://www.hydrogen.energy.gov/annual_review09_report.html.

Table 2 Parameters of compressed and liquid H₂ storage

Storage techniques	Storing energy (kJ kg^{-1})	Spent energy/ stored energy	Gravimetric energy content (MJ kg^{-1})	Volumetric energy content (MJ m^{-3})
Compressed H₂ (350 bar)	12 264	0.10	8.04	2492
Compressed H₂ (700 bar)	14 883	0.12	7.20	3599
Liquid H₂	42 600	0.36	16.81	3999

With reference to http://www.hydrogen.energy.gov/annual_review11_proceedings.html

Liquid hydrogen is another option to store hydrogen onboard. Comparatively, the energy density is nearly 2 times higher than that of the 700 bar compressed H$_2$; however, the energy cost to liquefy hydrogen reaches 30% or more of the actual hydrogen energy stored. There is also continual hydrogen loss when stored onboard (namely boil-off) due to thermal conduction, convection, and thermal radiation. One of the other drawbacks is the use of expensive multilayered vacuum superinsulated vessels. Another important practical issue is the 'cooling-down' losses during refilling of liquid hydrogen at gas stations. The entire transfer line between the liquid H$_2$ source and the vehicle tank system has to be cooled down to about −253.8 °C, and therefore, additional H$_2$ evaporation occurs. Clearly, these losses cannot be neglected and remain significant. There have been a few comprehensive reviews on compressed and liquid hydrogen published recently [26, 27], and the commercial employment of these techniques is still an open issue. However, currently, while most of the chemical storage systems to be discussed later remain at a research stage, compressed and liquid H$_2$ storage remain as choices for demonstration and evaluation purposes.

Porous materials are prone to adsorb hydrogen physically; however, due to the weak interaction of H$_2$ and sorbents, cryogenic conditions typically have to be applied. Materials with large surface areas and proper pore size of 2–3 nm are capable of adsorbing up to 7 wt.% of H$_2$ [12–14, 28, 29]. Representative sorbent materials include carbon materials [8–11, 30–32], MOFs [12, 16, 17, 33–35], and conjugated polymers [14]. A special note on hydrogen storage on MOFs was triggered by breakthroughs in material design and synthesis [12]. The interesting bonding nature of the metal and organic link creates a variety of pore structures and active centers, and the nature of the interaction of H$_2$ and the active centers has been a hot topic of study. It is obviously of scientific interest to further the research in this area; however, cryogenic adsorption in general is an energy-consuming process and has, in general, relatively low volumetric hydrogen storage density; hence, the remainder of this chapter will focus on alternative solid-state forms of H$_2$ storage.

4.06.3 Metal Hydrides

The homolytic dissociation of H$_2$ into atomic H followed by diffusion of the H in the lattice of metals, especially transition metals and alloys, leads to the formation of metal hydrides [2, 36]. Table 3 shows a list of conventional metal hydrides that have been extensively studied in the past. For example, the H content in terms of the volumetric hydrogen density of LaNi$_5$H$_6$ is 115 kg m^{-3}, which is higher than that of compressed hydrogen and liquid hydrogen. However, transition metals and their alloys have relatively low gravimetric hydrogen densities (normally < 3 wt.%). A recent work by Matsunaga et al. [37] on hybridizing metal hydrides with a high-pressure tank gives a certain level of promise for the improvement of gravimetric density. In addition to the search for new multicomponent metal alloys, current research also focuses on the reduction in size of Mg-based materials to enhance kinetics in dehydrogenation [16, 20].

4.06.4 Chemical Hydrides

There are a vast variety of natural and manmade chemical hydrides including H$_2$O, NH$_3$, alcohol, boranes, and hydrocarbons. The H–X (where X refers to O, N, B, C, etc.) bond is significantly stronger than that of a typical H–M bond of most of the interstitial metal hydrides [1–3]. Chemical hydrides that have been investigated for the purpose of hydrogen storage are mainly those

Table 3 Structure and hydrogen storage properties of typical metal hydrides

Type of metal hydrides	Metal	Hydrides	Structure	Mass% of hydrogen	P$_{eq}$, T
AB$_5$	LaNi$_5$	LaNi$_5$H$_6$	Hexagonal	1.4	2 bar, 298 K
AB$_3$	CaNi$_3$	CaNi$_3$H$_{4.4}$	Hexagonal	1.8	0.5 bar, 298 K
AB$_2$	ZrV$_2$	ZrV$_2$H$_{5.5}$	Hexagonal	3.0	10^{-8} bar, 323 K
AB	TiFe	TiFeH$_{1.8}$	Cubic	1.9	5 bar, 303 K
A$_2$B	Mg$_2$Ni	Mg$_2$NiH$_4$	Cubic	3.6	1 bar, 555 K

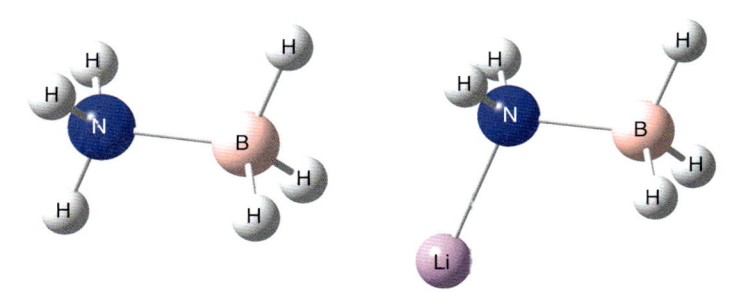

Figure 2 Molecular structures of AB and lithium amidoborane.

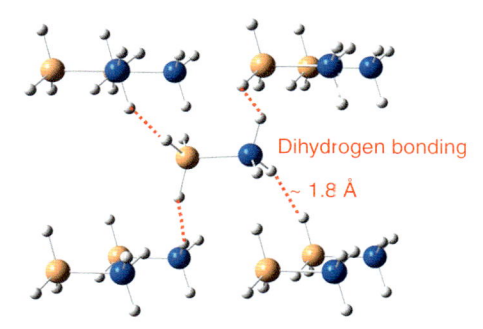

Figure 3 Packing of AB molecules in the crystal. Yellow, blue, and white balls are N, B, and H, respectively.

Table 4 Summary of dehydrogenation of AB, alkali and alkaline earth amidoboranes, and their derivatives

Reactions	Conditions[a]	Temperature (°C)	H (mass %)
nNH$_3$BH$_3 \rightarrow$ (NH$_2$BH$_2$)$_n$ + nH$_2 \rightarrow$ (NHBH)$_n$ + 2nH$_2$	Solid	70–200	12.9
NH$_3$BH$_3 \rightarrow$ NBH$_{6-x}$ + xH$_2$	SBA-15	50–100	6.7
	Ir-based catalyst/THF	Ambient temperature	6.7
	Ni-NHC catalyst/THF	60	16.5
LiNH$_2$BH$_3 \rightarrow$ LiNBH + 2H$_2$	Solid	75–95	10.9
	In THF	40–55	
NaNH$_2$BH$_3 \rightarrow$ NaH + BN + 2H$_2$	Solid	80–90	7.5
Ca(NH$_2$BH$_3$)$_2 \rightarrow$ Ca(NBH)$_2$ + 4H$_2$	Solid	90–245	8.0
Sr(NH$_2$BH$_3$)$_2 \rightarrow$ Sr(NBH)$_2$ + 4H$_2$	Solid	80–200	6.8
LiNH$_2$BH$_3$NH$_3$BH$_3 \rightarrow$ LiN$_2$B$_2$H + 5H$_2$	Solid	50–250	14.7
Ca(NH$_2$BH$_3$)$_2$·2NH$_3 \rightarrow$ Ca(BN$_2$H)$_2$ + 6H$_2$	Solid	75–300	8.9
Mg(NH$_2$BH$_3$)$_2$·NH$_3 \rightarrow$ MgB$_2$N$_3$H + 6H$_2$	Solid	50–300	11.8

[a] For solid-state dehydrogenation, most of the materials are under molten or semi-molten state.

containing H–B, H–N, and H–O bonds [4, 38, 39]. A distinctive feature of the most investigated chemical hydrides is the coexistence of both protonic and hydridic H atoms. Representative entities are NH$_3$BH$_3$ (ammonia borane, AB) [7, 24, 40–45], metal amidoboranes (MAB) [46–52], and H$_2$O–borohydride systems. **Figure 2** shows the molecular structures of AB and lithium amidoborane. H bonded with N has positive charge, which is opposite to H bonded with B. When a crystal is formed, the shortest distance between these two H atoms is found to be less than twice the van der Waals radius of H (see **Figure 3**). The exceptionally high chemical potentials for the combination of H$^-$ and H$^+$ to molecular H$_2$ and the formation of strong B–N or B–O bond are likely to be the driving forces for the dehydrogenation. For most of the chemical hydrides, dehydrogenation is an exothermic process. The increase in stability of the dehydrogenated product is the result of the formation of strong B–N or B–O covalent bond. In this section, the research activities on the development of AB and amidoboranes for hydrogen storage will be reviewed. **Table 4** presents the conditions applied in the dehydrogenation of AB, alkali and alkaline earth amidoboranes, and their derivatives.

4.06.4.1 Ammonia Borane

AB, first synthesized in 1955 [53], is a plastic crystalline solid adopting a tetragonal crystal structure with space group $I\bar{4}$ mm and lattice parameters of $a = b = 5.240$ Å and $c = 5.028$ Å at room temperature [54, 55]. As shown in **Figure 2**, this molecular crystal is stabilized by dihydrogen bonding between H(B) and H(N). The crystal melts at ~100 °C and decomposes to hydrogen (1 equiv.) between 70 and 112 °C to yield polyaminoborane (PAB, [NH$_2$BH$_2$]$_n$) according to eqn [1]. Subsequently, [NH$_2$BH$_2$]$_n$ decomposes with an additional 1 equiv. hydrogen loss, over a broad temperature range around 150 °C, forming amorphous polyiminoborane (PIB, [NHBH]$_n$) and a small fraction of borazine ([N$_3$B$_3$H$_6$]), according to eqns [2] and [3], respectively. The decomposition of [NHBH] to boron nitride (BN) occurs at temperatures in excess of 500 °C. This final step is not considered practical for hydrogen storage due to high temperatures needed for hydrogen release. Thermodynamic analyses and theoretical calculations show that hydrogen release from either AB or PAB or PIB is an exothermic process, revealing the irreversibility of hydrogen desorption from these materials.

$$n\text{NH}_3\text{BH}_3(s) \rightarrow [\text{NH}_2\text{BH}_2]_n(s) + n\text{H}_2(g) \quad [1]$$

$$[\text{NH}_2\text{BH}_2]_n(s) \rightarrow [\text{NHBH}]_n(s) + n\text{H}_2(g) \quad [2]$$

$$[\text{NH}_2\text{BH}_2]_n(s) \rightarrow [\text{N}_3\text{B}_3\text{H}_6]_{n/3}(l) + n\text{H}_2(g) \quad [3]$$

Figure 4 presents some of the likely forms of products from releasing the first and second equivalent molecules of H$_2$ from AB. The structure and composition of the product vary with the conditions applied during dehydrogenation. As an example, on catalytic dehydrogenation of AB by iridium (Ir) catalyst in tetrahydrofuran (THF), crystalline PAB is formed [43]. A recent report from He *et al.* [68] demonstrated the formation of crystalline linear PAB in the FeB-catalyzed solid-state dehydrogenation of AB at ~60 °C. However, in most cases, the solid product is essentially amorphous and is a mixture of linear, cyclic, branched, and cross-linked B–N structures.

Although it has an exceptionally high hydrogen content, AB has to overcome a few drawbacks to be practically viable. The first two challenges are the mass production of AB and energy-efficient regeneration of the used fuel [56, 57], while the kinetic-borne dehydrogenation of AB and the coproduction of unwanted gaseous products (such as borazine and NH$_3$) are to be alleviated. Moreover, severe material foaming in the dehydrogenation is also problematic. Tremendous efforts have been devoted to these issues since the first report on the dehydrogenation of AB for hydrogen storage by Wolf *et al.* [40], among which investigations on catalytic modification of AB or dispersing AB into porous materials attract significant attention [43–45, 58–71]. Dehydrogenation of AB in ionic liquids shows improved kinetics in comparison with neat AB [42]. Moreover, a number of intermediates and products have been identified by *in situ* nuclear magnetic resonance (NMR) and the density functional theory–gauge including/invariant atomic orbital (DFT–GIAO) calculations. As shown in **Figure 5**, different states of hybridization (sp^2 or sp^3) and bonding environments (with H or N) have chemical shifts ranging from −26.9 to +39.3 ppm. There are a few comprehensive reviews in this area to which the readers may like to further refer [24, 25, 56, 57].

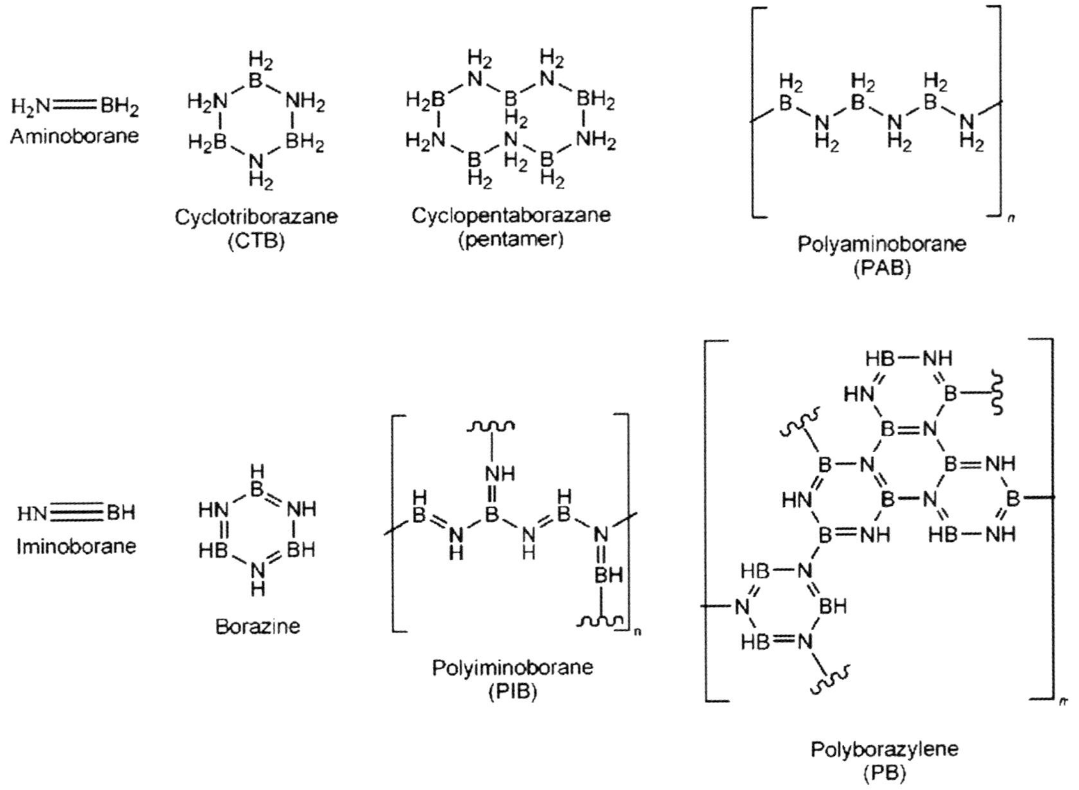

Figure 4 Molecular structures of possible dehydrogenation products [56].

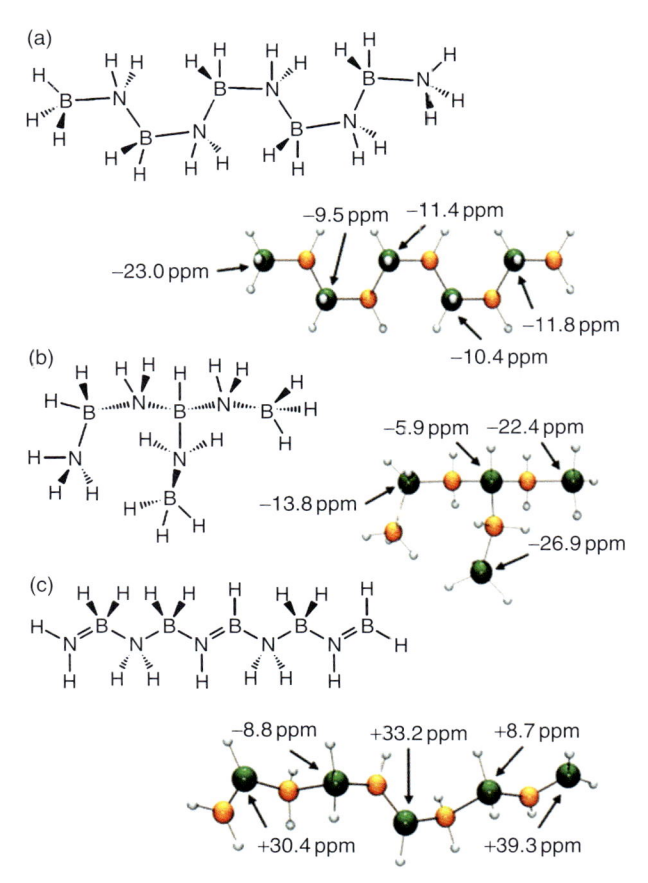

Figure 5 DFT–GIAO calculated ^{11}B NMR chemical shift for possible structures arising from the dehydropolymerization of AB [42].

4.06.4.1.1 Homogeneous catalytic dehydrogenation of AB

As summarized by Hamilton *et al.* [57] and Smythe and Gordon [56], a few homogeneous catalysts including Ru-, Ir-, and Ni-based complexes and Lewis acid (B(C$_6$F$_5$)$_3$) have been developed, which are effective in removing 1–2.5 equiv. H$_2$ from AB under mild conditions. **Figure 6** shows the time dependence of H$_2$ evolution from a AB/THF solution with different concentrations of (POCOPf)Ir(H)$_2$. With 1 mol.% of catalyst, ~1 equiv. H$_2$ can be released within 5 min. A quantitative yield of crystalline PAB was observed [43].

The dehydrogenation of AB by the Ni-N heterocyclic carbene (Ni-NHC) complex in a molar ratio of 10:1 shows unprecedented evolution of 2.5 equiv. H$_2$ at 60 °C [45]. The formation of Ni-NHC is by the reaction of biscyclooctadiene nickel (Ni(cod)$_2$) with Enders' NHC. Theoretical investigation suggests that the formation of the first transition state (highest energy barrier) is through transferring H(N) of AB to ligand carbene, which is different from the β-H elimination of AB in some other cases.

One way to activate AB by Lewis or Brønsted acid is by attracting a hydridic H(B) from AB to form the initiative cation [H$_2$BNH$_3$]$^+$ [63]. As shown in **Figure 7**, the overall process after the formation of the initiative cation resembles cationic polymerization and dehydrogeneration. One equivalent H$_2$ can be removed from AB at ambient temperature.

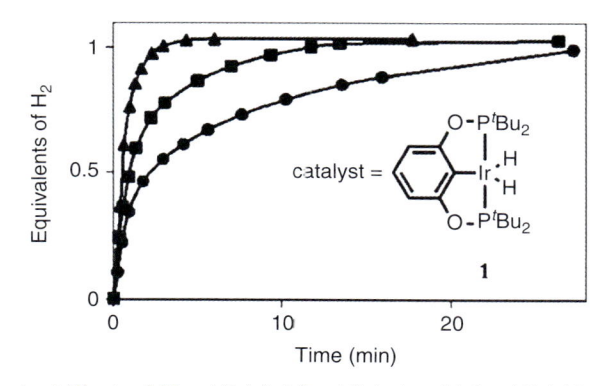

Figure 6 Amount of H$_2$ evolved per mole of AB using 0.25 mol.% (●), 0.5 mol.% (▲), and 1.0 mol.% (■) Ir catalyst [43].

Figure 7 Reaction of NH₃BH₃ with Lewis or Brønsted acid (A) results in the formation of borenium cation **2**. Subsequent reaction with another equivalent of NH₃BH₃ results in the formation of **3** with subsequent expulsion of H₂ and concomitant formation of **4** [63].

As shown above, the chemistry involved in the catalytic dehydrogenation of AB in solvent is considerably rich and worthy of detailed experimental and theoretical investigations. The use of the solvent allows sufficient mobility of both reactant and catalyst but will decrease the energy density of the system. It is a subject of system engineering to minimize the side effect of the solvent but retain the efficiency of homogeneous catalysis.

4.06.4.1.2 Solid-state dehydrogenation of AB

As mentioned in Section 4.06.4.1, the thermal decomposition of solid-state AB is a stepwise process having considerable kinetic barriers at each step. Efforts in alleviating the barrier in solid-state dehydrogenation are through dispersing AB into porous substrates [7] and introducing a catalyst in the material (solid form) [68].

An introductory work by Gutowska *et al.* demonstrated that, when dispersing AB onto porous SBA-15 nanoscaffold, hydrogen started to release at temperatures just above 50 °C and peaked at ~100 °C, which is considerably lower than that of neat AB. Moreover, the formation of borazine was largely depressed [7]. Further isothermal testing showed that the dispersed AB presented a significantly shortened induction period and reduced kinetic barrier. As shown in **Figure 8**, 1 equiv. H₂ can be released at 50 °C within 150 min. However, for pristine AB, it has to go through a ~100-min induction period and another 400–500 min to remove the same amount of H₂. A few successful attempts in using carbon cryogel, lithium catalysis and mesoporous carbon (Li-CMK-3), nano-BN, poly(methyl acrylate) (PMA), and so on, to improve the dehydrogenation properties of solid AB have been reported in the past 5 years [70, 72, 73].

Another approach in improving dehydrogenation of AB is via solid-state catalysis through the use of transition metals or alloys. He *et al.* reported that, upon the introduction of nano-sized Co- or Ni- or Fe-based catalyst to solid AB via the so-called coprecipitation method, ~1.0 equiv. or 6 wt.% of H₂ can be released at 59 °C (shown in **Figure 9**) [68]. It was observed that the presence of the nano-sized catalyst largely depressed the sample foaming and the coproduction of borazine. In the meantime, crystalline rather than amorphous PAB was formed (**Figure 10**), which should be derived from the catalyst-oriented growth of aminoborane and is significantly different from the ion-initiated dehydrogenation.

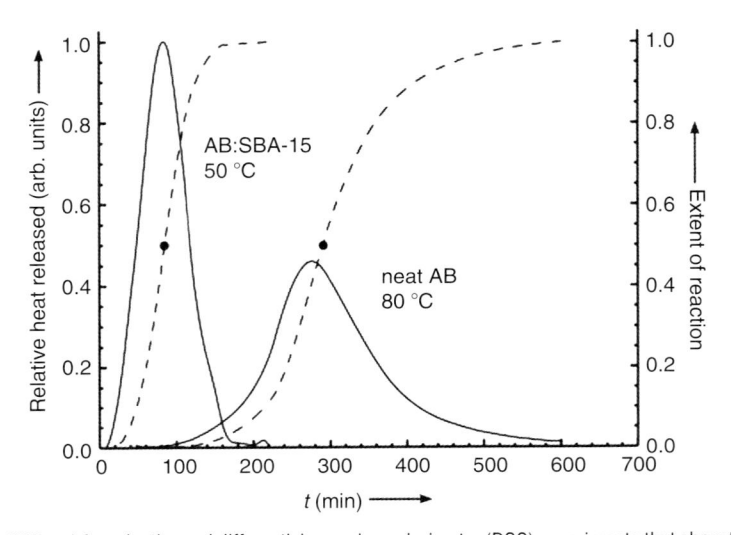

Figure 8 Scaled exotherms (solid lines) from isothermal differential scanning calorimetry (DSC) experiments that show the time-dependent release of H₂ from AB and AB:SBA-15 (1:1 w/w). The area under the curve for neat AB corresponds to $\Delta H_{rxn} = -21$ kJ mol⁻¹, and the area under the curve for AB:SBA-15 corresponds to $\Delta H_{rxn} = -1$ kJ mol⁻¹. The release of hydrogen from AB proceeds at a more rapid rate and at lower temperatures in SBA-15. The dashed line (-) is the integrated signal intensity; (•) is the point at which the reaction is 50% complete [7].

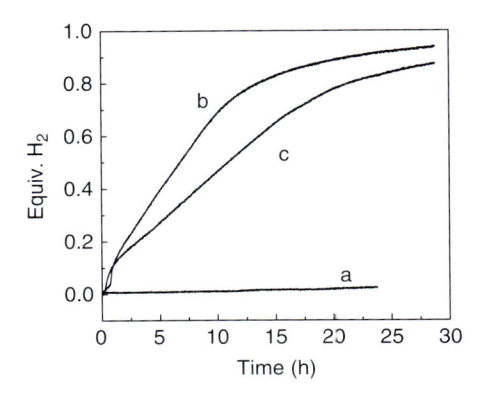

Figure 9 Volumetric hydrogen release measurements at 59 °C on the pristine (a), 2 mol.% Co-doped (b), and 2 mol.% Ni-doped (c) AB samples [68].

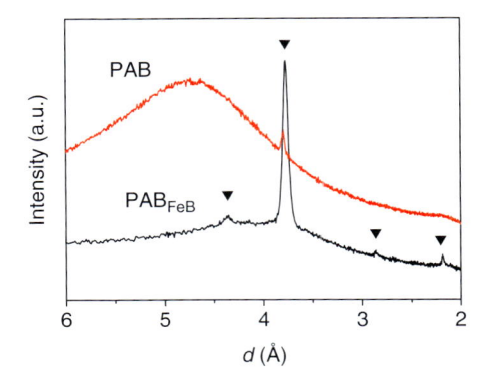

Figure 10 XRD patterns of the postdehydrogenated neat AB (80 °C) and 2.0 mol.% Fe-doped AB samples (60 °C). ▼, crystalline linear PAB.

4.06.4.2 Amidoboranes and Derivatives

4.06.4.2.1 Alkali and alkaline earth amidoboranes

As shown in the previous section, various methods have been employed to lower the decomposition temperature of AB through the use of additives and catalysts. A different approach has been applied recently in the manipulation of the thermodynamic properties of compounds through chemical alteration to AB, that is, through substituting one H in the NH_3 group in BH_3NH_3 with a more electron-donating element [46, 49]. The rationale behind this approach is to alter the polarity and intermolecular interactions (specifically the dihydrogen bonding) of AB to produce a substantially improved dehydrogenation profile. Lithium amidoborane ($LiNH_2BH_3$) [47, 49, 50, 52, 74, 75], sodium amidoborane ($NaNH_2BH_3$) [48, 49, 76], calcium amidoborane [46, 50], and strontium amidoborane [77] have been synthesized, which show substantially different dehydrogenation characteristics with respect to AB itself.

These alkali and alkaline earth amidoboranes (MABs) were synthesized mainly through the interactions of alkali or alkaline earth metal hydrides (LiH, NaH, CaH_2, and SrH_2) with AB (see eqn [4]), which lead to the replacement of hydrogen atom of AB by alkali or alkaline earth metals.

$$MH_x + xNH_3BH_3 \rightarrow M(NH_2BH_3)_x + xH_2 \quad [4]$$

where $x = 1$ when M is an alkali metal and $x = 2$ when M is an alkaline earth metal.

The replacement of the H of the NH_3 group in AB by alkali or alkaline earth element results in the alteration of the crystal structure and dehydrogenation property. As shown in **Figure 11**, $LiNH_2BH_3$ crystallizes in the orthorhombic space group Pbca with the lattice constants $a = 7.11274(6)$ Å, $b = 13.94877(14)$ Å, $c = 5.15018(6)$ Å, and $\underline{V} = 510.970(15)$ Å^3. The Li–N bond is essentially ionic and the B–H bond length is slightly longer than that in neat NH_3BH_3. $NaNH_2BH_3$ is of identical structure to $LiNH_2BH_3$ [49, 50]. $Ca(NH_2BH_3)_2$, on the other hand, is a monoclinic structure with $a = 9.100(2)$ Å, $b = 4.371(1)$ Å, $c = 6.441(2)$ Å, and $\beta = 93.19°$ (see **Figure 12**) [50]. Li or Na is coordinated with four NH_2BH_3 groups. Ca, on the other hand, sits in the center of an octahedron made of NH_2BH_3 groups. The THF adduct of $Ca(NH_2BH_3)_2$ was also determined [46]. It is interesting to note that, unlike Ca and Sr, no report on the formation of $Mg(NH_2BH_3)_2$ has appeared in the literature so far.

The experimental results show that more than 10 and 7 wt.% of hydrogen desorbs exothermically from $LiNH_2BH_3$ and $NaNH_2BH_3$, respectively, at around 91 °C (**Figure 13**) [49]. $Ca(NH_2BH_3)_2$, on the other hand, releases ~8 wt.% H_2 in the temperature range of 100–300 °C. In all the cases, borazine production is beyond the detection limit of mass spectrometry (MS). The induction period that is associated with the dehydrogenation of pristine NH_3BH_3 is absent from these amidoboranes, indicating that a different dehydrogenation mechanism is occurring. There are a few theoretical and experimental investigations on the dehydrogenation mechanism of these amidoboranes, especially of $LiNH_2BH_3$ [52, 75]. Kim *et al.* reported that the dehydrogenation of $LiNH_2BH_3$ is via abstracting H from the BH_3 group by Li [52]. An isotopic investigation also evidenced the bimolecular dehydrogenation.

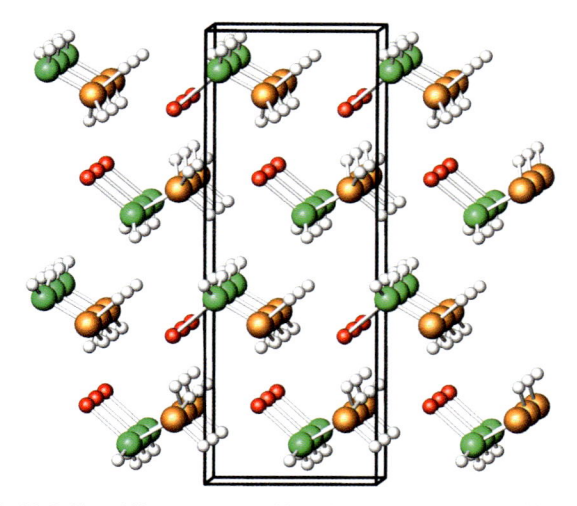

Figure 11 Crystal structure of LiNH$_2$BH$_3$. Li, B, N, and H are represented by red, orange, green, and white spheres, respectively [49].

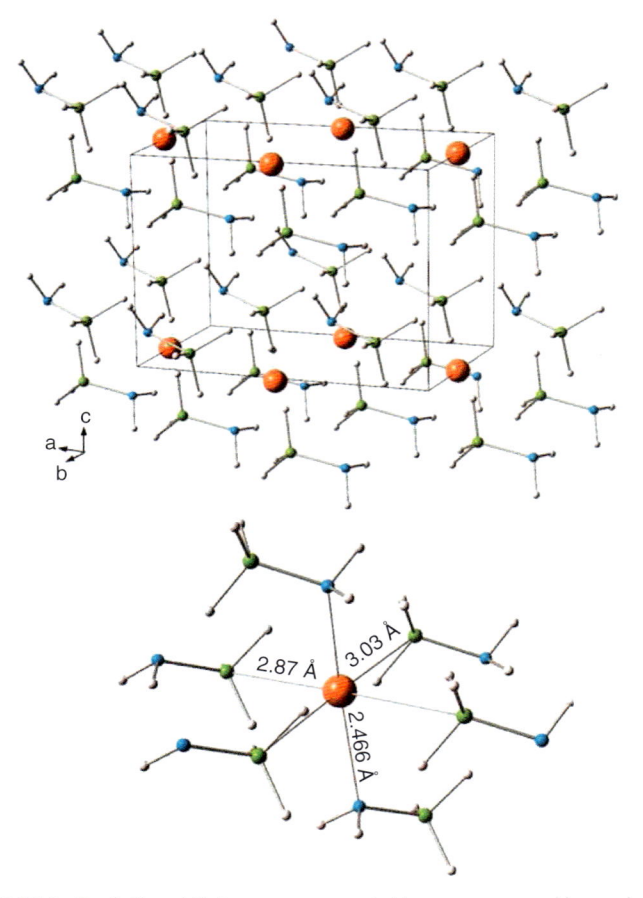

Figure 12 Crystal structure of Ca(NH$_2$BH$_3$)$_2$. Ca, B, N, and H atoms are represented by orange, green, blue, and white spheres, respectively [50].

4.06.4.2.2 Derivatives

A number of compounds and complexes derived from amidoboranes have been synthesized since 2009 [51, 78, 79]. NH$_3$ and THF are prone to adduct to amidoboranes. Amidoborane ammoniates can be synthesized either by exposing amidoboranes (such as Ca(NH$_2$BH$_3$)$_2$) to NH$_3$ or by reacting amides or imides with AB [51]. In general, amidoborane ammoniates were found to release H$_2$ at mild temperatures. Bowden *et al.* reported that when NH$_3$BH$_3$ reacts with LiNH$_2$, H$_2$ rather than NH$_3$ was released in the temperature range ~25–300 °C [79]. Chua *et al.* synthesized Ca(NH$_2$BH$_3$)$_2$·2NH$_3$ and Mg(NH$_2$BH$_3$)$_2$·NH$_3$ through the reaction of NH$_3$BH$_3$ with Ca(NH$_2$)$_2$ or MgNH, respectively [51]. In both cases, NH$_3$ adducts to metal cations and forms dihydrogen bonding

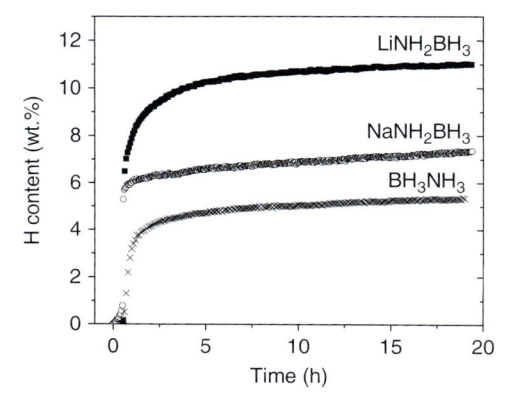

Figure 13 Hydrogen evolution from heating neat NH$_3$BH$_3$, LiNH$_2$BH$_3$, and NaNH$_2$BH$_3$ at 91 °C [49].

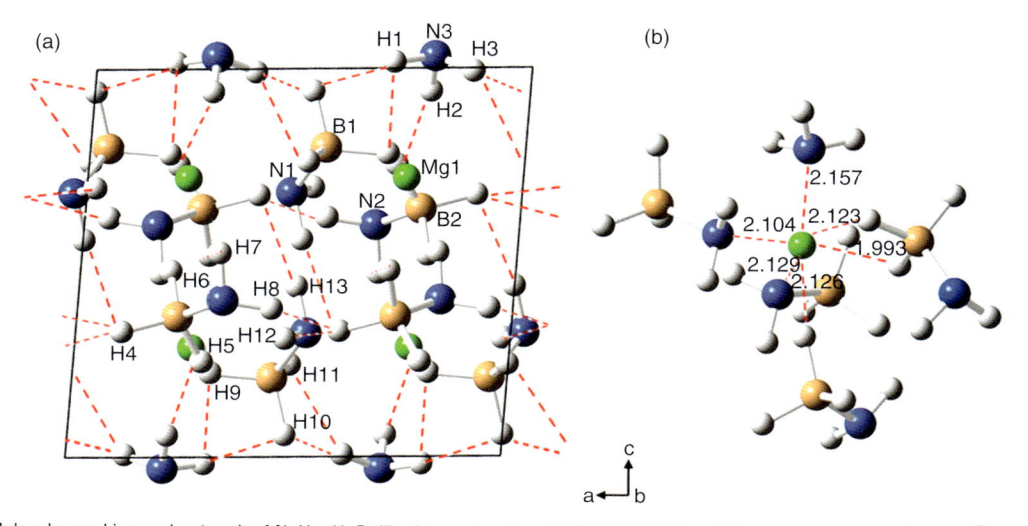

Figure 14 Molecular packing and network of N–H···H–B dihydrogen bonding in MgAB·NH$_3$ (a) and close contacts around the Mg^{2+} center (b).

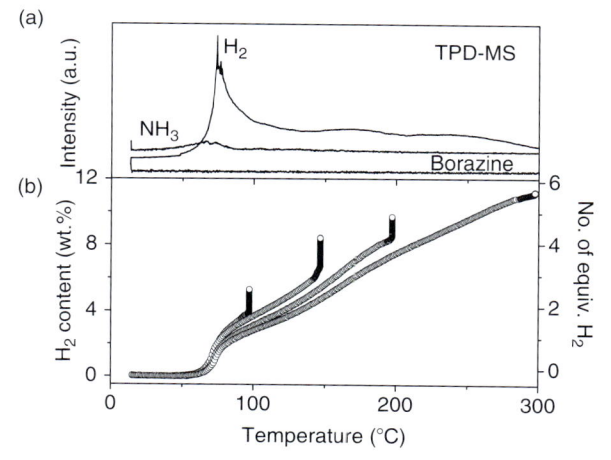

Figure 15 Temperature-programmed desorption (TPD)-MS spectra (a) and volumetric release (b) measurements on Mg(NH$_2$BH$_3$)$_2$·NH$_3$ at the heating rate of 2 (a) and 0.5 °C min^{-1} (b).

with nearby H(B). The shortest (N)H···H(B) distance in Mg(NH$_2$BH$_3$)$_2$·NH$_3$, for example, is around 1.92 Å (**Figure 14**). The difficulty in forming Mg(NH$_2$BH$_3$)$_2$ and the existence of its ammoniate indicate that the unstable crystal of Mg(NH$_2$BH$_3$)$_2$ (probably due to small but dense charged cation (Mg^{2+}) and big anion) can be stabilized by NH$_3$ through the establishment of coordination of a lone pair of N to Mg^{2+}. The thermal decomposition of Mg(NH$_2$BH$_3$)$_2$·NH$_3$ performed in a closed vessel demonstrated a stoichiometric conversion of NH$_3$ and desorption of ~11.2 wt.% H$_2$ (shown in **Figure 15**).

As shown above, chemical hydrides are capable of releasing large amounts of H$_2$ at relatively low temperatures. However, in most cases, hydrogen desorption is exothermic in nature, showing that these chemicals are kinetically stable. Intensive sunshine, impact, impurities in the material, and so on may trigger self-decomposition leading to auto-accelerated dehydrogenation, which may need serious consideration when applied practically.

4.06.5 Complex Hydrides

Complex hydrides have attracted considerable attention since 1997 when Ti was successfully introduced to NaAlH$_4$ system [6]. In the past 13 years, alanates, borohydrides, and amides have been extensively and intensively investigated. The following section will mainly report on the progress on borohydrides and amides. There have been significant amounts of review work on alanates in the past 10 years [3, 80–83]. Table 5 summarizes the systems developed over this period.

4.06.5.1 Borohydrides

Borohydrides, having a common formula of M(BH$_4$)$_n$, where M refers to the metal element and n the valence of M, have been extensively studied in the past decade. Representative systems are LiBH$_4$, Mg(BH$_4$)$_2$, and Ca(BH$_4$)$_2$.

Figure 16 shows the structure of LiBH$_4$, Mg(BH$_4$)$_2$, and Ca(BH$_4$)$_2$, respectively. LiBH$_4$ crystallizes in an orthorhombic structure (Pnma) at ambient temperature and transfers to a hexagonal structure (P6$_3$mc) at 135 °C [84–86]. Mg(BH$_4$)$_2$, on the other hand, transfers from a hexagonal structure to an orthorhombic structure at ~180 °C [87–89]. Three different polymorphs of Ca(BH$_4$)$_2$ have been reported up to date [90–92]. The structures of low-temperature α-Ca(BH$_4$)$_2$ (orthorhombic, space group Fddd) and high-temperature β-Ca(BH$_4$)$_2$ (tetragonal, P42/m) phases have been resolved [90, 91], and the third phase γ-Ca(BH$_4$)$_2$, of orthorhombic structure Pbca, was also reported [92]. Ca(BH$_4$)$_2$ undergoes phase transformation prior to its thermal decomposition.

Considerable attention has been paid to LiBH$_4$ due to its high hydrogen content (~18.4 mass%) [39, 85, 86]. However, hydrogen desorption from this chemical is highly endothermic (~67 kJ mol^{-1}) and, thus, requires temperatures higher than 300 °C. A few approaches have been introduced recently to destabilize LiBH$_4$. Comparatively, reacting LiBH$_4$ with chemicals, such as LiNH$_2$ [93–96], MgH$_2$ [22, 38, 97, 98], and CaH$_2$ [99–101], can considerably change the overall dehydrogenation thermodynamics due to the formation of more stable products. As examples, hydrogen desorption from the LiBH$_4$–2LiNH$_2$ mixture is an exothermic reaction [93, 96]; combination of LiBH$_4$ and MgH$_2$ in a molar ratio of 2:1 leads to ~25 kJ mol^{-1} H$_2$ decrease in enthalpy change compared with the pristine LiBH$_4$ [38]. As shown in Figure 17, hydrogen desorption from the composite starts at ~300 °C and rehydrogenation occurs at ~250 °C. The formation of the stable product MgB$_2$ alters the thermodynamics of the dehydrogenation.

Table 5   Dehydrogenation of borohydrides and amide–hydride combinations

Reactions	Mass% of H$_2$	Temperature (°C)[a]
Borohydrides		
2LiBH$_4$ → 2LiH + 2B + 3H$_2$	13.6	200–550
2LiBH$_4$ + MgH$_2$ = 2LiH + MgB$_2$ + 4H$_2$	11.5	270–440
Mg(BH$_4$)$_2$ → MgB$_2$ + 4H$_2$	14.8	290–500
3Mg(BH$_4$)$_2$·2(NH$_3$) → Mg$_3$B$_2$N$_4$ + 2BN + 2B + 21H$_2$	15.9	100–400
Ca(BH$_4$)$_2$ → CaH$_2$ + 2B + 3H$_2$	8.6	300–500
Zn(BH$_4$)$_2$ → Zn + B$_2$H$_6$ + H$_2$	2.1	90–140
Amide/hydride		
LiNH$_2$ + 2LiH = Li$_2$NH + LiH + H$_2$ = Li$_3$N + 2H$_2$	10.5	150–450
CaNH + CaH$_2$ = Ca$_2$NH + H$_2$	2.1	350–650
Mg(NH$_2$)$_2$ + 2LiH = Li$_2$Mg(NH)$_2$ + 2H$_2$	5.6	100–250
3Mg(NH$_2$)$_2$ + 8LiH = 4Li$_2$NH + Mg$_3$N$_2$ + 8H$_2$	6.9	150–300
Mg(NH$_2$)$_2$ + 4LiH = Li$_3$N + LiMgN + 4H$_2$	9.1	150–300
2LiNH$_2$ + LiBH$_4$ → 'Li$_3$BN$_2$H$_8$' → Li$_3$BN$_2$ + 4H$_2$	11.9	150–350
Mg(NH$_2$)$_2$ + 2MgH$_2$ → Mg$_3$N$_2$ + 4H$_2$	7.4	20[b]
2LiNH$_2$ + LiAlH$_4$ → LiNH$_2$ + 2LiH + AlN + 2H$_2$ = Li$_3$AlN$_2$ + 4H$_2$	5.0	20[b]–500
3Mg(NH$_2$)$_2$ + 3LiAlH$_4$ → Mg$_3$N$_2$ + Li$_3$AlN$_2$ + 2AlN + 12H$_2$	8.5	20[b]–350
Mg(NH$_2$)$_2$ + CaH$_2$ → MgCa(NH)$_2$ + 2H$_2$	4.1	20[b]–500
NaNH$_2$ + LiAlH$_4$ → NaH + LiAl$_{0.33}$NH + 0.67Al + 2H$_2$	5.2	20[b]
2LiNH$_2$ + CaH$_2$ = Li$_2$Ca(NH)$_2$ + 2H$_2$	4.5	100–330
4LiNH$_2$ + 2Li$_3$AlH$_6$ → Li$_3$AlN$_2$ + Al + 2Li$_2$NH + 3LiH + 15/2H$_2$	7.5	100–500
2Li$_4$BN$_3$H$_{10}$ + 3MgH$_2$ → 2Li$_3$BN$_2$ + Mg$_3$N$_2$ + 2LiH + 12H$_2$	9.2	100–400

[a] Experimental observation.
[b] Under ball milling condition.

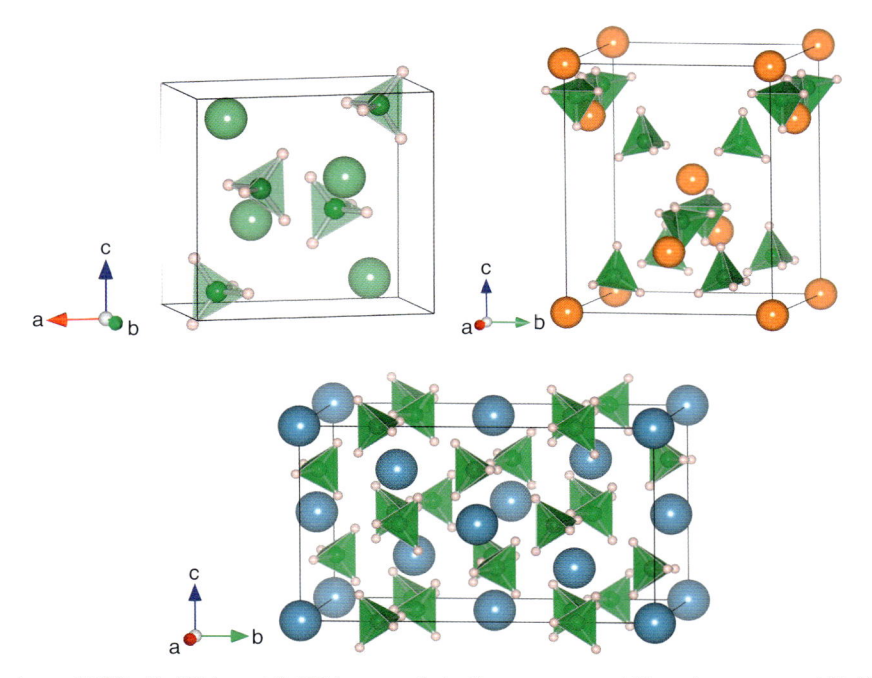

Figure 16 Crystal structures of LiBH$_4$, Mg(BH$_4$)$_2$, and Ca(BH$_4$)$_2$, respectively. Green, orange, and blue spheres represent Li, Mg, and Ca.

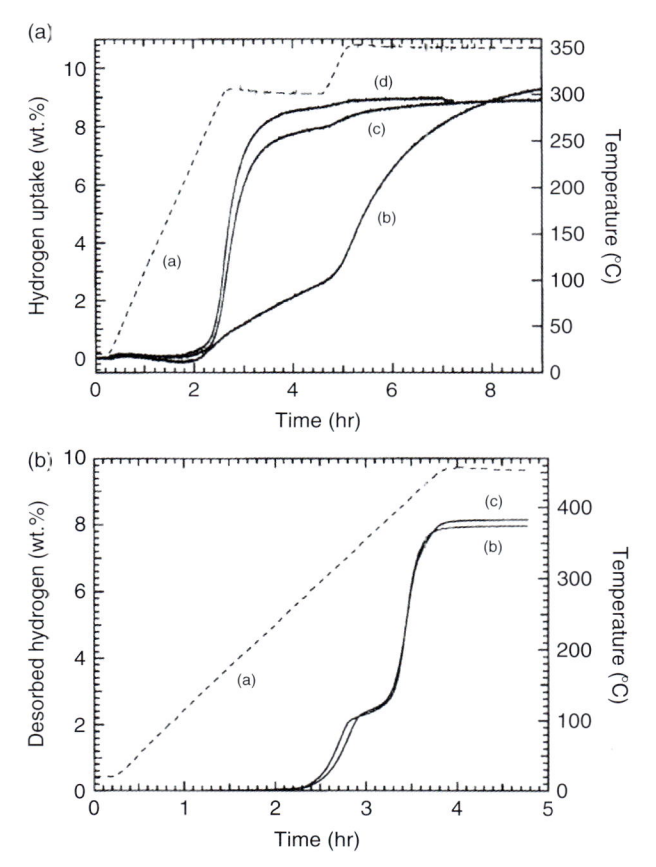

Figure 17 Hydrogenation and dehydrogenation of milled LiH + ½MgB$_2$ with 3 mol.% TiCl$_3$. (a) Hydrogen uptake during heating in 100 bar of hydrogen. Curve (a) shows the temperature profile. Curve (b) shows the initial uptake of hydrogen. Curves (c) and (d) show uptake during the second and third cycles, respectively. (b) Desorption following hydrogenation into a closed evacuated volume. Curve (a) shows the temperature profile. Curves (b) and (c), respectively, show the wt.% of desorbed hydrogen following the initial and second hydrogenation cycles that are shown in part (a) [38].

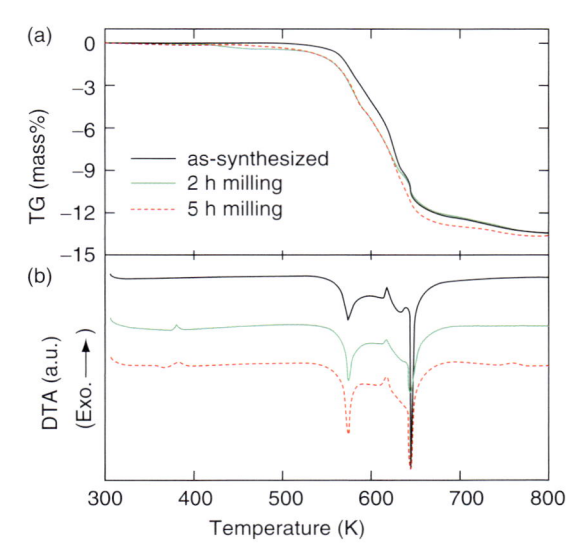

Figure 18 (a) Thermogravimetry and (b) differential thermal analysis curves of Mg(BH$_4$)$_2$ for as-synthesized and after 2 and 5 h milling [102].

There has been a discussion on whether the dehydrogenation is via a stepwise manner, that is, if the first step is via self-decomposition of LiBH$_4$ to LiH, B, and H$_2$ followed by MgH$_2$ + B to MgB$_2$ and H$_2$.

Having a hydrogen content of ~15 mass%, Mg(BH$_4$)$_2$ is another attractive hydrogen storage candidate [102–105]. Mg(BH$_4$)$_2$ can be synthesized via a metathesis of LiBH$_4$ and MgCl$_2$ [104–106]. At temperatures above 340 °C, it decomposes to hydrogen (see **Figure 18**) [103]; the first step in dehydrogenation has an enthalpy change of 39.3 kJ mol^{-1} H$_2$ and an entropy change of 91.3 J mol^{-1} H$_2$ [106]. An easy calculation from eqn [5] will give a temperature of ~150 °C to desorb 1.0 bar hydrogen. Obviously, it is ~70 °C higher than the operation temperature of the proton exchange membrane (PEM) fuel cell.

$$RT\ln(P) = \Delta H - \Delta S \times T \quad [5]$$

Ca(BH$_4$)$_2$ has a hydrogen capacity of 11.6 wt.% and a lower hydrogen desorption (thermal decomposition) temperature compared with that of LiBH$_4$ as predicted by thermodynamic analysis based on an *ab initio* calculation [107]. A previous study showed that Ca(BH$_4$)$_2$ desorbs 9.0 wt.% hydrogen at a temperature as high as 770 K, and CaH$_2$ is the only crystalline phase in the solid residue [108, 109]. Doping it with Ti or Nb species did not show obvious catalytic effect on decreasing the decomposition temperature [110].

Other borohydrides, such as Zn(BH$_4$)$_2$ [72], also decompose to hydrogen; however, these either tend to have poor thermodynamics or create unwanted side products (i.e., B$_2$H$_6$).

Nakamori *et al.* demonstrated an interesting relationship between the heat of formation of metal borohydrides and the electronegativities of metal in M(BH$_4$)$_n$ (M = Li, Na, Ca, Mg, Zn, etc.). Further investigation shows that the dehydriding temperature of M(BH$_4$)$_n$ decreases with the increase of the electronegativity of M [111]. It is worth noting that the dehydriding temperature obtained by the temperature-programmed desorption (TPD) technique [103] is not only a measure of the thermodynamic stability of a reactant but also reflects the kinetic barrier associated with the decomposition process. It is also worth highlighting that the chemical state of B in dehydrogenated products, which can bond with metals (such as MgB$_2$) or be in elemental or in amorphous B–H$_x$ states, will considerably change the dehydrogenation thermodynamic parameters [38, 112].

An amine complex of Mg(BH$_4$)$_2$, that is, Mg(BH$_4$)$_2$·2NH$_3$, was identified [113], which releases hydrogen endothermically at temperatures above 150 °C (see **Figures 19** and **20**). Although with side gaseous product(s) such as NH$_3$, this new chemical shows certain advantages over AB.

4.06.5.2 Amide–Hydride Systems

Studies on hydrogen storage over amide–hydride systems were initiated when researchers accidentally noticed that a mixture of metallic lithium and carbon nanotubes pretreated in a purified N$_2$ atmosphere absorbed large amounts of hydrogen at elevated temperatures (see **Figure 21**) [4]. Through X-ray diffraction characterizations, the hydrogenated solid-state sample was found to contain LiNH$_2$, LiH, and the unreacted carbon nanotubes. Further investigations revealed that the N$_2$-treated Li–C mixture converted to Li$_3$N and carbon nanotubes. The reversible hydrogen storage over Li$_3$N follows reaction [6], and ~10.5 mass% of hydrogen can be stored [4, 114].

$$Li_3N + 2H_2 = Li_2NH + LiH + H_2 = LiNH_2 + 2LiH \quad [6]$$

Thermodynamic analyses showed that hydrogen desorption from LiNH$_2$–2LiH and LiNH$_2$–LiH is endothermic with the heat of desorption of 80 and 66 kJ mol^{-1} H$_2$, respectively [4]. The operation temperature at 1.0 bar equilibrium H$_2$ pressure is above 250 °C for the LiNH$_2$–LiH (1:1 molar ratio) system, which is too high for practical applications.

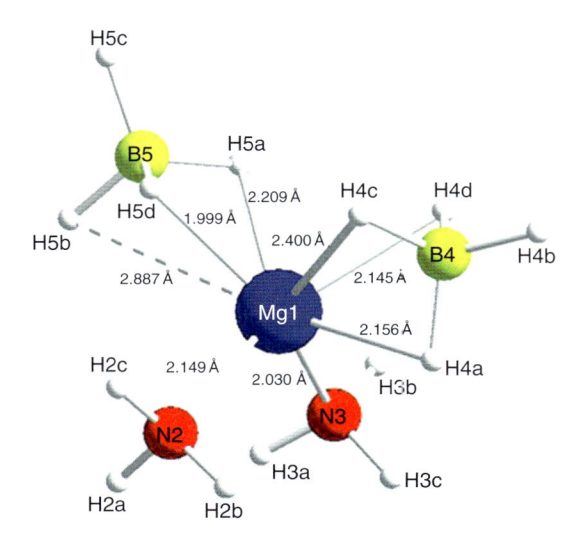

Figure 19 Molecular structure of Mg(BH$_4$)$_2$2NH$_3$ [113].

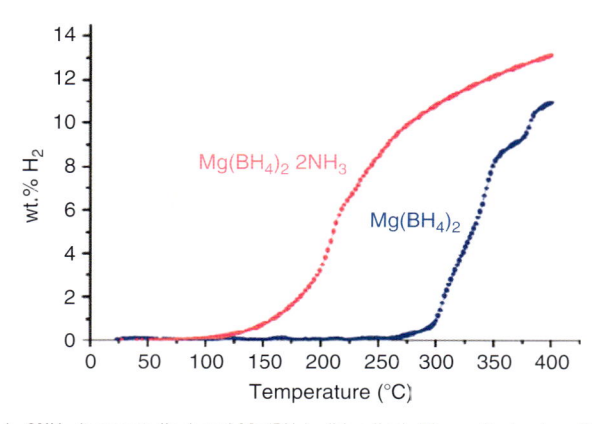

Figure 20 Gas evolution from Mg(BH$_4$)$_2$·2NH$_3$ (magenta line) and Mg(BH$_4$)$_2$ (blue line) The vertical axis calibration is wt.% H$_2$ and is based on the assumption that all the evolved gas is hydrogen [113].

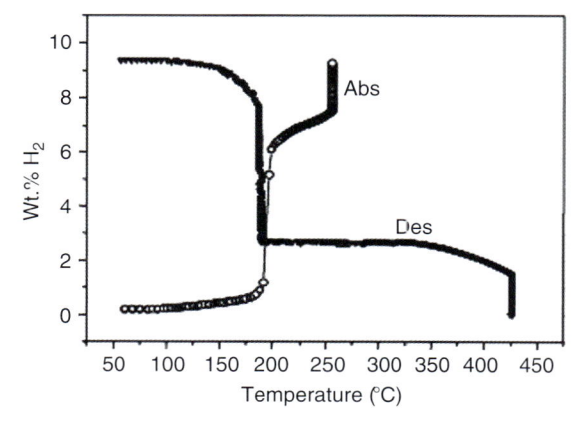

Figure 21 Weight variations during hydrogen absorption and desorption processes over Li$_3$N samples [4].

Li$_3$N has been regarded as a superior Li ion conductor. The structure of Li$_3$N is illustrated in **Figure 22**, which consists of Li and Li$_2$N layers, in which Li migrates along the Li$_2$N layer having a relatively low barrier. When hydrogen is pumped in, one-third of the Li will be removed from the Li$_3$N structure, which combines with H to form LiH. H replaces Li and bonds to N to form Li$_2$NH. Further hydrogenation results in the additional exchange between Li in Li$_2$NH and H in H$_2$ and the formation of LiNH$_2$ and LiH.

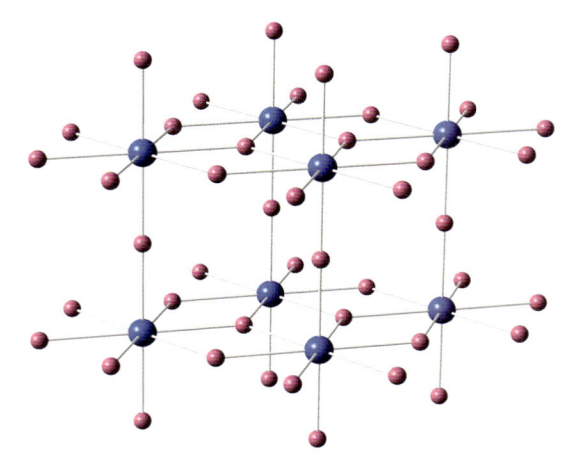

Figure 22 Crystal structure of Li$_3$N. N is in blue and Li in purple.

Due to a poorer electronegativity, H bonded with N is positively charged (H$^{\delta+}$). On the contrary, H in hydrides, especially ionic hydrides, is negatively charged (H$^{\delta-}$). The abnormally high potential of the combination of H$^{\delta+}$ and H$^{\delta-}$ to H$_2$ together with the strong electrostatic attraction between the N anion in amide and the metal cation in hydride will likely induce a direct reaction between the amide and hydride and lead to the release of H$_2$ [2, 115]. One can expect that such an interaction should exist in other amide–hydride combination systems. A variety of metal–N–H systems with different hydrogen capacities and thermodynamic parameters have been developed [23, 114, 116–155] (**Table 5**). As examples, the reaction between Mg(NH$_2$)$_2$ and MgH$_2$ in a molar ratio of ½ gives more than 7.4 mass% H$_2$ and the solid product of Mg$_3$N$_2$ [134]; more than 5 mass% of hydrogen can be released exothermically from a mixture of NaNH$_2$/LiAlH$_4$ (1:1 molar ratio) upon energetic ball milling [147].

The reactions of amides and complex hydrides including LiBH$_4$ [94, 96, 133, 154, 156–159], LiAlH$_4$, and Li$_3$AlH$_6$ [136, 138, 142, 144, 149] brought considerable interesting features to the amide–hydride system. It was reported that more than 11 wt.% of hydrogen can be desorbed from a mixture of 2LiNH$_2$–LiBH$_3$ exothermically in a temperature range of 250–350 °C (see **Figure 23**). Li$_3$BN$_2$ is the final product [93]. The dehydrogenation feature is significantly different from the highly endothermic self-decomposition of LiBH$_4$ and LiNH$_2$. Due to the exceptionally high hydrogen content, this system can be used for onboard hydrogen production, provided that the operation temperature can be substantially reduced. Attempts in catalyzing the dehydrogenation by introducing nano-sized Pd, Pt, Ni, and Co have successfully brought down the dehydrogenation temperature to ~150 °C [156, 160, 161]. However, further reduction of temperature may depend not only on the catalytic modification but also on the optimization of the physical state of the reactant. Experimental results show that the catalyzed dehydrogenation reaches the maximum rate upon the melting of Li$_3$BN$_2$H$_8$, indicating that the mobility of the reacting species (Li$_3$BN$_2$H$_8$) is essential to the effective contact of catalyst [161]. It is likely that an additive which can form an eutectic compound with Li$_3$BN$_2$H$_8$ could further enhance the reaction kinetics. Clearly, such an attempt has to be based on an in-depth structural understanding [94, 133, 159]. Yang et al. introduced MgH$_2$ to the LiBH$_4$–LiNH$_2$ system and observed a multiple-step reaction involving the formation of Li$_4$BN$_3$H$_{10}$,

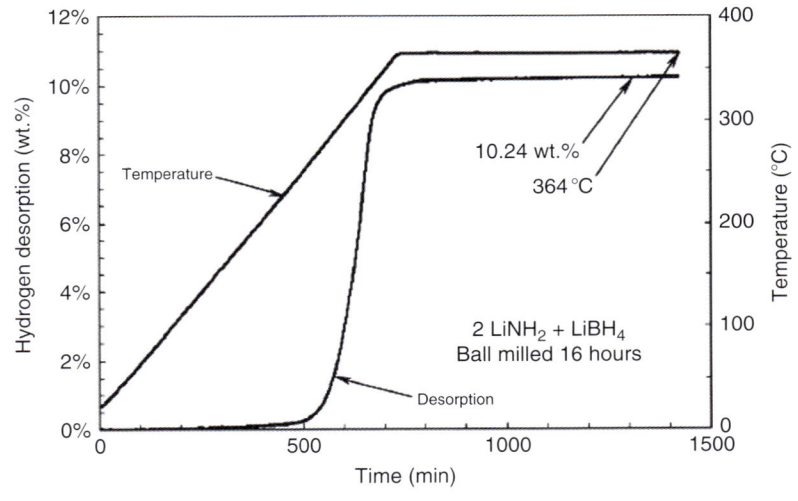

Figure 23 Volumetric measurement of thermal desorption from Li$_3$BN$_2$H$_8$ heating at 0.5 °C min^{-1} to 364 °C [93].

Li$_2$Mg(NH)$_2$, Li$_3$BN$_2$, and Mg$_3$N$_2$ [150]. Each step has different thermodynamic and kinetic parameters. Investigations on the interaction between LiNH$_2$ and LiAlH$_4$ revealed that the transition of [AlH$_4$]$^-$ to [AlH$_6$]$^{3-}$ is fairly easy in the presence of LiNH$_2$ [149]. From a 2LiNH$_2$–LiAlH$_4$ sample, 4 equiv. H was desorbed during a ball milling treatment. NMR measurements of samples collected at different intervals of ball milling showed that an Al–N bond was established upon the contact of these two chemicals, revealing a direct interaction between –NH$_2$ and [AlH$_4$]$^-$. Complete dehydrogenation at elevated temperatures results in the formation of Li$_3$AlN$_2$, which can only be partially rehydrogenated to LiNH$_2$, LiH, and AlN (**Table 5**) [149]. The LiNH$_2$–Li$_3$AlH$_6$ combination was also investigated [136, 138]. Different results were observed by different groups. Kojima *et al.* detected the formation of Li$_3$AlN$_2$, Li$_2$NH, Al, and LiH after the dehydrogenation of Li$_3$AlH$_6$–2LiNH$_2$ [136]. The Al–N bonding was not observed by Lu *et al.* A fully reversible reaction between Li$_3$AlH$_6$ and LiNH$_2$ (molar ratio 1:3) was reported [138]. Large amounts of hydrogen desorption from Mg(NH$_2$)$_2$–LiAlH$_4$ [142] and Mg(NH$_2$)$_2$–Li$_3$AlH$_6$ [144] were also observed, in which 6.2 wt.% of hydrogen can be reversibly stored in a Mg(NH$_2$)$_2$–Li$_3$AlH$_6$ combination at 300 °C.

Comparatively, the Mg(NH$_2$)$_2$–LiH system has attracted more attention due to its reversible nature and suitable thermodynamic parameters [5, 116, 117, 119, 122, 123, 128, 129, 139, 140, 145, 163–178]. A few Mg(NH$_2$)$_2$ and LiH combinations have been investigated thus far, which gave different reaction paths and hydrogen capacity [119, 140, 145, 179]. However, Mg(NH$_2$)$_2$–2LiH provides more 'usable' hydrogen at lower temperatures [117, 122]. The dehydrogenation of Mg(NH$_2$)$_2$ and 2LiH takes place in the temperature range of 150–250 °C, which gives 5.6 mass% hydrogen and a solid product Li$_2$Mg(NH)$_2$, which is a new compound of an orthorhombic structure (see **Figure 24**). Due to almost identical ion radii, Li$^+$ and Mg^{2+} are indistinguishable in the lattice, thus bringing particular interest to the crystallographic analyses [180]. Pressure–composition–temperature (PCT) measurements show that dehydrogenation of Mg(NH$_2$)$_2$ + 2LiH exhibits a pressure plateau and a slope region [117, 122]. The heat of hydrogen desorption within the pressure plateau is ~38.9 kJ mol^{-1} H$_2$. The results of a van't Hoff plot (see **Figure 25**) indicate that the temperature to desorb hydrogen at 1.0 bar equilibrium pressure is ~80 °C [162], which is clearly in the range of typical operational temperatures of PEM fuel cells. However, there is a severe kinetic barrier that probably originates from interface reactions and mass transport through the product layer, which provides a hurdle to low-temperature dehydrogenation [174]. Catalytic modification to the system is challenging partly due to the catalytic additives that have to be involved in the interface reactions and/or mass transport. Hu *et al.* introduced LiBH$_4$ to the system and lowered the energy barrier. It is observed that complete dehydrogenation and hydrogenation can be achieved at 140 and 100 °C, respectively [174]. More recently, Wang *et al.* introduced ~3 mol.% K in the Mg(NH$_2$)$_2$–2LiH system and enabled a full dehydrogenation and rehydrogenation cycle at a temperature near 100 °C (see **Figure 26**) [178]. Theoretical investigations indicated that K may bond with N and activate the N–H bond. It is rather interesting to understand the way K functions in the dehydrogenation and hydrogenation as it may shine a light on catalyst design for complex hydrides.

As mentioned earlier, the diverse combinations of amides and hydrides enable a series of novel chemical processes for hydrogen storage and production. On top of that, the superior bonding capability of N with metal and hydrogen allows the formation of a variety of new compounds, such as Li$_2$Mg(NH)$_2$ [122, 180], Li$_2$Ca(NH)$_2$ [146, 153], MgCa(NH)$_2$ [132], Li$_4$BN$_3$H$_{10}$ [93, 133], and Li$_2$BNH$_6$ [159]. Although a number of promising materials have been identified, the further development of amide–hydride systems for hydrogen storage largely relies on the proper match of N–H and N–M bonds in

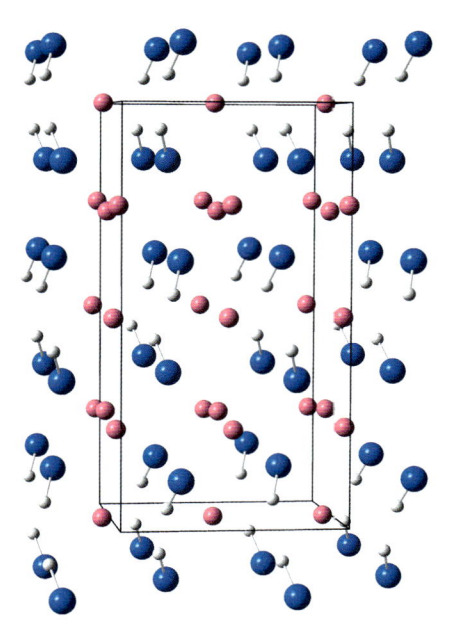

Figure 24 The crystal structure of Li$_2$Mg(NH)$_2$. Li and Mg are in purple, N in blue, and hydrogen in white.

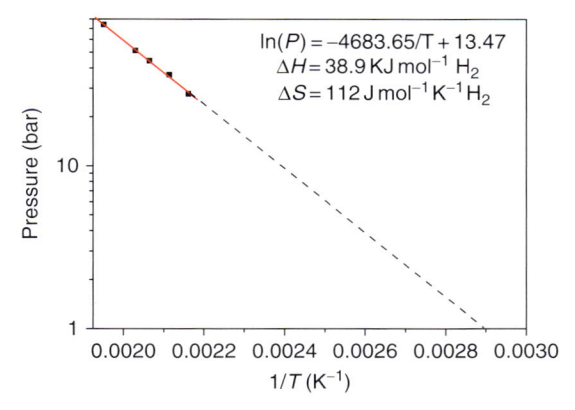

Figure 25 van't Hoff plot of Mg(NH$_2$)$_2$-2LiH system [162].

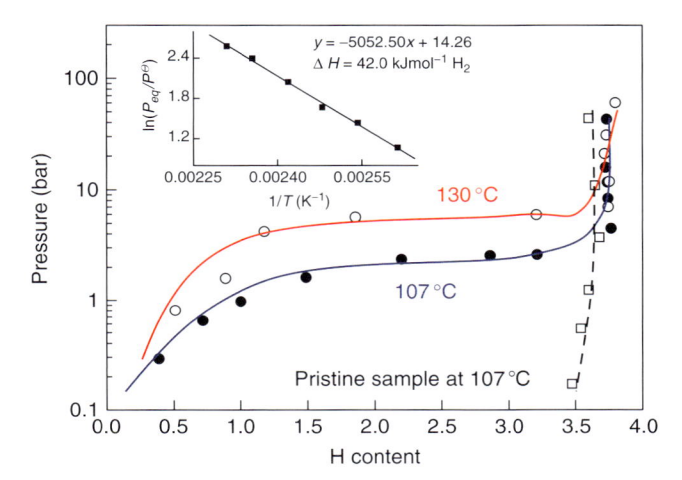

Figure 26 Pressure–composition–temperature (PCT) desorption isotherms of the K-modified samples at 107 (●) and 130 °C (○) and the post-milled pristine sample at 107 °C (□). For the pristine sample, the dehydrogenation is too slow to reach equilibrium. H content refers to the equivalent H atoms desorbed from the sorbent. The inset shows the van't Hoff plot of the K-modified sample [178].

amides and M–H bond in hydrides. In this regard, theoretical simulation is essential in predicting the potential systems [181]. In the meantime, in-depth understanding of the reaction mechanisms will also significantly benefit the kinetic optimization.

4.06.6 Pending Issues

The comparative H content in complex and chemical hydrides is high. More than 10 attracting systems have been developed within the past 10 years [3, 83, 182], and further promising systems are continually emerging. In the meantime, considerable new chemistry of B- and N-containing compounds has been accumulated, which will greatly facilitate the ongoing research and development. The broad range of materials and varieties of approaches in the material optimization and engineering enable these systems to be the most promising candidates for hydrogen storage.

There are a few common challenges in the chemical and complex hydride systems, one of which is material stability. Most of the chemical hydrides and some of the complex hydrides are kinetically stable and are reactive to moisture and oxygen. There are also by-products such as NH$_3$, borazine, and B$_2$H$_6$ in the dehydrogenation, which are toxic and may deteriorate the performance of, for example, a PEM fuel cell.

The other challenge the complex and chemical hydride systems have to overcome is the slow kinetics of the hydrogenation and dehydrogenation stages, which is an intrinsic property of solid-state reactions. The kinetic problem could be more prominent for a system of multiple phases and/or undergoing a stepwise reaction, where a catalyst is demanded. The effective catalytic modification depends strongly on the identification of the origin of the kinetic barrier(s); therefore, mechanistic understanding of the corresponding reaction is essential.

References

[1] Schlapbach L and Zuttel A (2001) Hydrogen-storage materials for mobile applications. *Nature* 414: 353.
[2] Grochala W and Edwards PP (2004) Thermal decomposition of the non-interstitial hydrides for the storage and production of hydrogen. *Chemical Reviews* 104: 1283.
[3] Orimo SI, Nakamori Y, Eliseo JR, et al. (2007) Complex hydrides for hydrogen storage. *Chemical Reviews* 107: 4111.
[4] Chen P, Xiong ZT, Luo JZ, et al. (2002) Interaction of hydrogen with metal nitrides and imides. *Nature* 420: 302.
[5] Chen P and Zhu M (2008) Recent progress in hydrogen storage. *Materials Today* 11: 36.
[6] Bogdanovic B and Schwickardi M (1997) Ti-doped alkali metal aluminium hydrides as potential novel reversible hydrogen storage materials. *Journal of Alloys and Compounds* 253: 1.
[7] Gutowska A, Li LY, Shin YS, et al. (2005) Nanoscaffold mediates hydrogen release and the reactivity of ammonia borane. *Angewandte Chemie International Edition* 44: 3578.
[8] Dillon AC, Jones KM, Bekkedahl TA, et al. (1997) Storage of hydrogen in single-walled carbon nanotubes. *Nature* 386: 377.
[9] Dresselhaus MS, Williams KA, and Eklund PC (1999) Hydrogen adsorption in carbon materials. *MRS Bulletin* 24: 45.
[10] Dillon AC and Heben MJ (2001) Hydrogen storage using carbon adsorbents: Past, present and future. *Applied Physics A: Materials Science & Processing* 72: 133.
[11] Darkrim FL, Malbrunot P, and Tartaglia GP (2002) Review of hydrogen storage by adsorption in carbon nanotubes. *International Journal of Hydrogen Energy* 27: 193.
[12] Rosi NL, Eckert J, Eddaoudi M, et al. (2003) Hydrogen storage in microporous metal-organic frameworks. *Science* 300: 1127.
[13] Dybtsev DN, Chun H, Yoon SH, et al. (2004) Microporous manganese formate: A simple metal-organic porous material with high framework stability and highly selective gas sorption properties. *Journal of the American Chemical Society* 126: 32.
[14] Kitagawa S, Kitaura R, and Noro S (2004) Functional porous coordination polymers. *Angewandte Chemie International Edition* 43: 2334.
[15] Pan L, Sander MB, Huang XY, et al. (2004) Microporous metal organic materials: Promising candidates as sorbents for hydrogen storage. *Journal of the American Chemical Society* 126: 1308.
[16] Seayad AM and Antonelli DM (2004) Recent advances in hydrogen storage in metal-containing inorganic nanostructures and related materials. *Advanced Materials* 16: 765.
[17] Rowsell JLC and Yaghi OM (2005) Strategies for hydrogen storage in metal-organic frameworks. *Angewandte Chemie International Edition* 44: 4670.
[18] Elias DC, Nair RR, Mohiuddin TMG, et al. (2009) Control of Graphene's properties by reversible hydrogenation: Evidence for Graphane. *Science* 323: 610.
[19] Berube V, Radtke G, Dresselhaus M, et al. (2007) Size effects on the hydrogen storage properties of nanostructured metal hydrides: A review. *International Journal of Energy Research* 31: 637.
[20] Varin RA, Czujko T, and Wronski Z (2006) Particle size, grain size and gamma-MgH$_2$ effects on the desorption properties of nanocrystalline commercial magnesium hydride processed by controlled mechanical milling *Nanotechnology* 17: 3856.
[21] Vajeeston P, Ravindran P, and Fjellvag H (2008) Novel high pressure phases of beta-AlH$_3$: A density-functional study. *Chemistry of Materials* 20: 5997.
[22] Alapati SV, Johnson JK, and Sholl DS (2006) Identification of destabilized metal hydrides for hydrogen storage using first principles calculations. *Journal of Physical Chemistry B* 110: 8769.
[23] Wolverton C, Siegel DJ, Akbarzadeh AR, et al. (2008) Discovery of novel hydrogen storage materials: An atomic scale computational approach. *Journal of Physics: Condensed Matter* 20: 064228.
[24] Marder TB (2007) Will we soon be fueling our automobiles with ammonia-borane? *Angewandte Chemie International Edition* 46: 8116.
[25] Stephens FH, Pons V, and Baker RT (2007) Ammonia – Borane: The hydrogen source par excellence? *Dalton Transactions* 36: 2613.
[26] Ahluwalia RK, Huaa TQ, Peng JK, et al. (2010) Technical assessment of cryo-compressed hydrogen storage tank systems for automotive applications. *International Journal of Hydrogen Energy* 35: 4171.
[27] Hua TQ, Ahluwalia RK, Peng JK, et al. (2011) Technical assessment of compressed hydrogen storage tank systems for automotive applications. *International Journal of Hydrogen Energy* 36: 3037.
[28] Lee H, Lee JW, Kim DY, et al. (2005) Tuning clathrate hydrates for hydrogen storage. *Nature* 434: 743.
[29] Morris RE and Wheatley PS (2008) Gas storage in nanoporous materials. *Angewandte Chemie International Edition* 47: 4966.
[30] Chen P, Wu X, Lin J, et al. (1999) High H$_2$ uptake by alkali-doped carbon nanotubes under ambient pressure and moderate temperatures. *Science* 285: 91.
[31] Baughman RH, Zakhidov AA, and de Heer WA (2002) Carbon nanotubes – The route toward applications. *Science* 297: 787.
[32] Zhao JJ, Buldum A, Han J, et al. (2002) Gas molecule adsorption in carbon nanotubes and nanotube bundles. *Nanotechnology* 13: 195.
[33] Chen BL, Ockwig NW, Millward AR, et al. (2005) High H$_2$ adsorption in a microporous metal-organic framework with open metal sites. *Angewandte Chemie International Edition* 44: 4745.
[34] Mueller U, Schubert M, Teich F, et al. (2006) Metal-organic frameworks – Prospective industrial applications. *Journal of Materials Chemistry* 16: 626.
[35] Sun DF, Ma SQ, Ke YX, et al. (2006) An interweaving MOF with high hydrogen uptake. *Journal of the American Chemical Society* 128: 3896.
[36] Akiba E and Iba H (1998) Hydrogen absorption by Laves phase related BCC solid solution. *Intermetallics* 6: 461.
[37] Matsunaga T, Kon M, Washio K, et al. (2009) TiCrVMo alloys with high dissociation pressure for high-pressure MH tank. *International Journal of Hydrogen Energy* 34: 1458.
[38] Vajo JJ, Skeith SL, and Mertens F (2005) Reversible storage of hydrogen in destabilized LiBH$_4$. *Journal of Physical Chemistry B* 109: 3719.
[39] Zuttel A, Rentsch S, Fischer P, et al. (2003) Hydrogen storage properties of LiBH$_4$. *Journal of Alloys and Compounds* 356: 515.
[40] Wolf G, Baumann J, Baitalow F, et al. (2000) Calorimetric process monitoring of thermal decomposition of B-N-H compounds. *Thermochimica Acta* 343: 19.
[41] Baitalow F, Baumann J, Wolf G, et al. (2002) Thermal decomposition of B-N-H compounds investigated by using combined thermoanalytical methods. *Thermochimica Acta* 391: 159.
[42] Bluhm ME, Bradley MG, Butterick R, et al. (2006) Amineborane-based chemical hydrogen storage: Enhanced ammonia borane dehydrogenation in ionic liquids. *Journal of the American Chemical Society* 128: 7748.
[43] Denney MC, Pons V, Hebden TJ, et al. (2006) Efficient catalysis of ammonia borane dehydrogenation. *Journal of the American Chemical Society* 128: 12048.
[44] Clark TJ, Whittell GR, and Manners I (2007) Highly efficient colloidal cobalt- and rhodium-catalyzed hydrolysis of H$_3$N center dot BH$_3$ in air. *Inorganic Chemistry* 46: 7522.
[45] Keaton RJ, Blacquiere JM, and Baker RT (2007) Base metal catalyzed dehydrogenation of ammonia-borane for chemical hydrogen storage. *Journal of the American Chemical Society* 129: 1844.
[46] Diyabalanage HVK, Shrestha RP, Semelsberger TA, et al. (2007) Calcium amidotrihydroborate: A hydrogen storage material. *Angewandte Chemie International Edition* 46: 8995.
[47] Xiong ZT, Chua YS, Wu GT, et al. (2008) Interaction of lithium hydride and ammonia borane in THF. *Chemical Communications* 44: 5595.
[48] Xiong ZT, Wu GT, Chua YS, et al. (2008) Synthesis of sodium amidoborane (NaNH$_2$BH$_3$) for hydrogen production. *Energy & Environmental Science* 1: 360.
[49] Xiong ZT, Yong CK, Wu GT, et al. (2008) High-capacity hydrogen storage in lithium and sodium amidoboranes. *Nature Materials* 7: 138.
[50] Wu H, Zhou W, and Yildirim T (2008) Alkali and alkaline-earth metal amidoboranes: Structure, crystal chemistry, and hydrogen storage properties. *Journal of the American Chemical Society* 130: 14834.
[51] Chua YS, Wu GT, Xiong ZT, et al. (2009) Calcium amidoborane ammoniate-synthesis, structure, and hydrogen storage properties. *Chemistry of Materials* 21: 4899.
[52] Kim DY, Singh NJ, Lee HM, et al. (2009) Hydrogen-release mechanisms in lithium amidoboranes. *Chemistry: A European Journal* 15: 5598.
[53] Shore SG and Parry RW (1955) The crystalline compound ammonia borane, H$_3$NBH$_3$. *Journal of the American Chemical Society* 77: 6084.
[54] Hughes EW (1956) The crystall structure of ammonia borane, H$_3$NBH$_3$. *Journal of the American Chemical Society* 78: 502.
[55] Lippert EL and Lipscomb WN (1956) The structure of H$_3$NBH$_3$. *Journal of the American Chemical Society* 78: 503.
[56] Smythe NC and Gordon JC (2010) Ammonia borane as a hydrogen carrier: Dehydrogenation and regeneration. *European Journal of Inorganic Chemistry* 2010: 509.

[57] Hamilton CW, Baker RT, Staubitz A, et al. (2009) B-N compounds for chemical hydrogen storage. *Chemical Society Reviews* 38: 279.
[58] Clark TJ, Lee K, and Manners I (2006) Transition-metal-catalyzed dehydrocoupling: A convenient route to bonds between main-group elements. *Chemistry: A European Journal* 12: 8634.
[59] Xu Q and Chandra M (2006) Catalytic activities of non-noble metals for hydrogen generation from aqueous ammonia-borane at room temperature. *Journal of Power Sources* 163: 364.
[60] Clark TJ and Manners I (2007) Transition metal-catalyzed dehydrocoupling of group 13-group 15 Lewis acid-base adducts. *Journal of Organometallic Chemistry* 692: 2849.
[61] Fulton JL, Linehan JC, Autrey T, et al. (2007) When is a nanoparticle a cluster? An operando EXAFS study of amine borane dehydrocoupling by Rh$_{4-6}$ clusters. *Journal of the American Chemical Society* 129: 11936.
[62] Paul A and Musgrave CB (2007) Catalyzed dehydrogenation of ammonia-borane by iridium dihydrogen pincer complex differs from ethane dehydrogenation. *Angewandte Chemie International Edition* 46: 8153.
[63] Stephens FH, Baker RT, Matus MH, et al. (2007) Acid initiation of ammonia-borane dehydrogenation for hydrogen storage. *Angewandte Chemie International Edition* 46: 746.
[64] Blaquiere N, Diallo-Garcia S, Gorelsky SI, et al. (2008) Ruthenium-catalyzed dehydrogenation of ammonia boranes. *Journal of the American Chemical Society* 130: 14034.
[65] Dietrich BL, Goldberg KI, Heinekey DM, et al. (2008) Iridium-catalyzed dehydrogenation of substituted amine boranes: Kinetics, thermodynamics, and implications for hydrogen storage. *Inorganic Chemistry* 47: 8583.
[66] Yan JM, Zhang XB, Han S, et al. (2008) Iron-nanoparticle-catalyzed hydrolytic dehydrogenation of ammonia borane for chemical hydrogen storage. *Angewandte Chemie International Edition* 47: 2287.
[67] Yao CF, Zhuang L, Cao YL, et al. (2008) Hydrogen release from hydrolysis of borazane on Pt- and Ni-based alloy catalysts. *International Journal of Hydrogen Energy* 33: 2462.
[68] He T, Xiong ZT, Wu GT, et al. (2009) Nanosized Co- and Ni-catalyzed ammonia borane for hydrogen storage. *Chemistry of Materials* 21: 2315.
[69] Kalidindi SB, Joseph J, and Jagirdar BR (2009) Cu2+-induced room temperature hydrogen release from ammonia borane. *Energy & Environmental Science* 2: 1274.
[70] Li L, Yao X, Sun CH, et al. (2009) Lithium-catalyzed dehydrogenation of ammonia borane within mesoporous carbon framework for chemical hydrogen storage. *Advanced Functional Materials* 19: 265.
[71] Li YQ, Xie L, Li Y, et al. (2009) Metal-organic-framework-based catalyst for highly efficient H$_2$ generation from aqueous NH$_3$BH$_3$ solution. *Chemistry: A European Journal* 15: 8951.
[72] Feaver A, Sepehri S, Shamberger P, et al. (2007) Coherent carbon cryogel-ammonia borane nanocomposites for H$_2$ storage. *Journal of Physical Chemistry B* 111: 7469.
[73] Zhao JZ, Shi JF, Zhang XW, et al. (2010) A soft hydrogen storage material: Poly(methyl acrylate)-confined ammonia borane with controllable dehydrogenation. *Advanced Materials* 22: 394.
[74] Kang XD, Fang ZZ, Kong LY, et al. (2008) Ammonia borane destabilized by lithium hydride: An advanced on-board hydrogen storage material. *Advanced Materials* 20: 2756.
[75] Lee TB and McKee ML (2009) Mechanistic study of LiNH$_2$BH$_3$ formation from (LiH)(4) + NH$_3$BH$_3$ and subsequent dehydrogenation. *Inorganic Chemistry* 48: 7564.
[76] Fijakowski KJ and Grochala W (2009) Substantial emission of NH$_3$ during thermal decomposition of sodium amidoborane, NaNH$_2$BH$_3$. *Journal of Materials Chemistry* 19: 2043.
[77] Zhang QG, Tang CX, Fang CH, et al. (2010) Synthesis, crystal structure, and thermal decomposition of strontium amidoborane. *Journal of Physical Chemistry C* 114: 1709.
[78] Wu CZ, Wu GT, Xiong ZT, et al. (2010) LiNH$_2$BH$_3$ center dot NH$_3$BH$_3$: Structure and hydrogen storage properties. *Chemistry of Materials* 22: 3.
[79] Graham KR, Kemmitt T, and Bowden ME (2009) High capacity hydrogen storage in a hybrid ammonia borane-lithium amide material. *Energy & Environmental Science* 2: 706.
[80] Jensen CM and Gross KJ (2001) Development of catalytically enhanced sodium aluminum hydride as a hydrogen-storage material. *Applied Physics A: Materials Science & Processing* 72: 213.
[81] Sandrock G, Gross K, and Thomas G (2002) Effect of Ti-catalyst content on the reversible hydrogen storage properties of the sodium alanates. *Journal of Alloys and Compounds* 339: 299.
[82] Schuth F, Bogdanovic B, and Felderhoff M (2004) Light metal hydrides and complex hydrides for hydrogen storage. *Chemical Communications* 40: 2249.
[83] Sakintuna B, Lamari-Darkrim F, and Hirscher M (2007) Metal hydride materials for solid hydrogen storage: A review. *International Journal of Hydrogen Energy* 32: 1121.
[84] Soulie JP, Renaudin G, Cerny R, et al. (2002) Lithium boro-hydride LiBH$_4$. *Journal of Alloys and Compounds* 346: 200.
[85] Miwa K, Ohba N, Towata S, et al. (2004) First-principles study on lithium borohydride LiBH4. *Physical Review B* 69: 245120.
[86] Lodziana Z and Vegge T (2004) Structural stability of complex hydrides: LiBH$_4$ revisited. *Physical Review Letters* 93: 145501.
[87] Ozolins V, Majzoub EH, and Wolverton C (2008) First-principles prediction of a ground state crystal structure of magnesium borohydride. *Physical Review Letters* 100: 135501.
[88] Her JH, Stephens PW, Gao Y, et al. (2007) Structure of unsolvated magnesium borohydride Mg(BH$_4$)$_2$. *Acta Crystallographica Section B: Structural Science* 63: 561.
[89] Filinchuk Y, Chernyshov D, and Dmitriev V (2008) Light metal borohydrides: Crystal structures and beyond. *Zeitschrift Fur Kristallographie* 223: 649.
[90] Miwa K, Aoki M, Noritake T, et al. (2006) Thermodynamical stability of calcium borohydride Ca(BH$_4$)$_2$. *Physical Review B* 74: 155122.
[91] Riktor MD, Sorby MH, Chlopek K, et al. (2007) In situ synchrotron diffraction studies of phase transitions and thermal decomposition of Mg(BH$_4$)$_2$ and Ca(BH$_4$)$_2$. *Journal of Materials Chemistry* 17: 4939.
[92] Buchter F, Lodziana Z, Remhof A, et al. (2008) Structure of Ca(BD$_4$)$_2$ beta-phase from combined neutron and synchrotron X-ray powder diffraction data and density functional calculations. *Journal of Physical Chemistry B* 112: 8042.
[93] Pinkerton FE, Meisner GP, Meyer MS, et al. (2005) Hydrogen desorption exceeding ten weight percent from the new quaternary hydride Li$_3$BN$_2$H$_8$. *Journal of Physical Chemistry B* 109: 6.
[94] Meisner GP, Scullin ML, Balogh MP, et al. (2006) Hydrogen release from mixtures of lithium borohydride and lithium amide: A phase diagram study. *Journal of Physical Chemistry B* 110: 4186.
[95] Filinchuk YE, Yvon K, Meisner GP, et al. (2006) On the composition and crystal structure of the new quaternary hydride phase Li$_4$BN$_3$H$_{10}$. *Inorganic Chemistry* 45: 1433.
[96] Aoki M, Miwa K, Noritake T, et al. (2005) Destabilization of LiBH$_4$ by mixing with LiNH$_2$. *Applied Physics A: Materials Science & Processing* 80: 1409.
[97] Vajo JJ, Salguero TT, Gross AE, et al. (2007) Thermodynamic destabilization and reaction kinetics in light metal hydride systems. *Journal of Alloys and Compounds* 446: 409.
[98] Bosenberg U, Doppiu S, Mosegaard L, et al. (2007) Hydrogen sorption properties of MgH$_2$-LiBH$_4$ composites. *Acta Materialia* 55: 3951.
[99] Pinkerton FE and Meyer MS (2008) Reversible hydrogen storage in the lithium borohydride-calcium hydride coupled system. *Journal of Alloys and Compounds* 464: L1.
[100] Jin SA, Lee YS, Shim JH, et al. (2008) Reversible hydrogen storage in LiBH$_4$-MH$_2$ (M = Ce, Ca) composites. *Journal of Physical Chemistry C* 112: 9520.
[101] Barkhordarian G, Jensen TR, Doppiu S, et al. (2008) Formation of Ca(BH$_4$)$_2$ from hydrogenation of CaH$_2$+MgB$_2$ composite. *Journal of Physical Chemistry C* 112: 2743.
[102] Li HW, Kikuchi K, Nakamori Y, et al. (2008) Dehydriding and rehydriding processes of well-crystallized Mg(BH$_4$)$_2$ accompanying with formation of intermediate compounds. *Acta Materialia* 56: 1342.
[103] Li HW, Kikuchi K, Nakamori Y, et al. (2007) Effects of ball milling and additives on dehydriding behaviors of well-crystallized Mg(BH$_4$)$_2$. *Scripta Materialia* 57: 679.
[104] Chlopek K, Frommen C, Leon A, et al. (2007) Synthesis and properties of magnesium tetrahydroborate, Mg(BH$_4$)$_2$. *Journal of Materials Chemistry* 17: 3496.
[105] Nakamori Y, Li HW, Miwa K, et al. (2006) Syntheses and hydrogen desorption properties of metal-borohydrides M(BH$_4$)$_n$ (M = Mg, Sc, Zr, Ti, and Zn; n=2-4) as advanced hydrogen storage materials. *Materials Transactions* 47: 1898.
[106] Matsunaga T, Buchter F, Mauron P, et al. (2008) Hydrogen storage properties of Mg[BH$_4$]$_2$. *Journal of Alloys and Compounds* 459: 583.
[107] Ozolins V, Majzoub EH, and Wolverton C (2009) First-principles prediction of thermodynamically reversible hydrogen storage reactions in the Li-Mg-Ca-B-H system. *Journal of the American Chemical Society* 131: 230.
[108] Kim JH, Jin SA, Shim JH, et al. (2008) Reversible hydrogen storage in calcium borohydride Ca(BH$_4$)$_2$. *Scripta Materialia* 58: 481.
[109] Kim JH, Jin SA, Shim JH, et al. (2008) Thermal decomposition behavior of calcium borohydride Ca(BH$_4$)$_2$. *Journal of Alloys and Compounds* 461: L20.
[110] Kim JH, Shim JH, and Cho YW (2008) On the reversibility of hydrogen storage in Ti- and Nb-catalyzed Ca(BH$_4$)$_2$. *Journal of Power Sources* 181: 140.

[111] Nakamori Y, Miwa K, Ninomiya A, et al. (2006) Correlation between thermodynamical stabilities of metal borohydrides and cation electronegativites: First-principles calculations and experiments. *Physical Review B* 74: 045126.
[112] Hwang SJ, Bowman RC, Reiter JW, et al. (2008) NMR confirmation for formation of $[B_{12}H_{12}]^{2-}$ complexes during hydrogen desorption from metal borohydrides. *Journal of Physical Chemistry C* 112: 3164.
[113] Soloveichik G, Her JH, Stephens PW, et al. (2008) Ammine magnesium borohydride complex as a new material for hydrogen storage: Structure and properties of $Mg(BH_4)_2$ center dot $2NH_3$. *Inorganic Chemistry* 47: 4290.
[114] Ichikawa T, Isobe S, Hanada N, et al. (2004) Lithium nitride for reversible hydrogen storage. *Journal of Alloys and Compounds* 365: 271.
[115] Xiong ZT, Chen P, Wu GT, et al. (2003) Investigations into the interaction between hydrogen and calcium nitride. *Journal of Materials Chemistry* 13: 1676.
[116] Leng HY, Ichikawa T, Hino S, et al. (2004) New metal-N-H system composed of $Mg(NH_2)_2$ and LiH for hydrogen storage. *Journal of Physical Chemistry B* 108: 8763, 12628.
[117] Luo WF (2004) ($LiNH_2$-MgH_2): A viable hydrogen storage system. *Journal of Alloys and Compounds* 381: 284.
[118] Nakamori Y, Kitahara G, and Orimo S (2004) Synthesis and dehydriding studies of Mg-N-H systems. *Journal of Power Sources* 138: 309.
[119] Nakamori Y and Orimo S (2004) Destabilization of Li-based complex hydrides. *Journal of Alloys and Compounds* 370: 271.
[120] Nakamori Y and Orimo S (2004) Li-N based hydrogen storage materials. *Materials Science and Engineering B: Solid State Materials for Advanced Technology* 108: 48.
[121] Orimo S, Nakamori Y, Kitahara G, et al. (2004) Destabilization and enhanced dehydriding reaction of $LiNH_2$: An electronic structure viewpoint. *Applied Physics A: Materials Science & Processing* 79: 1765.
[122] Xiong ZT, Wu GT, Hu HJ, et al. (2004) Ternary imides for hydrogen storage. *Advanced Materials* 16: 1522.
[123] Chen P, Xiong ZT, Wu GT, et al. (2005) Development of metal-N-H compounds for hydrogen storage. *Abstracts of Papers of the American Chemical Society* 230: U1642.
[124] Herbst JF and Hector LG (2005) Energetics of the Li amide/Li imide hydrogen storage reaction. *Physical Review B* 72: 125120.
[125] Hino S, Ichikawa T, Leng HY, et al. (2005) Hydrogen desorption properties of the Ca-N-H system. *Journal of Alloys and Compounds* 398: 62.
[126] Ichikawa T, Hanada N, Isobe S, et al. (2005) Hydrogen storage properties in Ti catalyzed Li-N-H system. *Journal of Alloys and Compounds* 404: 435.
[127] Isobe S, Ichikawa T, Hanada N, et al. (2005) Effect of Ti catalyst with different chemical form on Li-N-H hydrogen storage properties. *Journal of Alloys and Compounds* 404: 439.
[128] Nakamori Y, Kitahara G, Miwa K, et al. (2005) Hydrogen storage properties of Li-Mg-N-H systems. *Journal of Alloys and Compounds* 404: 396.
[129] Nakamori Y, Kitahara G, Miwa K, et al. (2005) Reversible hydrogen-storage functions for mixtures of Li_3N and Mg_3N_2. *Applied Physics A: Materials Science & Processing* 80: 1.
[130] Nakamori Y, Kitahara G, Ninomiya A, et al. (2005) Guidelines for developing amide-based hydrogen storage materials. *Materials Transactions* 46: 2093.
[131] Pinkerton FE (2005) Decomposition kinetics of lithium amide for hydrogen storage materials. *Journal of Alloys and Compounds* 400: 76.
[132] Xiong ZT, Hu JJ, Wu GT, et al. (2005) Hydrogen absorption and desorption in Mg-Na-N-H system. *Journal of Alloys and Compounds* 395: 209.
[133] Chater PA, David WIF, Johnson SR, et al. (2006) Synthesis and crystal structure of $Li_4BH_4(NH_2)_3$. *Chemical Communications* 42: 2439.
[134] Hu JJ, Wu GT, Liu YF, et al. (2006) Hydrogen release from $Mg(NH_2)_2$-MgH_2 through mechanochemical reaction. *Journal of Physical Chemistry B* 110: 14688.
[135] Hu JJ, Xiong ZT, Wu GT, et al. (2006) Hydrogen releasing reaction between $Mg(NH_2)_2$ and CaH_2. *Journal of Power Sources* 159: 116.
[136] Kojima Y, Matsumoto M, Kawai Y, et al. (2006) Hydrogen absorption and desorption by the Li-Al-N-H system. *Journal of Physical Chemistry B* 110: 9632.
[137] Liu YF, Xiong ZT, Hu JJ, et al. (2006) Hydrogen absorption/desorption behaviors over a quaternary Mg-Ca-Li-N-H system. *Journal of Power Sources* 159: 135.
[138] Lu J, Fang ZZ, and Sohn HY (2006) A new Li-Al-N-H system for reversible hydrogen storage. *Journal of Physical Chemistry B* 110: 14236.
[139] Luo WF and Sickafoose S (2006) Thermodynamic and structural characterization of the Mg-Li-N-H hydrogen storage system. *Journal of Alloys and Compounds* 407: 274.
[140] Xiong ZT, Wu GT, Hu JJ, et al. (2006) Investigations on hydrogen storage over Li-Mg-N-H complex – The effect of compositional changes. *Journal of Alloys and Compounds* 417: 190.
[141] David WIF, Jones MO, Gregory DH, et al. (2007) A mechanism for non-stoichiometry in the lithium amide/lithium imide hydrogen storage reaction. *Journal of the American Chemical Society* 129: 1594.
[142] Liu Y, Hu J, Wu G, et al. (2007) Large amount of hydrogen desorption from the mixture of $Mg(NH_2)_2$ and $LiAlH_4$. *Journal of Physical Chemistry C* 111: 19161.
[143] Liu YF, Hu JJ, Xiong ZT, et al. (2007) Investigations on hydrogen desorption from the mixture of $Mg(NH_2)_2$ and CaH_2. *Journal of Alloys and Compounds* 432: 298.
[144] Lu J, Fang ZZ, Sohn HY, et al. (2007) Potential and reaction mechanism of Li-Al-N-H system for reversible hydrogen storage. *Journal of Physical Chemistry C* 111: 16686.
[145] Osborn W, Markmaitree T, and Shaw LL (2007) Evaluation of the hydrogen storage behavior of a $LiNH_2$+MgH_2 system with 1 : 1 ratio. *Journal of Power Sources* 172: 376.
[146] Wu GT, Xiong ZT, Liu T, et al. (2007) Synthesis and characterization of a new ternary imide-$Li_2Ca(NH)_2$. *Inorganic Chemistry* 46: 517.
[147] Xiong ZT, Hu JJ, Wu GT, et al. (2007) Large amount of hydrogen desorption and stepwise phase transition in the chemical reaction of $NaNH_2$ and $LiAlH_4$. *Catalysis Today* 120: 287.
[148] Xiong ZT, Wu GT, Hu JJ, et al. (2007) Ca-Na-N-H system for reversible hydrogen storage. *Journal of Alloys and Compounds* 441: 152.
[149] Xiong ZT, Wu GT, Hu JJ, et al. (2007) Reversible hydrogen storage by a Li-Al-N-H complex. *Advanced Functional Materials* 17: 1137.
[150] Yang J, Sudik A, Siegel DJ, et al. (2007) Hydrogen storage properties of $2LiNH_2$+ $LiBH_4$+MgH_2. *Journal of Alloys and Compounds* 446: 345.
[151] Shaw LL, Osborn W, Markmitree T, et al. (2008) The reaction pathway and rate-limiting step of dehydrogenation of the $LiNH_2$+LiH mixture. *Journal of Power Sources* 177: 500.
[152] Sudik A, Yang J, Halliday D, et al. (2008) Hydrogen storage properties in $(LiNH_2)_2$-$LiBH_4$-$(MgH_2)X$ mixtures (X=0.0-1.0). *Journal of Physical Chemistry C* 112: 4384.
[153] Wu H (2008) Structure of ternary imide $Li_2Ca(NH)_2$ and hydrogen storage mechanisms in amide-hydride system. *Journal of the American Chemical Society* 130: 6515.
[154] Yang J, Sudik A, Siegel DJ, et al. (2008) A self-catalyzing hydrogen-storage material. *Angewandte Chemie International Edition* 47: 882.
[155] Kojima Y and Kawai Y (2004) Hydrogen storage of metal nitride by a mechanochemical reaction. *Chemical Communications* 40: 2210.
[156] Pinkerton FE, Meyer MS, Meisner GP, et al. (2006) Improved hydrogen release from $LiB_{0.33}N_{0.67}H_{2.67}$ with noble metal additions. *Journal of Physical Chemistry B* 110: 7967.
[157] Pinkerton FE, Meyer MS, Meisner GP, et al. (2007) Phase boundaries and reversibility of $LiBH_4$/MgH_2 hydrogen storage material. *Journal of Physical Chemistry C* 111: 12881.
[158] Chater PA, Anderson PA, Prendergast JW, et al. (2007) Synthesis and characterization of amide-borohydrides: New complex light hydrides for potential hydrogen storage. *Journal of Alloys and Compounds* 446: 350.
[159] Chater PA, David WIF, and Anderson PA (2007) Synthesis and structure of the new complex hydride $Li_2BH_4NH_2$. *Chemical Communications* 43: 4770.
[160] Pinkerton FE, Meyer MS, Meisner GP, et al. (2007) Improved hydrogen release from $LiB_{0.33}N_{0.67}H_{2.67}$ with metal additives: Ni, Fe, and Zn. *Journal of Alloys and Compounds* 433: 282.
[161] Tang WS, Wu G, Liu T, et al. (2008) Cobalt-catalyzed hydrogen desorption from the $LiNH_2$–$LiBH_4$ system. *Dalton Transactions* 37: 2395.
[162] Xiong ZT, Hu JJ, Wu GT, et al. (2005) Thermodynamic and kinetic investigations of the hydrogen storage in the Li-Mg-N-H system. *Journal of Alloys and Compounds* 398: 235.
[163] Ichikawa T, Tokoyoda K, Leng HY, et al. (2005) Hydrogen absorption properties of Li-Mg-N-H system. *Journal of Alloys and Compounds* 400: 245.
[164] Ichikawa T, Leng HY, Isobe S, et al. (2006) Recent development on hydrogen storage properties in metal-N-H systems. *Journal of Power Sources* 159: 126.
[165] Leng H, Ichikawa T, and Fujii H (2006) Hydrogen storage properties of Li-Mg-N-H systems with different ratios of $LiH/Mg(NH_2)_2$. *Journal of Physical Chemistry B* 110: 12964.
[166] Aoki M, Noritake T, Kitahara G, et al. (2007) Dehydriding reaction of $Mg(NH_2)_2$-LiH system under hydrogen pressure. *Journal of Alloys and Compounds* 428: 307.
[167] Janot R, Eymery JB, and Tarascon JM (2007) Investigation of the processes for reversible hydrogen storage in the Li-Mg-N-H system. *Journal of Power Sources* 164: 496.
[168] Liu YF, Hu JJ, Xiong ZT, et al. (2007) Improvement of the hydrogen-storage performances of Li-Mg-N-H system. *Journal of Materials Research* 22: 1339.
[169] Nakagawa T, Ichikawa T, Iida R, et al. (2007) Observation of hydrogen absorption/desorption reaction processes in Li-Mg-N-H system by in-situ X-ray diffractmetry. *Journal of Alloys and Compounds* 430: 217.
[170] Sorby MH, Nakamura Y, Brinks HW, et al. (2007) The crystal structure of $LiND_2$ and $Mg(ND_2)_2$. *Journal of Alloys and Compounds* 428: 297.
[171] Tsumuraya T, Shishidou T, and Oguchi T (2007) First-principles study on lithium and magnesium nitrogen hydrides for hydrogen storage. *Journal of Alloys and Compounds* 446: 323.
[172] Wang Y and Chou MY (2007) First-principles study of cation and hydrogen arrangements in the Li-Mg-N-H hydrogen storage system. *Physical Review B* 76: 014116.

[173] Yang J, Sudik A, and Wolverton C (2007) Activation of hydrogen storage materials in the Li-Mg-N-H system: Effect on storage properties. *Journal of Alloys and Compounds* 430: 334.
[174] Hu JJ, Liu YF, Wu GT, *et al.* (2008) Improvement of hydrogen storage properties of the Li-Mg-N-H system by addition of LiBH$_4$. *Chemistry of Materials* 20: 4398.
[175] Isobe S, Ichikawa T, Leng HY, *et al.* (2008) Hydrogen desorption processes in Li-Mg-N-H systems. *Journal of Physics and Chemistry of Solids* 69: 2234.
[176] Liu YF, Hu JJ, Wu GT, *et al.* (2008) Formation and equilibrium of ammonia in the Mg(NH$_2$)$_2$-2LiH hydrogen storage system. *Journal of Physical Chemistry C* 112: 1293.
[177] Ma LP, Wang P, Dai HB, *et al.* (2009) Catalytically enhanced dehydrogenation of Li-Mg-N-H hydrogen storage material by transition metal nitrides. *Journal of Alloys and Compounds* 468: L21.
[178] Wang JH, Liu T, Wu GT, *et al.* (2009) Potassium-modified Mg(NH$_2$)$_2$/2 LiH system for hydrogen storage. *Angewandte Chemie International Edition* 48: 5828.
[179] Leng HY, Ichikawa T, Hino S, *et al.* (2004) New metal-N-H system composed of Mg(NH$_2$)$_2$ and LiH for hydrogen storage. *Journal of Physical Chemistry B* 108: 8763.
[180] Rijssenbeek J, Gao Y, Hanson J, *et al.* (2008) Crystal structure determination and reaction pathway of amide-hydride mixtures. *Journal of Alloys and Compounds* 454: 233.
[181] Alapati SV, Johnson JK, and Sholl DS (2007) Using first principles calculations to identify new destabilized metal hydride reactions for reversible hydrogen storage. *Physical Chemistry Chemical Physics* 9: 1438.
[182] Chen P, Xiong ZT, Wu GT, *et al.* (2007) Metal-N-H systems for the hydrogen storage. *Scripta Materialia* 56: 817.

4.07 Alkaline Fuel Cells: Theory and Application

F Bidault, Imperial College London, London, UK
PH Middleton, University of Agder, Grimstad, Norway

© 2012 Elsevier Ltd.

4.07.1	Introduction	160
4.07.2	General Principles and Fundamentals of Alkaline Cells	160
4.07.2.1	Cathode Catalyst Materials	162
4.07.2.2	Platinum Group Metal Catalysts	162
4.07.2.3	Non-Platinum Group Metal Catalysts	163
4.07.2.4	Cathodes Performance	163
4.07.2.5	Anode Catalyst Materials	163
4.07.3	Alkaline Fuel Cells Developed with Liquid Electrolytes	165
4.07.3.1	Gas Diffusion Electrode for AFC	165
4.07.3.1.1	Electrode design	166
4.07.3.1.2	Materials used in electrode fabrication	166
4.07.3.1.3	Operational mechanism	167
4.07.3.1.4	Electrode modeling	167
4.07.3.1.5	Electrode fabrication	168
4.07.3.1.6	Electrode durability	169
4.07.3.2	Stack and System Design	170
4.07.3.3	System Achievements	172
4.07.3.3.1	Space systems	172
4.07.3.3.2	Terrestrial systems	173
4.07.4	Alkaline Fuel Cell Based on Anion Exchange Membranes	175
4.07.4.1	Anion Exchange Membrane Chemistry and Challenges	175
4.07.4.2	Review of the Main Classes of AEMs	177
4.07.4.3	Ionomer Development/Membrane Electrode Assembly Fabrication	178
4.07.4.4	Alkaline Anion Exchange Membrane Fuel Cells Performance	178
4.07.4.4.1	Hydrogen as fuel	178
4.07.4.4.2	Alcohol fuels	179
4.07.4.4.3	Sodium borohydride fuel	180
4.07.5	Conclusions	181
References		181

Glossary

Anion exchange membrane (AEM) A polymer electrolyte membrane that contains positively charged groups and conducts anions. In this chapter, we refer to AEMs that contain predominantly hydroxide (OH^-), carbonate (CO_3^{2-}), or hydrogen carbonate (HCO_3^-) anions.

Alkaline fuel cell A fuel cell that uses an aqueous alkali metal hydroxide electrolyte such as KOH solutions.

Alkaline membrane direct alcohol fuel cell A low-temperature polymer electrolyte fuel cell that contains an AEM and is supplied with alcohol/air (or O_2) at the anode/cathode.

Anion exchange membrane fuel cell A low-temperature polymer electrolyte fuel cell that contains an AEM and is supplied with H_2/air (or O_2) at the anode/cathode.

Ionomer An ionic conductor material that is used as catalyst binder and to improve the ionic conductivity in the active layer of the electrode. It also reduces the interfacial resistance between the membrane and the electrode during membrane electrode assembly fabrication. In this chapter, we refer to anionic ionomers that are anion conductive materials (counterpart of Nafion® for PEMFCs).

Proton exchange membrane fuel cell (PEMFC) A low temperature polymer electrolyte fuel cell that contains a proton exchange membrane and is supplied with H_2/air (or O_2) at the anode/cathode.

Proton exchange membrane A polymer electrolyte membrane that contains negatively charged or neutral ether groups and conducts protons (H+).

Quaternary ammonium A chemical functional group where a nitrogen atom is bonded to four other groups, via N–C bonds, and has a positive charge.

4.07.1 Introduction

Alkaline fuel cells (AFCs) were the first practically working fuel cells capable of delivering significant power, particularly for transport applications. The pioneering work of Francis Thomas Bacon in the 1930s at the University of Cambridge [1] led to a number of significant advances and innovations especially the development of porous, sintered nickel electrodes. Bacon demonstrated the first viable fuel cell power unit in the mid-1950s. This system was the starting point of a new technology using alkaline liquid electrolyte, which led to its use as the electrical power source in the Apollo missions to the Moon and later in the space shuttle Orbiter. This system was developed and studied extensively throughout the 1960s to the 1980s prior to the emergence of the proton exchange membrane fuel cell (PEMFC), which has subsequently attracted most of the attention of the developers. The main difficulties with these early AFCs were the management of the liquid electrolyte, which was difficult to immobilize and faced problems related to the absorption of carbon dioxide from ambient air which caused both loss in conductivity and precipitation of carbonate species. Whereas PEMFCs have shown significant progress during the past 10 years in terms of power density and durability, their predicted cost reduction remains problematic due to their reliance on the use of platinum (Pt) as catalyst and fluoropolymer backbone membrane (Nafion®) as electrolyte. These expensive materials have been a factor in precluding mass production and have limited the application of PEMFCs to niche markets or demonstration projects. In recent years, a resurgence of interest in AFCs has occurred with the development of anion exchange membranes (AEMs). Indeed, recent advances in materials science and chemistry enabled the production of membrane and ionomer materials which would allow the development of the alkaline equivalent to PEMFCs. The application of these AEMs promises a quantum leap in fuel cell viability because catalysis of fuel cell reactions is faster under alkaline conditions than acidic conditions [2]. Indeed, non-platinum catalysts perform very favorably in this environment and open a wide range of possible materials both on the cathode side and on the anode side, which make AEM fuel cell (AEMFC) a potential low-cost technology compared to PEMFC. New chemical routes are being developed for synthesizing different alkaline membranes not dependent on a fluoropolymer backbone. Use of such membranes could also reduce stack costs when compared with PEMFC.

In this chapter, the general principles of operation of AFCs are given showing the inherent advantages and disadvantages of the technology. This begins with a discussion of catalysts that can be used for both the traditional AFCs and the new generation of AEMFCs. The oxygen reduction reaction (ORR) and the hydrogen oxidation reaction (HOR) are explained for the alkaline case with special attention to the description of the ORR since this is where most of the recent innovations in catalyst designs have been focused. The main catalysts developed for ORR and HOR are given and typical performance data shown. These data are presented in Section 4.07.2 because the catalysts for both ORR and HOR can be applied to either AFCs or AEMFCs. The sensitivity of the electrolyte to CO_2 and its effect of cell performance are addressed. The development of liquid electrolyte AFCs is then covered starting from an electrode point of view going through stack designs to finish with systems achievements, performance, and durability. In a final part, the recent development of AEMs will be treated reviewing the state-of-the-art performance of these membranes addressing the different chemistries involved, stability, and performance in terms of conductivity. The diverse applications of these new membranes is also discussed listing the different fuels used, and where available the state-of the-art performance is also discussed. To avoid confusion, in this chapter the acronym AFC refers to liquid electrolyte AFCs and AEMFC refers to solid electrolyte AFCs using a membrane electrolyte.

4.07.2 General Principles and Fundamentals of Alkaline Cells

As can be seen in **Table 1**, the AFC can be operated over a wide range of temperatures from what is considered low temperature (~70 °C) to intermediate temperature (~250 °C) depending on the complexity of the system to run the stack and the performance required. Indeed, an increase in temperature above 100 °C would require a pressurized system to prevent the electrolyte from boiling. PEMFCs and AEMFCs are limited to low temperatures due to the degradation of the membrane at elevated temperatures.

The basic function of the alkaline cell is shown in **Figure 1**. The electrolyte is a hydroxide ion conductor which in the case of liquid electrolyte is readily achieved using a strong aqueous solution of potassium hydroxide (KOH) – typically 30–50 wt%. The corresponding pH can be as high as 15. The cathodic reaction (ORR) under alkaline conditions produces hydroxide ions that migrate through the electrolyte to the anode where they are consumed in the hydrogen reaction (HOR) to produce the overall product water. Some of the water formed at the anode diffuses to the cathode and reacts with oxygen to form hydroxyl ions in a continuous process. This defines one of the basic differences between AFC and PEM. In the PEM case, the product water is produced at the cathode. The overall reaction produces water and heat as by-products and generates four electrons per mole of oxygen, which travel via an external circuit producing the electrical current. The theoretical electromotive force (EMF) (at 24 °C and 1 atm pressure for pure H_2/O_2) is given by the ΔG value of -237.13 kJ mol, which is equivalent to an EMF of $+1.23$ V. If the system runs on air, the value is a little less at 1.2 V. In practice, values ranging between 1 and 1.1 V are achievable on open circuit [3].

A more obvious comparison can be drawn between the AFC and the phosphoric acid fuel cell (PAFC) – in that both use liquid electrolytes that are alkaline, in the first case, and phosphoric acid, in the latter case. Under similar operating conditions, the AFC offers the following advantages:

- Cell life may be longer than that of acid cells because of the greater compatibility between the alkaline electrolyte and practical cell materials especially metals such as nickel that is corrosion resistant at high pH and can be used in the construction of interconnects and end plates.

Table 1   Different types of low and intermediate temperature fuel cells

Fuel cell type	Electrolyte charge carrier	Principal catalyst	Typical operating temperature	Fuel compatibility	Primary contaminant
PEMFC (Proton exchange membrane)	Solid polymer membrane H$^+$	Platinum	60–80 °C	H$_2$, methanol	CO, sulfur and NH$_3$
AAEMFC (Alkaline anion exchange membrane)	Solid polymer membrane OH$^-$	Platinum Silver Nickel	40–60 °C	H$_2$, methanol …	CO, CO$_2$ and sulfur
PAFC (Phosphoric acid)	H$_3$PO$_4$ solution H$^+$	Platinum	150–220 °C	H$_2$	CO < 1%, sulfur
AFC (Alkaline)	KOH solution OH$^-$	Platinum Silver Nickel	70–250 °C	H$_2$	CO, CO$_2$ and sulfur

Cathode: $O_2 + 2H_2O + 4e^- \rightarrow 4OH^-$

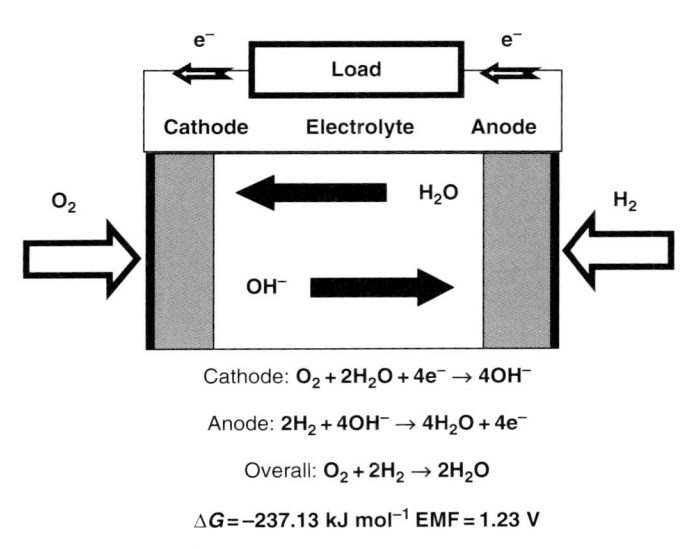

Anode: $2H_2 + 4OH^- \rightarrow 4H_2O + 4e^-$

Overall: $O_2 + 2H_2 \rightarrow 2H_2O$

$\Delta G = -237.13$ kJ mol^{-1} EMF = 1.23 V

Figure 1   Diagram showing the fundamentals of an alkaline fuel cell.

- Thermodynamic considerations show that the choice of possible catalysts is wider.
- AFCs can operate at higher thermodynamic efficiencies (up to 60% based on lower heating value (LHV)) on pure H$_2$ than PAFCs (50%).
- The cell component cost per m^2 of AFCs is substantially lower than that for PAFCs.

The power output and lifetime of alkaline cells are directly linked to the behavior of the cathode, where most of the polarization losses occur (at high current density of up to 80%). This is because the ORR is a sluggish reaction compared with the HOR occurring at the anode (the overpotential at the anode, operating at current densities of < 400 mA cm^{-2} is about 20 mV compared to at least 10–15 times this value experiences at the cathode). This is the principal reason why most catalyst developments have focused on the cathode.

Alkaline cells can realize a higher overall electrical efficiency (up to 60% LHV) than most other fuel cell types mainly because the ORR in alkaline media is more facile than that in acid media. As a consequence, higher voltages can be obtained at a given current density. This can be illustrated by comparing the performance of an AFC and PAFC running with similar H$_2$/O$_2$ fuel and oxidant and at a similar controlled current density of 100 mA cm^{-2}, at the same temperature of 70 °C, and with similar platinum electrodes. In the case of the PAFC, a potential of 0.67 V for 13.9 M H$_3$PO$_4$ was observed, whereas in the case of the AFC a potential of 0.89 V for 6.9 M KOH versus a hydrogen reference electrode was reported – the AFC producing an additional 0.22 V, a huge improvement. The higher voltage (performance) of the alkaline system was explained by the preferred formation of peroxide species in the alkaline medium that desorbs more readily than in the acid counterpart [4].

The ORR is a complex process involving four coupled proton and electron transfer steps. Several of the elementary steps involve reaction intermediates leading to a wide choice of reaction pathways. The exact sequence of the reactions is still not known, and identification of all reaction steps and intermediates and their kinetic parameters is required, which is clearly challenging. In acid electrolyte, the ORR reaction is electrocatalytic, but as pH values of acid become alkaline's, redox processes involving superoxide and peroxide ions start to play a role and become dominant in strongly alkali media as used in AFCs. The reaction in alkaline electrolytes may stop with the formation of the relatively stable HO_2^- solvated ion, which is easily disproportionated or oxidized to dioxygen. Although there is no consensus on the exact reaction sequence, two overall pathways take place in alkaline media:

1. Direct four-electron pathway

$$O_2 + 2H_2O + 4e^- \rightarrow 4OH^- \qquad [1]$$

2. Peroxide pathway or 'two + two-electron' pathway

$$O_2 + H_2O + 2e^- \rightarrow HO_2^- + OH^- \qquad [2]$$

with

$$HO_2^- + H_2O + 2e^- \rightarrow 3OH^- \qquad [3]$$

The peroxide produced may also undergo catalytic decomposition with the formation of dioxygen and OH^-, given by

$$2HO_2^- \rightarrow 2OH^- + O_2 \qquad [4]$$

Thermodynamic analysis can be used to explain the origin of the pH effect, showing that the overpotential required to facilitate the four-electron transfer process at high pH is relatively small compared to the potential required at low pH. At high pH, no specific chemical interaction between the catalyst and O_2 or O_2^- is required, whereas strong chemical interaction is necessary at low pH. It has also to be noted that the low activity of catalysts in acid media is exacerbated by the presence of spectator species adsorbed onto the electrode surface, which act to physically block the active sites and also lower the adsorption energy for intermediates, so retarding the reaction rate.

Due to the inherently faster kinetics for the ORR in alkaline media, a wide range of catalysts have been studied including platinum group metals (PGMs) such as Pt or silver (Ag), transition metals such as Co or Mn, diverse oxide materials such as perovskites or spinels, and pyrolyzed macrocycles. Whereas carbon supports show poor electrochemical activity in acidic media, carbon blacks, and graphites have been shown to catalyze the ORR in alkaline media with the formation of HO_2^- in a two-electron process, where high surface area carbon blacks such as Vulcan XC-72R (25 nm, 250 m^2g^{-1}) showed better activities compared with graphite. It is important to appreciate that the carbon support plays a role in the ORR and influences the kinetics of the catalyst supported on its surface. The performance of the catalyst/support system is directly linked to the physical and chemical characteristics of the carbon support.

4.07.2.1 Cathode Catalyst Materials

The power output and lifetime of AFCs are directly linked to the behavior of the cathode, for the reasons shown in Section 4.07.2. As a consequence, cathode development has attracted most of the attention of AFC developers to find the best catalyst and electrode structure to ally performance and stability.

4.07.2.2 Platinum Group Metal Catalysts

Platinum is the most commonly used catalyst for the electroreduction of oxygen and all of the PGMs reduce oxygen in alkaline media according to the direct four-electron process. At a very low Pt/C ratio, the overall number of electrons exchanged is approximately two due to the carbon contribution, but increases as the Pt/C ratio increases, reaching four electrons at 60% wt.Pt. Pt-based alloys have been studied and generally exhibit higher activity and stability than Pt alone. The enhanced electrocatalytic activity of Pt-alloy systems has been explained by a number of phenomenon, including (1) reduction in Pt–Pt bond distance thus favoring the adsorption of oxygen; (2) the electron density in the Pt 5d orbital; and (3) the presence of surface oxide layers. Due to the high cost of Pt, techniques have been developed to reduce loading. For example, monolayer deposition of Pt on non-noble metal nanoparticles showed improved catalytic properties with very small amounts of Pt. The carbon impregnation with hexachloroplatinic acid solution ($H_2PtCl_6 \cdot 6H_2O$) followed by metal reduction using heat treatment or wet chemical methods, have been widely used to produce a catalyst particle of size ranging between 2 and 30 nm.

Ag has also been studied as a potential replacement for Pt due to its high activity for the ORR and its lower cost. ORR occurs with the participation of two- and four-electron processes, depending on the surface state and, in particular, on its oxidation state and electrode potential. The size of the Ag particles affects the different catalytic activities for these two processes. Four electrons are exchanged during ORR on nanodispersed silver particles on carbon, with an optimum loading range between 20 and 30 wt%. The effect of electrolyte concentration is positive for silver catalyst but not for Pt catalyst, which is slightly hindered due to greater absorbed species coverage. Silver becomes competitive to Pt due to favored kinetics in high concentration alkaline media, but shows a strong propensity to dissolution at open-circuit voltages (OCVs) following reaction [5]:

$$4Ag + O_2 + H_2O \rightarrow 4Ag^+ + 4OH^- \qquad [5]$$

At an overpotential of 100–300 mV, this dissolution was found not to be significant. The impregnation of $AgNO_3$ in suitable solid support media such as carbon black is commonly used, associated with different techniques for reduction of the precursor to form metallic silver.

4.07.2.3 Non-Platinum Group Metal Catalysts

Recently, manganese oxides have attracted more attention as potential catalysts for both fuel cells and metal–air batteries because of their attractive cost and good catalytic activity toward O_2 reduction. The investigation of different manganese oxides dispersed on high surface area carbon black showed low activity for MnO/C and high activity for MnO_2/C and Mn_3O_4/C. The higher activity of MnO_2 was explained by the occurrence of a mediation process involving the reduction of Mn(IV) to Mn(III), followed by the electron transfer from Mn(III) to oxygen. The reaction is sensitive to the manganese oxide/carbon ratio in which, at lower ratios, the reaction proceeds by the two-electron pathway, evolving to an indirect four-electron pathway with disproportionation of HO_2^- into O_2 and OH^- at higher catalyst/carbon ratios. The catalytic activity for the disproportionation reaction has led to a new approach of dual system catalysis in which one catalyst is used for the reduction of O_2 through the two-electron process producing HO_2^-, which is subsequently decomposed by MnO_2, leading to a four-electron process. The MnO_2 catalytic activity was found to vary following its crystalline structure in the sequence: $\beta\text{-}MnO_2 < \lambda\text{-}MnO_2 < \gamma\text{-}MnO_2 < \alpha\text{-}MnO_2 \approx \delta\text{-}MnO_2$, in which higher activity seems to go with higher discharge ability proceeding through chemical oxidation of the surface Mn^{3+} ions generated by the discharge of MnO_2 rather than through a direct two-electron reduction. γ-MnOOH exhibits higher activity than γ-MnO_2; this has been explained by the fact that amorphous manganese oxide has more structural distortion and is more likely to have active sites compared to crystalline manganese oxides.

Pyrolyzed macrocycles on carbon support have been studied in alkaline media showing high activity toward the ORR. Cobalt phthalocyanine has been shown to reduce oxygen with similar kinetics to that of Pt. Electrodes made of Cobalt/Iron tetraphenylporphyrin (CoTPP/FeTPP) demonstrated good performance, outperforming electrodes made of silver catalysts. Increased surface area and structural changes are required to enhance the catalytic activity, which is obtained by chemical and heat treatments of the carbon and the porphyrins. This high catalytic activity was attributed to the combined effect of the macrocycle black and Co; however, poor stability has been shown where the loss of Co appeared to be important, leading to performance deterioration. $CoCO_3$ + tetramethoxyphenylporphyrin (TMPP) + carbon showed better performance than CoTMPP + carbon confirming the fact that the structure of the metal macrocycle is not responsible for catalytic activity, but its origin is due to the simultaneous presence of the metal precursor, active carbon, and a source of nitrogen, supposed already to be part of the catalytic process.

Perovskite-type oxides, which have an ABO_3-type crystal structure, have shown a high cathode activity in alkaline media proceeding by a two-electron pathway where HO_2^- is further reduced. Good performance has been reported with different catalyst composition such as $La_{0.5}Sr_{0.5}CoO_3$, $La_{0.99}Sr_{0.01}NiO_3$, $La_{1-x}A_xCoO_3$ (A = Ca, Sr), $Ca_{0.9}La_{0.1}MnO_3$ and $Pr_{0.6}Ca_{0.4}MnO_3$, and $La_{0.6}Ca_{0.4}CoO_3$. The catalyst support choice seemed to be crucial to obtain stable performance. Graphite supports appeared less stable than high surface area carbon black.

A spinel is a ternary oxide containing three different elements named after the mineral spinel $MgAl_2O_4$. The general structure is AB_2O_4 in which the choice of the B cation is critical as it plays an important role in the activity of the catalyst. Studies of $MnCo_2O_4$ catalysts have mainly indicated an ORR mechanism that involves a two-electron process with HO_2^- formation. The catalytic activity depends greatly on the preparation route; the decomposition of Co and Mn nitrates and subsequent heat treatment is most commonly used.

4.07.2.4 Cathodes Performance

A summary of the data found in a review article [5] describing cathode performance for different catalysts is given in **Tables 2** and **3**, which have been separated according to whether the measurements were made in oxygen or air. All the potentials are reported against an Hg/HgO reference electrode. This choice of reference electrode is preferred because of its good stability and reproducibility in strong alkaline conditions. In general a more positive value of potential indicates a more active cathode The KOH concentration was between 5 and 8 M and the electrolyte temperature varied between 25 and 70 °C as reported in the tables.

4.07.2.5 Anode Catalyst Materials

The anode in alkaline media has been much less studied than the cathode and remains a significant field for further work. Hydrogen, alcohol (such as methanol, ethanol, and ethylene glycol), borohydride, and hydrazine can be used as fuel in alkaline cells, which leads to a wide choice of catalyst depending on which fuel is employed. In this section, only catalysts developed for HOR are considered other fuels being discussed in Section 4.07.4.

HOR and hydrogen evolution reaction (HER) are the two important reactions in several technologies such as fuel cells, water electrolysis, and chlorine manufacturing industry. HER has been studied in a larger extent due to the development of alkaline electrolyzers, which is nowadays a mature and commercial technology aiming for an overall efficiency of 70% and current efficiency of up to 99%.

Table 2 Cathode performances using different catalysts with O_2

Catalyst	KOH temperature (°C)	KOH concentration (M)	Potential (V)	Current density (mA cm^{-2})
Pt/Pd/C	25	6	0.1	900
			0.2	1600
			0.3	2100
Ag/C	70	7	0.1	250
			0.2	540
La$_{0.5}$Sr$_{0.5}$CoO$_3$/C	25	6	0.1	250
			0.2	700
			0.3	1600
CoTPP/C	40	5	0.06	150
			0.14	600
			0.18	950
La$_{0.6}$Ca$_{0.4}$CoO$_3$/C	25	6	0.1	150
			0.2	500
			0.3	1000

Table 3 Cathode performance using different catalysts with air

Catalyst	KOH temperature (°C)	KOH concentration (M)	Potential (V)	Current density (mA cm^{-2})
Pt/CNT[a]/C	25	6	0.2	125
			0.5	520
Pr$_{0.8}$Ca$_{0.2}$MnO$_3$/C	60	8	0.1	115
			0.15	260
CoTMPP/C	25	5	0.1	140
			0.2	350
			0.25	500
MnO$_2$/C	25	8	0.2	91
			0.5	440
LaMnO$_3$/C	60	8	0.08	300
			0.1	400
MnCo$_2$O$_4$/C	60	6	0.1	150
			0.2	300

[a] CNT is an acronym for carbon nanotube.

Hydrogen reaction studies have shown that reaction kinetics is much slower in alkaline electrolyte than in acid ones where Pt is usually the best electrocatalyst. The accepted mechanism of HOR in alkaline media involves Tafel [6] and/or Heyrovsky [7] reactions, followed by Volmer reaction [8]:

$$H_2 \rightarrow H_{(ad)} + H_{(ad)} \quad [6]$$

$$H_2 + OH^-_{(aq)} \rightarrow H_{(ad)} + H_2O + e^- \quad [7]$$

$$H_{(ad)} + OH^-_{(aq)} \rightarrow H_2O + e^- \quad [8]$$

With the overall reaction

$$H_2 + 2OH^- \rightarrow 2H_2O + 2e^- \quad [9]$$

In alkaline media depending on the catalyst activity, Tafel and/or Heyrovsky reactions are the slow steps at low overpotential whereas diffusion of dissolved H_2 in the electrolyte has been proposed as the rate-determining step at high overpotential.

Pt, together with other PGMs (such as palladium (Pd)) as single, binary, ternary, or bimetallic combination, has been the preferred option for use in AFCs. Pt is the best electrocatalyst for HOR which has been extensively studied in acid media at low temperature mainly due to the development of PEMFC. In contrast, few studies can be found in alkaline media where it was demonstrated that in all alkaline pH range (7–15) the limiting process with Pt is always the diffusion of dissolved hydrogen which is due to the low solubility of H_2 in aqueous electrolytes.

As an alternative to Pt, high surface area nickel (Raney nickel) is among the most active non-noble metal catalysts toward HOR. Two different Tafel slopes were observed in the case of nickel catalysts which have been ascribed to polarization caused by

Table 4 Anode performances using different catalysts with H_2

Catalyst	Potential (V)	Current density (mA cm^{-2})
Pt/Pd	−0.910	80
	−0.895	200
	−0.882	300
Raney Ni	−0.912	100
	−0.898	200
	−0.880	300
Ml(NiCoMnAl)	−0.820	100

rate-determining surface diffusion of atomic hydrogen to the active site and by electron transfer accompanied by proton discharge. The catalytic activity and stability of Raney Ni is limited and suffers from progressive deactivation with time. Deactivation is mainly due to oxidation of the nickel and the formation of $Ni(OH)_2$ which passivates the electrode. This could be mitigated by doping with a few percentages of transition metals such as Ti, Cr, La, or Cu. An activation process is necessary prior to the use of the nickel electrode due to the oxidation of the surface when in contact with oxygen. The activation process involves the application of a cathodic current where Ni oxides are reduced along with hydrogen evolution.

Rare-earth-based AB_5-type hydrogen storage alloys (HSAs) have the ability to absorb hydrogen at room temperature. They have been investigated extensively as negative electrodes in rechargeable Ni/metal hydride batteries having many merits such as good electrochemical properties, mechanical and chemical stability in alkaline electrolyte, plenty of raw materials, and low cost. Diverse type of AB_5 HSAs have been investigated, such as $Ml(NiCoMnCu)_5$ or $Ml(NiCoMnAl)$ (Ml: La-rich mischmetal), showing much less activity and stability than Raney nickel and Pt catalysts toward HOR.

A summary of the data in the literature describing anode performance for different catalysts is given in **Table 4**. All the potentials are reported against an Hg/HgO reference electrode. The KOH concentration and temperature are 6 M and 55 °C, respectively. In the case of the anode, a more negative potential corresponds to a more active electrode.

The main disadvantage of alkaline cells is that carbon dioxide can react with the electrolyte to form carbonates (reaction [10]), decreasing the electrolyte conductivity (the conductivity of CO_3^{2-} being lower than that of OH^-), oxygen solubility, and electrode activity.

$$CO_2 + 2OH^- \rightarrow CO_3^{2-} + H_2O \quad [10]$$

The impact of CO_2 absorption differs in the case of liquid or solid electrolyte and is addressed separately in the respective sections dedicated to AFCs and AEMFCs.

4.07.3 Alkaline Fuel Cells Developed with Liquid Electrolytes

Since Bacon's first AFC design using KOH solution as electrolyte, a multitude of different designs have been developed, which have been demonstrated in almost all possible applications showing the adaptability and practicality of this technology. In this section, AFC technology will be described starting from electrode development considerations going through stack designs to finish with systems achievement given performance and durability.

In AFCs, KOH solution is almost exclusively used as the electrolyte because it has a higher ionic conductivity than sodium hydroxide solution, and potassium carbonate has a higher solubility product than sodium hydroxide, which renders the former less likely to precipitate.

Two main types of AFCs have been developed to date where the electrolyte can either be immobilized or be circulated. In an immobilized cell, or matrix cells, the electrolyte is fixed in a porous matrix (usually asbestos), whereas the electrolyte is free flowing between the electrodes and the circulates from cell to cell in the circulating cell design. The one common aspect of these cells is that they use porous electrode architectures referred to as gas diffusion electrodes (GDEs).

4.07.3.1 Gas Diffusion Electrode for AFC

The function of the GDE is more demanding for liquid electrolytes than solid electrolytes because it has to function as both a gas diffuser and containment for the liquid electrolyte, otherwise flooding of the gas channeling will occur with corresponding loss in performance. The degree to which flooding can be controlled has given rise to the term 'weeping' that refers to a gas diffusion layer (GDL) that still lets some of the liquid electrolyte into the gas chamber, but that can be countered. For these reasons, the development of properly functioning GDEs was one of the major breakthroughs in the Bacon cell of the 1950s. In those days, modern wet-proofing materials such as polytetrafluoroethylene (PTFE) were not available, so GDLs based on porous metal sinters were used, which controlled the impregnation of liquid electrolyte by a balance between capillary forces in the narrow pores of the substrate leading to liquid penetration and the barometric pressure of the gas from the opposite side of the sintered substrate. Care was required to control the pressure difference between the air and fuel sides of the stack. However, in the past few decades, the use of wet-proofing materials such as PTFE have considerably simplified and improved reliability to the point that low-cost manufacturing methods can be used to produce high-performance GDLs, as discussed in the next section.

4.07.3.1.1 Electrode design

Modern AFC electrodes consist of several PTFE-bonded carbon black layers, which fulfill different functions. The most common structure is the double-layer electrode structure shown in Figure 2 consisting of a backing material (BM), a GDL, and an active layer (AL).

The BM can be placed in the GDL, in the AL, or in between, following the stack design. It should have a high permeability to gases, high structural strength, good corrosion resistance, and high electronic conductivity. When used as current collector, nickel (being corrosion resistant to KOH) screens, meshes, or foams are commonly used, but carbon cloth or porous carbon paper can also be utilized in a similar way to the design of PEMFCs.

The GDL supplies the reactant gas to the AL and prevents the liquid electrolyte from passing through the electrode. However, some liquid is still prone to form on the gas side, possibly due to product water. This effect is often termed 'weeping'. The GDL can be made from pure porous PTFE where the porosity is achieved by mixing the PTFE suspension or powders with a pore former such as ammonium carbonate. When sintered at elevated temperature (usually below 320 °C), the ammonium carbonate filler decomposes, producing gas bubbles which create porosity in the PTFE film. When the GDL is required to be electronically conductive, it is mixed with conducting carbon black. The ratio of carbon/PTFE (25–60% PTFE) is a trade-off between the level of hydrophobic behavior of the PTFE and the conductivity of the carbon black. Ideally, the GDL should be completely water repellent and of metallic conductivity.

The AL contains the catalyst supported on carbon black and bonded together with PTFE. The carbon black is chosen to have a high surface area to maximize the power density. The level of PTFE in the AL is lesser than that in the GDL, typically the AL will contain between 2% and 25% PTFE, depending on the level of hydrophobicity required. The basic function of the PTFE in the AL is to bind the carbon black together, but still provide multiple three-phase contact points. A three-phase interface is created, where gas, electrolyte, and carbon-supported catalyst meet. Current collection is achieved by the use of a metallic grid or sheet that is bonded to or incorporated in the GDL. This allows the electrons generated in reactions [6] and [9] to be collected. Different structures depending on the nature of the carbon support, carbon/PTFE ratio, and electrode fabrication process can be obtained where electronic conductivity, ionic transport, and gas transport have to be provided.

4.07.3.1.2 Materials used in electrode fabrication

AFC electrodes can be made of different materials with different structures, but modern electrodes tend to use high surface area carbon-supported catalysts and PTFE to obtain the necessary three-phase boundary (TPB). Electrode performance in AFCs depends on catalyst surface area rather than catalyst weight. As with all other fuel cells, the catalyst loading is a critical parameter in determining performance. The nature of the catalyst support is also of prime importance to achieve high catalytic activity.

PTFE is a hydrophobic polymer material that has become the binding agent of choice since its commercial introduction in the 1950s by Dupont; although other materials are sometimes used (paraffin, polyethylene, polypropylene, wax, etc.). It is available either as dry powder additives or as a ready-made aqueous suspension (containing proprietary dispersants). Both of these forms have been used to make electrodes. PTFE can be present in the form of spherical particles, fibrils, or thin films on porous substrates. The PTFE penetrates deep into the subsurface of the carbon when the dispersion is mixed with the carbon black powder. However, generally it is necessary to melt the PTFE in order to provide a thin film over the entire surface of the carbon black. This process is usually called sintering and takes place at temperatures around 320 °C.

The electrical, chemical, and structural properties of carbon make it an ideal material for use in AFC electrodes [6]. Carbon blacks consist of carbon in the form of near spherical particles obtained by the thermal decomposition of hydrocarbons. High surface area is achieved in a separate step, by treatment with steam at a temperature in the range of 800–1000 °C. Specific surface areas of over

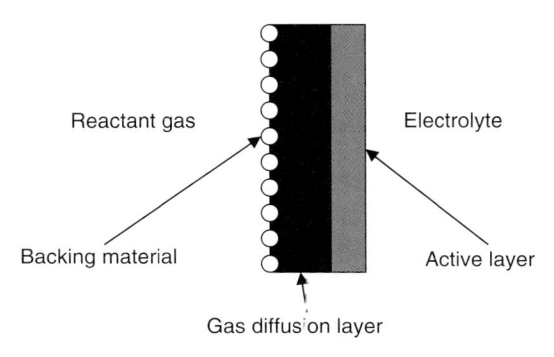

Figure 2 Design of a double-layer electrode.

$1000\,m^2\,g^{-1}$ can be obtained where porosity and surface area are the main characteristics of the carbon black structure [7]. Oxygen and hydrogen groups are introduced onto the carbon surface during the manufacturing process. The carbon–oxygen group is by far the most important and influences the physicochemical properties of carbon blacks. Formation of these groups by oxidative treatment in gaseous and liquid phases has been comprehensively studied since it influences electrode kinetics in alkaline media [8]. Despite the preference to use carbon black in GDE fabrication, alternative catalyst supports have been tried such as carbon nanofibers, and carbon nanotubes with improved electrode performance with the latest.

4.07.3.1.3 Operational mechanism

The electrochemical behavior of the GDE can be controlled by varying the structure of its component layers and in particular by varying the ratio of lyophobic and lyophilic pores within the carbon support. Two structures have been developed, each playing a different role within the electrode. The primary 'macro'structure is formed at distances greater than 1 µm and is created by the partial enclosure of the carbon particles by the PTFE. It forms the skeleton structure that ensures electronic conductivity throughout the electrode and also provides mechanical support. Different macrostructures can be obtained by varying the carbon particle size and shape, the carbon/PTFE ratio, and the electrode fabrication process. The secondary 'micro'structure, created by the pore system inside the carbon particles, depends on the surface area and pore structure of the carbon used. This structure is directly linked to the carbon manufacturing and activation process, which greatly influences the microporosity of the carbon particles. Indeed, the carbon particles have been shown to consist of macropores that are lyophobic and micropores (<0.01 µm) that are lyophilic. The lyophilic and lyophobic properties of the carbon depend on the nature of the surface groups, which can be selected by various thermal and chemical treatments. The lyophobic macropores have been shown to play an essential role in gas mass transport by acting as gas supplying channels. The ORR mechanism occurs in the lyophilic micropores which are filled with electrolyte and on the boundary of micro- and macropores. In the GDL, the transport of gas is determined by both the macro- and microstructures, since this layer is essentially free of liquid electrolyte.

In the AL, the macrostructure is filled with the liquid electrolyte, while the microstructure is free from electrolyte. This enables the gas to diffuse within the microstructure.

The TPB is formed in the outer regions of the carbon particle shell where it is covered by a film of liquid electrolyte at the interface between the carbon micro- and macrostructures. The carbon particles arrangement is described as a 'tight bed of packed spheres' where the large vacancies between the particles are filled with electrolyte ensuring the ionic transport and where the carbon pore system and hydrophobic channels created by the PTFE ensure the gas transport as shown in **Figure 3**.

The thicknesses of the different layers, can typically be in the range 100–500 µm, have to be optimized for electrode performance. The GDL thickness has to be as thin as possible to maximize oxygen accessibility, while the AL has to be optimized to maximize the reaction area constituted by the TPB.

4.07.3.1.4 Electrode modeling

Many publications have discussed the behavior of porous electrodes in AFCs. Whereas some authors have focused on specific issues such as the current distribution or the degree of catalyst utilization, the majority have tried to understand the overall mechanism of operation in the GDE related to the structure; considering factors such as gas diffusion and electrolyte penetration. Several models have been used such as the simple pore model [9], the thin-film model [10], or the dual scale of porosity model [11]. The concept of 'flooded agglomerates' [12] gives a satisfactory explanation for the behavior of PTFE-bonded GDEs and is in good accordance with experimental findings [13]. The operational mechanism of this structure, as shown in **Figure 4**, consists of catalyst particles that form porous agglomerates 'flooded' with electrolyte under working condition. The agglomerates are kept together by the PTFE, which creates hydrophobic gas channels. Reactant gases diffuse through the channels and dissolves in the electrolyte contained in agglomerates to react on available catalyst sites.

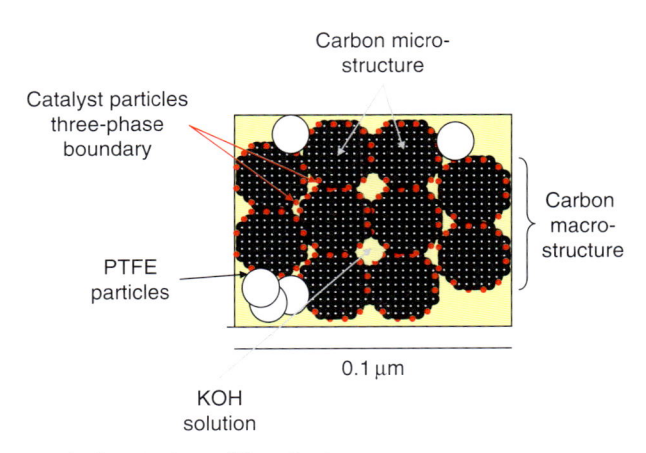

Figure 3 Scheme of the carbon macro- and microstructures of the active layer.

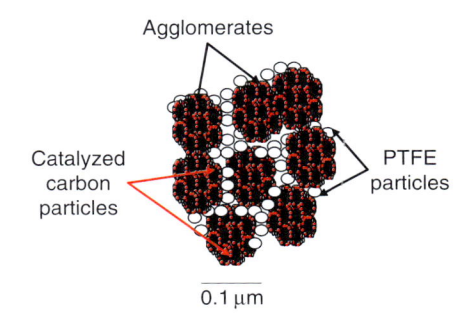

Figure 4 Schematic of the 'flooded agglomerate' model.

Further single cell (anode/electrolyte/cathode) models have shown that cathode reaction kinetics are particularly important in determining the overall cell performance, predicting that the diffusion of dissolved oxygen contributes most to the polarization losses at low potentials, while the electronic resistance contributes most at high cell potentials. As a consequence, cell performance can be increased by means of improved cathode fabrication methods, in which both gas–liquid and liquid–solid interfacial surface areas are increased and the diffusion path of dissolved oxygen to catalytic sites is reduced.

4.07.3.1.5 Electrode fabrication

Since different electrode structures lead to different electrode performance the electrode fabrication requires special attention where the gas permeability of the GDL and the wettability of the AL are the two main performance-limiting factors. Structural parameters of the different layers can be optimized by varying the carbon support used, the carbon/PTFE ratio and the fabrication conditions to obtain the best cathode performance. The electrochemical performance of the electrodes is also controlled by the initial porous structure and chemical surface properties of the active carbon, where different activities and gas transport hindrances depend on its process fabrication route. An activation step appears to improve the electrochemical activity and stability of the carbon black by mean of thermal, physical, and chemical treatments. Increased surface area, formation of a defined interpore structure and an increased surface activity by the formation of catalytically active groups on the surface occurs during such treatment. The activity of carbon black is proportional to its surface area, the higher the better. High temperature treatment leads to a higher surface area and as a consequence to a higher electrochemical activity. Carbon pretreatment needs to be specific to the type of carbon black. For example, the surface area has been found to increase significantly for Vulcan XC-72 in the presence of CO_2, whereas a N_2 atmosphere is required for Ketjenblack when heat treated at 900 °C [14].

Pressing, rolling, screen printing, and spraying methods are used in the production of AFC electrodes. The rolling method is the most commonly applied (**Figure 5**). The process shown is generic and variations including addition of filler materials such as sugar or ammonium carbonate along with various washing or drying steps. If PTFE powder is used and ground with the carbon, the method is referred to as the 'dry method'. If PTFE suspension and water are mixed with the carbon black, it is referred to as the 'wet method'.

The method of mixing the carbon black with the PTFE has a direct effect on the electrode activity and stability. Very fine networks of gas channels are needed in the AL to obtain high performance. Since diffusion of dissolved reactant gas is a limiting factor for high

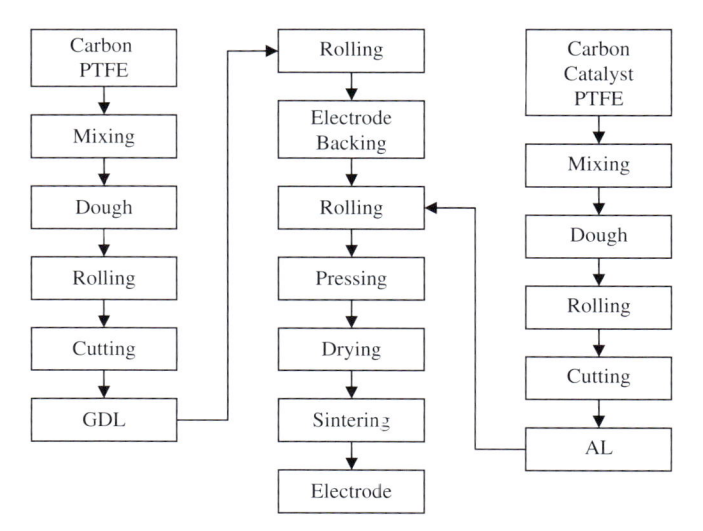

Figure 5 Electrode fabrication: the rolling method.

current generation, good dispersion of the carbon and PTFE particles is required to increase the number of gas dissolving sites and reduce the diffusion path length of dissolved gas to the catalyst sites, resulting in a performance increase.

The catalyst deposition method is critical since a high catalytic activity relies on a very fine and well-dispersed catalyst particle. In the case of platinum, the particle size is generally in the nanometer range [15]. The carbon impregnation of metal salt solution with further reduction of the metal is commonly used, and well known for its simplicity and ability to produce metal nanoparticles with nearly monodispersed size distribution and easy scale-up [16].

4.07.3.1.6 Electrode durability

On the cathode side, for Pt-based GDE, several degradation rates have been reported lying between 10 and 30 $\mu V\,h^{-1}$ over a period of 3500 h at 0.1 A cm^{-2} [17]. For silver-based GDE over 3500 h at 0.15 A cm^{-2}, a degradation rate of 17 $\mu V\,h^{-1}$ has been reported [18]. On the anode side, for a Pt/Pd-based GDE, a decay rate of 3.4 $\mu V\,h^{-1}$ for more than 11 500 h has been reported, whereas for Raney nickel-based GDEs a decay rate of 24 $\mu V\,h^{-1}$ over a period of 1500 h has been reported [19]. Several causes or effects have been proposed to explain the degradation of AFC electrode performance with time; they are described in the following sections. The understanding of these effects and their studies is very important in the development of increased AFC lifetimes. However, few studies have been found in the literature so far.

4.07.3.1.6(i) CO$_2$ effect

CO$_2$ not only decreases the concentration of OH– (when reacting to form CO$_3^{2-}$) but also decreases the electrolyte conductivity and interferes with the electrode kinetics, especially in porous electrodes. The presence of carbonate also increases the electrolyte viscosity which in turn leads to a decline in the limiting current because the diffusion of the various species involved in the reactions varies inversely with viscosity. In addition, and perhaps more significant, the electrolyte surface tension is modified leading to different interactions with the nonwetting properties of the porous electrode. Micropores may become inactive or less active if completely flooded with electrolyte. If left unchecked, the formation of precipitated carbonate (reaction [10]) can also lead to the blockage of the electrolyte pathways and electrode pores [20]. This can sometime happen when stacks are dismantled for inspection and the electrolyte is not washed off the individual cells properly before storage.

$$CO_3^{2-} + 2K^+ \rightarrow K_2CO_3 \qquad [11]$$

Thus, to avoid and mitigate these caveats, air is generally scrubbed to reduce the CO$_2$ content ranging between 5 and 30 ppm, depending on the technology used, before it enters the fuel cell [21]. Perhaps less obvious is the clean up on the fuel side. Pure hydrogen is no problem for the AFC, but if impure hydrogen made, for example, by gasification of natural gas or from biogas, then CO$_2$ can still enter the stack. So it is prudent to scrub the fuel side as well as the air side if there is any doubt about fuel purity. This dependency of CO$_2$ removal has often been cited as a reason not to develop or deploy AFC systems for terrestrial applications such as combined heat and power (CHP). However, scrubbing and gas cleanup methods have advanced in tandem to FC development that now render AFC applications viable [22].

Authors are not unanimous on the effect of CO$_2$ on electrode degradation [18, 20]. Whereas some authors attributes CO$_2$ to be the main factor determining electrode aging, others have demonstrated 3500 h of operation with a cathode in the presence of CO$_2$ concentrations 150 times that in air, asserting that CO$_2$ in air had no influence on the cathode, but rather degradation in the fuel cell performance was attributed solely to its impact on electrolyte conductivity. Based on published evidence, the CO$_2$ effect seems to be electrode structure dependent, wherein the pore structure of the electrode is crucial. A different CO$_2$ effect has been observed on electrode stability depending on the carbon support used. It was found that CO$_2$ had a strong effect on cathode stability when electrodes were prepared from activated carbon. No CO$_2$ dissolution or progressive wetting was observed with Asahi-90 black [17], which was explained by the small particle size of this carbon and its compact electrode structure.

4.07.3.1.6(ii) Corrosion effect

Some degradation reported in the literature [23] with increasing operating time was assigned to the corrosion of carbon and PTFE degradation caused by the KOH electrolyte. The carbon is slowly oxidized due to attack by the HO$_2^-$ radical formed as an intermediate during oxygen reduction. The discreet processes of electrocatalyst deterioration have been identified [24] as composed of corrosion, chemical dissolution, cathode hydrogenation, and metal intercalation. An increase in current density, temperature and ligand (OH$^-$) concentration was found to accelerate corrosion. A multicatalyst system has been proposed [25] to increase lifetime using the most stable support in compromised conditions (medium electrolyte concentration, etc.). PTFE was shown to lose some hydrophobicity after KOH exposure, which was attributed to surface chemical changes. It was shown that the contact angle reached a minimum; the higher the KOH temperature and concentration, the shorter the time taken to reach this minimum.

4.07.3.1.6(iii) Weeping/flooding effects

The reduction of the electrode performance over time is often caused by flooding of the electrode structure by the electrolyte, which reduces oxygen accessibility to reacting sites by blocking gas pores. This phenomenon has been described as the main parameter driving electrode degradation, showing an increasing cell capacitance over time due to greater electrode surface being in contact with the electrolyte [21]. The contact angle between the electrode surface and the electrolyte is potential dependent. The contact angle was found to decrease with a decrease in potential from the OCV, which increased wetting of the electrode. An increase in pH and temperature, especially at 90 °C with the condensation of the vapor in gas pores, both lead to flooding of the electrode [26]. The PTFE degradation also causes the decrease in hydrophobicity with time allowing more pores to be flooded, which hinders gas transport. Again the weeping effect seems to be electrode structure dependent, wherein the pore structure of the electrode is crucial [27]. A different weeping effect has been observed on electrode stability depending on the carbon support used. The use of acetylene black ensures a highly hydrophobic and homogeneous electrode structure with long-term durability, whereas oil-furnace carbon such as Vulcan XC-72R displayed excessive wettability [28]. Finally, the production of OH^- ions arising from the ORR in the active zone increases its concentration. The movement of water from the bulk electrolyte, or from condensation via the vapor phase to compensate this gradient, causes an increase in the size of the active zone with the result that the reaction zone moves through the electrode [29, 30].

4.07.3.2 Stack and System Design

Two main system configurations have evolved over the decades, in which the liquid electrolyte is either circulated or immobilized and is running in either monopolar or bipolar stack designs, leading to a wide range of possible stack/system configurations.

In immobilized systems, a porous matrix usually constructed from thin asbestos sheets is soaked with KOH solution. Asbestos, despite being hazardous in handling, was the preferred material in this application due to its exceptional stability and absorption properties. The capillary forces observed in asbestos are quite phenomenal and can be correlated with the ability of the asbestos structure to be almost infinitely cleavable, leading to nano-sized fibers. Paradoxically this is the same property that makes asbestos so harmful. The main advantages of immobilized systems are the simplicity of construction leading to robustness (less moving parts than in a circulating system) and weight savings compared with circulated systems. The excess of product water at the anode side is removed from the hydrogen loop as water vapor. The company Allis/Chalmers [31] developed a static water control design that was shown to follow load changes more quickly, as the matrix had a slowing down effect on the water equilibrium (**Figure 6**). The waste heat was removed by a coolant circulation. However, such matrix systems are very prone to degradation of the electrolyte due to impurities and require very pure hydrogen and oxygen to function reliably. Due to this, they are ideally suited for space and underwater applications where pure tanked oxygen and hydrogen is routinely used. For near zero gravity space applications, the use of a flowing liquid system with possible gas bubble formation was an obvious drawback for liquid circulating fuel cell systems, but not so for fixed-bed matrix systems. Moreover, the weight savings compared to heavier circulating systems and the fact that hydrogen is already used as propulsion fuel rendered immobilized systems the solution of choice for space applications as evidenced by the long history of reliable use from Apollo to Shuttle spacecraft of more than 40 years.

The circulation of the electrolyte through the stack has some advantages over the alternative immobilized systems. The use of a circulating electrolyte allows thermal and water management to be easily controlled. Moreover, impurities (e.g., carbon from electrodes or carbonates) can be easily removed and the OH^- concentration gradient is greatly decreased. Circulating electrolyte systems also minimize the build-up of gas bubbles in the gap between the electrodes. However, electrolyte leakage and parasitic losses due to the fact that each cell are linked by the KOH circulation loop (leading to shunt current) are challenging problems which needs to be carefully addressed. It should also be appreciated that the cost of KOH electrolyte is not so high and periodic replacement with fresh electrolyte is seen as a viable procedure during refurbishment of stacks in order to increase overall lifetime.

The electrolyte circulation loop consists of a KOH tank, a KOH pump, and a heat exchanger (**Figure 7**). The electrolyte of choice is usually a 30–40% KOH solution, which can be easily replaced when CO_2 absorption has reached an unacceptably high level. The electrolyte concentration level must be monitored because it is diluted during operation with the water produced in excess at the anode side and must be readjusted when needed.

The circulation of the electrolyte provides a very effective way of cooling the stack and heat recovery via a heat exchanger. During start up, the KOH is heated to the desired operating temperature, typically 70 °C. During operation, the heat exchanger is used to remove excess heat. This can be recovered for space heating applications. An air blower forces air into a CO_2 scrubber (usually containing soda lime), from where the air is directed to the air intake. The outlet air is directly exhausted to the atmosphere whereas the hydrogen is re-circulated or 'dead ended' for maximum efficiency. The hydrogen circulation is achieved by means of a

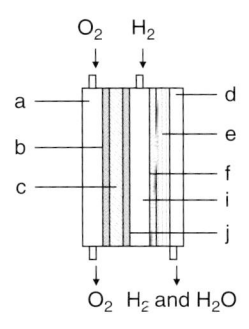

Figure 6 Allis/Chalmers static water vapor control. (a) Oxygen chamber, (b) porous oxygen electrode, (c) electrolyte, (d) moisture removal chamber, (e) porous support plaque, (f) moisture removal membrane, (i) hydrogen chamber, and (j) porous hydrogen electrode.

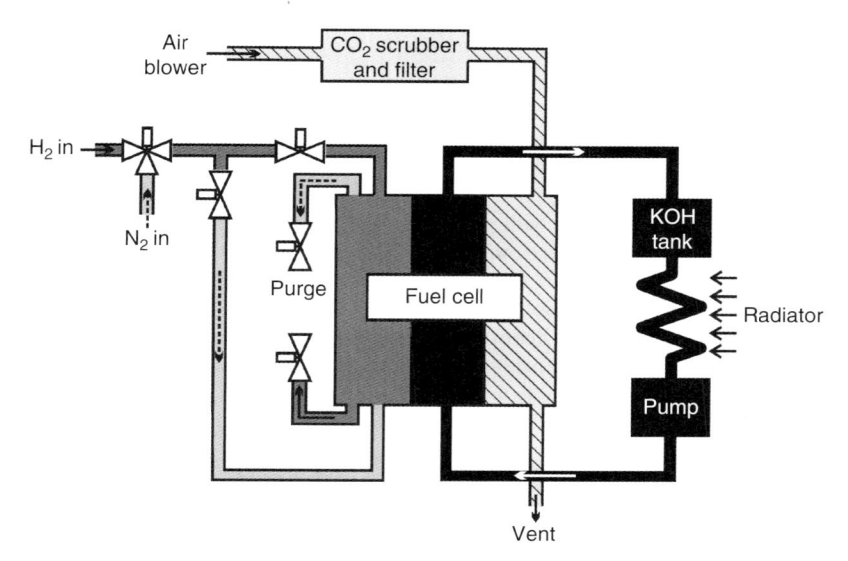

Figure 7 Schematic of a circulating electrolyte alkaline system.

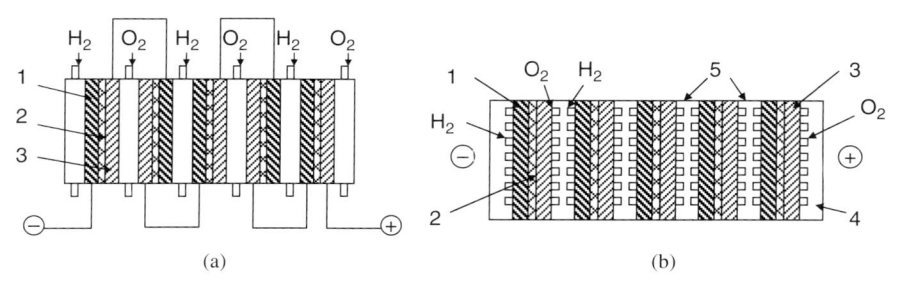

Figure 8 Scheme of an alkaline fuel cell stack in monopolar configuration (a) and bipolar configuration (b): (1) anode, (2) electrolyte/spacer, (3) cathode, (4) end plate and (5) bipolar plates.

venturi-based injector pump that facilitates the evacuation of the excess water that is subsequently collected in a water trap. The start-up/shut-down procedure is quick and easily performed by means of a nitrogen purge. No gas humidification system is required to run the stack, which is a big advantage compared to membrane electrolyte systems.

Both monopolar and bipolar stack designs have been demonstrated. In a monopolar stack design such as those developed by Elenco and Zetek, the current is directly collected on the BM of each electrode which is connected as shown in **Figure 8a**. The monopolar design requires each electrode to have a current collector extension to the BM, which normally protrudes through the side of the stack (see **Figure 13** for details). The main reason for developing this type of stack was to simplify the manufacture of the GDL allowing pure PTFE (an electrical insulator) to be used. The bipolar stack has the advantage of internal interconnection between the cells via the bipolar plates, but does require the GDL to be electronically conducting too.

The monopolar stack design presents several advantages: (1) low cost due to the avoidance of expensive bipolar plates. (2) stack thickness decreases as there is only one gas chamber between the two electrodes, (3) no mechanical pressure is required because cells are usually glued or welded together, (4) modularity of the power delivered by changing the external current connectors, and (5) the ability to disconnect a bad cell allowing continued operation (albeit with decreased performance) and facilitation of stack maintenance. However, the monopolar design is limited to a current density of up to 100 mA cm^{-2} due to the ohmic losses [32, 33] associated with long current collection path on the side of each electrode.

By contrast, the bipolar design (**Figure 8(b)**) demonstrates a uniform current density over all of the electrode surface and higher-terminal voltage with less power limitation and is therefore the preferred geometry for high-power applications. Reactant gases are distributed through channels engraved, machined, or incorporated in the bipolar plates and end plates.

The bipolar plates can be manufactured from pure stainless steel (X2CrNiMo18-14-3 grade) or other metal electroplated with nickel, silver, or even gold. A conductive polymer (mixture of carbon fillers and thermoplastic polymer such as polypropylene) can also be used to fabricate bipolar plate using injection molding as a cheap and mass production process. The downside is that the conductivity of such plates is much less than that for the metal ones.

A spacer, usually being made from polyethylene or polypropylene, is used to avoid any contact between the cathode and the anode. These spacers can be made of different structures such as meshes, porous plates, or nonwoven materials; they also ensure an even spacing for the electrolyte gap.

4.07.3.3 System Achievements

As discussed in the introduction, the starting point of all AFC systems was the system developed by Francis Thomas Bacon (**Figure 9**). Bacon's cell was constructed with sintered nickel anodes and lithiated nickel oxide cathodes using a circulated concentrated KOH solution as electrolyte (30–45 wt.%). Electrodes consisted of a double-layer structure of dual porosity where the electrolyte wetted the fine pores because of high capillary forces and larger pores stayed electrolyte free. The TPB was maintained by differential gas pressure since stable wet proofing agents, such as PTFE, were not available at that time. In the mid-1950s, Bacon demonstrated a 5 kW monopolar system operating with pure hydrogen and oxygen at relatively high temperature (200 °C) and pressure (45 bars), which showed a very good cell performance (~800 mA cm^{-2} at 0.8 V).

During the years, the general trend for AFCs systems development has been the decrease in operating conditions (temperature and pressure) aiming toward much simpler and reliable systems. This transition toward low-temperature and pressure systems was possible because of the improvement of electrode performance enable by the development of new materials to fabricate them (e.g., PTFE). Fully developed AFC systems can be separated in two main categories: space systems, which are usually pressurized systems without any cost limitation running on pure hydrogen/oxygen, and terrestrial systems, which are commonly atmospheric pressure low-temperature systems being developed with low-cost materials running on hydrogen/air.

4.07.3.3.1 Space systems

The NASA's first manned space capsule (Mercury Program) was powered by battery. As the flights became longer, the battery technology became limited and the decision was taken to switch to fuel cells. During the Gemini program, a PEMFC was used, but the system was found to be highly inefficient and not reliable due to problems related to the membranes (pinholes). In order to solve these problems, Pratt & Whitney Aircraft, a division of United Technologies Corporation (UTC), was contracted by NASA to develop an alkaline system (**Figure 10(a)**). This system was based on Bacon's work and powered the Apollo missions to the moon. High Pt loading (40 mg cm^{-2}) was incorporated to the initial sintered nickel electrode from Bacon's design to boost performance in spite of lowering the operating pressure to 0.3 Mpa. The electrolyte was a circulated, highly concentrated KOH solution (85%) running at high temperature (over 100 °C) to keep it liquid. The electrodes were 2.5 mm thick and circular with a diameter of 200 mm. Thirty-one cells were stacked together and connected electrically in series, and then three stacks were connected in parallel. The nominal power of one stack was 1.5 kW and its weight was 110 kg [31].

Figure 9 Dr. Francis Thomas Bacon next to his 5 kW system.

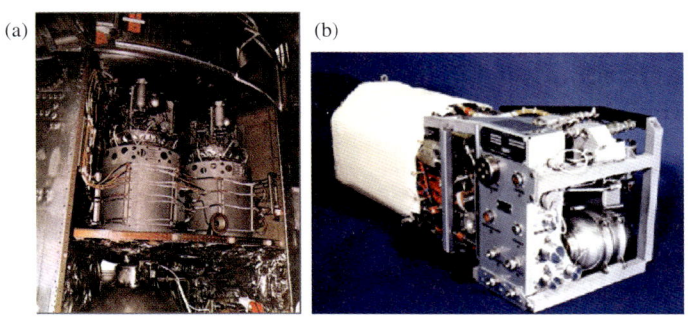

Figure 10 (a) The NASA Apollo and (b) Orbiter fuel cell systems.

Later on, NASA again selected AFCs for their space shuttle Orbiter fleet mainly because of their power generating efficiencies that approached efficiency of 70%. The shuttle systems (**Figure 10(b)**), developed by UTC, consisted of 32 cells with 465 cm^2 of active area each provided power and drinking water for the astronauts. Each shuttle was equipped with three 12 kW stacks (maximum power rating = 436 A at 27.5 V) aiming at an 8 times increase in power and weighing 18 kg less than the original Apollo design. The systems were low-temperature systems operated at 92 °C and 0.45 Mpa. The stacks had a bipolar configuration with lightweight, silver-plated magnesium foils as the bipolar plates also aiding the heat transfer. The electrolyte was 35–45 wt% immobilized KOH solution in an asbestos separator. The anode was PTFE-bonded carbon loaded with a 10 mg cm^{-2} Pt/Pd (ratio 4:1) loading, pressed on a silver-plated nickel screen. The cathode consisted of a gold-plated nickel screen with 10 wt% Pt (related to 90% Au). Water was removed via the anode gas in a condenser and a centrifugal separating device. The temperature was controlled by the circulation of heat-exchanging liquid. The Orbiter system has given an impressive performance (up to 1.1 A cm^{-2} at 900 mV) and durability (up to 15 000 h).

The European Space Agency (ESA) also launched an AFC development program for its manned space ship HERMES, which was stopped for various reasons before the development of a practical system. This program included subcontractors such as Varta, Siemens, and Elenco, who also developed systems for terrestrial applications.

4.07.3.3.2 Terrestrial systems
The following is a nonexhaustive list of AFC systems that have shown significant performance or technical achievements.

4.07.3.3.2(i) The Allis/Chambers system
On the basis of the Bacon fuel cell system, Allis/Chalmers built the first large vehicle equipped with a fuel cell in the late 1950s. It was a farm tractor powered by a 15 kW stack (consisting of 1000 cells), which was able to pull a weight of about 1.5 tons (**Figure 11(a)**). After this achievement, Allis/Chambers have focused their R&D on bipolar stacks using nickel-plated magnesium bipolar plates for fuel cell-powered golf carts (**Figure 11(b)**), submersibles, and forklifts. The cell consisted of Pt/Pd coated porous sintered nickel electrodes where the KOH electrolyte was immobilized in asbestos sheets. Their development of a static water vapor control method for removing the reaction water, which included an additional moisture removal membrane on the anode side, became a model for many matrix cells (**Figure 6**).

4.07.3.3.2(ii) The Union Carbide Corporation (UCC) system
In early 1960s, UCC developed the first modern electrode design allying the catalytic properties of Pt supported activated carbon with the advantages of PTFE bonding to obtain active, thin, wet-proofed electrodes. They developed circulating electrolyte systems running at 70 °C. UCC developed the first fully fuel cell car powered by a 150 kW unit for the General Motors 'Electrovan' in 1967 (**Figure 12(a)**). This system consisted of 32 modules with a top output of 5 kW each running under H_2/O_2 both in liquid form. Whereas the overall system was much too heavy (3400 kg) for transportation applications, this van had a driving range of 200 km and a top speed of 105 km h^{-1}. The lifetime was poor (~1000 h) due to cell reversal problems in this high-voltage system (400 V).

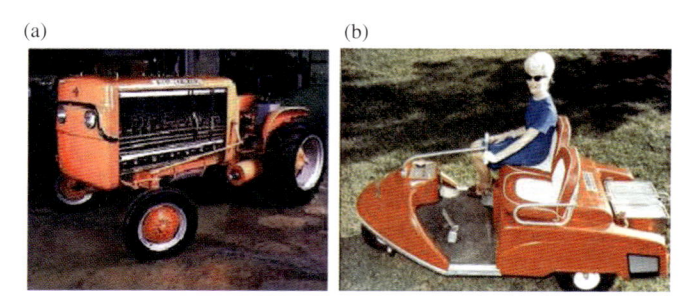

Figure 11 The Allis/Chalmers farm tractor (a) and golf cart (b).

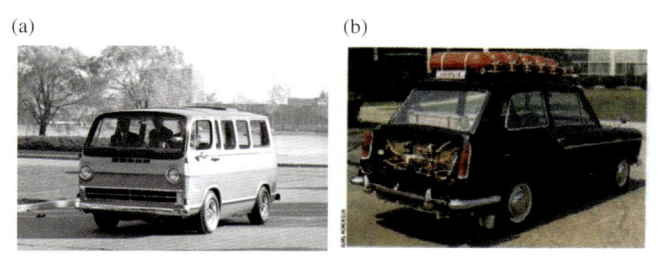

Figure 12 (a) the General Motors 'Electrovan' and (b) Kordesch's Austin A 40.

In the early 1970s, K.V. Kordesch built a 6 kW H_2/air fuel cell–lead acid battery hybrid car. He drove his Austin A 40 (**Figure 12(b)**) for 3 years on public roads showing that an electric automobile could be powered by a fuel cell/battery hybrid system and that such system can be easily started and shut down, which is no more complicated than any other assembly of batteries [34].

4.07.3.3.2(iii) The Siemens fuel cell system

In the late 1970s, Siemens developed a 7 kW system (49 V, 143 A) that consisted of 70 cells operating at 400 mA cm^{-2} at 0.8 V per cell in 7 M KOH at 80 °C. The system ran under pure H_2/O_2 at a pressure of 0.2 MPa. The main difference between Siemens and most other AFC developers involved the use of Raney catalysts (60 mg cm^{-2} Ag, containing Ni, Bi, and Ti as sintering inhibitors at the cathode and 120 mg cm^{-2} Ni containing Ti at the anode). The system was bipolar with a circulating electrolyte, but was fitted with asbestos diaphragms on every electrode to prevent gas leakage on the electrolyte side. The expected lifetime of the system was about 3000 h and the power deterioration was 5% per 1000 h. Siemens's R&D efforts led mainly to the development of systems for submarines.

4.07.3.3.2(iv) The Elenco fuel cell system

This monopolar system, developed in the 1970s, was operated with a circulating 7 M KOH electrolyte at 70 °C. The anode and cathode ALs were rolled into multilayer carbon GDE with PTFE as the binding agent. The GDL consisted of a porous hydrophobic PTFE foil, which was pressed onto the nickel mesh. The electrodes (thickness 0.4 mm) were mounted onto injection-molded frames where 24 cells were stacked in modules using a vibration welding method. Due to the low temperature, the fact that the system ran atmospheric air and the very small amount of noble metal catalysts (0.15–0.30 mg cm^{-2}), the current densities were low (0.7 V at 100 mA cm^{-2}). Power degradation was about 4% per 1000 h. Elenco's R&D efforts led to the demonstration of a 200 kW AFC system for a hybrid bus.

In more recent years, AFC companies have focused on the design of circulating electrolyte low-temperature atmospheric systems running on H_2/air for backup power, stationary, and mobile applications. The aim was to achieve a low cost fuel cell suitable for mass production. The UK-based company, Zetek [35] (previously Zevco and later Eident Energy [36]) have been the most successful AFC company to date, being at some point the largest fuel cell developer in Europe. Zetek demonstrated an AFC-powered London taxi in 1999 (max speed: 113 km h^{-1} with a range of 100 miles) and the first AFC-powered boat in 2000 (Hydra project). The technology was the continuation of Elenco's design based on injection-molded plastic frames for housing the electrodes and low Pt loading carbon supported electrodes (**Figure 13**). Low-cost electrode production was ensured by the use of standard industrial processes such as rolling (calendaring) and pressing.

The latest performance of a module at Eident Energy is given in **Table 5**. The stand-alone module was made of 24 cells connected in series (6 cells)/parallel (4 groups of 6 cells). The dimension of the surface of the cell was 16.8 × 16.8 cm. Connected in this

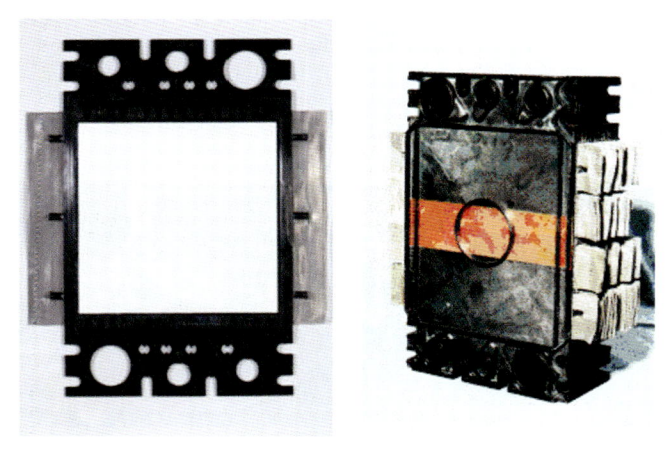

Figure 13 Zetek Injection-molded plastic frame and friction welded stack module.

Table 5 Summary of the performance of the latest Eident Energy module

Pt loading (mg cm^{-2}) Cathode Anode	Power At 53% E.Eff vs. LHV (W per module)	Power density[a] Wl^{-1} Wkg^{-1}	Life time[b] (kh)	Degradation rate (μVh^{-1})	Cost (euro kW^{-1})[c]
0.26 0.17	590	77.6 98	>5	32	430

[a] Module dimension: 98 mm × 250 mm × 310 mm (=7.60 l), weight: 6.0 kg including 1 l of electrolyte. Calculations made for a total efficiency of 51% vs. LHV.
[b] The definition of lifetime in the table is given as being 30% current loss at nominal module voltage (4.0 V).
[c] The cost is calculated as the bill of material at prices quoted on 25 May 2003, for volumes of material equivalent to a 50-unit production.

fashion, a module current of 108 A corresponded to a current density of 0.1 A cm^{-2} and a module operating voltage of 4 V corresponded to a cell voltage of 0.67 V (equivalent to an electrochemical efficiency of 53% vs. the LHV).

In a much smaller scale than Zetek, companies such as Astris Energi (Canada) [37] and Gaskatel (Germany) [38] have developed stacks on Ag cathodes and Ni anodes. The Astris-E8 was a 2.4 kW system with an electrical efficiency of 55% rated for a 2000 h lifetime. The stack cost (materials only) was claimed to be 220 euro Kw^{-1}. The Eloflux design from Gaskatel is based on flexible porous electrodes fabricated with low-cost materials such as carbon. The module is claimed to be highly efficient without any exhaust delivering up to 0.5 kW l^{-1}.

Nowadays, most companies involved in the development of AFCs have even ceased their AFC activity, which is the case of UTC switching for PEMFC, or have closed such as Zetek and Astris. Only a few companies remain active in the field such as Gaskatel, which still proposes its Eloflux design or AFC Energy PLC which is the only listed AFC company in the world targeting large-scale, stationary applications.

From an academic point of view, the most active universities and research institutions have been the German Aerospace Research Establishment (DLR), Germany with Dr. Erich Gulzow and notably the technical University Graz with Prof. Kordesch in Austria, which has been the strongest and most consistent advocate for AFC research, developing and promoting this technology for over 30 years.

The interest in AFC by the scientific community has dropped dramatically since the emergence of the PEMFC and AFC technologies have become largely stagnant during the past two decades. There are no obvious technical or economic reasons for the relative neglect that AFC has received. It is believed that AFC technology still has the potential to yield major improvements, especially in durability with modest R&D investment.

4.07.4 Alkaline Fuel Cell Based on Anion Exchange Membranes

Recently, AFCs have diversified into the realm of polymer-based electrolytes using anionic conducting membranes. The so-called AEMFCs are the alkaline equivalent to the well-known PEMFCs and are attracted increasing attention because the widespread commercialization of PEMFCs still remains a challenge. After more than 30 years of development, cost is still a major issue with PEMFCs, which is mainly due to three critical factors: (1) the dependence on Pt group catalysts whose cost are exacerbated by supply shortages and monopolies, (2) the use of expensive fluorinated polymer electrolytes, and (3) the use of relatively expensive bipolar plate materials; there are only few suitable materials which are stable with respect to contact with Nafion® – a superacid. The cost of the bipolar plates can be as much as one third of the cost of the entire PEMFC stack. The AEMFC alkaline analogue has some distinct advantages to help to mitigate these drawbacks with PEM technology as discussed in the remainder of this chapter.

Recent advances in materials science and chemistry has led to the production of AEMs (and ionomers) that conduct hydroxide anions (OH$^-$) and/or (bi)carbonate anions (HCO$_3^{-1}$/CO$_3^{2-}$) rather than protons (H$^+$, H$_3$O$^+$). The application of these AEMs promises a significant leap forward in fuel cell viability. The main advantages that conventional alkaline cells offer over acidic cells such as larger repertoires of effective catalyst and materials resistant to corrosion still apply to AEMFCs but with several other additional important advantages: (1) improved CO$_2$ tolerance due to the prevention of carbonate precipitation because of the lack of mobile cations (normally K$^+$); (2) avoidance of weeping or seeping out of KOH solution; and (3) water and ionic transport within the OH$^-$ anion conducting electrolytes is favorable; the electroosmotic drag transports water away from the cathode (preventing flooding on the cathode, a major issue with PEMFCs and direct methanol fuel cells (DMFCs)). This process also mitigates the 'crossover' problem in DMFCs; and (4) nonfluorinated membranes are feasible and promise significant membrane cost reductions.

4.07.4.1 Anion Exchange Membrane Chemistry and Challenges

Solid polymer electrolytes (SPEs) are conveniently divided into two classes, differentiated by the ionic mode of conduction within the polymer structure; these are termed ion-solvating polymer and ion-exchange polymer (AEM). Ion-solvating polymer membranes are ionically conductive solids based on the migration of cations and anions through the membrane. Typically, KOH solution is dissolved in a matrix polymer that effectively immobilizes the liquid, but is still essentially an electrolyte with freely mobile anions and cations as is the case with liquid KOH. Therefore, such immobilized electrolytes suffer from the disadvantage of poor CO$_2$ tolerance and associated carbonate formation. On the other hand AEMs are free from mobile cations such as Na$^+$ and K$^+$, which give a much better tolerance to CO$_2$. It is believed that the future of alkaline SPEs lies with the development of AEMs, whose properties are described in the remainder of this chapter.

AEMs are solid polymer membranes composed of a polymer backbone onto which functional cationic end groups are tethered (typically quaternary ammonium (QA)). The ionic conductivity is ensured by mobile anions associated with the cationic end groups.

Figure 14 shows a generic chemical reaction steps to convert a backbone polymer to an AEM polymer with QA as cationic end groups. Two pathways are considered, depending on if the polymer chain contains phenyl groups (such as for the polysulfone) or not. In the case where phenyl groups are already present, a chloromethylation reaction is necessary to functionalize the polymer. The chloromethylation is achieved by different chemical treatments, which are not discussed in detail here [39]. In the case where phenyl groups are not present in the polymer chain, vinylbenzyl chloride (VBC) can be radiation grafted onto the polymer chain. In both cases, functionalized benzylic chloromethyl groups react typically with an amine (quaternization reaction) to yield QA. The cationic end group is then alkalinized by treatment with KOH to yield a hydroxide ion-conducting AEM.

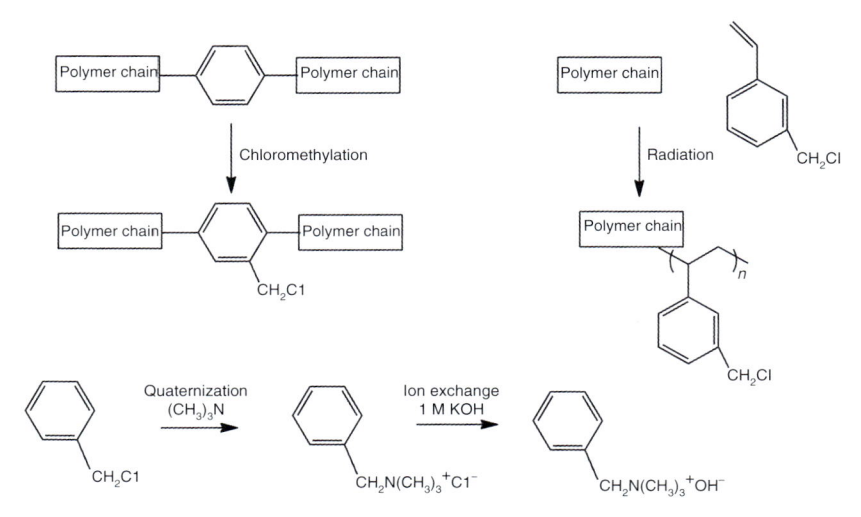

Figure 14 Generic chemical reaction steps to convert a polymer to an AEM polymer with QA as cationic end groups.

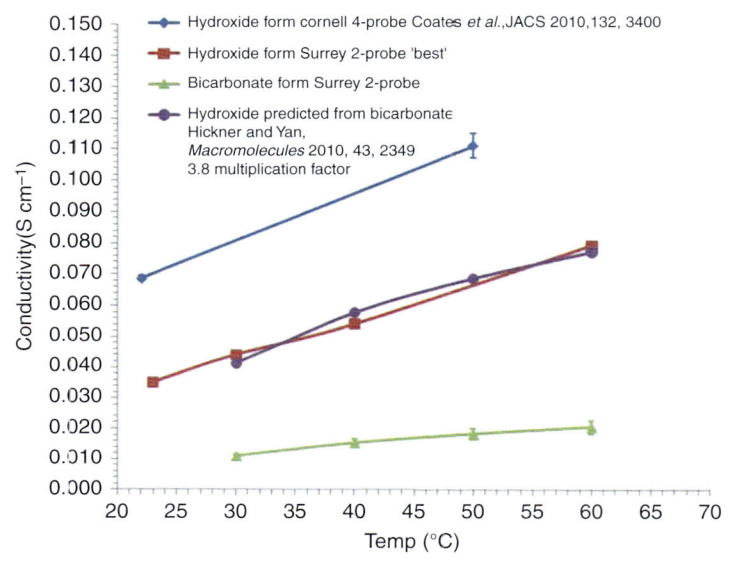

Figure 15 Typical AEM conductivities vs. temperature from Surrey University in its OH⁻ form and bicarbonate form.

The two foremost challenges to be considered with the development of AEMs (especially using OH^- as anions) are the ionic conductivity and chemical stability of the membrane.

Indeed, the electrochemical mobility of OH^- anions is less than that of H^+ (more correctly H_3O^+) in most media and functional groups (such as $-NMe_3OH$) do not strongly dissociate as the case for sulfonic acid groups (SO_3H) present in PEM membranes such as Nafion®. Thus, typical OH^- conductivities in AEMs are much lower than that of H^+ in PEMs. To illustrate this point, some typical AEM conductivities versus temperature are given in **Figure 15**. Moreover, AEM conductivities are considerably lowered when relative humidity values are less than 100% due to the requirement for higher numbers of water molecules necessary for complete dissociation and also that only a fraction of the total number of water molecules present in the membrane are directly associated with the ionic group (most of the water forms aggregates outside the ionic groups). It has to be noted that AEM conductivities are also lowered when exposed to air due to the reaction of OH^- anions with CO_2 forming HCO_3^{-1}/CO_3^{2-} (**Figure 15**). During AEMFC operations, the drop in ionic conductivity with carbonate ions can be mitigated in the so-called 'self-purging' mechanism where the increase in ionic current increases the production of OH^- at the cathode resulting in an overall increase in ionic conductivity of the membrane. AEMFCs can also function with carbonate anions instead of hydroxide ions in a so-called 'carbonate cycle' where CO_2 reacts at the cathode to form CO_3^{2-}, which then migrates to the anode to react with H_2 forming water and CO_2.

AEM ionic conductivity can be enhanced by increasing the number of functional cationic groups (increasing the polymer's ion-exchange capacity (IEC)). However, this approach is limited by the fact that the increase in the fixed charge concentration leads to the degradation of the mechanical properties of the membrane (excessive swelling when hydrated or brittleness when dry). It has

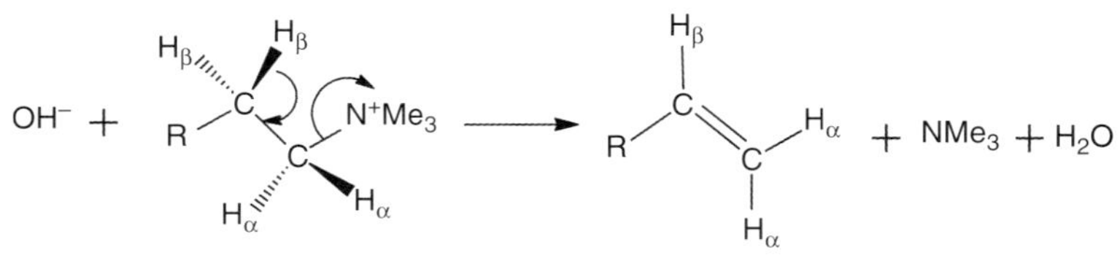

Figure 16 The Hoffman elimination reaction.

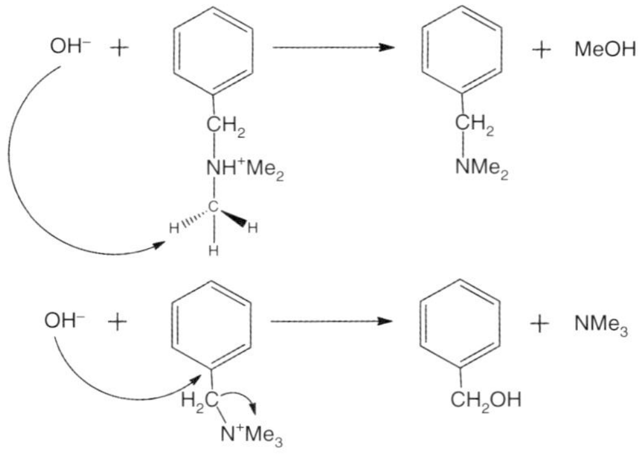

Figure 17 The direct nucleophilic substitution reactions.

to be noted that the excessive swelling of a membrane also leads to the decrease in its conductivity because the effective phase concentration of fixed charges is reduced.

The chemical stability of AEMs is one of the main concerns because OH⁻ anions are effective nucleophiles. Indeed, the main chemical degradation process of AEMs appears to be from nucleophilic attacks on the cationic end groups by OH⁻ anions. A decrease in cationic end groups causes a decrease of the ionic conductivity of the membrane. The presence of β-hydrogen atoms allow the Hoffman elimination reaction to occur wherein OH⁻ anions attack a hydrogen atom on the beta carbon relative to the cation. As a consequence of this attack, a double bond is formed between the beta and the alpha carbons, the cation being released and a molecule of water being produced (**Figure 16**).

In the absence of β-hydrogen atoms, direct nucleophilic attacks occur on the QA end groups. OH⁻ anions attack either the methyl group to form an alcohol or the C–C bond between the alpha and the beta carbons to cleave the cationic end group (**Figure 17**). There are ongoing research efforts to obtain a better understanding of AEM degradation mechanisms, which is a key requirement to the success of AEMFCs.

4.07.4.2 Review of the Main Classes of AEMs

Recent AEM studies have focused particularly on quaternizable polymers containing QA groups because the alternatives quaternized pyridinium and phosphosium are reported to suffer from a lack of thermochemical stability in alkaline media. A wide range of materials have been studied such as aminated poly(oxyethylene) [40], methacrylates [41], radiation-grafted poly(vinylidene fluoride) (PVDF) [42], poly(tetrafluoroethen-co-hexafluoropropylene) (FEP) [43], crosslinked poly(vinyl alcohol) (PVA) [44], aminated poly(phenylene) polyethersulfone (PES) [45], poly(phthalazinon ether sulfone ketone) (PPESK) [46], polysulfone (PS) [47], poly(epichlorhydrin) [48, 49], and poly(2,6-dimethyl-1,4-phenylene oxide) (PPO) [50]. The most frequent quaternizing agents include alkyliodides, trialkylamines, N,N,N',N'-tetramethylalkyl-1,n-diamines, polyethyleneimine, 1,4-diazabicyclo-[2.2.2]--octane (DABCO), and 1-azabicyclo-[2.2.2]-octane [51, 52]. Among these materials, aromatic polymers are the preferred candidates for fuel cell applications due to their excellent thermal and mechanical properties as well as their resistance to oxidation and stability in alkaline conditions.

In academia, important developments have been made from Varcoe and coworkers (University of Surrey) [53], who prepared AEMs by radiation grafting of VBC onto completely or partially fluorinated polymers. Their S80 membrane, which is a radiation-grafted poly(ethylene-co-tetrafluoroethylene) (PETFE)-based AEMs, demonstrated good chemical stability in 1 M KOH up to 80 °C and high ionic conductivity when fully hydrated (at 60 °C ~0.06 S cm⁻¹ for comparison Nafion PEMs ~ 0.1 S cm⁻¹).

Commercial AEMs are available from Solvay (Belgium-Morgane ADP), which is a crosslinked fluorinated polymer with QA groups, Fumatech (Germany-FAA), which is a perfluorosulfonic polymer, and Tokuyama (Japan-A201 and A901), which are both QA-containing polyolefinic(aliphatic)-type AEMs. Some properties of these membranes alongside properties of the Surrey membrane (S80) are summarized in **Table 6** [54].

Table 6 Properties of diverse AEMs

Properties	S80	Morgane ADP	FAA	A201	A901
Thickness dry-hydrated (μm)	63–80	133–154	130–150	28–30	10–11
Ion-exchange capacity (mmol g^{-1})	1.28	1.3	1.2	1.7	1.7
OH– conductivity (mS cm^{-1})	35 25 °C 100% RH	9 30 °C 100% RH	42 25 °C 100% RH	42 23 °C 90% RH	38 23 °C 90% RH

4.07.4.3 Ionomer Development/Membrane Electrode Assembly Fabrication

Anionic membrane electrode assembly (MEA) fabrication methods and materials have not yet advanced to the level of MEA production in PEM systems. This is mainly due to the novelty of the anionic membrane materials and the lack of suitable anionic ionomers to bind the catalyst to the surface of the membrane, which is normally done using hot pressing techniques. Nafion has the advantage of being easily dispersed in liquid form, whereas the anionic membranes currently have limited solubility. A good ionomer is primordial for good electrode performance because it maximizes ionic contact between catalyst reaction sites in the AL and the membrane. Current anion exchange binders demonstrate poor ionic conductivities and stabilities, which limit MEA performance. Different research groups have developed diverse solutions to this ionomer problem such as the use of Nafion dispersion as a binder and the use of KOH solution at the electrode/AEM interface. The chemistry of the ionomer needs to be compatible with the chemistry of the membrane. Some quaternized polymers, which are made from 4-vinylpyridine monomer and some polysulfone-based alkaline ionomer, have also been under investigation. Surrey developed an anionic ionomer (SION1), which is a metal-cation-free ionomer allowing the use of their AEMs under air where the CO_3^{2-} appeared to operate as well as an OH– form MEA. The SION1 contains β-hydrogen atoms allowing the Hofmann elimination degradation mechanism to occur and limiting the thermal stability under 60 °C. A β-hydrogen-free anionic ionomer is currently being investigated. Commercial ionic ionomers are scarce. Fumatech has developed an anionic ionomer for their FAA AEMs. Their HEM exhibits an IEC of 1.6 mmol g^{-1} and a conductivity of 17 mS cm^{-1}. Tokuyama has been working on two anionic ionomers, which are insoluble to water, methanol, and ethanol. Their A3 and AS-4 are hydrocarbon-based polymers containing QA groups, which exhibit IECs of 0.7 and 1.3 mmol g^{-1} and conductivities of 2.6 and 13 mS cm^{-1}, respectively. The lack of suitable low boiling point, water-soluble organic solvents for catalyst ink preparation, and the fact that (depending on the AEM chemistry) hot pressing is not always possible all add to complicate and limit the anionic MEA fabrication process.

4.07.4.4 Alkaline Anion Exchange Membrane Fuel Cells Performance

In this section, the authors will give general principles, views, and state-of-the-art performance obtained with AEMFCs using hydrogen, methanol, and sodium borohydride as fuels without going through an exhaustive review process. The idea is to give a concise summary of catalysts, AEMs, and ionomers used during testing and also showing typical AEMFC performance with the different fuels considered.

AEMFCs can run with different fuels such as hydrogen, alcohols (methanol or ethanol and ethylene glycol), or boron- and nitrogen-containing fuels such as sodium borohydride (or hydrazine). Some of the properties of the suitable fuels are given in **Table 7**.

4.07.4.4.1 Hydrogen as fuel

$$\text{Anode: } H_2 + 2OH^- \rightarrow 2H_2O + 2e^- \; (E^0 = -0.83 \text{ V}) \quad [12]$$

$$\text{Cathode: } \tfrac{1}{2}O_2 + H_2O + 2e^- \rightarrow 2OH^- \; (E^0 = +0.40 \text{ V}) \quad [13]$$

$$\text{Overall: } H_2 + \tfrac{1}{2}O_2 \rightarrow H_2O \; (E^0 = +1.23 \text{ V}) \quad [14]$$

Different membranes have been tested by the Surrey University group alongside their own membranes. As a general comment, it is believed that the main source of performance loss is due to mass transport of H_2O to the cathode AL as water is a reactant of the ORR in AEMFCs. Even with the use of 100% RH gas supplies, the primary source of H_2O to the cathode appeared to be the excess water produced and back transported from the anode. Using commercial Toray carbon paper electrodes (435 μm thick containing Pt/C (20% mass) catalyst at 0.5 mg$_{Pt}$ cm^{-2} loading, PTFE binder) from E-TEK treated with their ionomer SION1 at both the anode and the cathode sides, they obtained a peak power of 230 mW cm^{-2} and a maximum current of 1.3 A cm^{-2} under H_2/O_2 at 50 °C with their

Table 7 Properties of fuels what can be used in AEMFCs

Fuel	Specific energy density (kWh kg^{-1})	Volumetric energy density (kWh l^{-1})	Density at 20 °C (g cm^{-3})
Hydrogen	33	0.18	0.071
Methanol	6.1	4.8	0.79
Ethanol	8.0	6.3	0.79
Propanol	9.1	7.4	0.81
Ethylene glycol	5.3	5.8	1.11
Sodium borohydride	9.3	10	1.07

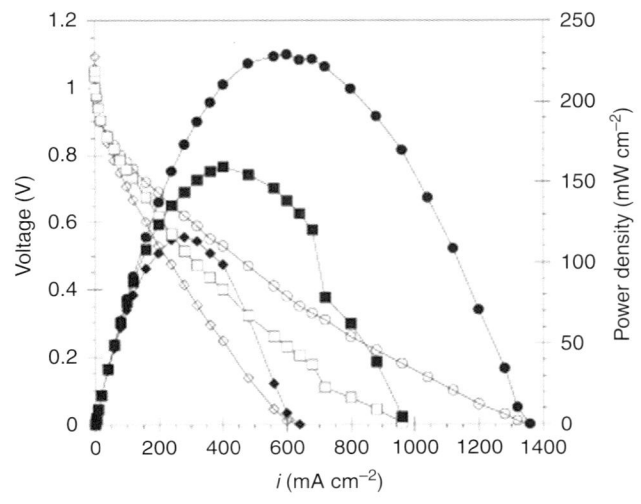

Figure 18 Fuel cell performance at 50 °C, anode: 0.5 mg cm^{-2} Pt prefabricated carbon paper electrode; cathode: 0.5 mg cm^{-2} Pt carbon paper electrode. With (♦) S80 (AAEM, 85 μm fully hydrated thickness); (■) S50 (AAEM 46 μm fully hydrated thickness); and (●) S20 (AAEM, 17 μm fully hydrated thickness). The open symbols represent the V_{cell} vs. i plot and the filled symbols represent the P_{cell} vs. i plot.

S20 (Figure 18). For comparison, a peak power of 260 mW cm^{-2} was obtained with an AAEM from Tokuyama under the same testing conditions using SION1 as ionomer.

A team at Wuhan University, which has developed QA-polysulfone-based alkaline anion exchange membranes (AAEMs) and ionomers, has reported a peak power of 52 mW cm^{-2} at 60 °C under H$_2$/O$_2$ using Ni catalyst at the anode and Ag catalyst at the cathode [55]. Under the same testing condition switching pure O$_2$ with air, they have demonstrated a peak power of 28 mW cm^{-2} at 0.47 V with Pt catalyst (Pt/C, 0.5 mg$_{Pt}$ cm^{-2}, from Johnson Matthey) and a peak power of 30 mW cm^{-2} at 0.42 V with Ag catalyst (Ag/C, 2 mg$_{Ag}$ cm^{-2}, from E-TEK). A team from the University of South Carolina in collaboration with Tokuyama has demonstrated a peak power of 177 mW cm^{-2} and an OCV of 0.97 V with a CoFeN/C cathode catalyst and Pt anode catalyst using A201 membrane and AS-4 ionomer from Tokuyama under H$_2$/O$_2$ at 50 °C. They demonstrated 196 mW cm^{-2} and an OCV of 1.04 V with Pt/C in the same experimental conditions [56]. A peak power of 365 mW cm^{-2} at 0.40 V has been reported by Wang's team at Penn State University using Tokuyama's A901 AEM and AS-4 ionomer at 50 °C under H$_2$/O$_2$ with Pt/C catalyst (0.4 mg$_{Pt}$ cm^{-2}). The power dropped at 212 mW cm^{-2} with purified air (<1 ppm of CO$_2$) and 113 mW cm^{-2} with atmospheric air showing the influence of carbonate form (CO$_3^{2-}$) on cell performance. The cell durability appeared also to suffer from CO$_3^{2-}$ species demonstrating 120 h testing under pure oxygen and only 11 h under atmospheric air. It was believed by the authors that the CO$_3^{2-}$ species accumulate at the anode, creating an undesirable pH gradient, which disrupts anode electrokinetics. This explanation is not consistent with other experiments, which showed that O$_2$/CO$_2$ mixtures could improve cell performance due to 'carbonate cycle', which requires no water unlike with the formation of OH$^-$ [57]. Acta S.p.A in collaboration with a team in the University of Pisa has developed and tested alkaline MEAs with and without PGM cathodes demonstrating, respectively, 400 and 200 mW cm^{-2} under H$_2$/Air (CO$_2$ free) at 50 °C. A durability test was shown where the power density dropped of a third of the initial power density when CO$_2$ free air was switched with atmospheric air being then stable for 50 h. There is still no consensus on the real impact and mechanism degradation involving carbonate forms where HCO$_3^-$ could be the cause of most problems and not CO$_3^{2-}$ [58].

4.07.4.4.2 Alcohol fuels

The development of AEMs has also boosted research in alkaline direct alcohol fuel cells (ADAFCs) where liquid alcohol fuels offer a much higher volumetric energy density than hydrogen (Table 7). Even taking into account the thermodynamic disadvantage

Table 8 Typical ADAFCs performances obtained with methanol, ethanol, and ethylene glycol

Fuel	Anode	Cathode	Electrolyte	Temperature (°C)	Maximum power (mW cm^{-2})
Methanol	PtRu	Pt Black	Nafion 115, Surrey	50	31
Methanol	PtRu	Pt Black	S80, Surrey	50	2.2
Ethanol	PtRu	Pt Black	S80, Surrey	50	2.1
Ethylene Glycol	PtRu	Pt Black	S80, Surrey	50	2
Methanol + KOH	PtRu/C	Pt/C	A201, Tokuyama	20	6.8
Ethanol + KOH	PtRu	Pt/C	A201, Tokuyama	20	58
Ethylene Glycol + KOH	PtRu/C	Pt/C Ag/C LaSrMnO/C	A-006, Tokuyama	80	25 20 18
Ethanol + KOH	Pd$_2$Ni$_3$/C	Fe-Co, Acta SpA	A201, Tokuyama	60	90
Ethanol + KOH	Ni-Fe-Co, Acta SpA	Fe-Co, Acta SpA	A201, Tokuyama	40	60

induced by the pH difference across the membrane (due to the production of carbonate at the anode side), the electrokinetic advantage in alkaline media open the possibility of a larger repertoire of catalysts for the fuel oxidation and for the fuel tolerance on the cathode side. The faster kinetics in alkaline media also allow a wider range of fuels (such as ethanol or ethylene glycol) to be considered.

Methanol, which is the simplest alcohol (no C–C bonds), has been the most studied of all alcohols. It reacts with OH$^-$ to form water and CO_2 as shown below:

$$\text{Anode: } CH_3OH + 6OH^- \rightarrow +5H_2O + 6e^- \, (E^0 = -0.81 \text{ V}) \quad [15]$$

$$\text{Cathode: } ^3/_2 O_2 + 3H_2O + 6e^- \rightarrow 6OH^- \, (E^0 = +0.40 \text{ V}) \quad [16]$$

$$\text{Overall: } CH_3OH + ^3/_2 O_2 \rightarrow 2H_2O + CO_2 \, (E^0 = +1.21 \text{ V}) \quad [17]$$

Running an alkaline membrane direct methanol fuel cell (AMDMFC) in comparison to a DMFC (the PEM equivalent) offers two main advantages: the reduction of the fuel crossover because the conductive species moves from the cathode to the anode (which allow the use of thinner membrane thus improving FC performance) and the water management of the cell is more easily facilitated because the water reacts at the cathode and is formed at the anode, which limits the effect of flooding. Even with these advantages, DMFC demonstrates higher power output than AMDMFC (**Table 8**).

Alcohols other than methanol have been investigated with AEMs showing encouraging performances. Ethanol and ethylene glycol have shown better performance than methanol even if the oxidation of these fuels to CO_2 is not complete because of the higher energy required to break the C–C bond. Good performance has been obtained with ethanol using Pd catalysts (Pd being the most active catalyst for ethanol oxidation reaction (EOR)) and non-PGM catalyst systems (**Table 8**), which seems promising.

For all ADAFCs considered in the literature studies have shown that the presence of OH$^-$ in the fuel stream is mandatory in order to obtain acceptable performance, which is expected since OH$^-$ is a reactant in the alcohol oxidation reaction. Hence, OH$^-$ from the membrane is not enough to ensure fast kinetics at the anode side and requires the addition of OH$^-$ in the fuel stream, which limits durability due to the carbonization of the fuel. For example, KOH can be added to the alcohol fuel in much the same way that water is added to methanol for the DMFC. Typical ADAFC performances are given in **Table 8** with methanol, ethanol, and ethylene glycol from a good review article from Antolini [59]

4.07.4.4.3 Sodium borohydride fuel

Sodium borohydride (NaBH$_4$), which contains 10.6% by mass hydrogen, has often been proposed as an alternative hydrogen storage material and more recently as a fuel in the direct borohydride fuel cells (DBHFCs). NaBH$_4$ is stable in alkaline media (not the case in neutral or acidic conditions) and has been demonstrated using AEMs as electrolyte.

The electrochemical reaction and potential are as follow:

$$\text{Anode}: BH_4^- + 8OH^- \rightarrow BO_2^- + 6H_2O + 8e^- \, (E^0 = -1.24 \text{ V}) \quad [18]$$

Table 9 Some performance of DBHFCs with cationic and anionic membranes

Anode	Cathode	Membrane	Oxidant	Temperature (°C)	Maximum power (mW cm^{-2})
Ni-Pt/C	Pt/C	Nafion 212	O_2	60	221
Au/Ti	Pt/C	Nafion 117	O_2	85	82
Pt-Ni/C	Non-platinum catalyst	Morgane ADP, Solvay	Air	RT	115
Pt/C	Non-platinum catalyst	Morgane ADP, Solvay	Air	RT	200
Au	MnO_2	AEM, Surrey University	Air	RT	28

$$\text{Cathode: } 2O_2 + 4H_2O + 8e^- \rightarrow 8OH^- \ (E^0 = +0.40 \text{ V}) \quad [19]$$

$$\text{Overall: } BH_4^- + 2O_2 \rightarrow H_2O + BO_2^- \ (E^0 = +1.64 \text{ V}) \quad [20]$$

One of the main problems of DBHFCs is that the hydrolysis reaction occurs in parallel and competes with the oxidation reaction on catalyst sites leading to a decrease in fuel efficiency. The hydrolysis reaction happens at varying extents depending of temperature, concentration, type of catalyst, and potential. Pt and Ni have been demonstrated to be active toward the BH_4^- hydrolysis reaction unlike Au and Ag, which have shown little or no activity.

Hydrogen evolution from hydrolysis of water or from the incomplete borohydride oxidation (reaction [20]) occurs also during cell operation and is another problem in DBHFCs. The hydrolysis of water can be minimized by running the cell at high current increasing anode potentials.

$$BH_4^- + 4OH^- \rightarrow BO_2^- + 2H_2O + 2H_2 + 4e^- \quad [21]$$

Considering that BH_4^- is an anion, the use of cation exchange membranes (CEMs) is more effective in the suppression of BH_4^- crossover than AEMs. Nevertheless, DBHFCs using AEMs have demonstrated good performance at room temperature under air with alternative Pt catalyst as can be seen in **Table 9** (results from diverse review article [60–62]).

4.07.5 Conclusions

Since Bacon's first alkaline cell using KOH solution as an electrolyte, a multitude of different designs have been developed, which have been demonstrated in almost all possible applications, showing the adaptability and practicality of this technology. The interest in AFCs by the scientific community has dwindled over the years due to the rise and supremacy of PEMFCs and the AFC technology has become largely stagnant during the past two decades; however, there are no obvious technical or economic reasons to justify the neglect that AFCs have received. The future of AFCs seems to lie with the development of AEMs. Indeed, recent advances in materials science and chemistry enabled the production of membrane and ionomer materials, which allow the development of the alkaline equivalent to PEMFCs. The application of these AEMs promises a huge leap in fuel cell viability because fuel cell reactions are faster under alkaline conditions than under acidic conditions. As a consequence, larger repertoires of catalysts (both anodic and cathodic) and fuels are available where, for example, non-platinum catalysts such as silver and nickel perform more favorably in alkaline media. Currently, however, most studies still employ Pt group catalysts and alternative catalysts to platinum need to be further demonstrated. Encouraging performance has been demonstrated with diverse fuels (ethanol and sodium borohydride) showing the potential of this emerging technology. However, while the AAEM fuel cells hold great promises, developments still need to be made to achieve higher membrane conductivity and durability. The interactions between carbonates, ions, and AEMs have still to be fully understood alongside degradation mechanisms of the different membranes systems. The lack of good ionomers is a major limitation factor in AEM MEA performance, which does not compare now with PEM MEAs. Current performance levels show promise for low-temperature, low-power fuel cell applications. AEMFCs are still at an early stage of development but show a great potential for a low-cost fuel cell technology. Increasing attention can be seen from the scientific community for AEMs and their applications around the world where intensive activities can be seen in Japan and China and rising interest in Europe and USA.

References

[1] Perry ML (2002) *Journal of the Electrochemical Society* 149: S59.
[2] Bockris JOM and Appleby AJ (1986) *Energy* 11: 95.
[3] Larminie J and Dicks A (2004) *Fuel Cell Systems Explained*, 2nd edn., ch. 5, pp. 121–139. Chichester, UK: Wiley.
[4] Blurton KF and McMullin E (1969) *Energy Conversion* 9: 141–144.
[5] Bidault F, Brett DJL, Middleton PH, and Brandon NP (2009) Review of gas diffusion cathodes for alkaline fuel cells. *Journal of Power Sources* 187(1): 39–48.
[6] Dicks AL (2006) *Journal of Power Sources* 156: 128–141.

[7] Donnet J, Bansal R, and Wang M (1993) *Carbon Black*. New York: Marcel Dekker.
[8] Kinoshita K and Bett JAS (1973) *Carbon* 11: 403–411.
[9] Austin LG (1965) *Industrial & Engineering Chemistry Fundamentals* 4: 321.
[10] Srinivasan S and Hurwitz HD (1967) *Electrochimica Acta* 12: 495–512.
[11] Markin VS (1963) *Russian Chemical Bulletin* 12: 1551.
[12] Giner J (1969) *Journal of the Electrochemical Society* 116: 1124.
[13] Vogel W, Lundquist J, and Bradford A (1972) *Electrochimica Acta* 17: 1735–1744.
[14] Pirjamali M and Kiros Y (2002) *Journal of Power Sources* 109: 446–451.
[15] Bagotzky VS, Khrushcheva EI, Tarasevich MR, and Shumilova NA (1982) *Journal of Power Sources* 8: 301–309.
[16] Lima FHB and Ticianelli EA (2004) *Electrochimica Acta* 49: 4091–4099.
[17] Sato M, Ohta M, and Sakaguchi M (1990) *Electrochimica Acta* 35: 945–950.
[18] Gulzow E and Schulze M (2004) *Journal of Power Sources* 127: 243–251.
[19] Kiros Y and Schwartz S (2000) Long-term hydrogen oxidation catalysts in alkaline fuel cells. *Journal of Power Sources* 87(1–2): 101–105.
[20] Rolla A, Sadkowski A, Wild J, and Zoltowski P (1980) *Journal of Power Sources* 5: 189–196.
[21] Gouerec P, Poletto L, Denizot J, *et al.* (2004) *Journal of Power Sources* 129: 193–204.
[22] McLean GF, Niet T, Prince-Richard S, and Djilali N (2002) *International Journal of Hydrogen Energy* 27: 507–526.
[23] Tomantschger K, Findlay R, Hanson M, *et al.* (1992) *Journal of Power Sources* 39: 21–41.
[24] Korovin NV (1994) *Electrochimica Acta* 39: 1503–1508.
[25] Rotenberg Y, Srinivasan S, Vargha-Butler EI, and Neumann AW (1986) *Journal of Electroanalytical Chemistry* 213: 43–51.
[26] Burchardt T (2004) *Journal of Power Sources* 135: 192–197.
[27] Wagner N, Schulze M, and Gulzow E (2004) *Journal of Power Sources* 127: 264–272.
[28] Maja M, Orecchia C, Strano M, *et al.* (2000) *Electrochimica Acta* 46: 423–432.
[29] Hull M and James H (1977) *Journal of the Electrochemical Society* 124: 332.
[30] Baugh L, Cook J, and Lee J (1978) *Journal of Applied Electrochemistry* 8: 253.
[31] Cifrain M and Kordesch KV (2003) In: Vielstich W, Lamm A, Gasteiger H (eds.) *Handbook of Fuel Cells*, p. 267. New York: Wiley.
[32] Burchardt T, Gouerec P, Sanchez-Cortezon E, *et al.* (2002) *Fuel* 81: 2151–2155.
[33] De Geeter E, Mangan M, Spaepen S, *et al.* (1999) *Journal of Power Sources* 80: 207–212.
[34] Kordesch K, Gsellmann J, Cifrain M, *et al.* (1999) *Journal of Power Sources* 80: 190–197.
[35] Burchardt T, Gouerec P, Sanchez-Cortezon E, *et al.* (2002) Alkaline fuel cells: Contemporary advancement and limitations. *Fuel* 81: 2151–2155.
[36] Gouérec P, Poletto L, Denizot J, *et al.* (2004) The evolution of the performance of alkaline fuel cells with circulating electrolyte. *Journal of Power Sources* 129(2): 193–204.
[37] Astris Energi Inc. (2006) Astris AFC electrodes pass 5000h test. *Fuel Cells Bulletin* 2006(10): 8.
[38] Stafell I and Ingram A (2010) Life cycle assessment of an alkaline fuel cell CHP system original research. *International Journal of Hydrogen Energy* 35(6): 2491–2505.
[39] Varcoe JR and Slade RCT (2005) Prospects for alkaline anion-exchange membranes in low temperature fuel cells. *Fuel Cells* 5(2): 187–200.
[40] Mamlouk M Characterization and application of anion exchange polymer membranes with non-platinum group metals for fuel cells. *Proceedings of the Institution of Mechanical Engineers; Part A; Journal of Power and Energy* 225(2): 152–160.
[41] Luo Y, Guo J, Wang C, and Chu D Quaternized poly(methyl methacrylate-*co*-butyl acrylate-*co*-vinylbenzyl chloride) membrane for alkaline fuel cells. *Journal of Power Sources* 195(12): 3765–3771.
[42] Zhang F, Zhang H, Qu C, and Ren J Poly(vinylidene fluoride) based anion conductive ionomer as a catalyst binder for application in anion exchange membrane fuel cell. *Journal of Power Sources* 196(6): 3099–3103.
[43] Slade RCT and Varcoe JR (2005) Investigations of conductivity in FEP-based radiation-grafted alkaline anion-exchange membranes. *Solid State Ionics* 176(5–6): 585–597.
[44] Xiong Y, Fang J, Zeng QH, and Liu QL (2008) Preparation and characterization of cross-linked quaternized poly(vinyl alcohol) membranes for anion exchange membrane fuel cells. *Journal of Membrane Science* 311(1–2): 319–325.
[45] Li L and Wang Y (2005) Quaternized polyethersulfone Cardo anion exchange membranes for direct methanol alkaline fuel cells. *Journal of Membrane Science* 262(1–2): 1–4.
[46] Fang J and Shen PK (2006) Quaternized poly(phthalazinon ether sulfone ketone) membrane for anion exchange membrane fuel cells. *Journal of Membrane Science* 285(1–2): 317–322.
[47] Wang G, Weng Y, Chu D, *et al.* (2009) Developing a polysulfone-based alkaline anion exchange membrane for improved ionic conductivity. *Journal of Membrane Science* 332(1–2): 63–68.
[48] Stoica D, Ogier L, Akrour L, *et al.* (2007) Anionic membrane based on polyepichlorhydrin matrix for alkaline fuel cell: Synthesis, physical and electrochemical properties. *Electrochimica Acta* 53(4): 1596–1603.
[49] Vassal N, Salmon E, and Fauvarque JF (2000) Electrochemical properties of an alkaline solid polymer electrolyte based on P(ECH-*co*-EO. *Electrochimica Acta* 45(8–9): 1527–1532.
[50] Xu T, Liu Z, Li Y, and Yang W (2008) Preparation and characterization of Type II anion exchange membranes from poly(2,6-dimethyl-1,4-phenylene oxide) (PPO). *Journal of Membrane Science* 320(1–2): 232–239.
[51] Komkova EN, Stamatialis DF, Strathmann H, and Wessling M (2004) Anion-exchange membranes containing diamines: preparation and stability in alkaline solution. *Journal of Membrane Science* 244(1–2): 25–34.
[52] Park J-S, Park S-H, Yim S-D, *et al.* (2008) Performance of solid alkaline fuel cells employing anion-exchange membranes. *Journal of Power Sources* 178(2): 620–626.
[53] Poynton SD, Kizewski JP, Salde RCT, and Varcoe JR (2010) Novel electrolyte membranes and non Pt-catalysts for low temperatures fuel cells. *Solid State Ionics* 181(3–4): 219–222.
[54] Varcoe JR, Kizewski JP, Halepoto DM, *et al.* (2009) Fuel cells – Alkaline fuel cells | Anion-exchange membranes. In: Garche J (ed.) *Encyclopedia of Electrochemical Power Sources*, pp. 329–343. Amsterdam: Elsevier.
[55] Lu S, Pan J, Huang A, *et al.* (2008) Alkaline polymer electrolyte fuel cells completely free from noble metal catalysts. *Proceedings of the National Academy of Sciences of the United States of America* 105(52): 20611–20614.
[56] Li X, Popov BN, Kawahara T, and Yanagi H Non-precious metal catalysts synthesized from precursors of carbon, nitrogen, and transition metal for oxygen reduction in alkaline fuel cells. *Journal of Power Sources* 199(4): 1717–1722.
[57] Lim PC, Ge S, and Wang C-Y (2008) High performance MEA for alkaline membrane fuel cells operating without liquid electrolyte. *ECS Meeting Abstracts* 802(11): 1073–1073.
[58] Piana M, Boccia M, Filpi A, *et al.* H2/air alkaline membrane fuel cell performance and durability, using novel ionomer and non-platinum group metal cathode catalyst. *Journal of Power Sources* 195(18): 5875–5881.
[59] Antolini E and Gonzalez ER Alkaline direct alcohol fuel cells. *Journal of Power Sources* 195(11): 3431–3450.
[60] de Leon CP, Walsh FC, Pletcher D, *et al.* (2006) Direct borohydride fuel cells. *Journal of Power Sources* 155(2): 172–181.
[61] Liu BH and Li ZP (2009) Current status and progress of direct borohydride fuel cell technology development. *Journal of Power Sources* 187(2): 291–297.
[62] Ma J, Choudhury NA, and Sahai Y A comprehensive review of direct borohydride fuel cells. *Renewable and Sustainable Energy Reviews* 14(1): 183–199.

4.08 PEM Fuel Cells: Applications

AL Dicks, The University of Queensland, Brisbane, QLD, Australia

© 2012 Elsevier Ltd. All rights reserved.

4.08.1	Introduction	184
4.08.2	Features of the PEMFC	185
4.08.2.1	Proton-Conducting Membranes	185
4.08.2.2	Modified PFSA Membranes	188
4.08.2.3	Alternative Sulfonated Membrane Materials	188
4.08.2.4	Acid–Base Complex Membranes	189
4.08.2.5	Ionic Liquid Membranes	189
4.08.2.6	High-Temperature Proton Conductors	189
4.08.3	Electrodes and Catalysts	190
4.08.3.1	Anode Materials	190
4.08.3.2	Cathode Materials	190
4.08.3.3	Preparation and Physical Structure of the Catalyst Layers	191
4.08.3.4	Gas Diffusion Layers and Stack Construction	192
4.08.4	Humidification and Water Management	194
4.08.4.1	Overview of the Problem	194
4.08.4.1.1	Airflow and water evaporation	194
4.08.4.1.2	Humidity of PEMFC air	194
4.08.4.2	Running PEMFCs without Extra Humidification (Air-Breathing Stacks)	194
4.08.4.3	External Humidification	195
4.08.5	Pressurized versus Air-Breathing Stacks	197
4.08.5.1	Influence of Pressure on Cell Voltage	197
4.08.5.2	Other Factors Affecting Choice of Pressure – Balance of Plant and System Design	198
4.08.6	Operating Temperature and Stack Cooling	199
4.08.6.1	Air-Breathing Systems	199
4.6.06.2	Separate Reactant and Air or Water Cooling	199
4.08.7	Applications for Small-Scale Portable Power Generation Markets (500 W–5 kW)	200
4.08.7.1	Market Segment	200
4.08.7.1.1	Auxiliary power units	200
4.08.7.1.2	Backup power systems	200
4.08.7.1.3	Grid-independent generators and educational systems	202
4.08.7.1.4	Low-power portable applications (< 25–250 W)	202
4.08.7.1.5	Light traction	203
4.08.7.2	The Technologies	205
4.08.7.2.1	The DMFC	205
4.08.7.2.2	The RMFC	208
4.08.7.2.3	The DLFC	208
4.08.7.2.4	The MRFC	208
4.08.8	Applications for Stationary Power and Cogeneration	208
4.08.8.1	Prospects for Stationary Fuel Cell Power Systems	208
4.08.8.2	Technology Developers	209
4.08.8.3	System Design	209
4.08.8.4	Cogeneration and Large-Scale Power Generation	214
4.08.9	Applications for Transport	214
4.08.9.1	The Outlook for Road Vehicles	214
4.08.9.2	Hybrids	215
4.08.9.3	PEMFCs and Alternative Fuels	217
4.08.9.4	Buses	217
4.08.9.5	Fuel Cell Road Vehicle Manufacturers	218
4.08.9.6	Planes, Boats, and Trains	218
4.08.10	Hydrogen Energy Storage for Renewable Energy Systems and the Role of PEMFCs	221
References		223
Further Reading		225
Relevant Websites		225

Glossary

Air stoichiometry (λ) The ratio of volumetric airflow to that which would be required for the stoichiometric combustion of fuel. Thus, $\lambda = 2$ has twice the airflow that would be required for complete combustion of the fuel. The excess airflow is used to cool the fuel cell.

Nafion™ One of the first polyfluorinated sulfonic acid polymers produced by DuPont in the 1960s. Nafion first referred to a sodium polyfluorinated sulfonate membrane that could be ion-exchanged with acid to yield a proton-conducting membrane.

Open-circuit voltage (OCV) A voltage developed between the anode and cathode of a fuel cell with no load connected.

Power density A measure of power in Watts expressed per unit mass (e.g., $W\,kg^{-1}$) or per unit volume (e.g., $W\,l^{-1}$).

Transport number The fraction of the total current carried by a given ion in an electrolyte. Also known as transference number.

4.08.1 Introduction

A fuel cell is a device that produces direct current (DC) by directly converting the chemical energy embodied in a fuel. The concept has been around since the 1830s when pioneering work was carried out by William Grove in the United Kingdom and Friedrich Schoenbein in Switzerland [1]. The earliest experiments were carried out at ambient temperature using a liquid electrolyte, typically sulfuric acid, and platinum electrodes. Such acid fuel cells use the principle that the electrolyte is able to conduct protons (H^+ ions) that migrate from the negatively charged anode or fuel electrode to the cathode or positively charged air electrode. The fuel cell produces electricity (DC) as long as fuel is supplied to the anode and oxidant (commonly air) is supplied to the cathode. The operating principle of the acid fuel cell is shown in **Figure 1**, and is described in more detail in section 4.08.2.

The proton-exchange membrane fuel cell (PEMFC), also known as the solid-polymer fuel cell (SPFC), was first developed in the 1960s by the General Electric (GE) in the United States for use by the National Aeronautics and Space Administration (NASA) on their first 'Gemini' manned space vehicles. Instead of the liquid proton-conducting electrolyte of the earlier cells, a solid or quasi-solid proton-conducting material was used. Early materials were based on polymers such as polyethylene, and the first NASA fuel cells employed polystyrene sulfonic acid (PSA). In 1967, DuPont introduced a novel fluorinated polymer based on a polytetrafluoroethylene (PTFE) structure with the trademark Nafion™. PTFE is the material that was used to coat nonstick cookware and is highly hydrophobic (nonwetted by water). The Nafion material provided a major advance for fuel cells and the material thus became the preferred electrolyte for PEMFCs for much of the following 30 years.

Several companies set about developing PEMFC technology for terrestrial power applications following the success in the Gemini spacecraft, but it was Ballard Power Systems, a Canadian company, that produced the first practical system in the late 1980s [2]. Ballard started making battery systems for the military and required power sources that would run longer. They were the first to see the inherent advantages of PEMFCs for field operations where a reliable power source operating at close to ambient temperature would make them virtually undetectable compared with the traditional engine generators that could easily be detected by their sound or their heat signature using infrared-sensitive cameras. Ballard first concentrated on developing stationary PEMFC systems at the scale of 3–5 kW. These sparked much interest and before long, the PEMFC was being proposed for zero-emission vehicles. Using

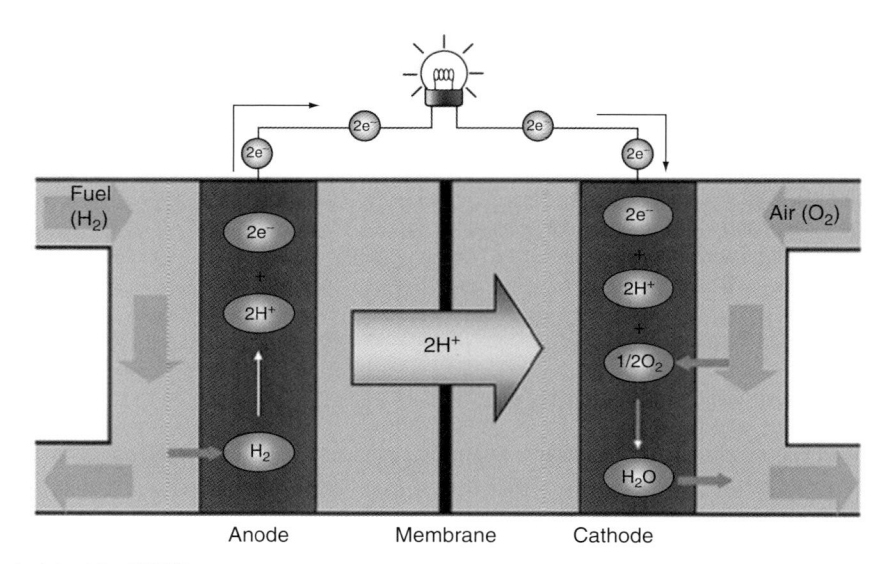

Figure 1 Operating principle of the PEMFC.

pure hydrogen as fuel, the only emission from a vehicle employing a PEMFC is water. Ballard instigated a program to demonstrate the PEMFC in a 21-seat bus, and this created much interest among vehicle manufacturers as well as the R&D community worldwide.

In the early 1990s, legislation by California set the challenge for low-emission vehicles and a worldwide interest in fuel cell vehicles (FCVs) started to emerge. In 1993, the Partnership for a New Generation of Vehicles (PNGV) program was set up and sponsored by the US government and the US automobile manufacturers which in turn spawned even more R&D in PEMFC technology. In 1997, the field had a terrific boost by the injection of substantial capital from Ford and DaimlerChrysler into Ballard Power Systems. New fledgling companies were formed and before long all the major auto companies had fuel cell development or demonstration programs.

The preferred fuel for the PEMFC is pure hydrogen, and while oxygen is the preferred oxidant, air can be used although there is a significant performance penalty for using air. Other types of fuel cells, for example, the molten carbonate fuel cell (MCFC) and solid-oxide fuel cell (SOFC) that operate at much higher temperatures than PEMFCs, are able to directly electrochemically oxidize other fuels such as natural gas. At the lower operating temperature of the PEMFC (typically around 80 °C), the fuel is limited to hydrogen that readily absorbs on the Pt catalyst, or alcohols such as ethanol or methanol which also absorb and chemically dissociate on Pt. The high electrochemical activity of such alcohols has given rise to a particular form of PEMFC known as the direct methanol fuel cell (DMFC), which is being developed for small-scale stationary and portable applications such as in consumer electronic devices [3].

Apart from the SOFC, the PEMFC is unique in that it uses a solid electrolyte, operates at around ambient temperature, and generates a specific power (W kg^{-1}) and power density (W cm^{-2}) higher than any other type of fuel cell. It is worth remarking that the United States' Department of Energy (US DOE), 2010, targets of 650 W kg^{-1} and 650 W l^{-1} for an 80 kW PEMFC stack were achieved in 2006 by Honda with a novel vertical 100 kW flow stack that is used in the FCX Clarity car. The stack has a volumetric power density of almost 2.0 kW l^{-1} and weight density of 1.6 kW kg^{-1} [4]. In 2008, Nissan also claimed to have achieved 1.9 kW l^{-1}. Hydrogen PEMFCs typically achieve cell area power densities of 800–1000 mW cm^{-2} at a working cell voltage of 0.8 V (**Figure 2**) [5]. Cost is the perhaps the most challenging barrier to widespread commercialization of the PEMFC [6]. This is partly due to the platinum used in the electrodes (currently loaded at around 0.2 mg cm^{-2}) and the cost and lifetime of the membrane.

The unique features of the PEMFC are described in the next section, and these lead to important consequences in the way this type of fuel cell has to be operated, relating to humidification and water management, pressurization, and heat management. Each unique feature affects the way that the fuel cells are being developed for different applications as described in the sections that follow.

4.08.2 Features of the PEMFC

4.08.2.1 Proton-Conducting Membranes

As shown in **Figure 1**, the PEMFC comprises a porous anode and cathode and a nonporous cation-conducting electrolyte membrane. The conducting cation is taken to be the proton (H$^+$), although in most cases this is in the form of hydrated protons or hydronium ions (H$_3$O$^+$). The passage of fuel (hydrogen) through the porous anode liberates electrons and creates protons at the interface between the anode and electrolyte. The protons migrate through the electrolyte to the cathode where they react with oxygen and electrons fed via the external circuit to produce water. Thus, there are two half-cell reactions occurring at the electrodes:

$$\text{Anode:} \quad H_2(g) \rightarrow 2H^+ + 2e^- \quad E° = 0 \text{ V}_{SHE} \tag{1}$$

$$\text{Cathode:} \quad {}^1/_2 O_2(g) + 2H^+ + 2e^- \rightarrow H_2O\,(l) \quad E° = 1.229 \text{ V}_{SHE} \tag{2}$$

$$\text{Overall reaction:} \quad H_2(g) + {}^1/_2 O_2(g) \rightarrow H_2O(l) \quad E° = 1.229 \text{ V}_{SHE} \tag{3}$$

The membrane serves the dual role of keeping the fuel and oxidant separate, that is, is nonporous to hydrogen and oxygen, and providing a conducting path for the protons. In fact, the membrane has several important requirements: (1) good ionic conductivity but low electronic conductivity, (2) low gas permeability, (3) dimensional stability (resistance to swelling), (4) high mechanical strength and integrity, (5) chemical stability with high resistance to dehydration, oxidation, reduction, and hydrolysis, (6) high cation transport number, (7) surface properties allowing easy bonding to catalyst, and (8) homogeneity. The ionomer Nafion has stood the test of time as a PEMFC membrane on account of its high ionic conductivity, chemical stability, and good mechanical strength. Indeed, these features make the PEMFC probably the most robust of all fuel cell types, enabling it to withstand an extraordinary amount of abuse without seriously affecting the performance. In comparison, the MCFC and SOFC are far more fragile, needing to be slowly brought up to the operating temperature, safeguarded from over pressurization and their anodes protected from inadvertent oxidation.

Prior to the introduction of PSA as used in the GE fuel cells, earlier materials that had been investigated for membranes were as follows:

- Phenolic resins, made by polymerization of phenolsulfonic acid with formaldehyde
- Partially sulfonated PSA, made by dissolving PSA in ethanol-stabilized chloroform and sulfonated at room temperature
- An interpolymer of cross-linked polystyrene and divinylbenzene sulfonic acid in an inert matrix – this possessed very good physical properties, better water uptake capacity, and proton conductivity than earlier materials.

Table 1 Early membrane materials for PEMFCs

Time	Membrane	Power density (kW m^2)	Lifetime (thousand of hours)
1959–1961	Phenol sulfonic acid	0.05–0.1	0.3–1
1962–1965	Polystyrene sulfonic acid	0.4–0.6	0.3–2
1966–1967	Polytrifluorostyrene sulfonic	0.75–0.8	1–10
1968–1970	Nafion experimental	0.8–1	1–100
1971–1980	Nafion production	6–8	10–1000

Source: Son J-Ek (2004) Hydrogen and fuel cell technology. *Korean Journal of Chemical Engineering* 42(1): 1–4 [7].

Table 1 lists the performance of some of these materials in comparison with the early Nafion and later production material.

Nafion was the first of a class of materials that are known as perfluoro sulfonic acids (PFSAs). The structure of a PFSA comprises three domains:

1. A PTFE-like backbone that is hydrophobic
2. Side chains of $-O-CF_2-CF-O-CF_2-CF_2-$
3. Clusters of sulfonic acid moieties $-SO_3^-H^+$ that are hydrophilic.

The molecular structure of Nafion and other commercial PFSAs is illustrated in Table 2.

When the membrane of PFSAs becomes hydrated, the protons in the sulfonic acid moieties become attached to water molecules as hydronium (H_3O^+) ions. The sulfonic functional groups aggregate to form hydrophilic nanodomains, which act as water reservoirs [8]. It is these clusters of water molecules that become the means of conduction of hydronium ions (Figure 2). Thus, the hydrogen ions are able to migrate through the electrolyte by virtue of the fact that it is hydrated.

The ionic conductivity of the membrane depends not only on the degree of hydration, which depends on the temperature and operating pressure, but also on the availability of the sulfonic acid sites. For example, the conductivity of Nafion membranes quoted in the literature varies widely depending on the system, pretreatment, and equilibrium parameters used. At 100% relative humidity (RH), the conductivity is generally between 0.01 and 0.1 S cm^{-1} and drops by several orders of magnitude as the humidity decreases [9–13]. Therefore, the degree of hydration has a very marked influence on the ionic conductivity and therefore the performance of the cell. The effect of the availability of sulfonic acid sites, usually expressed as the membrane equivalent weight (EW), is relatively small. Values of EW between 800 and 1100 (equivalent to acid capacities of between 1.25 and ~0.90 mEq g^{-1}) are acceptable for most membranes because the maximum ionic conductivity can be obtained in this range. The low EW of 800 of the Dow membrane, listed in Table 2, gives rise to higher specific proton conductivity and therefore improved performance compared with Nafion with an EW of 1100.

The conductivity of the PFSA can be improved by reducing the thickness of the material, and several different Nafion materials have been produced (Table 1). However, thin materials are inherently less robust and small amounts of fuel crossover can occur with consequent reduction in the observed cell voltage.

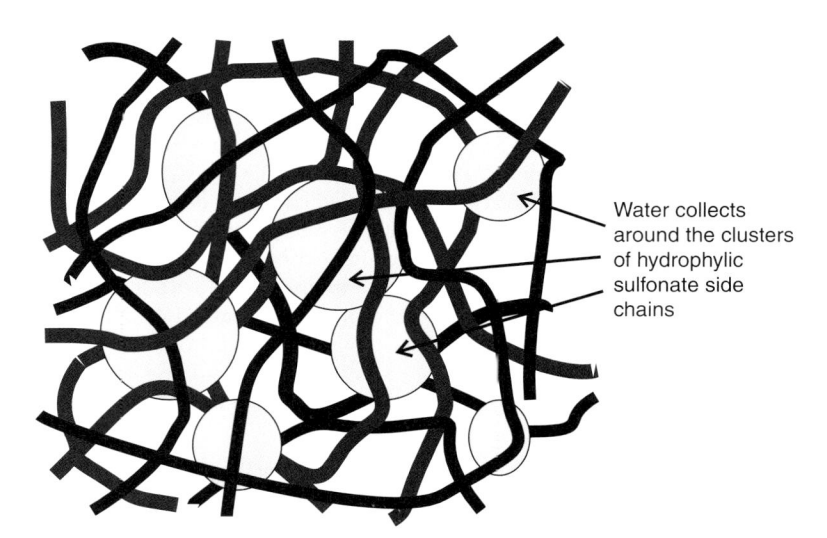

Figure 2 Water forms the conduction path for hydrated protons in the PFSA structure. Adapted from Larminie J and Dicks AL (2003) *Fuel Cell Systems Explained*, 2nd edn. John Wiley & Sons. ISBN-10: 047084857X [3].

Table 2 Structure of Nafion and other PFSAs

$$-(CF_2CF_2)_x-(CF_2CF)_y-$$
$$-(OCF_2CF)_m-O-(CF_2)_n-SO_3H$$
$$CF_3$$

Structure parameter	Trade name and type	Equivalent weight	Thickness (μm)
$m = 1, x = 5–13.5, n = 2, y = 1$	Dupont		
	Nafion 120	1200	260
	Nafion 117	1100	175
	Nafion 115	1100	125
	Nafion 112	1100	80
	Asashi Glass		
$m = 0, 1, n = 1–5$	Flemion - T	1000	120
	Flemion - S	1000	80
	Flemion - R	1000	50
$m = 0, n = 2–5, x = 1.5–14$	Asashi Chemicals Aciplex - S	1000 ~ 1200	25 ~ 100
$m = 0, n = 2, x = 3.6–10$	Dow Chemical Dow	800	125

Source: Lee JS, Quan ND, Hwang JM, et al. (2006) Polymer electrolyte membranes for fuel cells. *Journal of Industrial Engineering Chemistry* 12(2): 175–183 [8].

Since the molecular structure of the PFSA incorporates a PTFE backbone, the membranes are strong and chemically stabile in both oxidizing and reducing environments. Table 1 shows that Nafion exhibited a lifetime significantly greater than previous nonfluorinated membrane materials. PFSAs also exhibit very high proton conductivities with Nafion being around $0.1\,\mathrm{S\,cm^{-1}}$ at normal levels of hydration.

One of the most successful new approaches to membrane development has been the use of composite materials. In this respect, the Gore Select™ material is now widely used among fuel cell developers. This material comprises a very thin base material (typically 0.025 mm thick) of expanded PTFE prepared by a proprietary emulsion polymerization process that gives rise to a microporous structure. An ion-exchange resin, typically perfluorinated sulfonic acid, perfluorinated carboxylic acid, or other material, is incorporated into the structure with the aid of a suitable surfactant.

A major disadvantage of the PFSA membranes is their high cost, due to the inherent expense of the fluorination step. Another disadvantage of all of these membranes is that they are not able to operate above 100 °C at atmospheric pressure due to the evaporation of water from the membrane. Higher operating temperatures can be achieved by running the cells at elevated pressures, but this has a negative effect on system efficiency. Above 120 °C, the PFSA materials undergo a glass transition (i.e., a structural change from an amorphous plastic state to a more brittle one) that also severely limits their usefulness. Membranes that could operate at higher temperatures without the need for pressurization would therefore bring significant benefits [14–16]:

1. *CO catalyst poisoning.* Carbon monoxide concentrations in excess of about 10 ppm at low temperatures (< 80 °C) will poison the electrocatalyst used in the PEMFC. As the operating temperature increases, so the tolerance of catalyst improves. Phosphoric acid fuel cells (PAFCs) that operate at 200 °C will tolerate CO concentrations in the fuel stream of above 1%.
2. *Heat management.* Operating at high temperatures has the advantage of creating a greater driving force for more efficient stack cooling. This is particularly important for transport applications to reduce balance of plant equipment (e.g., radiators). Furthermore, high-grade exhaust heat can be useful for fuel processing, for example, in providing heat for the endothermic steam reforming of natural gas.
3. *Prohibitive technology costs.* The prospects of nonfluorinated high-temperature membranes with the potential savings from a reduction in electrocatalyst loading form a very strong economical driving force to develop fuel cells that operate at high temperatures.
4. *Humidification and water management.* The pressurization needed to reach temperatures beyond 130 °C and maintain high humidities would likely outweigh any efficiency gains of going beyond this temperature. Membranes that are capable of operating at reduced humidity would not require pressurization. In addition, it is less likely that they will be affected by the significant water management problems of polymer membranes.
5. *Increased rates of reaction and diffusion.* As the temperature increases, the reaction and interlayer diffusion rates increase. Additionally, the reduction of liquid water molecules will increase the exposed surface area of the catalysts and improve the ability of the reactants to diffuse into the reaction layer.

For these reasons, many researchers have been investigating alternative membrane materials that are not fluorinated and that may be able to operate at higher temperatures.

4.08.2.2 Modified PFSA Membranes

Two approaches have been taken to modify or functionalize PFSA membranes to improve water management so that they can operate at high temperatures. The first approach is to make thinner membranes, which has the advantage of reducing internal ionic resistance but is limited by the need to have mechanically strong materials. Strength may be improved, as in the case of the Gore membranes, for example, by reinforcing the material using a porous PTFE sheet. This approach has enabled developers to reduce the thickness of the PFSA to 5–30 µm while maintaining acceptable mechanical properties.

An alternative approach has been to incorporate another material into the nanostructure of the PFSA to make a composite material. The earliest examples were the inclusion of small particles of inorganic hygroscopic oxides such as SiO_2 or TiO_2 [9]. This was achieved by using sol–gel methods with the aim of water becoming absorbed on the oxide surface thereby limiting water loss from the cell by 'electro-osmotic drag'. Unfortunately, the incorporation has normally led to a much reduced proton conductivity of the PFSA. Better results have been obtained by incorporating other proton-conducting materials into the PFSA nanostructure. Examples have been silica-supported phosphotungstic acid and silicotungstic acid, zirconium phosphates, and materials such as silica alkoxides produced using (3-mercaptopropyl)methyldimethoxysilane (MPMDMS) [17]. Methods of modifying the PFSA membranes have been reviewed by Lee *et al.* [8].

4.08.2.3 Alternative Sulfonated Membrane Materials

The high cost of manufacturing the PFSAs has led researchers to seek alternative materials for PEMFCs, particularly for high-temperature operation and also for application in DMFCs for which the traditional PFSAs suffer from severe methanol crossover through the membrane from anode to cathode. Reviews by Johnson Matthey [18] and researchers at Sophia University, Japan [19], identified over 60 alternatives to PFSAs. Of these, the hydrocarbon polymers have attracted a lot of interest, despite the fact that materials such as PSA, phenol sulfonic acid resin, and poly(trifluorostyrene sulfonic acid) were investigated during the 1960s but later fell out of favor on account of their low thermal and chemical stability.

Alternative fluorinated polymers that have been made include trifluorostyrene, copolymer-based α,β,β-tryfluorostyrene monomer, and radiation-grafted membranes. Of the nonfluorinated polymers, the most studied are sulfonated poly(phenyl quinoxalines), poly(2,6-diphenyl-4-phenylene oxide), poly(aryl ether solfone), acid-doped polybenzimidazole (PBI), partially sulfonated polyether ether ketone (SPEEK), poly(benzyl sulfonic acid)siloxane (PBSS), poly(1,4-phenylene), poly(4-phenoxybenzoyl-1,4-phenylene) (PPBP), and polyphenylene sulfide. These and other polymers can be used as backbone structures for proton-conducting electrolytes and may easily be sulfonated using sulfuric acid, chlorosulfonic acid, sulfur trioxide, or acetyl sulfate. Most of these polymers can also be modified to give more entanglement of the side chains thereby increasing the physical robustness of the materials. Some of these materials do have improved thermal stability, but unfortunately most have generally lower ionic conductivities than Nafion at comparable ion-exchange capacities. Many of the materials are also more susceptible than Nafion to oxidative or acid-catalyzed degradation.

Workers at Stanford Research Institute (SRI) recognized that chemical degradation by oxidation [20] may be reduced by utilizing purely aromatic polymers, such as polyphenylene(s), which are inherently more thermochemically stable than many of the other fluorinated and nonfluorinated polymers. By creating high-molecular-weight polyphenylenes via a Diels–Alder condensation reaction, they generated a sulfonated polyphenylene that provides a very promising solution to producing proton-exchange membranes (PEMs) with high molecular weight, good hydrogen fuel cell performance, and improved operating temperature capabilities.

Researchers at Sandia National Laboratory have also developed novel high-molecular-weight hydrocarbon polymers [21]. Their approach, as with some of the materials developed during the 1990s by Ballard Advanced Materials, has been to produce block copolymers. These are polymers that are built up using building blocks of two or more different molecular subunits or polymerized monomers, joined by covalent bonds. Such block copolymers have the advantage of forming regular and uniform nanostructures, and many examples of such block copolymers of polystyrene, for example, are now in widespread use in the plastics and adhesives industry. The ideas generated by Sandia were spun out into the new company PolyFuel Ltd in 1999 after some 14 years of research into applied membranes.

PolyFuel's patented hydrocarbon membrane material self-assembles nanoscale proton-conducting channels that are engineered to be significantly smaller than those in the more common fluorocarbon membranes. The polymer matrix is also claimed to be much tougher and stronger, so that it does not swell to the same degree as fluorocarbon membranes do. The net effect is that more of the water and, in the case of the DMFC, methanol remain on the fuel side of the fuel cell. The result is a more efficient fuel cell that for a given power output is significantly smaller, lighter, less expensive, and longer running than those using more conventional polymers. PolyFuel's patents [22] describe a range of block copolymers that are built up of nonionic and ionic regions having the formula:

$$\{-L_1-[-(A_aB_b)_n]_{1-z}-L_2-[(S_xC_c-S_yD_d)_o]_zL_3\}_j$$

where $[(A_aB_b)_n]$ comprises a nonionic block and $[(S_xC_c-S_yD_d)_o]$ comprises an ionic block. A and C are phenyl, napthyl, terphenyl, aryl nitrile, substituted aryl nitrile, organopolysiloxane, or various aromatic or substituted aromatic groups. B and D are $-O-Ar_5-R_2-Ar_6-O-$, where R_2 is a single bond, a cycloaliphatic hydrocarbon of the formula C_nH_{2n-2}, and Ar_5 and Ar_6 are aromatic or substituted aromatic groups, and where B and D can be the same or different. S is an ion-conducting moiety and L_1, L_2, and L_3 are single bonds or additional groups.

Many of the world's leading portable fuel cell system developers such as NEC, Sanyo, and Samsung have been claiming to use PolyFuel and similar membranes [23], but hydrocarbon membranes have been developed by other organizations such as Gas Technology Institute (GTI) in the United States. GTI has worked extensively over the past 5 years on a major PEM development program, with an emphasis on options that utilize low-cost starting materials and more simplified manufacturing approaches when compared with conventional materials. The cost of the material (raw materials and film-processing costs) is estimated at less than $10 m^{-2}$. Performance has matched conventional Nafion, and positive long-term tests have achieved durability in excess of 5000 h (with tests ongoing). GTI has evaluated this new membrane for suitability in PEMFC and DMFC stacks [24].

4.08.2.4 Acid–Base Complex Membranes

Sulfuric acid was one of the first electrolytes used in fuel cells and, like phosphoric acid, is an excellent conductor of hydrogen ions when in an anhydrous state. The PAFC, which has developed in parallel with PEMFCs, has the electrolyte immobilized in a ceramic matrix, usually silicon carbide impregnated with PTFE. In an attempt to avoid the difficulties associated with hydrated polymers in which protons are conducted as hydronium ions, many research groups have sought to immobilize an anhydrous acid such as H_2SO_4, H_3PO_4, or HCl by complexing it within a basic polymer. Polymers that have been investigated for use in such systems include polyethylene oxide (PEO), polyvinyl alcohol (PVA), polyacrylamide (PAM), polyvinylpyrrolidone (PVP), polyetheleneimine (PEI), various polyamino silicates, and PBI. In these materials, the acid molecule is attached to the polymer via hydrogen bonding and can be thought of as a solution of acid in polymer. The acid provides the means of proton conduction and, as would be expected, the higher the acid content, the greater is the proton conductivity of the membrane. High acid contents unfortunately also reduce the mechanical stability of the membrane particularly above 100 °C. Inevitably, the acids are not perfectly anhydrous and a certain amount of water is often added to improve conductivity and mechanical properties. Other methods that have been examined to improve mechanical stability include using highly cross-linked polymers or addition of inorganic filler or plasticizer. Plasticizers such as polypropylene carbonate, dimethylformamide (DMF), and glycols result in an electrolyte with gel-like properties rather than the more rigid form exhibited by PFSAs. However, unlike PFSAs, the acid–base polymer complex membranes are relatively inexpensive and have been investigated for a wide variety of applications. Of the many possible acid–base complex polymers, $PBI-H_3PO_4$ has probably been investigated the most, especially for the DMFC [25, 26].

4.08.2.5 Ionic Liquid Membranes

Rather than using water in a sulfonated polymer to provide the conducting path for protons, many developers have opted for ionic liquids. These materials are organic liquids that become ionized under the influence of an electrical potential. The molecular structure comprises an anion, such as BF_4^-, PF_6^-, NO_3^-, $CFSO_3^-$, and $CH_3CO_2^-$, and a cation, such as tetraalkylammonium, tetraalkylphosphonium, trialkylsulfonium, N-alkylpyridinium, and the like. Organic ionics that are liquid at room temperature are expensive, but they do have unique properties such being nonvolatile and nonflammable, with high ionic conductivity and good thermal and chemical stability. These properties have made them very attractive for a variety of applications including advanced batteries, double-layer capacitors, supercapacitors, and dye-sensitized solar cells. In ionic liquid/polymer membranes, the nitrogen sites of the cations can act as proton acceptors with the acidic sulfonic groups of the host polymer serving as proton donors. Rather than the ionic liquid being a separate phase from the polymer, it is possible to attach the imidazole group directly to the backbone of the polymer to prevent loss during use. Some such membranes have been prepared and evaluated in PEMFCs. Clearly, there is much more that can be done, and ionic liquids could provide an alternative to the PFSAs or hydrocarbon polymers that at present remain the preferred choices for fuel cell developers.

4.08.2.6 High-Temperature Proton Conductors

There are a range of materials that are proton conductors that do not fall into the categories listed so far. These are mainly inorganic solid acid materials and ceramic oxides. The ceramic oxides are a class of materials that normally become ionic conductors at temperatures of several hundred degrees. Of the inorganic solid acids, phosphates such as those of cesium, tungsten, zirconium, and uranium have received considerable attention in recent years [9]. Cesium phosphate conducts protons through the bulk, whereas for zirconium, tungsten, and uranium phosphates, conductivity is a surface phenomenon. The latter are water-insoluble layered compounds containing intercalated hydronium ions and have reasonable room temperature conductivity. Complex acids, known as heteropolyacids, such as $H_3PMo_{12}O_{40} \cdot H_2O$ and $H_3PW_{12}O_{40} \cdot nH_2O$, show very high conductivity at room temperature ($\sim 0.2\ S\ cm^{-1}$) when the water of hydration (n) is high, but they dehydrate rapidly on increasing the temperature, with a concomitant fall in conductivity. Some success has been achieved recently in intercalating Brønsted bases (i.e., a functional group or part of a molecule that accepts H^+ ions) with the inorganic acids and heteropolyacids, but one of the greatest issues with such materials is the fabrication of structurally and mechanically robust membranes.

4.08.3 Electrodes and Catalysts

4.08.3.1 Anode Materials

On either side of the membrane in a PEMFC are the two electrocatalysts. On the fuel side, the oxidation of hydrogen to release protons proceeds via a fast reaction over an active metal catalyst. At the normal operating range of temperatures of PEMFCs and DMFCs, the metal has to be platinum or a Pt metal alloy. The rate of reaction at the anode is controlled by the adsorption of hydrogen on the metal and the subsequent dissociation into protons and electrons is a facile reaction. Consequently, the anode reactions contribute very little to the voltage loss in a practical fuel cell.

The main concern at the anode of the PEMFC is the effect of carbon monoxide. The CO molecule reacts rapidly with Pt and is absorbed in preference to hydrogen (the strength of the Pt–CO bond being higher than the Pt–H bond). This poisoning of the anode catalyst is a problem for hydrogen that is obtained by reforming of hydrocarbon fuels (e.g., natural gas), since there is always some residual CO present in such fuel gases. Pt catalysts can only tolerate a few ppm of CO in the fuel before the poisoning effect becomes significant. For this reason, most PEMFC systems require removal of all but the last traces (up to 10 ppm) of CO from the fuel stream. Surface Pt–CO that is formed at the anode can be removed by oxidation (e.g., by applying a positive potential to the anode), but over time, this leads to gradual deactivation of the Pt catalyst.

An approach that has been successfully employed to improve the CO tolerance of anode catalysts is to use Pt–Ru alloys. At the nanoscale, the elements are segregated and the CO which is strongly adsorbed onto Pt can get oxidized by oxygen or hydroxyl species that form on the neighboring Ru sites. In the DMFC, methanol is adsorbed onto the Pt and then dehydrogenates into CO and similar fragments. Thus, it is found that Pt–Ru catalysts that are good as DMFC anode catalysts also tend to be somewhat tolerant to CO for PEMFCs.

4.08.3.2 Cathode Materials

On the cathode side of the fuel cell, Pt has also been found to be the best metal for catalysis of the oxygen reduction reaction (the reaction of oxygen molecules with protons and electrons to produce water). However, the reaction mechanism at the cathode is not as simple as that at the anode. This is because of the relative strength of the O–O bond (492 kJ mol^{-1}) compared with the H–H bond (432 kJ mol^{-1}), the formation of highly stable Pt–O or Pt–H surface species, and the possible formation of a partially oxidized peroxide (H_2O_2) species. The mechanism appears to be dependent on the type of catalyst and there are several possible steps that may occur. Broadly, the reduction of the oxygen molecule in aqueous solution, particularly in acidic media, proceeds through either one of the two major pathways, and they are as follows:

1. The direct four-electron reduction reaction to H_2O:

$$O_2 + 4H^+ + 4\bar{e} \leftrightarrow 2H_2O \quad E° = 1.229 \text{ V} \quad [4]$$

2. The parallel pathway, the two-electron reduction reaction to hydrogen peroxide, H_2O_2:

$$O_2 + 2H^+ + 2\bar{e} \leftrightarrow H_2O_2 \quad E° = 0.695 \text{ V} \quad [5]$$

followed by the reduction of adsorbed peroxide to H_2O:

$$H_2O_2 + 2H^+ + 2\bar{e} \leftrightarrow 2H_2O \quad E° = 1.76 \text{ V} \quad [6]$$

where $E°$ represents the thermodynamic potentials at standard conditions.

The four-electron mechanism is the most favored reaction pathway since it produces a high cell voltage for a H_2/O_2 fuel cell. In practice, the theoretical open-circuit (OC) potential is never achieved on account of the slow reaction (adsorption of oxygen) giving rise to a high overpotential.

The high overpotential on Pt and the high cost of the material has provided an incentive for researchers to seek alternative catalyst materials for the PEM cathode. By making the Pt more dispersed on the support material, the amount of platinum used in the fuel cell, for a given power output, has been significantly reduced over the past 20 years, but an alternative to Pt seems as elusive as it was decades ago.

Several groups of materials have been investigated as potential non-Pt cathode catalysts [27]. These include carbons doped with iron and cobalt, and transition metal nitrides, but perhaps the largest group of nonprecious metal systems that have received attention are the macrocyclic compounds. The simplest of these comprise a central metal atom, such as one of the transition elements, for example, iron, cobalt, nickel, or copper, surrounded by chelate ligands via a nitrogen atom. As examples, the phthalocyanine complexes of copper and nickel have been found to be stable as PEM cathode catalysts.

Examples of more complex macrocyclics are naturally occurring pigments such as the hemes, which give red color to the blood, and chlorophyll, the green pigment involved in photosynthesis. The first of these is a type of porphyrin, which comprises a highly aromatic molecule (containing a large number of delocalized pi electrons), incorporating bridging nitrogen atoms (pyrrole groups). The nitrogen atoms provide Lewis acid sites enabling metals to be complexed within the molecule. Various porphyrin complexes have been investigated as cathode catalysts, and examples include iron and cobalt complexes of tetramethoxyphenylporphyrin (TMPP) and tetraphenylporphyrin (TPP).

Probably the next most studied class of materials for use as PEM cathode catalysts have been the nonprecious metal chalcogenides. These first received the attention of researches to replace Pt in the 1970s when various transitional metals sulfides such as CoS showed a distinctive oxygen reduction reaction at the cathode [28]. Over the past 40 years, several binary and ternary metal chalcogenides have been prepared and tested as potential PEMFC catalysts. As with the macrocyclics, none of these materials have proved to be as active and durable as supported Pt.

In recent years, various electronic and ionic-conducting polymers have been investigated for applications, such as organic photovoltaic devices. Polyaniline (pani), polypyrrole (Ppy), and poly(3-methylthiophene) (P3MT) have been recognized as conducting polymers for some years. Incorporation of nickel or cobalt as complexes into these heterocyclic polymers has yielded some potentially good cathode catalysts, but performance in PEMFCs has so far proved inadequate with current densities of only around $2\,mA\,cm^{-2}$. In 2009, researchers at Monash University reported that poly(3,4-ethylenedioxythiophene) (PEDOT, a proton-conducting polymer), exhibited activity for oxygen reduction [29], but the activity appears to be highly dependent on the method of preparation, and it is too early to say how the durability of the material compares to the traditional Pt catalysts.

4.08.3.3 Preparation and Physical Structure of the Catalyst Layers

The basic structure of the electrodes in different designs of PEMFC is similar, though the details vary. The anodes and the cathodes are essentially the same too – indeed in many PEMFCs they are identical.

Carbon is normally used as the catalyst support as it not only serves to disperse the active metal but also provides electronic conductivity to enable a high current to be drawn from the fuel cell. Supported platinum catalyst has been traditionally prepared by a wet chemistry approach that starts with a compound such as chloroplatinic acid that is absorbed on high-surface-area carbon blacks. Suitable carbon blacks can be obtained from Cabot Corporation (Vulcan XC-72R, Black Pearls BP 2000), Ketjen Black International, Chevron (Shawinigan), Erachem, and Denka, and are produced by the pyrolysis of hydrocarbons [30]. The absorbed compound yields finely dispersed Pt particles when thermally decomposed, as illustrated in **Figure 3**. These images showed the Pt catalysts with different supports and loadings.

More recently, other methods of depositing the active metal onto carbon have been investigated. Wee *et al.* reviewed the promising fabrication methods that have reduced Pt loading with increased catalyst utilization that have been published since 2000. The current emerging methods include a modified thin-film method, electrodeposition, and sputter deposition, and also new approaches such as dual-ion-beam-assisted deposition, electroless deposition, electrospray method, and direct Pt sols deposition [32].

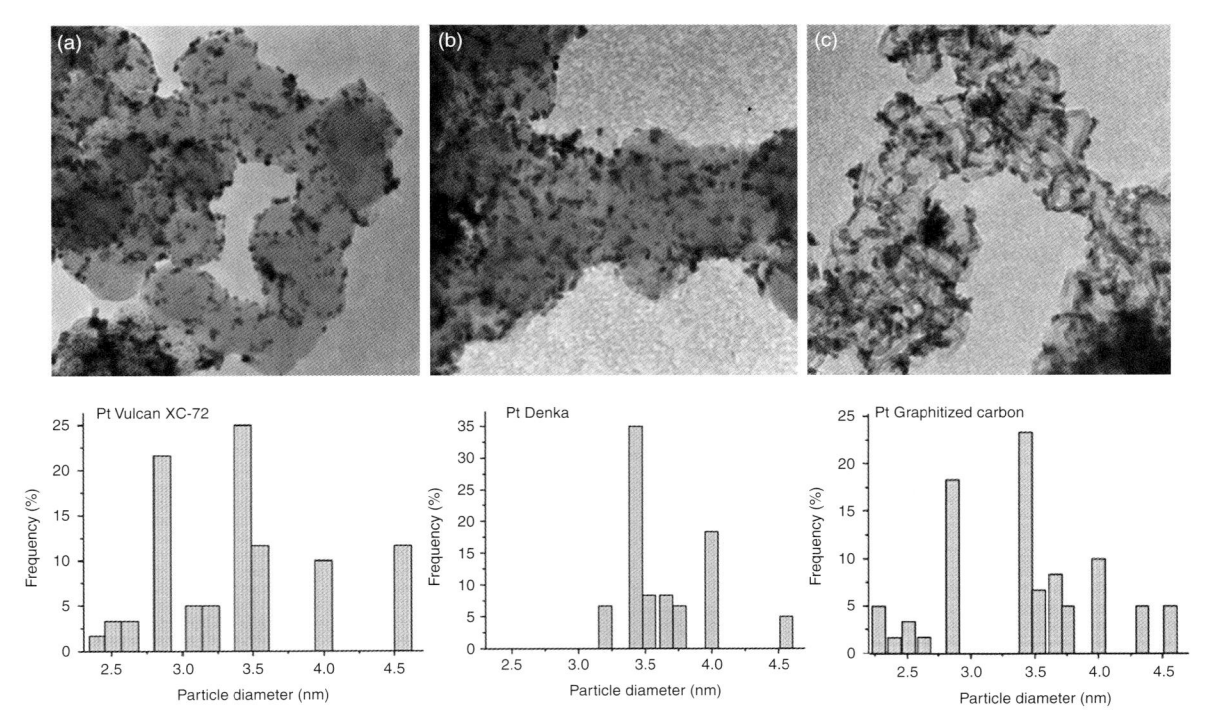

Figure 3 Transmission electron microscope images of Pt/C catalysts with histograms of Pt particle size distribution: (a) Pt/Vulcan XC-72R (40 wt%); (b) Pt/Denka (40 wt%); (c) Pt/graphitized carbon (50 wt%). Adapted from Ignaszak A, Ye, S, and Gyenge E (2009) A study of the catalytic interface for O_2 electroreduction on Pt: The interaction between carbon support meso/microstructure and ionomer (Nafion) distribution. *The Journal of Physical Chemistry C* 113(1): 298–307 [31].

192 PEM Fuel Cells: Applications

The traditional Pt–carbon catalyst is prepared in the form of an aqueous dispersion or 'ink' that is used to paint or coat a thin layer onto a porous and conductive material such as carbon cloth or carbon paper. For the coating step, one of two alternative methods is used, though the end result is essentially the same in both cases.

In the 'separate electrode method', a thin layer of the carbon-supported catalyst is fixed, using proprietary techniques, to a thicker layer of porous carbon. PTFE will often be added also, because it is hydrophobic, and so, in the case of the cathode, will expel the product water to the electrode surface where it can evaporate. As well as providing the basic mechanical structure for the electrode, the carbon paper or cloth also diffuses the gas onto the catalyst and so is often called the 'gas diffusion layer' (GDL). Such an electrode with catalyst layer is then fixed to each side of a polymer electrolyte membrane. A fairly standard procedure for doing this is described in several papers (e.g., Lee et al. [33]). First, the electrolyte membrane is cleaned by immersing in boiling 3% hydrogen peroxide in water for 1 h, and then in boiling sulfuric acid for the same time, to ensure as full protonation of the sulfonate group as possible. The membrane is then rinsed in boiling deionized water for 1 h to remove any remaining acid. The electrodes are then put onto the electrolyte membrane and the assembly is hot pressed at 140 °C at high pressure for 3 min. The result is a complete membrane electrode assembly (MEA).

The alternative method involves 'building the electrode directly onto the electrolyte'. The platinum on carbon catalyst is fixed directly to the electrolyte, thus manufacturing the electrode directly onto the membrane, rather than separately. This can be obtained by two ways, either using the 'decal transfer' method, which is casting the catalyzed layer onto a PTFE blank before transferring it onto the membrane or direct coating it onto the membrane. The catalyst, which will often (but not always) be mixed with PTFE, is applied to the electrolyte membrane using rolling methods (e.g., Bever [34]), or spraying (e.g., Giorgi et al. [35]), or an adapted printing process (Ralph et al. [36]).

Whichever of the coating methods is chosen, the result is a structure as shown, in idealized form, in **Figure 4**. The carbon-supported catalyst particles are joined to the electrolyte on one side, and the gas diffusion (current collecting, water removing, physical support) layer on the other side. The hydrophobic PTFE that is needed to remove water from the catalyst is not shown explicitly, but will almost always be present.

In the early days of PEMFC development, the catalyst was used at the rate of 28 mg cm^{-2} of platinum. In recent years, the usage has been reduced to around 0.2 mg cm^{-2} with an increase in power. The basic raw material cost of the platinum in a 1 kW PEMFC at such loadings would be about $10 – a small portion of the total cost [37]. The development of PEMFC using Pt catalyst strongly depends on the electrode fabrication method and the loaded substrate.

4.08.3.4 Gas Diffusion Layers and Stack Construction

The GDL on either side of the MEA will normally be carbon cloth or paper, of about 0.2–0.5 mm thickness. GDL is a slightly misleading name for this part of the electrode, as it does much more than diffuse the gas. It also forms an electrical connection

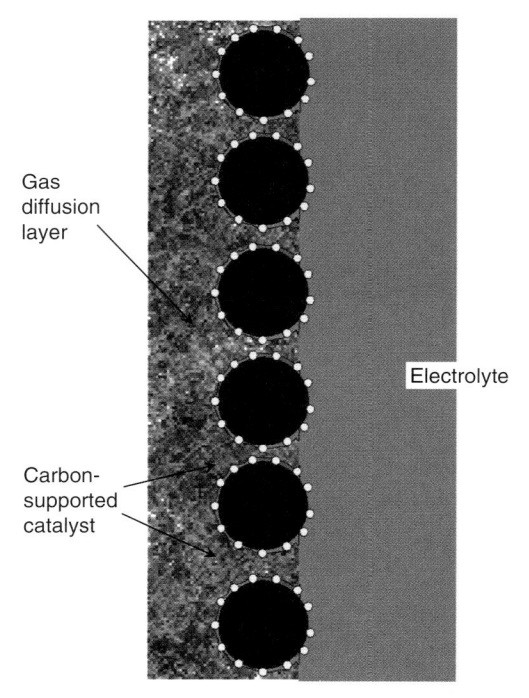

Figure 4 Simplified and idealized structure of a PEMFC electrode. Adapted from Larminie J and Dicks AL (2003) *Fuel Cell Systems Explained*, 2nd edn. John Wiley & Sons. ISBN-10: 047084857X [3].

between the carbon-supported catalyst and the bipolar plate, or other current collector. In addition, it carries the product water away from the electrolyte surface, and also forms a protective layer over the very thin (typically ~30 μm) layer of catalyst. The GDLs on either side of the membrane contact the bipolar plate, which is used in planar stacks to electrically connect one cell to the next, and also provide a means for bringing the reacting gases to and from either side of the fuel cells. This is achieved by channels embedded into either side of the bipolar plate. Each channel forms a flow field for hydrogen on the one side or oxidant (air) on the other side of the plate to be brought to the surface of the GDL. The design of the bipolar plates is a subject in its own right and is influenced by the operating temperature and pressure of the fuel cell. A schematic of a bipolar plate sandwiched between two fuel cell MEAs is shown in **Figure 5**. In this design, the bipolar plate also serves to cool the stack with cooling channels embedded within it.

The first bipolar plates were made of graphite with parallel channels for the gases machined into the surface of each side of the plates. While this was adequate for initial evaluation, it soon became evident that machined graphite is far too expensive for commercial application. Ideally, a bipolar plate should have the following properties:

- The electrical conductivity should be >10 S cm^{-1}.
- The heat conductivity must exceed 20 W m^{-1} K^{-1} for normal integrated cooling fluids or exceed 100 W m^{-1} K^{-1} if heat is removed only from the edge of the plate.
- The gas permeability must be < 10^{-7} mbar l s^{-1} cm^{-2}.
- It must be corrosion-resistant when in contact with acid electrolyte, oxygen, hydrogen, heat, and humidity.
- It must be reasonably stiff, flexural strength >25 MPa.
- The cost should be as low as possible, and the production cycle should be reasonably short.
- It must be as thin and light as possible to minimize stack volume and weight.

Most manufacturers now employ either metal bipolar plates, which can be made to the appropriate shape by stamping, or plates made of a composite material by injection moulding. A more complete description of the production of bipolar plates is given in

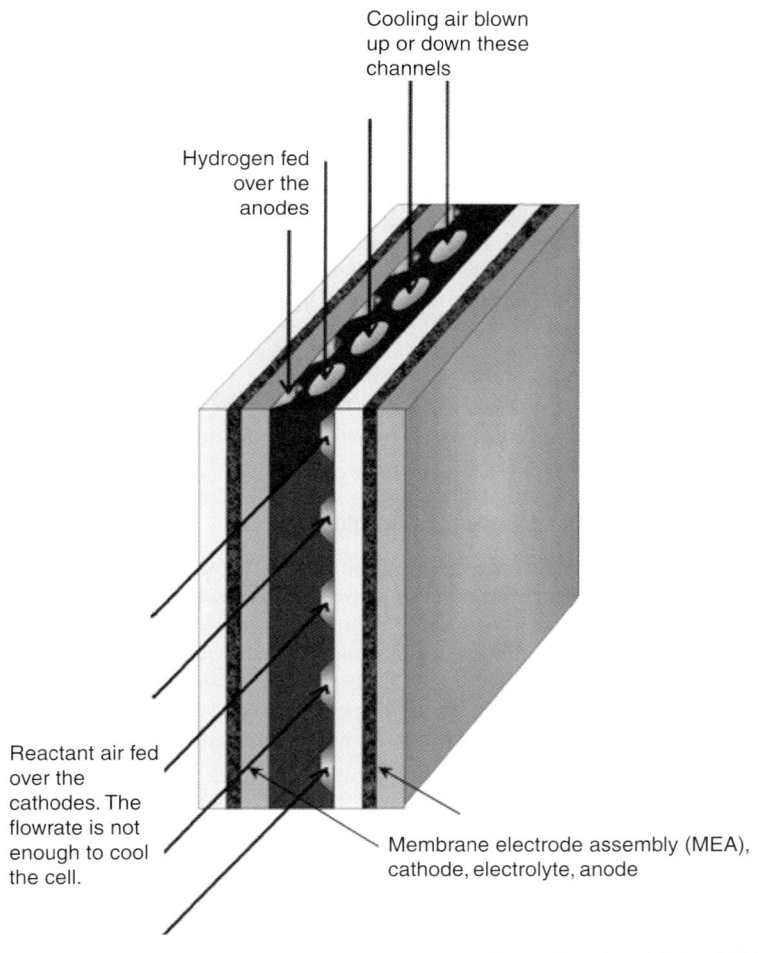

Figure 5 Two MEAs and one bipolar plate modified for separate reactant and cooling air. Adapted from Larminie J and Dicks AL (2003) *Fuel Cell Systems Explained*, 2nd edn. John Wiley & Sons. ISBN-10: 047084857X [3].

References 3 and 30. Many different flow field designs have been evaluated over the past few years, and it is also worth commenting that different cell topologies have also been investigated. While the planar cell configuration remains the most widely adopted, tubular and other designs have been tested, particularly for small-scale applications.

4.08.4 Humidification and Water Management

4.08.4.1 Overview of the Problem

A critical issue for conventional PEMFCs that employ PFSA membranes is the need to maintain an adequate level of humidification of the membrane to achieve optimal proton conductivity.

In the PEMFC, water forms at the cathode, and in a well-designed air-breathing cell, this water would keep the electrolyte at the correct level of hydration. Air would be blown over the cathode, and as well as supplying the necessary oxygen it would dry out any excess water. As the membrane electrolyte is very thin, water would diffuse from the cathode side to the anode, and throughout the whole electrolyte a suitable state of hydration would be achieved without any special difficulty.

Unfortunately, this is not the case in most PEMFCs. One problem is that during operation of the cell, the H^+ ions moving from the anode to the cathode pull water molecules with them. In this electro-osmotic drag, typically between 1 and 5, water molecules are 'dragged' for each proton. This means that, especially at high current densities, the anode side of the electrolyte can become dried out – even if the cathode is well hydrated. Another major problem is the drying effect of air at high temperatures. At temperatures of about 60 °C or over, the air will always dry out the electrodes faster than water is produced by the H_2/O_2 reaction. These problems of drying out are usually solved by humidifying the air, the hydrogen, or both, before they enter the fuel cell. Yet another complication is that the water balance in the electrolyte must be correct throughout the cell. Again, this can be addressed by good engineering of the stack and system to allow the correct amount of external humidification for the operating conditions of the stack.

4.08.4.1.1 Airflow and water evaporation

Except for the special case of PEMFCs supplied with pure oxygen, it is universally the practice to remove the product water using the air that flows through the cell. The air will also always be fed through the cell at a rate faster than that needed just to supply the necessary oxygen. If it were fed at exactly the 'stoichiometric' rate, there would be very great loss in cell voltage caused by 'concentration losses'. This is because the exit air would be completely depleted of oxygen. In practice, the stoichiometry (λ) will be at least 2. Problems arise because the drying effect of air is nonlinear in its relationship to temperature.

4.08.4.1.2 Humidity of PEMFC air

The humidity of the air in a PEMFC must be carefully controlled. The air must be dry enough to evaporate the product water, but not so dry that it dries too much – it is essential that the electrolyte membrane retains a high water content. The humidity should be above 80% to prevent excess drying, but must be below 100%, or liquid water would collect in the electrodes. Fortunately, it is possible to calculate the humidity of the cathode exit stream of a PEMFC for a given set of operating conditions, and fundamentally cell humidity can be increased by the following:

- Lowering the temperature, which unfortunately increases voltage losses
- Lowering the airflow rate and hence the air stoichiometry, which could be done a little, but also reduces cathode performance
- Increasing the operating pressure, which unfortunately adds to parasitic losses in the system (see next section).

4.08.4.2 Running PEMFCs without Extra Humidification (Air-Breathing Stacks)

By operating at suitable temperatures and airflow rates, it is possible to run a PEMFC that does not get too dry without using any extra humidification. It has been found that at temperatures of above 60 °C, external humidification of the reactant gases will be essential in PEMFCs. This rule-of-thumb has been confirmed by many experimental studies, and leads to the conclusion that providing the operating temperature is kept low, it is possible to avoid external humidification (and the resulting system complexity) and design what has become known as an air-breathing stack. This feature makes choosing the optimum operating temperature for a PEMFC difficult – the higher the temperature, the better the performance, mainly because the cathode overvoltage reduces. However, once over 60 °C, the humidification problems increase, and the extra weight and cost of the humidification equipment can exceed the savings coming from a smaller and lighter fuel cell.

The key to running a fuel cell without external humidification is to set the air stoichiometry so that the RH of the exit air is about 100%, and to ensure that the cell design is such that the water is balanced within the cell. One way of doing this is to have the air and hydrogen flows in the opposite directions across the MEA, as described by Büchi and Srinivasan (**Figure 6**) [38]. The water flow from anode to cathode is the same in all parts, as it is caused by the electro-osmotic drag, and is directly proportional to the current. The back diffusion from cathode to anode varies, but is compensated for by the gas circulation. Other aids to an even spread of humidity are narrow electrodes and thicker GDLs, which hold more water.

The key to correct PEMFC water balance is control of the airflow rate and temperature. If the temperature can be kept low, and an adequate flow of air maintained, then the overall membrane humidity can be maintained, although there may be some regions

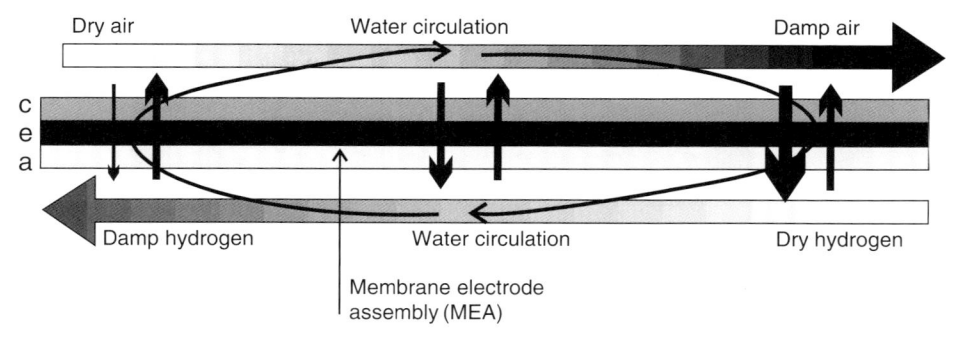

Figure 6 Contraflow of reactant gases to spread humidification [38].

(particularly the cell inlet) that become dry. This is the case for systems for small portable power supplies of a few watts, and even with slightly larger systems (such as for laptops), it may be possible to have an air-breathing stack operating at atmospheric pressure in which an adequate airflow is achieved using a high-efficiency blower. One of the best sources of data and further discussion of the issues of running a PEMFC without humidification of the gases is given by Büchi and Srinivasan [38].

4.08.4.3 External Humidification

Although small fuel cells can be operated without additional or external humidification, in larger cells this is rarely done. Operating temperatures of over 60 °C are desirable to reduce losses, especially the cathode activation voltage loss. Also, it makes economic sense to operate the fuel cell at maximum possible power density, even if the extra weight, volume, cost, and complexity of the humidification system are taken into account. With larger cells, all these are proportionally less important. Three points should be made regarding the principle of external humidification:

- First, it is often not the case that only the air is humidified. To spread the humidity more evenly, sometimes the hydrogen fuel is humidified as well.
- Second, the humidification process involves evaporating water in the incoming gas. This will cool the gas, as the energy to make the water evaporate will come from the air. In pressurized systems, this is positively helpful as it will help offset the heating that inevitably occurs when the gas is compressed.
- Third, we should note that the quantities of water to be added to the air, and the benefits in terms of humidity increase, are all much improved by operating at higher pressure. The effect of cell operating pressure will be considered later.

There is no standard method of applying external humidification for PEMFCs, and a study of systems that have been developed shows that different manufacturers have adopted different approaches. In laboratory test systems, the reactant gases of fuel cells are humidified by bubbling them through water, whose temperature is controlled. This 'sparging' of the gas is fine for experimental work but is not a practical proposition for larger commercial systems.

One of the easiest methods of controlling humidification is the direct injection of water as a spray. This has the further advantage that it will cool the gas, which will be necessary if it has been compressed or if the fuel gas has been formed by reforming some other fuel and is still hot. The method involves the use of pumps to pressurize the water, and also a solenoid valve to open and close the injector. It is therefore fairly expensive in terms of equipment and parasitic energy use. Nevertheless, it is a mature technology, and is widely used, especially on larger fuel cell systems.

Another approach is to directly inject liquid water into the fuel cell through specially designed flow fields in the bipolar plates [39]. The flow field shown in **Figure 7** is like a maze with no exit. The gas is forced through the bipolar plate and into the electrode, driving the water with it. If the flow field is well designed, this will happen all over the electrode.

In an ideal system, the water that is generated by the fuel cells would be recirculated within the system to humidify the inlet gases. In practice, this is difficult as it requires separation or condensation of the water as liquid and then reinjection into the inlet streams. One method of achieving this is to use a PEM membrane. The principle is shown in **Figure 8**.

The warm, damp air leaving the cell passes over one side of a membrane, where it is cooled. Some of the water condenses on the membrane. The liquid water passes through the membrane and is evaporated by the drier gas going into the cell on the other side. Such a humidifier unit can be seen on the top of the fuel cell system shown in **Figure 9**.

A more novel approach was described by Watanabe [40] as 'self-humidification', where the electrolyte is modified, not only to retain water but also to produce water. Retention is increased by impregnating the electrolyte with particles of silica (SiO_2) and titania (TiO_2), which are hygroscopic materials. Nanocrystals of platinum are also impregnated into the electrolyte, which is made particularly thin. Some hydrogen and oxygen diffuse through the electrode and, because of the catalytic effect of the platinum, react, producing water. This, of course, uses up valuable hydrogen gas, but it is claimed that the improved performance of the electrolyte justifies this parasitic fuel loss.

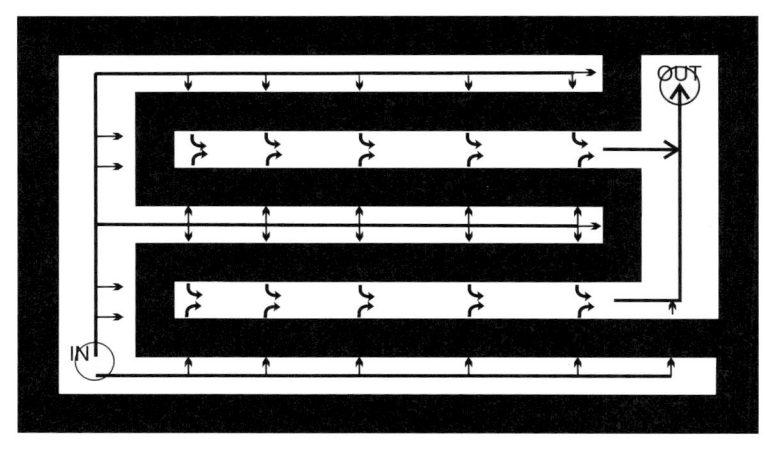

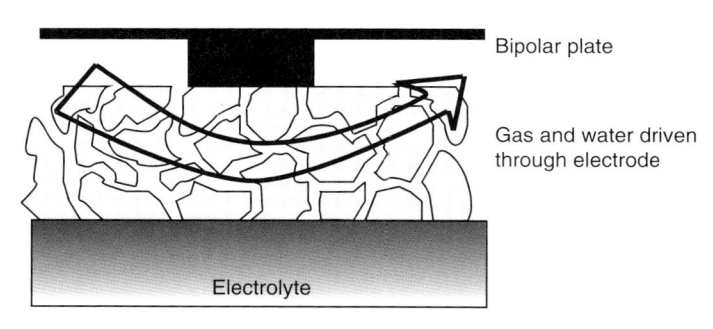

Figure 7 Diagrams to show the principle of humidification using interdigitated flow fields. Adapted from Wood DL, Yi JS, and Nguyen TV (1998) Effect of direct liquid water injection and interdigitated flow field on the performance of proton exchange membrane fuel cells. *Electrochimica Acta* 43(24): 3795–3809 [39].

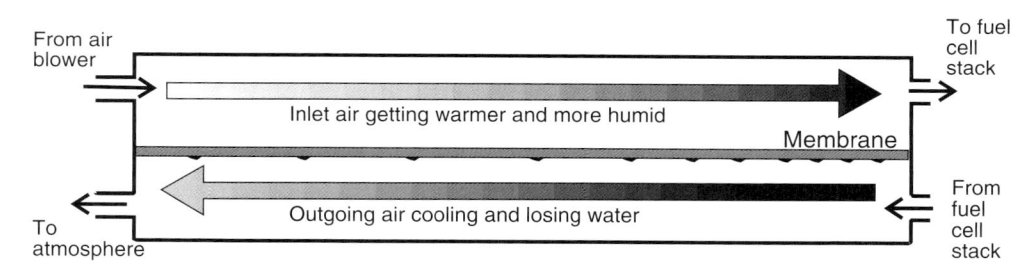

Figure 8 Humidification of reactant air using exit air, as demonstrated by the Paul Scherrer Institute (1999).

A particular issue arises with water management in the case of the direct methanol variant of the PEMFC. This is because a substantial amount of water needs to be added to the methanol so that the reactions proceed via:

$$\text{Anode:} \quad CH_3OH + H_2O = CO_2 + 6H^+ + 6e^- \qquad [7]$$

$$\text{Cathode:} \quad 6H^+ + 1.5O_2 + 6e^- = 3H_2O \qquad [8]$$

$$\text{Net reaction:} \quad CH_3OH = CO_2 + 2H_2O \qquad [9]$$

There is net transfer of water (with the protons) from the anode side of the fuel cell to the cathode side. In the DMFC, carrying water with the fuel severely reduces the system's energy density because water has no energy content. While it is possible to recycle some of the water, this would make for a complex system, and the need for a methanol–water mixture is regarded as a necessary drawback for the DMFC. An approach taken by MTI Micro in the Mobion® system is to use a passive control of direct methanol addition. MTI have been developing a micro-DMFC, which is the size of an electronics chip. Protected by a substantial suite of patents, the MTI microchip system has recently delivered over 62 mW cm^{-2}, producing more than 1800 Wh kg^{-1} of energy from 100% methanol fuel

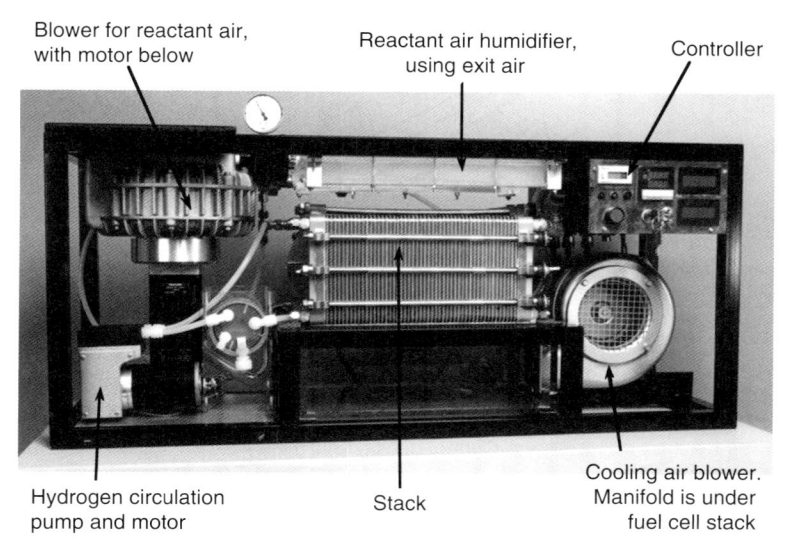

Figure 9 A 2 kW PEMFC by Paul Scherrer Institute, Switzerland.

feed. The latest Mobion® fuel cell on a chip is 50% smaller than the initial device produced at the beginning of 2007, and uses a system of 'fluid conditioning' to control the humidity of the cell. The combination of significant size reductions and improvements in power performance and efficiency are critical if fuel cells are to be used inside portable electronic devices.

4.08.5 Pressurized versus Air-Breathing Stacks

4.08.5.1 Influence of Pressure on Cell Voltage

Although small PEMFCs are operated at normal air pressure and may be air-breathing, larger fuel cells of 10 kW or more are invariably operated at higher pressures. The basic issues around operating at higher pressure are the same as for other engines, such as diesel and petrol internal combustion engines (ICEs), only with these machines the term used is 'supercharging' or 'turbocharging'. Indeed, the technology for achieving the higher pressures is essentially the same. The purpose of increasing the pressure in an engine is to increase the specific power to get more power out of the same size engine. Hopefully, the extra cost, size, and weight of the compressing equipment will be less than the cost, size, and weight of simply getting the extra power by making the engine bigger. It is a fact that most diesel engines are operated at above atmospheric pressure – they are supercharged using a turbocharger. The hot exhaust gas is used to drive a turbine, which drives a compressor and which compresses the inlet air to the engine. The energy used to drive the compressor is thus essentially 'free', and the turbocharger units used are mass-produced, compact, and highly reliable. In this case, the advantages clearly outweigh the disadvantages. However, with fuel cells the advantage/disadvantage balance is much closer. Above all, it is because there is little energy in the exit gas of the PEMFC (this is not the case for high-temperature fuel cells such as the MCFC or SOFC) and any compressor has to be driven largely or wholly using the electrical power produced by the fuel cell; in other words, it creates a parasitic load on the fuel cell. For a PEMFC, the issue of whether to operate at elevated pressure comes down to a question of optimization, where a balance has to be achieved between the benefits of potentially increased power, per kilogram or liter by increasing the operating pressure versus reduction of power through increased parasitic loads of compressor(s), and internal heat management. The question of heat management is most important where the fuel cell is integrated with a fuel processor that consumes heat, or where the energy of the exhaust is captured, for example, in a cogeneration system. These issues will be dealt with in more detail in Section 4.08.5.2.

The increase in power resulting from operating a PEMFC at higher pressure is mainly the result of the reduction in the cathode activation overvoltage. This is illustrated in **Figure 10**.

Increased operating pressure raises the exchange current density, which has the apparent effect of lifting the open-circuit voltage (OCV). The OCV is really also raised, as described by the Nernst equation. As well as these benefits, there is also sometimes a reduction in the mass transport losses, with the effect that the voltage begins to fall off at a higher currents. The effect of raising the pressure on cell voltage can be seen from the graph of voltage against current shown in **Figure 10**. In simple terms, for most values of current, the voltage is raised by a fixed value.

It may also be apparent from **Figure 10** that this voltage 'boost' with pressure, ΔV is proportional to the logarithm of the pressure rise. This is both an experimental and a theoretical observation, and intuitively it means that there will be a pressure above which any benefits in terms of increasing cell voltage are outweighed by the increased parasitic load on the system. An analysis of the benefits for a simple model system are given in Larminie and Dicks [3], in which the benefits of increasing pressure peak around a pressure of around 3 bar where the net benefit in terms of increasing cell potential amounts to about 17 mV per cell. Above 3 bar, these benefits tend to diminish.

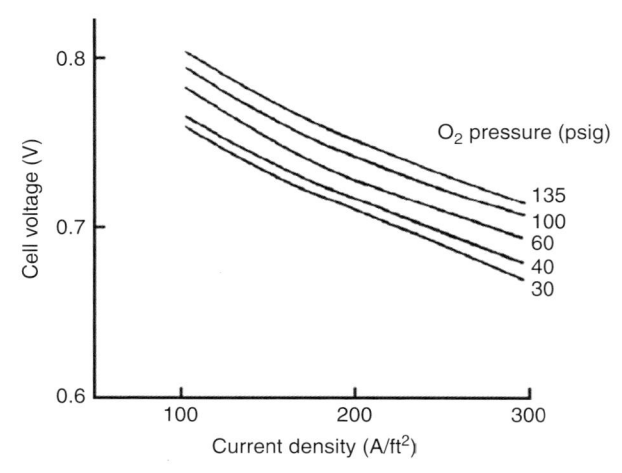

Figure 10 Influence of O_2 pressure on PEFC performance (93 °C, electrode loadings of 2 mg cm^{-2} Pt, H_2 fuel at 3 atm). Adapted from LaConti A, Smarz G, and Sribnik F (1986) New membrane-catalyst for solid polymer electrolyte systems. Final Report prepared by Electro-Chem Products, Hamilton Standard for Los Alamos National Laboratory under Contract No. 9-X53-D6272-1, Figure 29, p. 49 [41].

4.08.5.2 Other Factors Affecting Choice of Pressure – Balance of Plant and System Design

The increased power of a PEMFC that arises from operating at elevated pressures is also influenced by the 'balance of plant'. That is to say, by the system design needed to bring pure hydrogen as well as air to the stack, how these streams are humidified, how the stack is cooled, and what happens to any exhaust heat from the anode and cathode exhaust streams. So although it is the simplest to quantify, the voltage boost is not the only benefit from operating at higher pressure. Similarly, loss of power to the compressor is not the only loss.

One of the most important gains with increasing pressure can be shown by **Figure 11**. This shows a schematic arrangement for a pressurized PEMFC that incorporates a steam reformer and turbine/compressor for pressurizing the stack. If hydrogen is being produced by the steam reforming of natural gas, thermodynamics suggests that the reforming should be carried out at high temperatures and low pressures. In practice, the reforming is carried out under moderately elevated pressures (up to about

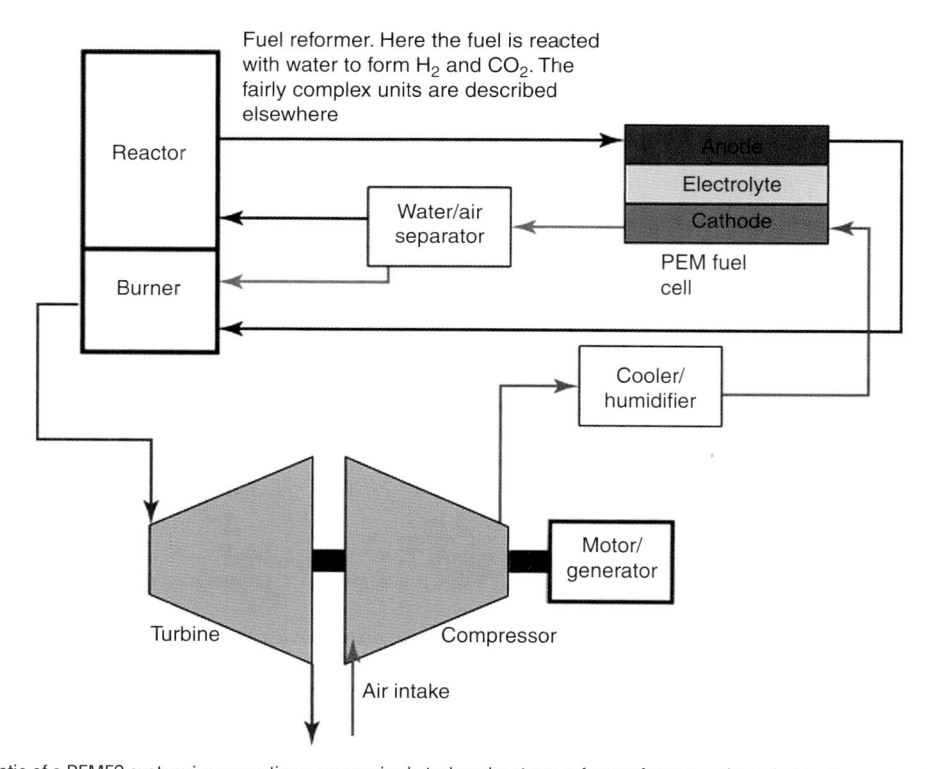

Figure 11 Schematic of a PEMFC system incorporating a pressurized stack and a steam reformer for converting a fuel such as natural gas to hydrogen [3].

10 bar) to keep the size of the reformer to a minimum (the size is dictated by the kinetics of the chemical processes). To avoid loss of exergy in transferring the hydrogen from the reformer to the fuel cell stack, both reformer and fuel cell should be operated at similar pressures (even so there will be a need for intercooling between the two). In the system of **Figure 11** there is a burner, which is needed to provide heat for the fuel reformation process. The exhaust from this burner can be used by a turbine to drive the compressor. The fuel for the burner is provided by the exhaust gas from the anode of the fuel cell. Thus, it can be seen that although the reformer system may influence the choice of operating pressure, integration of the reformer with the fuel cell stack also requires careful consideration of energy flows.

Humidification also influences the choice of operating pressure. Humidification of the inlet air to a PEMFC is a great deal easier if the air is hot and needs cooling, because there is plenty of energy available to evaporate the water. Since air is heated by compression, humidification is easier at elevated pressures. However, the main benefit is that less water is needed to achieve the same RH at higher pressures, and at higher temperatures the difference is particularly great. In practice, it has been found difficult to arrange adequate PEMFC humidification at temperatures above 80 °C unless the system is pressurized to about 2 bar or more.

Another practical consideration is that inevitably there will be a pressure drop along the fuel and oxidant channels of a fuel cell stack. Therefore, some degree of compression will be required for both of these streams to overcome the pressure drops, especially in the case where the size of the stack has been minimized, resulting in narrow gas channels.

On the negative side for compressors or blowers, there are the issues of size, weight, cost, and noise. It must be borne in mind that some sort of air blower for the reactant air would be needed whatever pressure is employed, so it is the extra size, weight, and cost of higher pressure compressors compared with lower pressure blowers that is the issue. The practical issue of product availability means that this difference will often be quite small for fuel cells of power in the region of tens of kilowatts, but could become significant for very large system. Again, it is worth stating that most small systems (< 1 kW) in practice operate at approximately ambient air pressure. It is the larger systems (>5 kW) that may benefit by operating at higher pressure.

4.08.6 Operating Temperature and Stack Cooling

4.08.6.1 Air-Breathing Systems

In a fuel cell, only a fraction of the energy of the incoming fuel is converted into electricity. A standard fuel cell text will show that the voltage produced by any fuel cell is always less than the theoretical OC potential. This is caused by a number of internal losses within the system, some relating to the kinetics of the reactions (activation losses) and some relating to simple resistive or ohmic losses. For a PEMFC, typically around half of the energy results in DC power, the remainder is manifest as heat. How this heat is removed from the stack depends greatly on the size of the fuel cell. With fuel cells below 100 W, it is possible to use purely convected air (through the cathode channels and around the cell housing) to cool the cell and provide sufficient airflow to evaporate the water, without recourse to any fan. This is done with a fairly open-cell construction with a cell spacing of between 5 and 10 mm per cell [42]. However, for a more compact fuel cell, small fans can be used to blow the reactant and cooling air through the cell, though a large proportion of the heat will still be lost through natural convection and radiation.

For fuel cell stacks greater than about 100 W, a lower proportion of the heat is lost by convection and radiation from and around the external surfaces of the cell and cathode channels, and an alternative cooling method is required.

4.6.06.2 Separate Reactant and Air or Water Cooling

For cell stacks greater than about 100 W, cooling is achieved by employing separate cooling channels within the stacks. For stacks in the range from about 100 to 1000 W, air is blown through these cooling channels, as shown in **Figure 5**. Alternatively, separate cooling plates can be added, through which air is blown.

The issues of when to change from air cooling to water cooling are much the same for fuel cells as they are for other engines, such as ICEs. Essentially, air cooling is simpler, but it becomes harder and harder to ensure that the whole fuel cell is cooled to a similar temperature as it gets larger. Also, the air channels make the fuel cell stack larger than it needs be – 1 kg of water can be pumped through a much smaller channel than 1 kg of air, and the cooling effect of water is much greater.

With fuel cells, the need to water cool is perhaps greater than with a petrol engine, as the performance is more affected by variation in temperature. On balance PEMFCs, above 5 kW will be water-cooled, those below 2 kW will be air-cooled, with the decision for cells in between being a matter of judgment.

One factor that will certainly influence the decision of whether or not to water cool will be the question of "what is to be done with the heat." If it is to be just lost to the atmosphere, then the bias will be toward air cooling. On the other hand, if the heat is to be recovered, for example, in a small domestic combined heat and power (CHP) system, then water cooling becomes much more attractive. The method of water cooling a fuel cell is essentially the same as for air, as shown in **Figure 5**, except that water is pumped through the cooling channels. In practice, cooling channels are not always needed or provided at every bipolar plate.

Now we can reconsider the issue of operating temperature since it also affects the issue of stack cooling. If we limit the operating temperature of the PEMFC to around 80 °C, then the temperature of the cooling water will be somewhat lower and its usefulness is limited. If the operating temperature of the stack could be increased, through the use of alternative membranes, as described in Section 4.08.3, then more valuable heat at a higher grade will be available from the cooling outlet of the fuel cell stack, as well as the outlet of the cathode. Indeed, operating at greater temperature, it is conceivable that separate stack cooling could be eliminated altogether and it means that cathode air could cool the stack on its own.

It should be evident from the previous discussion that PEMFCs may find a niche in several market segments. Small-scale air-breathing systems of below 100 W could be applied to consumer electronics products as well as a number of specialized applications that require stable DC power for prolonged periods. It is in this market that the hydrogen fuel cell competes head on with a range of battery technologies. At a larger scale, say from 1 to 10 kW, hydrogen fuel cells could be used for domestic power generation, or if the heat from the stack is recovered, for domestic-scale cogeneration (sometimes referred to as CHP), especially if the hydrogen could be obtained from a readily available fuel such as natural gas by steam reforming. This application is likely to be a challenge on account of the complexity of integrating fuel processor and fuel cell stack. Yet, larger systems (above a few kilowatts) will have to compete with alternative technologies, such as diesel generators, ICE generators, or even gas turbine systems that are able to provide stationary power, as well as other fuel cell systems such as the SOFC and MCFC. Such systems, combined with hydrogen storage, may be useful for renewable energy applications that are wind- or solar-powered. At this larger scale, PEMFCs may also come into their own in providing the best opportunity for electric vehicles. The following sections describe the main market segments that are currently the focus of PEMFC developers, with emphasis on differentiating the technical differences demanded by each type of application.

4.08.7 Applications for Small-Scale Portable Power Generation Markets (500 W–5 kW)

4.08.7.1 Market Segment

It has been clear for some time that fuel cells have huge potential for uses in a vast number of applications in people's everyday lives. At the same time, there is a perception that the technology has been oversold, many promises made that have not materialized, that commercial systems are always '5 years away', and the reality is that only a relatively small number of fuel cell manufacturers have available products for the general population. Even with this caveat, business analysts continue to predict substantial business prospects for the technology. For example, an Energy Business Report in 2008 predicted that fuel cell revenue worldwide is expected to exceed US$18.6 billion in 2013 [43].

For the purpose of this section, we are defining portable as fuel cell systems below about 5 kW. (It should be noted that there is no universal definition of portable systems. The last review by FuelCellToday on Small Stationary Fuel Cells (March 2009), for example, defines the range as below 10 kW.) Portable fuel cells are promising for growth due to the fact that they are comparatively close to commercialization, or are already there [44]. There is a great demand for small power supply alternatives that are longer lasting than batteries, refuelable when away from electricity sources, and have a high energy density [45]. Market growth during 2009 was projected to be approximately US$400 million [46], is expected to be the fastest growth market in 2012, and will be particularly favorable toward DMFCs [47]. While some business projections can be amazingly optimistic, a recent survey by FuelCellToday claimed [48] that some 15.31 MW of portable fuel cell systems were already shipped in 2010 and that there was a rapid 10-fold increase in numbers of portable systems sold in 2010 compared with 2009. This is largely due to the substantial increase in shipments of educational fuel cell units (including fuel cell toys), which exceeded 100 000 units in the past year. This reflects the aggressive building of market share that has occurred by the likes of Horizon and Heliocentris. FuelCellToday [48] forecasts that 40 million portable fuel cells could be shipped annually by 2020, with small portable fuel cells (1–100 W) seeing the most shipments by that time.

Portable power systems are grouped into applications in the following descriptions which focus on the various technologies and key developers.

4.08.7.1.1 Auxiliary power units

Auxiliary power units (APU) are most often used in vehicles for onboard electrical services, typically in airplanes, boats, or heavy-duty trucks. In all of these cases, the intention is to use the fuel that is used for propulsion (diesel, aviation, or logistic fuel) for supplying the auxiliary fuel cell. The design of fuel cell APUs then becomes dominated by the design of the fuel reformer for converting the fuel to a hydrogen-rich gas for the fuel cell. This is explored in Section 4.08.8.2, which describes the reformer and its integration in stationary fuel cell systems. To keep the reforming systems simple, most fuel cell APU development has focused on the use of the SOFC rather than the PEMFC. The higher operating temperature of the SOFC also allows for better heat management between the fuel reformer and the fuel cell stack. It is possible that with the development of PEMFCs that operate at high temperatures, the integration of a fuel reformer may become more cost-effective, in which case developers may then turn to the PEMFC as a robust solution for APU applications in the future.

4.08.7.1.2 Backup power systems

The PEMFC was recognized by early developers as a good technology for emergency backup power systems where there is a requirement for high energy and power density, and the ability to start up quickly from ambient conditions. Uninterruptible power supplies (UPS) also need to sustain a wide dynamic range with fast response. Compared with batteries, hydrogen-fueled PFMFCs offer longer continuous run times, with robustness and durability that can withstand harsh environmental condition, such as low ambient temperatures. If a PEMFC stack is held in a standby condition (i.e., with hydrogen admitted to the anode and air to the cathode), it is able to be switched on within the time of single cycle at mains frequency (50 or 60 Hz), although most fuel cell backup power systems also incorporate a battery as well as the PEMFC stack. Systems that have been developed as backup supplies include the following:

ElectraGen system of IdaTech (3 or 5 kW)
ReliOn systems from 200 W to 2 kW
GenCore5 from Plug Power (5 kW)
Premion T-4000 from P21 (4 kW)
PureCell Model 5 from UTC (5 kW)
Altergy Freedom Power™ systems (1–30 kW)

Examples of backup systems are shown in **Figures 12** and **13**.

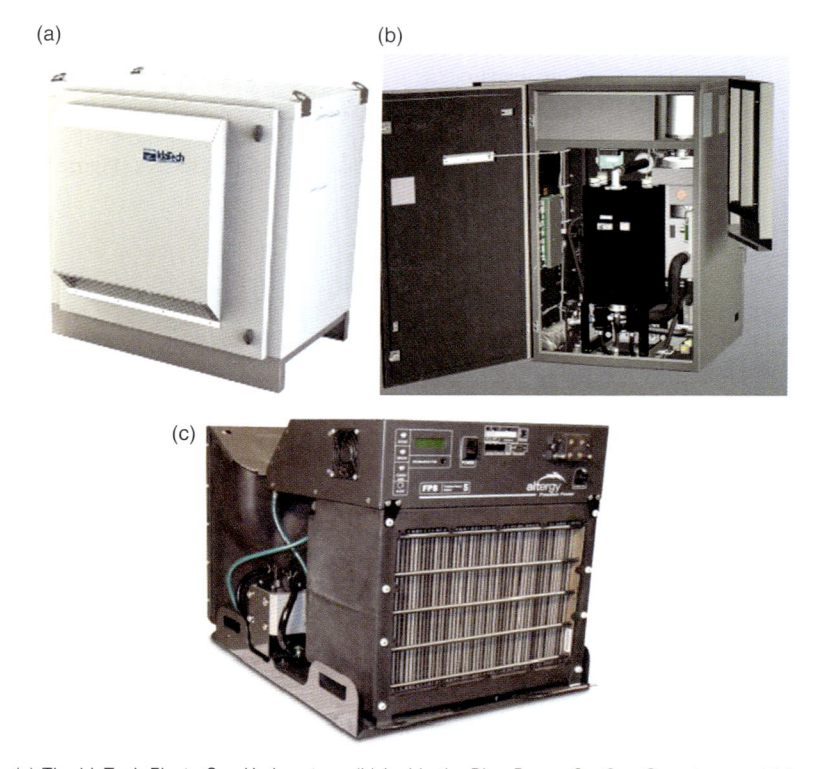

Figure 12 Backup power. (a) The IdaTech ElectraGen H$_2$-I system; (b) inside the Plug Power GenCore® system; and (c), stack assembly used in the Altergy Freedom Power systems.

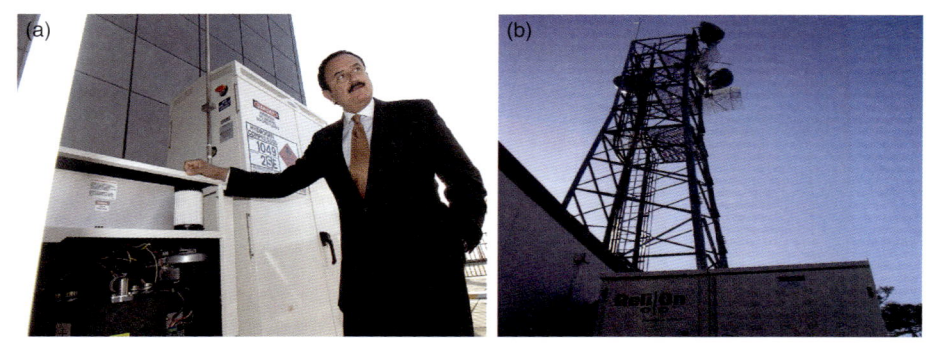

Figure 13 Hydrogen-fueled PEMFC systems used for backup power in remote installations in Australia: (a) Telstra Next G Telecoms System and (b) Queensland Rail. Photos courtesy: SEFCA.

4.08.7.1.3 Grid-independent generators and educational systems

Grid-independent generators are used for on-site services in areas that are not connected to the electricity supply grid. In contrast to backup supplies, grid-independent generators run continuously and therefore stack lifetime is important. Examples of grid-independent generators are as follows:

ZSW-UBZM unit (1 kW)

Ballard/Heliocentris Nexa unit 1200 (1.2 kW)

It is to be noted that a large number of the Ballard systems were supplied to educational establishments and these represent a significant early market segment. The leading developers of educational systems are now Heliocentris and Horizon Fuel Cell Technologies, although other companies are also producing small air-breathing stacks for school use, as can be supplied by the FuelCellStore (www.fuelcellstore.com). Heliocentris started their range of portable systems with the Ballard 1.2 kW Nexa system, but now build their own stacks for the Nexa system, which includes a kit with an optimally adapted DC/DC converter for energy systems up to about 4 kW (**Figure 14**). The Heliocentris product range also includes many smaller systems for education applications (the Dr Fuel Cell® range), and larger systems for training and research Horizon produces a wide range of educational fuel cell kits and portable air-breathing PEMFC stacks in the range from 12 W to 5 kW (www.horizonfuelcell.com).

4.08.7.1.4 Low-power portable applications (<25–250 W)

This market sector includes systems to power mobile and cordless phones, pagers, radios, small consumer electronic devices, notebooks, and professional camcorders. In this sector, the fuel cell of choice has been the DMFC, although Angstrom Power produce systems fueled by hydrogen stored in the form of a hydride. Examples of the devices (**Figure 15**) include:

Angstrom Microdot™

Toshiba Dynario (5 V, 400 mA)

Medis Xtreme 24-7 (3.8–5.5 V, 1 A)

UltraCell XX25TM (25 W) (also used in military applications)

Smart Fuel Cell EFOY class (systems from 25 to 90 W)

Protonex M250-B (including methanol reformer)

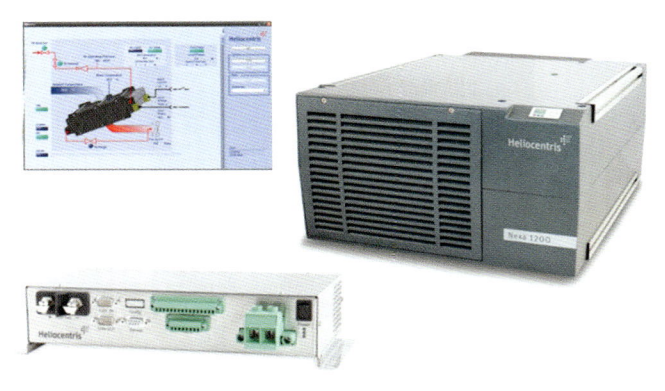

Figure 14 Ballard/Heliocentris Nexa 1200 unit and integration kit.

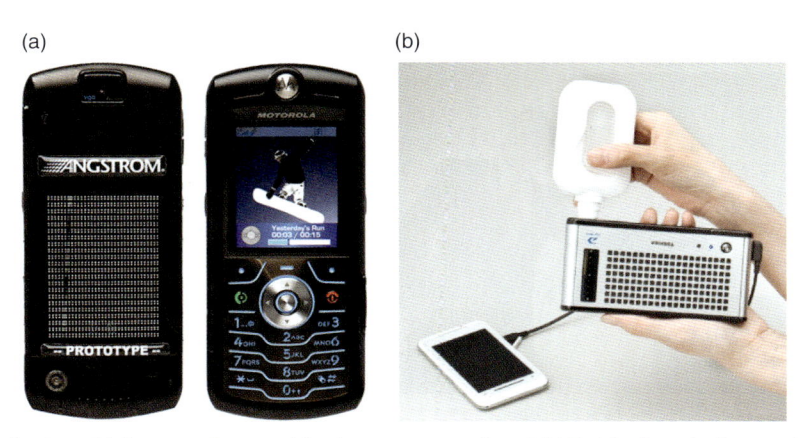

Figure 15 Small-scale applications: (a) Angstrom Power mobile phone power supply and (b) Toshiba Dynario direct methanol mobile phone charger.

4.08.7.1.5 Light traction

This market sector has become one of the most significant to emerge over the past 2 years. It includes light traction vehicles such as forklift trucks, recreation vehicles (golf buggies), airport tugs, wheelchairs, scooters, and motorbikes. In each of these applications, the PEMFC is being used increasingly on account of its high energy and power density, operating close to ambient temperature, fast start-up, and load-following capabilities.

Two-wheeled transport – motorcycles, scooters, mopeds, and bicycles – offer excellent opportunities for university groups and other enterprising organizations to build and demonstrate PEMFC power, and many examples have been built over the past 10–15 years. A large market in Asia exists for scooters and motorbikes, and fuel cell and fuel cell/battery hybrids have been successfully developed by several companies for these applications. Examples are given in **Figures 16–19**. Systems with PEMFC or DMFC stacks giving as little as 250 W up to 3 kW have been supplied by fuel cell manufacturers (e.g., Asia Pacific Fuel Cell Technologies, Horizon Fuel Cell Technologies, Intelligent Energy, Protonex, and SFC Smart Fuel Cell) to system integrators such as Stalleicher, City Com, GUF, ElBike, Suzuki, van Raam, Manhattan Scientifics, Masterflex, Meyra, Palcan, and Vectrix.

Golf carts, airport shuttles, and neighborhood vehicles have also been useful for demonstrating PEMFC technologies. For example, several fuel cell companies have installed fuel cells into the Global Electric Motorcars (GEM) hybrid neighborhood vehicles. Personal wheelchairs and carts have been built by S.A. Bessel who incorporated 0.35 kW PEMFC stacks and metal hydride storage in wheelchairs developed under the European HyChain project. Service trucks developed by H2 Logic incorporate a PEMFC hybrid drive train and low-pressure hydride storage.

Forklift trucks powered by PEMFCs have the following advantages over the more common lead–acid battery-powered systems that have been the preferred option for a number of years:

- Warehouse space to store batteries on charge is eliminated
- Performance of batteries decline with use and typically do not last for a full 8 h shift, whereas PEMFCs give their full performance as long as there is stored hydrogen
- PEMFC forklifts can be recharged with hydrogen in typically 3 min, so the downtime required for charging or swapping batteries is eliminated
- The systems perform well in refrigerated warehouses.

Figure 16 Suzuki Crosscage fuel cell motorbike (2007) and the Burgmann fuel cell scooter (2009), each powered by an Intelligent Energy PEMFC stack.

Figure 17 Hydrogen powered bicycle from Shanghai Pearl Hydrogen Power Company.

Figure 18 A Microcab FCV with Royal Mail livery (United Kingdom). Developed in conjunction with the Birmingham University; this uses a 1.5 kW PEMFC stack and has a range of up to 100 miles on a full charge of hydrogen.

Figure 19 New Holland fuel cell tractor.

An economic case (Economics of Fuel Cell Solutions for Material Handling, Ballard, April 2009; http://www.ballard.com/files/pdf/Case_Studies/Material_Handling_Economic_Benefits_041510.pdf) can be made for the adoption of PEMFCs in forklift trucks because of these attributes, and significant numbers are now being taken up by warehouses. In 2010, Plug Power supplied over 500 of its GenDrive® fuel cell units and manufactured and shipped over 650 units to forklift manufacturers. The latest estimate by Fuel Cells 2000 is that over 1300 PEMFC forklift trucks have been shipped or are in the pipeline for the US markets alone. **Table 3** gives an economic lifecycle cost comparison between PEMFC and battery-powered forklifts.

Current developers of PEMFC systems for forklift trucks (mainly for the North American market) include Oorja Protonics, Ballard Power Systems, Plug Power (in 2008, Plug Power entered into a 2-year agreement with Ballard Power Systems to purchase fuel cell stacks for its electric forklift truck applications), Nuvera Fuel Cells, and Hydrogenics. Interestingly of the 30 companies that have purchased PEMFC forklifts in North America, in 10 locations hydrogen-fueled PEMFC systems are used for the whole forklift truck fleet. These are listed in **Table 4**.

Table 5 gives some details of the manufacturers developing small-scale PEMFCs for this market segment. This list is not exhaustive, and it is apparent, from an analysis of the market over the past 12 months, that there is ongoing rationalization and consolidation of the business among developers.

Table 3 Economic and lifecycle costs of PEMFC and battery-powered forklift trucks [49]

	3 kW PEMFC paired with integral NiMH battery for pallet trucks			8 kW fuel cell paired with integral ultracapacitor, for sit-down rider trucks		
	Battery-powered (two batteries per truck)	PEMFC-powered, with no tax incentive	PEMFC-powered, with $1K kW^{-1} tax incentive	Battery-powered (two batteries per truck)	PEMFC-powered, with no tax incentive	PEMFC-powered, with $1K kW^{-1} tax incentive
Net present value of capital costs	17 654	23 685	21 004	43 271	63 988	56 440
Net present value of O&M costs (including cost of the fuel)	127 539	52 241	52 241	76 135	65 344	65 344
Net present value of total costs of the system	145 193	76 075	73 245	119 405	129 332	121 784

Table 4 Organizations using dedicated PEMFC forklift trucks

Company	Location	PEMFC supplier	No. of forklifts
Bridgestone Tyre	Aiken County, South Carolina	Plug Power	43
Central Grocers	Joliet, Illinois	Plug Power	220
Fedex	Springfield, Missouri	Plug Power	35
Fedex	Toronto, Ontario, Canada	Hydrogenics	NA
Martin Brower	Stockton, California	Oorja Protonics	15
Nestlé Waters	Bottling facility, Dallas, Texas	Plug Power	32
Super Store Industries	Lathrop, California	Oorja Protonics	NA
Sysco	Front Royal, Virginia	Plug Power	100
Sysco	Houston, Texas	Plug Power	98
Walmart	Balzac, Alberta, Canada	Plug Power/Ballard	60–75

As can be seen from **Table 5**, the types of system under development for the small-scale portable market are the DMFC, the reformer methanol fuel cell (RMFC), the PEMFC, and the direct liquid fuel cell (DLFC).

4.08.7.2 The Technologies

The PEMFC has been described in detail in the first half of this chapter. A few words about the variants, the DMFC, the RMFC, the DLFC, and the mixed-reactant fuel cell (MRFC), are now needed.

4.08.7.2.1 The DMFC

The term DMFC is generally used to describe PEMFCs in which liquid methanol is used instead of hydrogen. The advantages of using a liquid fuel as opposed to gaseous hydrogen are obvious, namely that the liquid is easier to store and transfer. In all of the cases where a liquid fuel is used, the fuel cell operates more like a battery in that when the liquid fuel is exhausted, so the fuel cell stops working. Recharging can be achieved by replacing a canister of the liquid fuel. The difficulties with the DMFC are largely (1) poor electrode kinetics and (2) crossover of the methanol from the anode to cathode through the fuel cell membrane. A great deal of research over the past few years has been carried out to address the issue of methanol crossover, but it is far from resolved. Most researchers have attempted to modify the PFSA membrane by incorporating other materials to impede the crossover, such as polyaniline, and various inorganic supramolecular structures, such as nanoscale particles of TiO_2. The reader is directed to the paper by Hogarth et al. [9] for a discussion of this research. Unfortunately, while these materials lead to a reduction in crossover to some extent, it is usually accompanied by a reduction in proton conductivity, resulting to a loss of performance.

In the DMFC, a mixture of methanol and water is admitted to the anode side of the fuel cell. Inevitably, much of the water is transferred (with protons) via the membrane to the cathode side. The use of dilute methanol, together with the relative inefficiency of the DMFC caused by methanol crossover, has hampered the widespread uptake of the technology. As mentioned in Section 4.08.3, some novel approaches, such as that of the MTI micro system, appear to have merit, but, in general, there is slow progress in the commercialization of the DMFC for portable systems. The 2010 review by FuelCellToday claimed that of the portable units shipped in 2010, only 4% were DMFCs, the remainder were largely PEMFC systems.

Table 5 Manufacturers developing PEMFCs for the portable and small-scale stationary market

Company	Product name	Fuel cell type	Power	Comments
Altergy (www.altergy.com)	Freedom Power™	PEMFC	1–30 kW	Altergy is Californian company that has developed fuel cell stacks and systems for the UPS market, with the capability to produce many thousands of units per annum. The company has distribution deals through Eaton and Gulf Platinum Group in the Middle East. The company's Freedom Power product line has been certified in California, and the Earthsmart™ system has powered several high-profile media events such as golden globe awards ceremony.
Angstrom Fuel Cells (www.angstrompower.com)	Microdot™	RMFC		Angstrom has demonstrated the Microdot™ fuel cell for use in mobile phones (currently coupled with a Motorola handset). The company also has compact hydrogen storage technology developed using metal hydride reformulation.
Casio (www.casio.co.jp)		RMFC	19.4 W	Current version of the fuel cell is designed for laptop and other small applications. The internal multilayered microreactor reformer operates at 280 °C, with outer casing temperature of 40 °C. The compact unit employs three chemical reactors, which reform the hydrogen from methanol and render emissions harmless (i.e., the CO is converted to CO_2) [50].
CMR Fuel Cells (www.cmrfuelcells.com)		DMFC		CMR is a developer of fuel cell stacks for mobile applications in DMFCs, and has demonstrated a laptop-sized power cell [51].
Horizon Fuel Cell Technology (www.horizonfuelcell.com)	H-12 to H-5000	PEMFC	2 W–5 kW	A range of small PEMFC and DMFCs are produced largely for the education market, researchers, and hobbyists. Included is the MinPak 2 W personal power center employing an air-breathing PEMFC and metal hydride hydrogen storage cartridge. Horizon range of PEMFC stack products range from 12 W to 5 kW.
Heliocentris (www.heliocentris.com)		PEMFC	50 W–1.2 kW	Heliocentris produce a range of educational products starting at 50 W integrator training system to systems based on the Nexa 1.2 kW PEMF originally supplied by Ballard.
NEAH power systems (www.neahpower.com)		DMFC		NEAH is focusing on the portable market in the range of small electronics to small motorized vehicles, in both military and civilian applications. The company is concentrating efforts on the development of porous silicon electrodes, the modular design of fuel cells, and the integration of the modules and associated interactions. On top of this, NEAH is working on anaerobic options for fuel cell systems for underwater applications, and so on.
NEC (www.nec.com)				NEC has in the past had a strong fuel cell research division. The research centered on small electronics, first with a laptop powered by methanol and next with the NEC Flask Phone. These products were supposed to be heading toward commercialization; however, no recent information was available on the status of NEC's projects.

Company	Model	Type	Power	Description
Samsung SDI (ww.samsungsdi.com)		DMFC, PEMFC	25 W, 200 W	Samsung SDI has an extensive research effort taking place. It is demonstrating its 25 W DMFC for military and small power applications (largely laptops) with a range of 72 h. It is presently developing PEMs, which reform liquefied petroleum gas (LPG) into hydrogen (as an integrated unit) for small-scale power generation (for boats, mobile uses). Samsung SDI's future interest lies in the development of SOFCs for large-scale and vehicle applications [52].
SFC (www.sfc.com)	EMILY 2200	DMFC	90 W	Smart Fuel Cell (SFC) has an extensive range of fuel cell products. This product uses a water and methanol blend directly in the fuel cell. The company has already commercialized its products and these are aimed at a variety of markets (with outputs of 90–250 W).
Sony (www.sony.com)		DMFC	0.55–3 W	Sony has unveiled a number of small-scale DMFCs. The fuel cells are designed for use in small electronics and have been demonstrated as hybrids with lithium-ion batteries, which recharge with surplus power produced by the cell [53]. These are still prototype technologies.
Toshiba (www.toshiba.com)		DMFC		Toshiba has been concentrating efforts on small-scale DMFCs for mobile phone and laptop applications [54]. It has researched both active and passive technology and has demonstrated several prototypes. The company is quiet about its present status; however, it seems to be concentrating on development of battery chargers. The company is expected to have a product available in the very near future [55].
UltraCell (www.ultracellpower.com)	XX25/XX55	PEMFC	25 W, 55 W	UltraCell's products are proven and commercialized. The technology is largely utilized in military and other mobile/remote applications. UltraCell focuses on the small-scale methanol reforming technology to provide a versatile mobile power source [56].

4.08.7.2.2 The RMFC

The RMFC is essentially a PEMFC in which the hydrogen is obtained by the steam reforming of methanol. This reaction is a facile one and can be carried out at quite moderate conditions (250 °C and atmospheric pressure) over a supported metal catalyst (typically comprising copper/zinc oxide). Over the past 10–15 years, several companies have developed methanol reformers for both mobile and stationary power applications. In September 1997, DaimlerChrysler presented the NeCar 3. This was based on the Mercedes A-Class vehicle platform, and utilized a highly responsive fuel processor employing a 20 l reformer, a 5 l combustor, and 20 l selective oxidizer to convert methanol to hydrogen with an overall efficiency of 98–100%. Three years later, in 2000, the NeCar 5 used a more compact methanol reformer that fueled a Ballard 75 kW PEMFC stack. In this landmark vehicle, the reformer was located with the stack, under the passenger compartment. Capable of a range of over 400 km before refueling, the NeCar 5 completed an endurance run of more than 1100 km at the end of 2001 in California.

UltraCell has taken the lead in developing RMFCs for portable power systems, and is currently marketing products with outputs of 25 and 55 W, aimed at military applications, remote area satellite systems, mobile computing, and remote area surveillance [56].

4.08.7.2.3 The DLFC

Research and development in DMFCs has been in progress for at least 15 years, but it is only in the past 10 years that other liquid fuels have been considered for PEMFC systems. In the direct formic acid fuel cell (DFAFC), for example, formic acid is oxidized to carbon dioxide and water:

$$\text{Anode:} \quad HCOOH \rightarrow CO_2 + 2H^+ + 2e^- \quad [10]$$

$$\text{Cathode:} \quad {}^1\!/_2\, O_2 + 2H^+ + 2e^- \rightarrow H_2O \quad [11]$$

$$\text{Net reaction:} \quad HCOOH + {}^1\!/_2\, O_2 \rightarrow CO_2 + H_2O \quad [12]$$

Once dismissed on account of the high cathode overpotential, researchers at the University of Illinois at Urbana-Champaign found that under certain conditions the performance of the DFAFC appeared to be better than the DMFC. The finding stimulated a fair amount of interest in the research community and this was taken up by the Vancouver-based spin-out company Tekion (www.tekion.com), who signed a deal with BASF in 2003–04 to develop the technology. So far, that has not led to a commercial product.

Other liquids have been proposed as fuels for PEMFCs, including alcohols such as propan-2-ol and ethanol. Unfortunately, the electrochemical oxidation of such fuels can give rise to unwanted side products, crossover still appears to be an issue, and so far nothing has emerged from the laboratory suggesting a commercial product to be on the horizon.

4.08.7.2.4 The MRFC

This technology has been around in concept since the early 1990s. The MRFC uses a very different approach that could be applied to the design and operation of all types of fuel cell stacks, and not just DMFCs. MRFCs, in which the fuel and oxidant within a cell are allowed to mix, rely upon the selectivity of anode and cathode electrocatalysts to separate the electrochemical oxidation of fuel and reduction of oxidant. A review of MRFCs by Shukla, Raman, and Scott [57] has highlighted the advantages of the MRFC: no need for gas-tight structure within the stack, providing relaxation of sealing the reactant/product delivery structure; simplified manifolding and lower cost than conventional designs (with the potential to reduce PEM stack component costs by around a third and to raise volumetric power densities by an order of magnitude). The disadvantages are that selective catalysts are required, high ohmic resistance between neighboring cells, and the fact that crossover of fuel is inevitable. Research published by UTC and the University of Texas at Austin have, nonetheless, independently shown that the MRFC can perform as well as the DMFC. So far, CMR appears to be the only company committed to developing the MRFC [51].

4.08.8 Applications for Stationary Power and Cogeneration

4.08.8.1 Prospects for Stationary Fuel Cell Power Systems

The stationary electricity generation market is shaping up to be the next commercial-scale application for fuel cells. By 2014, stationary power-generating fuel cells are expected to account for half of the annual global fuel cell revenue [59]. The 2010 review by FuelCellToday claims that 4000 units were shipped during the year to the small stationary market (defined as under 10 kW), which also includes UPS systems.

Allowable costs for stationary power systems are considerably high, due to the increased efficiencies associated with fuel cells. A 2007 report [58] on the topic of allowable fuel cell cost for smaller-scale power generation (domestic) found a target price for a PEMFC system of €220–420 kW^{-1}. This is contrasted with an expected fuel cell price of between €300 and €900 kW^{-1} (**Table 6**).

As for distributed and industrial electricity markets, the allowable costs for fuel cell systems have been estimated at US$1300 kW^{-1}, and up to US$1800 kW^{-1} for high-efficiency systems, which incorporate combined turbines or other heat recovery methods [59].

Table 6 Economic comparison of 1 kWe fuel cells [58]

	AFC	PAFC	PEMFC	SOFC
Estimated high-volume manufacturing cost	€325–€675	?	€300–€900	€300–€600
Target sale price	€120–€230	€660–€1100	€220–€420	€510–€970
Estimated lifetime (years)	0.5–1.1	3.5–6.0	0.8–2.2	1.7–5.4
Payback period (years)	1.2–3.2	?	1.1–4.1	1.0–2.5
Probability of economic benefit (total savings more than purchase cost)	0.01	?	0.17	0.88

4.08.8.2 Technology Developers

Table 7 is a listing of major companies involved in the development of fuel cells for a range of stationary power applications using fuel cells of a moderate size. This includes manufacturers of a more general nature (including DuPont which supplies other companies with its membrane products). The list also includes fuel cell manufacturers who focus on logistics and handling applications for fuel cells, and companies involved in electrolysis and other applications.

Table 8 is a listing of suppliers and developers of fuel cells for stationary power generation. This includes larger backup systems, small home-size units, which can recover heat, community, and business-sized fuel cell systems. A number of companies are not represented in the table, including General Motors and Intelligent Energy, for example, who are listed elsewhere.

4.08.8.3 System Design

Reference to the list of developers shows that stationary power systems are either fueled by hydrogen directly or by hydrogen that is generated by the conversion of a fuel such as methanol or natural gas. Systems that are fueled by hydrogen directly are those that are applied to providing backup power, or incorporated into renewable energy systems that use the hydrogen as an energy storage medium. More discussion of the use of PEMFCs in renewable energy systems is given in Section 4.08.10. Backup power is a particular niche market for PEMFCs. As noted in the previous section, compared with diesel engine backup power supplies, the PEMFC provides low footprint and weight, zero emissions, and the ability to start up quickly from a standby condition. The PEMFC can also provide good DC power for remote telecoms towers, as demonstrated by Telstra and Queensland Rail in Australia (**Figure 13**). On the other hand, Diverse Energy in the United Kingdom (www.diverse-energy.com) is investigating the use of anhydrous ammonia for this purpose, since liquid ammonia is easy to store and is also easy to dissociate chemically into its constituent elements of hydrogen and nitrogen. Diverse Energy is also promoting the use of PEMFC and ammonia storage for powering remote telecoms towers in developing countries.

For systems that require the hydrogen to be generated from natural gas, it is necessary to integrate a fuel processor within the fuel cell system. SOFC and MCFC operate at temperatures high enough for the exhaust heat from the cell to be utilized in the reforming reactions. Indeed, 'internal reforming', where the fuel conversion is carried out within the fuel cell stack, makes the MCFC and SOFC particularly attractive for systems that are fueled by natural gas or other hydrocarbon fuels, such as biogases. This feature is not available with PEMFCs, and the low-grade exhaust heat from the stack is not able to be used in the chemical conversion of fuel. Inevitably this means that compared with the MCFC and SOFC, PEMFC systems are inherently less efficient at converting the chemical energy within hydrocarbon fuels into electricity.

Converting a hydrocarbon fuel such as natural gas (whose principal component is methane) to a hydrogen-rich gas has been done in industry for many decades by a catalytic process that involves the steam reforming reaction:

$$CH_4 + H_2O = 3H_2 + CO \quad \text{(endothermic)} \qquad [13]$$

or the partial oxidation reaction:

$$CH_4 + O_2 = 2H_2 + CO_2 \quad \text{(exothermic)} \qquad [14]$$

or a thermoneutral combination of the two reactions (often referred to as autothermal reforming). These processes are carried out at elevated temperatures over a supported metal catalyst. Other reactions that can occur over the catalyst include the shift reaction:

$$H_2O + CO = H_2 + CO_2 \qquad [15]$$

and carbon formation reactions, which are usually avoided by adding steam in excess of that required by the stoichiometry of reaction [13]. The product gas from a reformer, which is essentially a mixture of hydrogen, carbon oxides, and steam, is usually passed through another reactor or two where the shift reaction (15) is brought to equilibrium at lower temperatures, thereby increasing the yield of hydrogen. Even with the addition of shift reactors, the gas produced contains a significant amount of CO that has to be lowered to less than a few ppm to be acceptable as a PEMFC feed gas. This is most commonly carried out in a separate reactor in which a small amount of air is introduced to selectively or preferentially oxidize the CO to CO_2. Even if this is done, the presence of a substantial amount of CO_2 in the inlet to the PEMFC can give rise to the formation of CO within the stack by the

Table 7 Major developers of fuel cells for various medium-sized stationary power applications and materials handling

Company	Product name	Fuel cell type	Power	Comments
DuPont (www.dupont.com)				DuPont has vast experience in the production of high-tech MEAs. DuPont supplies membranes to a host of other fuel cell suppliers for use, and concentrates efforts on better membrane technology. DuPont has membranes to suit almost all fuel cells ranging from small-scale PEM and DMFCs up to stationary and mobile PEMs.
Enerfuel (www.ener1.com/?q=content/enerfuel-main)		PEMFC		Enerfuel is developing hybrid power systems that combine high-temperature PEMFCs with lithium-ion batteries. The units are designed to provide power for backup supply, extended range vehicles, and stationary energy storage/supply applications.
Hitachi (www.hitachi-hitech.com/global)		PEMFC, DMFC,	~100 to 300 W	Hitachi has had a fuel cell program in operation since the 1960s and shifted focus to DMFCs in 2001. The company has several portable DMFC prototypes ready, with an output of 100 W and similar. Hitachi signed a development agreement with the UK Center for Process Innovation in 2009 [60].
H2 Logic (www.h2logic.com)		PEMFC		H2 Logic produces fuel cell solutions for materials handling applications. This includes PEM electrolyzers, refueling equipment, and the fuel cell battery replacement.
Horizon (www.horizonfuelcell.com)		PEMFC	0.3 W–15 kW	Horizon has a 1–5 kW range of products useful for stationary power. Horizon has many off-the-shelf products available, and is largely focusing on the small fuel cell market. In particular, its products are being marketed as educational materials. It provides complete fuel cell systems, which incorporate air cooling and self-humidification. Horizon's fuel cells are also used in toys, consumer electronics, portable power, backup power, and transportation.
Intelligent Energy (www.intelligent-energy.com)		PEMFC	50 W–1 kW	Intelligent Energy has a range of fuel cells available. It has air-cooled models in sizes ranging from 50 W to 1 kW, and evaporative cooling employed on models in sizes 1.5 kW to 30 kW (PEMs). These can be added to give a range of outputs up to 120 kW. Intelligent Energy's fuel cells are designed to be versatile and have been used in a wide range of applications, and generally works in the following markets: aerospace and defence, motive power, distributed generations, and portable power and oil and gas.
IRD (www.ird.dk)		PEMFC, DMFC	100–1800 W	IRD has fuel cell stack components and stacks and complete systems available for sale. The DMFC systems are typically used for mobile applications, power backup, and battery charging applications. The PEMFC is designed for stationary CHP generation, with a power output of 1.5 kW and heat output of 1.5 kW.
ITM Power (www.itm-power.com)	ClStack	PEMFC	Up to 1 kW	ITM Power produces fuel cell systems and electrolyzers. The company has been concentrating efforts on reduction of fuel cell cost through redevelopment of membranes, and methods of reducing platinum loading in cells. The company has achieved its target of cell price reaching $250 kW^{-1}. The company has been demonstrating its electrolyzer technology and is integrating its technologies. It is focusing on using renewable electricity to produce hydrogen in its electrolyzer, and using this hydrogen in modified ICEs, or for other energy applications (such as heating).
NDC Power (www.ndcpower.com)	Sequoia, Yosemite, Eos	PEMFC, DLFC	3 W–15 kW	NDC Power has a successful history of providing fuel cells to the military. The Sequoia is a 15 kW PEMFC, while Yosemite models are configurations between 1 and 15 kW size and can be used for both stationary and mobile purposes. The Eos DLFC uses a platinum-free catalyst, and is fueled by a 50% ethanol mixture. These cells are designed for small electronics equipment, up to 500 W size. The company is focusing its energies on cost reduction through development of nonprecious metal catalysts and by simplification of the balance of plant.

Nedstack (www.nedstack.com)	PEMFC	2–100 kW and multi-MW scalability	Nedstack PEMFC products are aimed at three sectors: small stationary, large stationary, and transportation. Stack and complete systems can be purchased and the company has a host of projects underway or completed. Heat recovery is also an option on larger systems. Present price is estimated at €1000 kW^{-1}. Nedstack is investigating use of fuel cells for large transport applications, including trains, buses, shipping, and road haulage.
Nuvera (www.nuvera.com)	PEMFC	5–90 kW	Nuvera has hydrogen PEMs used mainly in logistics applications. The company has developed many integrated technologies, and has proven reformer technology available for all fuel cell sizes, which can utilize many different fuels. Nuvera produces a refueling station with integrated reformer technology, which is intended for use in industrial forklift operations.
Oorja Protonics (www.oorjaprotonics.com)	DMFC		Oorja Protonics has available fuel cell systems designed for use in forklifts, and other vehicles in the materials handling industry. The company utilizes a DMFC in conjunction with batteries and this is fitted to existing machinery (or adapted as necessary).
QinetiQ (www.qinetiq.com)	PEMFC		QinetiQ is developing materials for PEMFC, DMFC, novel stack designs, systems integration, diesel processing, and small-scale H$_2$ generators. The company has available (mostly used in military applications) several small-scale portable devices for laptop charging, up to multi-kW systems.
Trulite (www.trulitetech.com)	PEMFC KH4	150 W	Trulite has developed a 150 W backup power generation system. The hydrogen is stored as sodium borohydride, and this is reacted to hydrogen as needed. Trulite also integrates the fuel cell system with solar or wind power systems to capture this energy and convert it to hydrogen.

Table 8 Fuel cell developers for stationary power generation systems

Company	Product name	Power	Comments
ClearEdge Power (www.clearedgepower.com)	CE5	5 kW	ClearEdge Power has a 5 kW CE5 CHP unit designed for small office or home and comes with a 5-year warranty on all parts, maintenance, and service. It is fueled by natural gas or propane that is reformed in a 'fuel processor' module.
Eneos Celltech	ENE.FARM	750 W	Eneos Celltech is a joint venture between Sanyo Electric and Nippon Oil and is developing both PEM and SOFC residential units. It shipped its first ENE.FARM units in May 2009 and had predicted manufacturing 10 000 PEM units per year by 2010, ramping up to 40 000 units per year by 2015. It has PMEFC units running on city gas, LPG, and kerosene, with audited carbon dioxide saving of around a third per annum per unit installed. The six companies of Tokyo Gas, Osaka Gas, Toho Gas, Saibu Gas, Nippon Oil (ENEOS), and Astomos Energy are involved in manufacture and marketing of the ENE.FARM units.
Hydrogenics (www.hydrogenics.com)	HyPM™XR, FCXR, HyUPS	12–30 kW (can be scaled to 200 kW)	Hydrogenics has a large knowledge base concerned with PEMs and hydrogen generation methods. A fair amount of research has gone into integration of renewable technology with generation of hydrogen for complete remote power solutions, and up to 60 Nm^3 hydrogen produced per hour. The company tailors units to suit conditions, and systems are well suited to remote power production. Hydrogen production is typically achieved using a separate electrolyzer; however, a PEM production method, which utilizes the same fuel cell stack, is soon to be available. Hydrogenics' fuel cells have also been used in buses, forklifts, and other utility vehicles. Hydrogenics has a number of companies, which act either as direct distributors or integrators of its stationary HyPM pro. These include Bell and Commscope in the United States, Gulf International Trading Group in the Middle East, and APC globally. The HyPM-XR is intended for integration in UPS data centers and the HyUPS for mobile phone. Masts. Both are UL certified. The HyUPS Eco-Enclosure available via CommScope is UL50 and GR487 Zone 4 compliant.
IdaTech (www.idatech.com)	Extragen™ H2 and Extragen™ ME	250 W–250 kW	IdaTech plc designs, develops, and manufactures extended run backup power fuel cell products for Telecom applications requiring 100 W to 15 kW of backup power. IdaTech's products are based on the company's fuel processing, purification, and fuel cell system integration capabilities. The company manufactures reformers (particularly methanol reformers), which it integrates into its fuel cell systems. It has a supply agreement with Ballard for use of their stacks. The company manufacturers a line of ElectraGen units, which can be adapted for extended run time, critical power, or power to remote locations. In cases with the external reformer, which IdaTech has developed, the methanol is steam-reformed, membrane-separated, and the CO slip is catalytically converted to CO_2. In 2009, IdaTech won a deal to supply up to 30 000 5 kW UPS systems to the Indian ACME company. The initial order for 310 systems for delivery in 2009 was completed out of a total 445 units shipped during the year. In 2010, over 350 units of the next generation ElectraGen™H2 and ElectraGen™ ME were sold. IdaTech purchased the LPG off-grid and backup power business of PlugPower in 2010.

Matsushita	1 kW	Matsushita delivers products under the brand names Panasonic and National. It produced 650 PEMFC stacks into the Japanese demonstration program up to 2008. The company is working with Tokyo Gas, Toho Gas, and Saibu Gas to supply fuel to a 1 kW PEMFC system. During 2008, the company announced the plan to invest ¥50 billion by 2015 to expand PEMFC manufacturing capacity to reduce capital cost down to ¥500 000 per fuel cell system, which should ensure a payback of 16–17 years (i.e., shorter than that for PV systems).
Plug Power (www.plugpower.com)	Gensys	5 kW	The Plugpower Gensys reforms LPG into hydrogen for entry into a low-temperature PEMFC. The Gensys is sold as an integrated unit, while the company is also supplying stacks for forklift and material handling applications, where fuel cell output is rated at 14 kW.
P21 GmbH (http://www.p-21.de/cms/front_content.php?idcat=21)	1–21 kW (the Premion T-4000 is a 4 kW system)	Premion T-4000	P21 is developing UPS systems for the telecommunications industry only. Originally a spin-out from the Manessman/Vodaphone group, P21, is now supplying PEM UPS systems to customers around the globe. While not yet fully commercial, yet it is anticipated that P21 will be one of the European market leaders of UPS systems within the next few years.
ReliOn (www.relion-inc.com)	500 W–12 kW	ReliOn produces backup fuel cells with a range of outputs. The fuel cells typically operate on stored hydrogen. The company is focused on smaller-scale backup power solutions for the applications in the fields of telecommunications, government, and utilities (i.e., substations). Systems are optimized for reliable and dependable power supply.

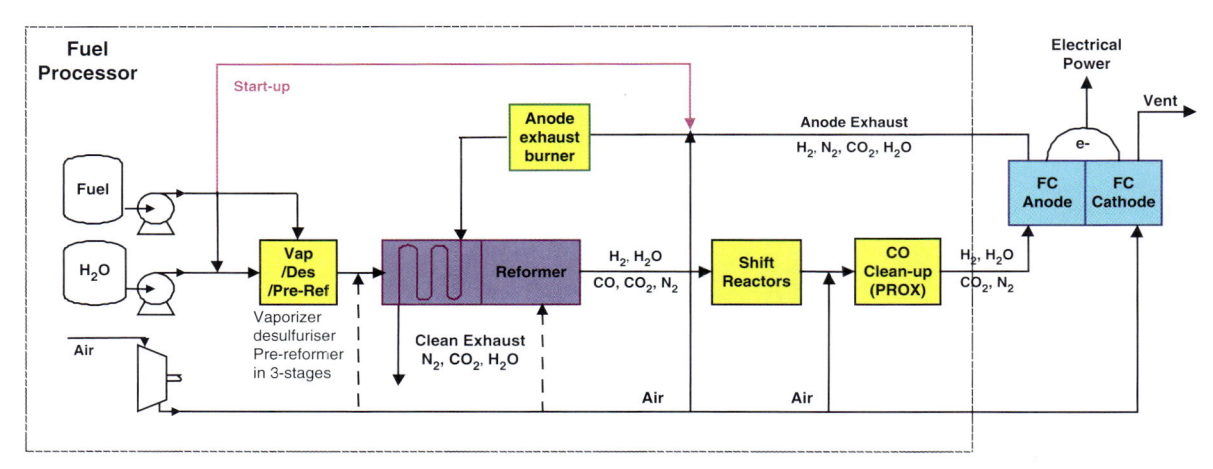

Figure 20 Schematic of conventional fuel processor for a PEMFC system.

reverse shift reaction. **Figure 20** shows the essential elements of a fuel processor based on conventional chemical conversion technologies. This schematic formed the basis of fuel processors used in early stationary power plant by Ballard Power Systems and others. Most recently, some manufacturers (a notable example being IdaTech) have developed fuel processors that include membranes to separate the hydrogen from the carbon oxides. This reduces the need for multiple reactors such as shift and preferential oxidation, and also reduces issues associated with carbon oxides and nitrogen entering the anode compartments of the PEMFC stack.

4.08.8.4 Cogeneration and Large-Scale Power Generation

Cogeneration or CHP systems take the heat that is generated during the generation of electricity and utilize it for applications such as providing hot water, space heating, and the like. A natural gas-fueled stationary power system employing a PEMFC stack at best converts about 40–50% of the energy in the fuel into electricity. The remainder ends up mainly as low-grade heat because the stacks operate at relatively low temperatures (below 100 °C). It is possible to recover this energy for providing hot water for domestic systems, or for space heating applications. System modeling has shown that PEMFC systems that integrate a natural gas fuel conversion system may have some heat available at a higher grade, but no manufacturer is currently promoting PEMFCs for cogeneration.

4.08.9 Applications for Transport

4.08.9.1 The Outlook for Road Vehicles

Recent concerns with global warming, the depletion of fossil fuel supplies, and local air pollution have focused attention around the world on the energy used in transport. There is the realization of the need to reduce local emissions to improve the health of the community, and the need to reduce carbon emissions to address global climate concerns. There is also a desire among many nations to move to alternative fuels as traditional supplies of petroleum products become more constrained. So developers are looking at both improving the technology within vehicles to increase energy conversion efficiency (which has a positive CO_2 benefit with existing fuels) and to decrease emissions. At the same time, a wide variety of alternative fuels are being explored, hydrogen being considered a long-term option with the benefit of zero emissions, provided the hydrogen is obtained using renewable energy.

With these issues in mind, fuel cycle analyses have been carried out in many countries to identify the preferred primary fuels to use for reducing CO_2 emissions from transport. This is a complex subject area and what may be the best option in one country or locality may not be most suitable for another. When considering fuel cells in transport, the PEMFC offers perhaps the best option in terms of energy density, ease of start-up, responsiveness to load changes and general robustness. At the same time, the PEMFC is most ideally suited to running on pure hydrogen, so if it is to be used in a vehicle, then onboard storage of the hydrogen has to be considered as well as how the hydrogen is produced, distributed, and delivered to the vehicle.

The dream of a fuel cell car or FCV has been around since the 1960s when it was evident that FCVs could provide a number of advantages over vehicles built around the ICE. In addition to the quietness and high torque, even at low speeds, that is afforded by other electric vehicles, FCVs offer the following characteristics:

- Hydrogen-fueled vehicles have zero tailpipe emissions
- High-energy conversion efficiency when the PEMFC is used as a component in an electric drive trains
- Low weight of fuel cell and hydrogen storage, especially when compared with batteries

- More freedom in locating the fuel cell, motor, and other components than in ICE vehicles
- Ability to hybridize PEMFC, batteries, and supercapacitors to provide increased pulling power or tractive force, and capture the energy released when braking
- Fast charge rates for gaseous hydrogen, comparable with petrol, diesel, or natural gas
- Vehicle range similar to conventional vehicles. (Early FCVs had a limited range with compressed hydrogen. This stimulated researchers to develop solid-state storage systems for hydrogen, and at the same time led Ballard Power Systems and others to target buses as a niche market. Buses have the advantage of more space (in the roof) than cars to store the compressed gas. They also have the benefit of having well-defined routes and return to the depot each day for refueling that can be monitored and controlled privately. Most recently, compressed hydrogen stored at 700 bar has been shown to provide range for cars comparable with ICEs.)

Against these advantages are the two disadvantages of high capital cost (especially of the fuel cell) and the various issues surrounding the development of a hydrogen fueling infrastructure. During the early 1990s, concepts were proposed in which a transition from gasoline-fueled vehicles toward hydrogen FCVs could be achieved by producing vehicles that would incorporate a gasoline or methanol reformer and fuel cell system. This would have provided the advantages of being able to use a readily available liquid fuel and infrastructure and a vehicle range comparable with ICEVs. Gasoline and methanol FCV projects, however, were soon abandoned as developers realized both the technical difficulties of mass-producing small reliable reformers and the marginal increase in efficiency to be gained in using a reformer – fuel cell and electric drive train over the conventional ICE drive train.

By the mid-1990s, the slow progress on the development of battery electric vehicles (BEVs) had led most automakers to the view that FCVs offered the best prospects for the ultimate zero-emission vehicle. Hydrogen as an energy carrier has the advantage that it can be produced from a large variety of primary energy sources. In the longer term, hydrogen could be produced from renewable energy sources (using the renewable energy to split water by electrolysis or photocatalysis), and in the near term, hydrogen can be produced economically by reforming fossil fuels. In 1997, Ford and Daimler made significant investments in Ballard Power Systems, which suggested that these companies at least viewed FCVs as a serious future option for road transport. Within a short space of time, leading automotive original equipment manufactures (OEMs) also set up R&D programs in FCVs as a strategic long-term option. Oil companies such as BP and Shell became involved in hydrogen vehicle demonstration programs as they also saw the FCV as a strategic opportunity to supply fuel into the future, and already such companies had a wealth of experience in producing hydrogen for their own refineries.

It is worth pointing out that the enthusiasm for PEMFCs in vehicles has been tempered by the relatively short lifetime of the cells. Automotive fuel cells have unique operation modes, compared with stationary applications, which cause accelerated degradation of the fuel cell components:

- *Start–stop*. Each time the fuel cell is turned on and off, air can be admitted to the anode causing swelling and contraction of the membrane, and corrosion of carbon in the GDL.
- *Load cycle*. Each time load is increased (during vehicle acceleration) or decreased (during braking), the Pt catalyst can experience high-voltage cycling, which leads to gradual dissolution of the Pt especially on the cathode side.
- *Low-temperature start-up or running*. Below 0 °C, the water will turn to ice in the GDL, catalyst, and membrane structure.

The low-temperature performance can be addressed to some extent by modification of the membrane chemistry and topology of the flow fields. Platinum dissolution in the catalyst layers, especially on the cathode side, and carbon support corrosion on the anode side continues to be a more intractable problem. At cathodic potentials, platinum in the catalyst can dissolve slightly in acidic electrolytes particularly under voltage cycling conditions (such as would be produced under acceleration or deceleration of the vehicle). Platinum dissolution leads to a loss of active catalyst surface area due to either (1) diffusion of dissolved platinum species in the membrane or (2) Ostwald ripening (i.e., the 'dissolution' of small crystals or 'sol' particles and the redeposition of the dissolved species on the surfaces of larger crystals or sol particles. It occurs because small particles have a higher surface energy, hence total Gibbs energy than larger ones) of Pt inside the cathode electrode, particularly near the cathode–membrane interface leading to a loss of Pt surface area due to growth of catalyst particles. If the fuel cell is not subject to aggressive swings on potential on either the cathode or anode side, such effects can be minimized.

On the anode side, carbon support corrosion is also accelerated during start–stop cycles due to the introduction of slugs of air in the flow field forming a so-called hydrogen–air front. These give rise to localized oxygen reduction reaction occurring, which consumes protons from the neighboring cathode compartment. A good understanding of carbon support corrosion has developed recently [61], and it can be reduced to some extent by using acetylene blacks or fully graphitized carbon as the catalyst support. Nevertheless, to minimize carbon corrosion and platinum dissolution caused by start–stop cycles, automotive fuel cell systems are now generally hybridized with batteries to reduce the number of voltage cycles experienced by the fuel cell during operation.

4.08.9.2 Hybrids

Today, the global fleet of road vehicles is dominated by gasoline cars and diesel buses and trucks. In some countries there are a small number of vehicles running on alternative fuels such as ethanol or ethanol–gasoline blends, or on liquefied petroleum gas (LPG, a mixture predominantly of butane and propane), or compressed natural gas vehicle (CNGV). There are few electric vehicles at present, but the situation is changing markedly. The steady improvements in the reliability of nickel–metal hydride batteries, and

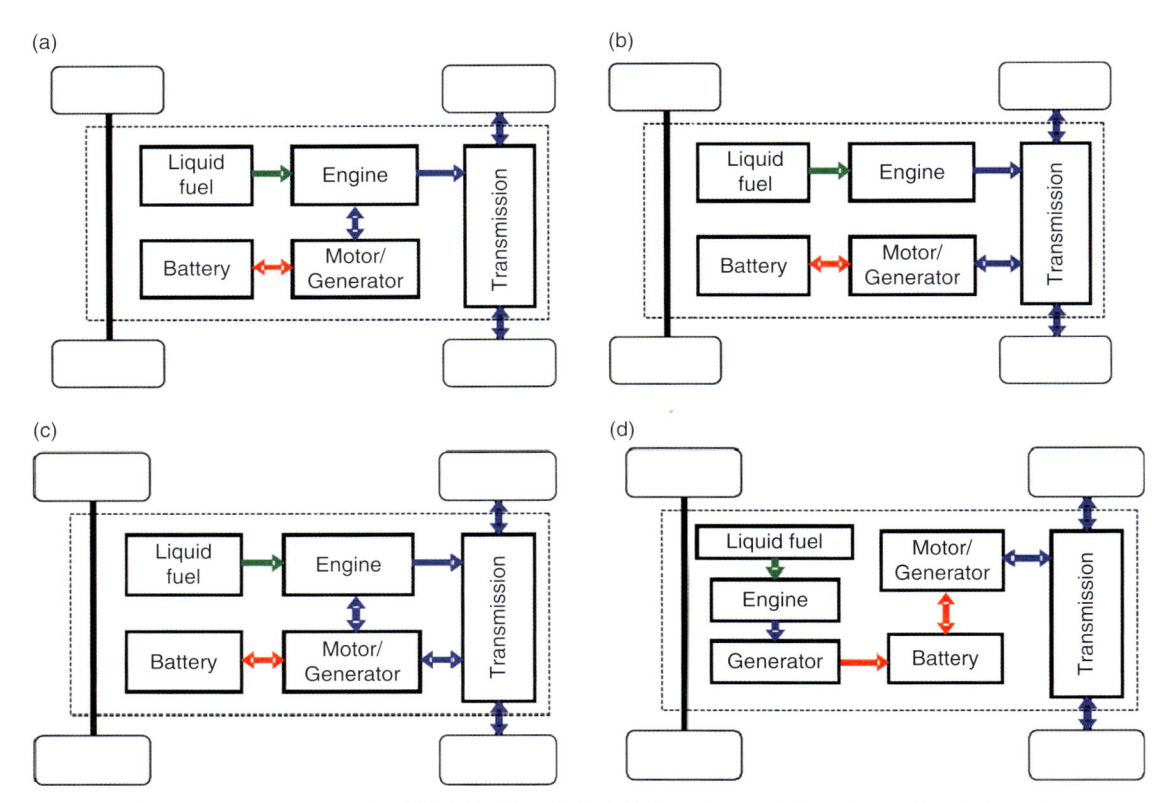

Figure 21 Hybrid electric vehicle drive trains: (a) mild hybrid; (b) parallel hybrid; (c) series–parallel hybrid; and (d) series hybrid.

promising research on alternative battery chemistries, have led in the past decade to the introduction of gasoline hybrid vehicles. These range from mild parallel hybrids through to parallel and then series hybrid configurations (**Figure 21**).

The most basic of these are known as mild hybrids in that the bulk of the motive power is provided by a gasoline-fueled ICE. A battery and electric motor provides additional power for acceleration and the ability to store energy recovered during braking. In the mild hybrid, the engine and electric motor are configured in parallel, that is, they are both mechanically coupled to the wheels. With mild hybrids the electric motor does not have sufficient power by itself to power the vehicle. Examples of cars using mild parallel hybrid configurations are the Honda Insight, Honda Civic Hybrid, and the Mercedes-Benz S400 BlueHYBRID.

One of the best-known hybrid cars has been the Toyota Prius. This is an example of a vehicle that uses a power-split or series–parallel hybrid configuration. In such vehicles, the electric motor is much larger than in the mild hybrid, and can develop sufficient power to drive the vehicle without need for the ICE for short distances. This provides an advantage for stop–start driving in town. Other examples of cars using such power trains are the Ford Escape, the Lexus Gs450, and LS600.

In series hybrid vehicles, all of the power to the wheels is provided by the electric motor. The electricity is provided by the battery, which is kept charged by the ICE. Perhaps the best-known example of a series hybrid configuration is to be found in the diesel–electric locomotive in which a diesel engine drives an electrical generator whose output provides power to the traction motors. The series hybrid configuration has the advantage over parallel hybrids of better traction, since the engine can be run at a steady state delivering maximum power at all times, irrespective of speed of the vehicle. Toyota (Hino) introduced a small series hybrid diesel bus in 1997.

With the development of electric hub motors for cars, it may not be too long before series hybrid cars start to emerge, with the ICE reducing in size as more energy is provided by the electric motors, and less traction is required from the ICE. At the same time, we are likely to see the introduction of other road vehicles such as BEVs for short commuter trips, hybrid variants including plug-in hybrid electric vehicles (PHEVs) in which the charge in the battery can be topped up using off-peak grid power, and conversely the battery could provide additional power for stationary applications during periods of high demand. The development of the lithium battery has also renewed interest in BEVs and hybrids as it offers the prospect of more compact and reliable energy storage onboard. Exactly how each of these different technologies will emerge is subject to much debate, but it is clear that most of the OEMs are moving toward electric drive trains of one form or other. Once these are established for BEVs or hybrids, introducing a fuel cell and hydrogen storage will be a logical progression in the development of the technologies. It should be no surprise therefore that in September 2009, the leading vehicle manufacturers in fuel cell technology (Ford Motor Company, General Motors Corporation/Opel, Honda Motor Co., Kia Motor Corporation, Renault/Nissan Toyota Motor Corporation, and Daimler AG) made a joint statement regarding development and introduction of FCVs, anticipating that from 2015 onwards a significant number of fuel cell hybrid electric vehicles (FCHEVs) would be commercially available. A few hundred thousand worldwide are expected, and early in

2010, Toyota announced that the purchase price would be similar to that of conventional HEVs, retailing at around $50 000 [62]. Whether such plans can be realized will depend on the development of an appropriate hydrogen delivery infrastructure. It is therefore interesting that in May 2010 an agreement was reached between New Energy and Industrial Technology Development Organization of Japan (NEDO) in Japan and the government of North Rhine Westphalia in Germany to jointly develop hydrogen delivery systems for the expected introduction of commercial vehicles in 2015 [63].

4.08.9.3 PEMFCs and Alternative Fuels

Although hydrogen is best suited to use with PEMFCs, there are many technical, economic, and safety issues associated with its use. Much attention is being given to alternative fuels that can replace gasoline or diesel in transport. Compressed natural gas and LPG are already widely used in regions of the world where there is economic benefit. Bioethanol and biodiesel, and liquid fuels produced from natural gas or coal via gas-to-liquids or coal-to-liquids processes, are also being considered. Of these alternative fuels, natural gas can be converted to hydrogen using well-developed processes as mentioned earlier. Onboard conversion of natural gas to hydrogen is fraught with technical difficulties associated with miniaturizing the reformer, which necessarily needs to run at high temperatures (typically above 800 °C), and the fact that CO_2 would be emitted from the vehicle (i.e., it would not longer be zero emission). Onboard reforming of ethanol should be easier than natural gas being carried out at lower temperatures (below 300 °C), but this has not seriously been considered so far by the major automotive OEMs. Biodiesel and diesel or gasoline obtained from coal or natural gas could in principle be reformed to hydrogen onboard, but again higher reforming temperatures are required and, as mentioned earlier, the OEMs abandoned onboard reforming because of the challenges associated with developing the technology. It is possible that the development of catalysts for microchannel reactor technology that has emerged over the past 10 years could help in the development of onboard reformers [64, 65]. Such technology offers the prospect of much more compact systems for reforming that take advantage of high heat and mass transfer rates that can be achieved with thin-film catalysts. Microchannel reactors could reduce the scale of systems by up to 2 orders of magnitude, and if that can be done, it would change the landscape of fuel utilization for future PEMFC systems.

4.08.9.4 Buses

While the fuel cell car provides a vision for clean transportation in the future, hydrogen-fueled buses are a significant niche for PEMFC application, offering a number of benefits:

- Infrastructure and delivery of hydrogen is simplified since buses on urban routes are refueled at central depots
- Safe dispensing of hydrogen can be done by trained operators
- Hydrogen can be stored in compressed form in the roof space of buses, as with natural gas vehicle buses
- Buses mainly use well-defined routes, so the danger or 'running out' of fuel is minimized
- There is flexibility in locating fuel cell stacks, motors, and fuel, allowing the floor of fuel cell buses to be lowered and giving improved access for disabled passengers
- Space for fuel cell stacks and balance of plant is not so constrained as in a car
- Greater passenger miles for buses should enable a reduction of per capita emissions compared with cars.

For these reasons, Ballard Power Systems demonstrated a bank of their early 5 kW fuel cell stacks in a 21-seat bus as early as 1993. Other developers soon followed with various designs of fuel cell bus, including vehicles running on methanol, but it was not until 2003 that the first major demonstration took place. This was the European CUTE program, which demonstrated 30 Mercedes Citaro buses that had been converted to take Ballard fuel cell stacks. The buses were tested on hydrogen made from different sources in 10 cities within Europe and Perth in Western Australia. The 3-year CUTE program was extended and then followed by another program (HyFLEET:CUTE), which ran to 2009. Both of these programs were exceptionally successful, demonstrating a high level of driver and public acceptance with over 140 000 h of fuel cell operation and the vehicles covering more than 2 200 000 km. The availability or reliability of the fuel cell stacks, which was between 90 and 95%, demonstrated the suitability of the fuel cell bus for regular service in urban fleets.

Development of the Daimler/Ballard fuel cell system during the HyFLEET:CUTE program paved the way for the next generation of Mercedes fuel cell bus, which is the first to be built specifically for a fuel cell system and power train. It is an innovative hybrid design that combines some of the best features of the Citaro BluTec diesel–electric hybrid bus with PEMFC stacks that have a projected average service life of 6 years. This new Citaro FuelCELL Hybrid (**Figure 22**) uses two 60 kW (80 kW peak) stacks (modeled on those used in the B-Class F-CELL car), which drive two 80 kW electric wheel hub engines. The PEMFC stacks are complemented by a 27 kWh, 330 kg liquid-cooled lithium-ion battery that is independently capable of delivering 250 kW to the hub engines. This enables the bus to run for several kilometers on battery power alone, and through the capture of energy from braking and other improvements means that the hydrogen requirement is 50% less than in the previous Citaro buses. The range of 250 km is provided by 35 kg of hydrogen stored at 350 bar pressure.

Interestingly, the Daimler/Citaro was not the first fuel cell hybrid bus to be built. That achievement went to Toyota and its truck division Hino, for their first jointly developed vehicle in 2001. Modeled on this demonstration, three buses were then built in 2006 and have been in more or less continuous operation since then, in Nagoya Japan. The buses use bodies built by Hino with the fuel

Figure 22 Mercedes Citaro FuelCell hybrid bus (Courtesy: Mercedes).

cell and electric drive trains developed by Toyota. Hydrogen is stored in the buses at 350 bar and this supplies two 90 kW PEMFC systems. These, alongside a nickel–metal hydride battery provides the electricity for two 80 kW motors.

The Korean automaker Hyundai demonstrated its first fuel cell bus in Germany in 2006. This was followed by the launch of its second-generation fuel cell hybrid bus at the 2009 Seoul motor show [66]. The fuel cell hybrid incorporated two 100 kW fuel cell systems that had been developed entirely by Hyundai, feeding three 100 kW electric motors. A significant innovation in this bus was the use of a 450 V, 100 kW, and 42.8 F supercapacitor rather than rechargeable batteries.

In Canada, Ballard Power Systems teamed up with New Flyer Industries to produce twenty 12 m low-floor buses for operation during the Olympic Winter Games in Vancouver and Whistler. These feature a 130 kW fuel cell supplied with hydrogen stored in a 350 bar tank. Hybridized with a nickel–metal hydride battery, the buses have a range of some 500 km.

In the United States, several fuel cell hybrid buses have been in use in California and Connecticut. These were manufactured by Van Hool in conjunction with UTC Power who provided the PEMFC stacks. The latest Van Hool hybrid bus is 13.1 m long with three axles. It has seating for 34 passengers with an additional 70 standing. It incorporates a 120 kW UTC fuel cell and 17.8 kWh of battery capacity which both power 170 kW electric motors supplied by Siemens. Compressed hydrogen is stored at 350 bar in eight cylinders, which is sufficient to provide a range of 350 km.

As of the beginning of 2011, the total number of fuel cell buses demonstrated is 126. Of these, several universities have incorporated fuel cell stacks into buses: The University of Delaware (5), Glamorgan (1), Hamburg (1), Tsinghua (China) (9), Rome 'La Spezia' (1), and Texas (2). The most recent listing of vehicles can be found on the Web site of www.fuelcells2000.org.

4.08.9.5 Fuel Cell Road Vehicle Manufacturers

Table 9 shows a list of companies who are developing fuel cell technology for transport applications. This includes both companies who are developing their own fuel cell technology for vehicular use and automotive OEMs who are utilizing fuel cells supplied by others in their vehicles. As much up-to-date information has been included as was available, although much is not readily accessible as car companies need to protect their competitive positions. In some cases it is known that although prototypes have existed for some time no recent developments have been reported.

4.08.9.6 Planes, Boats, and Trains

According to the latest review of transport fuel cells by FuelCellToday [88], the aerospace industry and, notably, unmanned aerial vehicles (UAVs), represent some 6% of the market for transport fuel cells. Boats (marine and submarine) and trains by contrast capture some 12% of the current market. In all of these applications, PEMFCs tend to be the preferred fuel cell technology except at the larger scale (e.g., providing the hotel load on ocean-going ships) where MCFC or even SOFC have been targeted.

Small manned airplanes using PEMFCs have been developed independently by Boeing using an Intelligent Energy PEMFC stack and DLR (German Space Agency) using a stack provided by BASF Fuel Cells. The Boeing plane was airborne in 2008 and the DLR a year later. Two consortia of organizations have also developed manned planes. The first was a project funded by the European Community and involving Turin Polytechnic, Intelligent Energy (20 kW PEMFC stack supplier), SkyLeader, APL, Mavel Electronics, and the University of Pisa. Taxiing tests were completed for this plane in 2009. The second project was a US consortium involving

Table 9 Fuel cell companies and developers involved in automotive applications

Company	Product name	Power (fuel cell)	Comments
Audi	H2A2	66 kW	Audi, which comes under the umbrella of the Volkswagen group, released a fuel cell version of its A2 car called the A2H2. This hybrid vehicle is equipped with a 66 kW Ballard fuel cell stack. The combined PEFC and battery system can deliver up to 110 kW [67].
Ballard Power Systems (www.ballard.com)		Up to 150 kW	Ballard has interests in both the mobile and stationary power generation markets. Mobile applications include many bus propulsion systems, and material handling operations (forklifts). Ballard has two heavy-duty transportation stacks available, with outputs of 75 and 150 kW. Ballard also has a CHP generation unit designed for residential size users, with an output of 1.2 kW. The company has available larger units for backup power, and telecommunication applications. According to the company's Web site, Ballard is expanding its applications in the telecommunications markets [68].
Daimler, Mazda, Mercedes-Benz (Ballard) (www.daimler.com)	B-Class, Citaro (bus)		An alliance exists between Daimler, Mazda, Mercedes-Benz, and Ballard. Daimler has been working extensively on fuel cell projects since the early 1990s, producing its first fuel cell car, the NeCar 1 in 1994. Over the next 10 years, Daimler produced a range of FCVs, including cars fueled with methanol and hydrogen, has an extensive amount of testing completed, and a large fleet of FCVs currently in use around the world. By the end of 2009, Daimler FCVs had accumulated over 4 000 000 km. The most recent products (there are a number of variants which have been improved upon over the years) include the Mercedes B-Class with a 90 kW Ballard PEMFC stack operating on H2 stored onboard compressed to 700 bar. Introduced in 2009, the B-Class F-CELL has cold-start ability at -15 °C, a lithium-ion battery, more efficient stack, software designed to protect the PEMFC during idling, giving it significant benefits over previous Daimler FCVs. Mercedes Citaro Fuelcell buses were used during the European CUTE and HyFLEET:CUTE projects that ran from 2003 to 2009. The Ballard PEMFC stacks used in 36 buses performed exceptionally well during these trials for 12 public transport agencies on three continents. An availability of over 90% even in the most remote cities demonstrated reliability over more than 2 200 000 km traveled. From the end of 2009, 30 new Citaro FuelCELL Hybrid buses will be rolled out to European cities [69, 70].
Fiat	600, Panda		Fiat has demonstrated fuel cell technology in its Panda and 600 models. The fuel cells are adapted and developed jointly with Nuvera. The Panda model utilizes the fuel cell power directly, without an intermediate battery. The company is currently working on releasing small fleets of the fuel cell Panda vehicle [71–73].
Ford (Ballard) (www.ford.com)			Ford is testing a Focus FCV, which utilizes a Ballard fuel cell. The program is focusing on research to increase power density, decrease loading of precious metals in catalysts, and is investigating fuel storage methods [74].
GM/Opel		93 kW	GM has had several decades of involvement in fuel cell research, and after several concept cars and prototypes, produced the Equinox in 2007. This is the fifth-generation fuel cell product from GM. As with the Mercedes B-Class, this has 4.5 kg hydrogen onboard stored at 700 bar, and with a 35 kW nickel–metal hydride battery achieves a range of over 320 km and top speed of 160 km h^{-1} using a 94 kW electric motor. The GM-Equinox is in operation throughout the United States, Japan, Korea, and Germany, with over 100 FCVs being tested by regular citizens in the community. In Europe, the same technology is used by Opel in the HydroGen4. So far, the combined vehicles have traveled over 1 million miles [75].
Honda (www.honda.com)	Clarity	100 kW	Honda has produced its own fuel cell in the Honda FCX vehicle, which it has designed to complement the fuel cell system. The Honda V-flow system is designed to lie in an up-right position, so that the individual cells are in a horizontal configuration, with the intention of better space utilization within the vehicle. The fuel cell itself is a PEM of 100 kW output, and battery storage integration. Has also got an experimental 'Home Energy Station' which has been a project undertaken in conjunction with Plug Power. The house uses solar cells, integrating this power with micro-CHP for home energy production and refuelling of the Honda vehicle [76–78].

(Continued)

Table 9 (Continued)

Company	Product name	Power (fuel cell)	Comments
Hyundai, Kia (www.worldwide.hyundai.com)		100 kW	Hyundai and Kia are in an alliance on fuel cell developments with a 100 kW PEMFC as the current platform for tests. The first-generation FCV from Hyundai was the Sant Fe in 2001. This was followed by the Tucson SUV in 2004. This was fitted with a UTC PEMFC, supplying an 80 kW engine. The Borrego FCEV from Kia uses a 115 kW air-breathing stack, which is capable of starting in temperatures as low as −30 °C. In future vehicles, Hyundai and Kia propose to use supercapacitors for energy recovery lost through braking, and surplus charge from the fuel cell [79]. The Hyundai i-Blue was launched in 2009 with a 100 kW stack and a lithium-ion battery. The range is 600 km on 115 l of hydrogen. This has developed into the third-generation Hyundai FCV known as the ix35 [80].
Morgan, (QinetiQ) (www.morgan-motor.co.uk)	LIFECar	4 × 6 kW	The Morgan LIFECar sports car is a light (600 kg) car with separate electric motors in all four wheels. The car utilizes four QinetiQ modular 6 kW fuel cells and uses supercapacitors to recover braking energy [81].
Nissan, Renault	X-Trail FC, Scenic	130 kW	Nissan started fuel cell R&D in 1996 and in 2003 introduced the X-trail FCV that incorporated a 60 kW UTC PEMFC stack, a lithium-ion battery, an 85 kW engine, and 250 bar hydrogen giving a range of 350 km. In 2008, Nissan started a partnership with Renault for fuel cell development. Renault has adapted the technology for use in the Renault Scenic model. Compared with earlier versions, the latest vehicles use a 130 kW PEMFC, but the stack size has reduced from 90 to 68 l. Nissan and Renault are focusing efforts on commercializing the technology through catalyst and membrane developments. Already Pt loading has been reduced by 50%, leading to a PEM stack cost reduction of 35% [82].
PSA Citroen Peugeot (www.psa-peugeot-citroen.com)	TaxiPAC and H$_2$O		PSA Citroen Peugeot has two variants of FCVs; TaxiPAC and H$_2$O demonstration vehicles. Taxi has 5.5 kW fuel cell, couple to nominal electric motor of 22 kW (max 36 kW). Hydrogen PEMFC. H$_2$O model uses a fuel of sodium borohydride, and this is reformed into hydrogen gas, and the remaining sodium borate is returned to the 'residue storage tank'. Same dimensions for electric motor and PEMFC. Fuel cell is called the genepac is of modular design, with one, two, or four 20 kW individual units being combined for one entire cell. Genepac was developed in partnership with the French Atomic Energy Commission. PSA has another project called the Quark; a small one person vehicle with a 1.5 kW FC.
Toyota (www.toyota.com)		90 kW	Unlike Daimler and GM, Toyota took the decision in the early 1990s to develop its own PEMFC stacks, and has developed a number of prototype vehicles over the past 15 years. The Highlander SUV provides the latest demonstration of Toyota fuel cell technology. Released in 2008, the FCHV is a hybrid incorporating a very efficient PEMFC fueled by hydrogen at stored onboard at 700 bar, a Ni-metal hydride battery with an energy management enabling a range of up to 800 km to be achieved. With cold-start ability down to −30 °C, this provides Toyota with a competitive edge compared with conventional ICE vehicles. Toyota's aim: "In 2015, our plan is to bring to market a reliable and durable FCV with exceptional fuel economy and zero emissions, at an affordable price" [83, 84].
Volkswagen (www.volkswagen.com)	Passat, Space Up! Blue	55 kW+	Volkswagen has demonstrated fuel cells in its Passat models. There are 22 vehicles that were developed by researchers at Tongji University, China; all are road-worthy. There is a range of different fuel cell configurations utilized in these vehicles. Volkswagen has also been developing its own high-temperature fuel cell. A 55 kW version of the fuel cell has been demonstrated in a prototype vehicle – the Space Up! Blue. No further details on this prototype were available [6, 85–87].

Figure 23 Fuel Cell Locomotive underground. Source: Fuelcell Propulsion Institute.

UQM Technologies, NASA, American Ghiles Aircraft, Electrochemical Systems, Selco Technology, Diamond Aircraft, Analytic Energy Systems, Lockwood Aviation, and Lynntech (stack supplier). This plane was a PEMFC battery hybrid and was first flown in 2005.

Some 20 UAVs have been demonstrated to date. The earliest took flight in 2003 and included a Hornet developed under a DARPA-sponsored research contract and a NASA Helios plane using a 25 kW PEMFC. Most UAVs use compressed hydrogen, the exceptions being a Global Observer UAV launched in 2005, a UAV built by Korea Advanced Institute of Technology in 2007, both of which ran on liquid hydrogen, and a Puma battery/PEMFC hybrid built by the US Air Force Laboratory in 2007, which employed a metal hydride for onboard hydrogen storage. The size of stack used in the UAVs depends on the payload and duty, and test flights of over 24 h have been commonly reported [89].

One of the earliest applications of PEMFCs was in submarines, where their compactness, low operating temperature, and zero emissions (when run on hydrogen) make them ideal for providing the power for the 'hotel load,' water for the crew, and contributing to the power for propulsion. Orders for Siemens 300 kW PEMFC systems were placed by the navies in Germany, Greece, South Korea, and Italy in 2002. Smaller systems from several PEMFC developers have been employed in a range of pleasure boats and yachts over the past 10 years, and hybrid systems are starting to emerge that combine solar, fuel cell, and diesel engines for marine applications, an example being a ferry built for San Francisco by Hornblower and Statue Cruises and planned for launch in 2011 [89].

Trains would at first sight seem an odd choice for PEMFC applications in view of the need for hydrogen infrastructure and issues of onboard storage, but in 2002, an underground mining locomotive was demonstrated by Vehicle Projects LLC (**Figure 23**). The 4 ton locomotive engine was powered by two 17 kW Nuvera PEMFC stacks coupled with reversible metal hydride storage, and has been working on a regular basis at the Placer Dome's Campbell mine in Red Lake Ontario, Canada, since October 2002. The advantages of a zero-emission vehicle for underground mining applications are self-evident. More recently (2009), the same Vehicle Projects company incorporated two 125 kW Ballard fuel cell stacks into a military locomotive that can also serve as a mobile backup power supply, and last year, China announced the introduction of its first light locomotive powered by hydrogen fuel cells. This incorporates a high-efficiency permanent magnet motor and was developed by the China North Vehicle Yongji Electric Motor Corporation and the Southwest Jiaotong University.

4.08.10 Hydrogen Energy Storage for Renewable Energy Systems and the Role of PEMFCs

A key issue with renewable energy is that of the intermittency of supply. Energy storage is required for periods when the sun does not shine or the wind speed falls below that needed to turn turbine blades. Even the cyclical nature of wave and tidal power requires storage to provide regularity of supply. While batteries provide a solution for short-term storage, there are serious disadvantages with most battery systems in terms of degradation over time, reliability, and disposal/recycle of the battery components. An option for the provision of a continuous renewable power supply lies in the coupling of a renewable electricity source with a hydrogen generation and storage system. The stored hydrogen can be utilized in a fuel cell for generating electricity when the renewable source is not available, or simply burned to provide heat, or used for FCVs. At present, most interest in this topic involves using wind power and/or photovoltaic solar panels to produce the electricity [90, 94].

The production of hydrogen from renewable energy sources is achieved by using an electrolyzer, which converts electricity and water into gaseous hydrogen and oxygen. Electrolyzers operate like a fuel cell in reverse. They incorporate a cathode and anode, which are supplied with DC electricity. Industrial electrolyzers were originally based on alkaline electrolytes, but more recently ion-conducting membranes similar to those found in PEMFCs have been employed. As with PEMFCs, the membrane needs to be supplied with water and kept hydrated. Hydrogen and oxygen are released in gaseous form from the electrolyte, and captured at the separate ends of the stack.

An alternative to using an electrolyzer for generating hydrogen from renewables and a fuel cell for consuming it for electricity generation is to combine the electrolyzer and fuel cell into a single device. This has become known as the unitized regenerative fuel cell (URFC). Among other benefits, the URFC should be lower in capital cost due to there being only one stack, smaller physical footprint, and potentially lower maintenance costs compared with using separate units [91, 92]. However, the requirement to fulfill the duties of both electrolyzer and fuel cell also brings some technical challenges, which have not yet been fully addressed. These are associated with the balance of plant, the passage of reactants, the control system, the integration of the energy supply, and the materials of construction, particularly the electrode catalysts which have different requirements for each mode of operation [92].

For an integrated renewable energy and hydrogen generation system to be effective, the efficiency of the electrolyzer with regard to the hydrogen quantity produced for a certain power input is an important consideration for the feasibility of such a system [93]. Table 10 shows findings from an investigation into renewable hydrogen electrolysis undertaken by the National Renewable Energy Laboratories (NREL) in 2009 [94]. The table lists efficiencies for both the individual stacks and the system as a whole. LHV refers to the lower heating value of hydrogen (33.3 kWh kg^{-1}) and HHV refers to the higher heating value (39.4 kWh kg^{-1}). Hydrogen produced by electrolysis when converted back into electricity using a PEMFC results in a round-trip energy efficiency that may be as low as 15–20% compared with a battery which may be over 80%. This is due to a multiplying effect of all of the energy losses encountered in converting power to hydrogen, losses involved in storing the hydrogen (e.g., heat lost during adsorption and desorption on a metal hydride), and especially losses involved in converting the hydrogen to electricity in a PEMFC.

A hydrogen production and storage system will usually require extra units of infrastructure, including storage tanks for hydrogen (high-pressure vessels, or solid-state storage medium), a compressor (if the pressure of the electrolyzer is insufficient for the required storage capacity), maximum power point tracker (MPPT) for integration of PV/wind and electrolyzer, and required electrical inverters and other power supply conditioners. In designing a renewable energy system, care therefore needs to be taken for matching the different components to reduce conversion losses [95], and to keep capital cost low so that the cost of electricity remains acceptable. For example, the NREL in the United States found that using a maximum power point tracking (MPPT) device between PV panels and electrolyzer increased the power reaching the electrolyzer by 10–20% [94], whereas Andrews has shown that the MPPT may actually be eliminated by matching the performance curves of PV panels and electrolyzers [96]. In addition, the conversion energy conversion efficiency of the PEMFC may be improved significantly by capturing the heat produced by the fuel cell for a cogeneration or CHP application [95].

There are several manufacturers of electrolyzers, and of these Hydrogenics (http://www.hydrogenics.com), Proton Energy Systems (http://www.protonenergy.com) and ITM Power (http://www.itm-power.com) are developing technology for integration with renewable energy. Both Hydrogenics and Proton Energy Systems are also investigating URFCs, but as yet do not have commercial products available.

There have been many demonstrations and modeling studies of PEMFC systems integrated with renewable energy sources. The ultimate factor in considering the feasibility of such systems incorporating hydrogen production, storage, and utilization will be the economics, and an investigation into cost comparisons was included in the NREL report cited earlier [94]. Although a price index does not currently exist for the sale of hydrogen, a nominal figure of US$1–$2 kg^{-1} was employed in a recent economic scoping analysis [97]. In contrast, the NREL report found optimized hydrogen production from electrolysis to cost US$5.83 kg^{-1} from a baseline of US$6.25 kg^{-1} (for wind generation) [94]. In 2009, the US DOE set a target price of hydrogen production from wind power of US$3.10 kg^{-1} by 2012. The price of hydrogen is sure to depend on its method of production (electrolysis has historically been regarded as the most expensive method), the cost of fuel and indeed the geographic region. Unlike the price of electricity, which is closely related to the cost of fuel, there is a wide divergence in the price of hydrogen, which currently makes any rigorous economic analysis almost impossible.

At this stage, it is therefore perhaps worth recapping the view from the developers of PEMFC systems for transport applications who claim that the PEMFC will have a role in future zero-emission vehicles, not because it is inherently better or less costly than a battery but because it technically complements the battery (and supercapacitor). The PEMFC provides a steady output of power from hydrogen, giving the vehicle extended range, whereas the battery and supercapacitor are best suited to capture the energy from

Table 10 NREL efficiency findings for PEM and alkaline electrolyzers [94]

Efficiency	PEM electrolyzer LHV	PEM electrolyzer HHV	Alkaline electrolyzer LHV	Alkaline electrolyzer HHV
Stack efficiency				
Low current	80% (5A)	95% (5A)	78% (30A)	92% (30A)
Rated current	63% (5A)	75% (135A)	59% (220A)	70% (220A)
System efficiency				
Low current	0% (15A)	0% (15A)	0% (35A)	0% (35A)
Rated current	49% (135A)	57% (135A)	35% (220A)	41% (220A)

braking and providing the burst of power required for vehicle acceleration. For stationary applications, there are many battery technologies that are technically capable of providing short-term storage for renewable energy systems. But for periods longer than a few days or weeks, batteries lose their charge and over time degrade. Perhaps, it will be in this application area that hydrogen and the PEMFC can provide the sustainable solution for long-term energy storage.

References

[1] Bossel U (2000) *The Birth of the Fuel Cell 1835–1845*. European Fuel Cell Forum. ISBN: 3-905592-06-1.
[2] Koppel T (2001) *Powering the Future: The Ballard Fuel Cell and the Race to Change the World*. Toronto, Canada: John Wiley & Sons. ISBN-10: 0471646296.
[3] Larminie J and Dicks AL (2003) *Fuel Cell Systems Explained*, 2nd edn. Chichester, UK: John Wiley & Sons. ISBN-10: 047084857X.
[4] Honda FCX Clarity Specifications (2011) http://automobiles.honda.com/fcx-clarity/specifications.aspx (accessed 29 September 2011).
[5] Baker R and Zhang J (2011) Proton exchange membrane or polymer electrolyte membrane (PEM) fuel cells. In: Nagy Z (ed.) *Electrochemistry Encyclopedia*. Cleveland, OH: Case Western Reserve University. http://electrochem.cwru.edu/encycl/art-f04-fuel-cells-pem.htm (accessed 29 September 2011).
[6] Satyapal S (2009) EERE Fuel Cell Technologies Program. *Presented at the Fuel Cells Project Kick-off*. 30 September 2009. Washington, DC: US Department of Energy.
[7] Son J-Ek (2004) Hydrogen and fuel cell technology. *Korean Journal of Chemical Engineering* 42(1): 1–4.
[8] Lee JS, Quan ND, Hwang JM, et al. (2006) Polymer electrolyte membranes for fuel cells. *Journal of Industrial Engineering Chemistry* 12(2): 175–183.
[9] Hogarth WHJ, Diniz da Costa JC, and Lu GQ(M) (2005) Solid acid membranes for high temperature (>140 °C) proton exchange membrane fuel cells. *Journal of Power Sources* 142(1–2): 223–237.
[10] Alberti G and Casciola M (2003) Composite membranes for medium-temperature PEM fuel cells. *Annual Review of Materials Research* 33: 129–154.
[11] Yang C, Costamagna P, Srinivasan S, et al. (2001) Approaches and technical challenges to high temperature operation of proton exchange membrane fuel cells. *Journal of Power Sources* 103: 1–9.
[12] Costamagna P, Yang C, Bocarsly AB, and Srinivasan S (2002) Nafion® 115/zirconium phosphate composite membranes for operation of PEMFCs above 100°C. *Electrochimica Acta* 47: 1023–1033.
[13] Atkins JR, Sides CR, Creager SE, et al. (2003) Effect of equivalent weight on water sorption, PTFE-like crystallinity, and ionic conductivity in bis[(perfluoroalkyl)sulfonyl] imide perfluorinated ionomers. *Journal of New Materials for Electrochemical Systems* 6: 9–15.
[14] Damay F and Klein LC (2003) Transport properties of Nafion (TM) composite membranes for proton-exchange membranes fuel cells. *Solid State Ionics* 162–163: 261–267.
[15] Epping-Martin K and Kopasz JP (2009) The US DOEs high temperature membrane effort. *Fuel Cells* 9(4): 356–362.
[16] Wannek C (2010) High-temperature PEM fuel cells: Electrolytes, cells and stacks. In: Stolten D (ed.) *Hydrogen and Fuel Cells, Fundamentals Technologies and Applications*, p. 17. Wiley-VCH Verlag GmbH.
[17] Ladewig BP, Knott RB, Hill AJ, et al. (2007) Physical and electrochemical characterization of nanocomposite membranes of Nafion and functionalized silicon oxide. *Chemistry of Materials* 19(9): 2372–2381.
[18] Glipa X and Hogarth M (2001) *ETSU Technical Report* F/02/00189/REP DTI/Pub URN 01/893. Harwell, UK: Department of Trade and Industry.
[19] Rikukawa M and Sanui K (2000) Synthesis of proton-conducting electrolytes based on poly(vinylidene fluoride-co-hexafluoropropylene) via atom transfer radical polymerization. *Progress in Polymer Science* 25: 1463–1502.
[20] Nurang S and Ventura S (2001) High Temperature Polymer Electrolytes. US Patent 6,248,480, 19 June 2001.
[21] Fujimoto CyH, Hickner MA, Cornelius CJ, and Loy DA (2005) Ionomeric poly(phenylene) prepared by Diels–Alder polymerization: Synthesis and physical properties of a novel polyelectrolyte. *Macromolecules* 38(12): 5010–5016.
[22] Cao S, Xu H, Jeanes T, et al. (2006) Ion conductive block copolymers. US Patent 7,094,490 B2. August 2006.
[23] Hoffman P (2006) Briefly noted: Polyfuel membrane. *The Hydrogen & Fuel Cell Letter* 21(1): 80. ISSN: 1080-8019.
[24] IAGS Energy Security (2003) GTI reports significant results from direct methanol fuel cell membrane. Potomac, MD: IAGS Energy Security. Institute of Analysis of Global Security. http://www.iags.org (accessed 29 September 2003).
[25] McConnell VP (2009) High-temperature PEM fuel cells: Hotter, simpler, cheaper. *Fuel Cells Bulletin* 2009(12): 12–16.
[26] Mader J, Xiao L, and Schmidt T Benicewicz B (2008)Polybenzimidazole/acid complexes as high temperature membranes. In: Abe A, Albertsson A-C, Dusek K, et al. (eds.) *Advances in Polymer Science*, vol. 216, 63–124. Germany: Springer.
[27] Yongjun Feng NA-V (2008) Nonprecious metal catalysts for the molecular oxygen-reduction reaction. *Physica Status Solidi B* 245(9): 1792–1806.
[28] Baresel D, Sarholz W, Scharner P, and Schmitz J (1974) Übergangs-Metallchalkogenide als Sauerstoff-Katalysatoren für Brennstoffzellen. *Berichte der Bunsengesellschaft* 78: 608–611.
[29] Winther-Jensen B, Winther-Jensen O, Forsyth M, and MacFarlane DR (2008) High rates of oxygen reduction over a vapor phase-polymerized PEDOT electrode. *Science* 321: 671–674.
[30] Dicks AL (2006) The role of carbon in fuel cells. *Journal of Power Sources* 156(2): 128–141.
[31] Ignaszak A, Ye, S, and Gyenge E (2009) A study of the catalytic interface for O_2 electroreduction on Pt: The interaction between carbon support meso/microstructure and ionomer (Nafion) distribution. *The Journal of Physical Chemistry C* 113(1): 298–307.
[32] Wee J-H, Lee K-Y, and Kim SH (2007) Fabrication methods for low-Pt-loading electrocatalysts in proton exchange membrane fuel cell systems. *Journal of Power Sources* 165(2): 667–677.
[33] Lee SJ (1998) Effects of Nafion impregnation on performance of PEMFC electrodes. *Electrochimica Acta* 43(24): 3693–3701.
[34] Bevers D, Wagner N, and VonBradke M (1998) Innovative production procedure for low cost PEFC electrodes and electrode/membrane structures. *International Journal of Hydrogen Energy* 23(1): 57–63.
[35] Giorgi L, Antolini E, Pozio A, and Passalacqua E (1998) Influence of the PTFE content in the diffusion layer of low-Pt loading electrodes for polymer electrolyte fuel cells. *Electrochimica Acta* 43(24): 3675–3680.
[36] Ralph TR, Hards GA, Keating JE, et al. (1997) Low cost electrodes for proton exchange membrane fuel cells. *Journal of the Electrochemical Society* 144(11): 3845–3857.
[37] Gasteiger HA, Kocha S, Sompalli B, and Wagner FT (2005) Activity benchmarks and requirements for Pt, Pt-alloy, and non-Pt oxygen reduction catalysts for PEMFCs. *Applied Catalysis B* 56(9).
[38] Büchi FN and Srinivasan S (1997) Operating proton exchange membrane fuel cells without external humidification of the reactant gases: Fundamental aspects. *Journal of the Electrochemical Society* 144(8): 2767–2772.
[39] Wood DL, Yi JS, and Nguyen TV (1998) Effect of direct liquid water injection and interdigitated flow field on the performance of proton exchange membrane fuel cells. *Electrochimica Acta* 43(24): 3795–3809.
[40] Watanabe M, Uchida H, Seki Y, et al. (1996) Self-humidifying polymer electrolyte membranes for fuel cells. *Journal of the Electrochemical Society* 143(12): 3847–3852.
[41] LaConti A, Smarz G, and Sribnik F (1986) New membrane-catalyst for solid polymer electrolyte systems. *Final Report Prepared by Electro-Chem Products, Hamilton Standard for Los Alamos National Laboratory under Contract No. 9-X53-D6272-1*. Los Alamos, NM: Los Alamos National Laboratory.

[42] Daugherty M, Haberman D, Stetson N, et al. (1999) Modular PEM fuel cell for outdoor applications, pp. 69–78. *Proceedings of the European Fuel Cell Forum Portable Fuel Cells Conference.* Lucerne, Switzerland.
[43] Energy Business Reports (2008) Fuel cell technology and market potential. http://www.energybusinessreports.com/shop/item.asp?itemid=790 (accessed 26 September 2009).
[44] Crawley G (2006) 2006 Portable Survey. Hertfordshire, UK: FuelCellToday.com. http://www.fuelcelltoday.com/media/pdf/surveys/2006-Portable.pdf (accessed 26 September 2009).
[45] Dyer CK (2002) Fuel cells for portable applications. *Journal of Power Sciences* 106(1–2): 31–34.
[46] Georgi D and Georgi S (2005) CES 2011 - Battery Powered Products Fads, Figures and Forecasts. Newark, IL: Teksym Corporation. http://www.batteriesdigest.com/BatteriesDigestCES2011.html (accessed 25 September 2009).
[47] Freedonia (2008) Fuel cells to 2012: Market research, market share, market size, sales, demand forecast, market leaders, company profiles, industry trends. Cleveland, OH: The Freedonia Group. http://www.freedoniagroup.com/Fuel-Cells.html (accessed 25 September 2009).
[48] The Fuel Cell Today Industry Review (2011) http://www.fuelcelltoday.com/media/1351623/industry_review_2011.pdf (accessed 27 December 2011).
[49] DOE Energy Efficiency and Renewable Energy Information Center (2008) Early markets: Fuel cells for materials handling equipment. DOE Energy Efficiency and Renewable Energy Information Center, USA. www.hydrogen.energy.gov (accessed November 2008).
[50] Fuel Cells (2000). Micro Fuel Cells - Market Info. http://www.fuelcells.org/info/charts/MicroMarket.pdf (accessed 27 December 2011).
[51] CMR Fuel Cell (2009) Products. Cambridge, UK: CMR Fuel Cells. http://www.cmrfuelcells.com/index.php?option=com_content&task=blogcategory&id=8&Itemid=6 (accessed 27 September 2010).
[52] Samsung SDI (2009) The introduction of fuel cell. Seoul, South Korea: Samsung SDI. http://www.samsungsdi.com/generation/fuel-cell-battery.jsp (accessed 25 September 2010).
[53] Yomogida H (2008) Sony unveils ultrasmall hybrid fuel cell. Tokyo, Japan: Nikkei Electronics. http://techon.nikkeibp.co.jp/english/NEWS_EN/20080502/151303/ (accessed 27 September 2010).
[54] Toshiba (2009) Toshiba Launches Direct Methanol Fuel Cell in Japan as External Power for Mobile Electronic Devices (Press Release). http://www.toshiba.com/taec/news/press_releases/2009/dmfc_09_580.jsp (accessed 27 December 2011).
[55] Hunt SR (2009) Toshiba's fuel cell charger arriving this quarter. Thousand Oaks, CA: TG Daily. http://www.tgdaily.com/content/view/41264/145/ (accessed 27 September 2010).
[56] UltraCell (2009) Technology. Livermore, CA: Ultracell. http://www.ultracellpower.com/sp.php?fuel (accessed 27 September 2010).
[57] Shukla AK, Raman RK, and Scott K (2005) Advances in mixed-reactant fuel cells. *Fuel Cells* 5(4): 436–447.
[58] Green K, Kendall K, and Staffel I (2007) Cost targets for domestic fuel cell CHP. *Journal of Power Sciences* 181(2): 339–349.
[59] Mitchell WL and Teagan WP (1996) Potential markets for fuel cell/gas turbine cycles. Washington, DC: DOE. http://www.osti.gov/bridge/servlets/purl/475277-moRBKG/webviewable/475277.pdf (accessed 7 September 2010).
[60] Hitachi (2010) Hitachi to take part in direct methanol joint evaluation in the UK with CPI and Hitachi-High Technologies. Tokyo, Japan: Hitachi Ltd. http://www.hitachi.com/New/cnews/090224.pdf (accessed 10 November 2010).
[61] Gasteiger HA, Baker DR, Carter RN, et al. (2010) Electrocatalysis and catalyst degradation challenges in proton exchange membrane fuel cells. In: Stolten D (ed.) *Hydrogen Fuel Cells*, pp. 1–16. Wiley-VCH Verlag GmbH.
[62] Ohnsman A (2011) Toyota advances hydrogen fuel cell plans amid industry's battery-car push. Tokyo, Japan: Bloomberg. 13 January 2011. aohnsman@bloomberg.net (accessed 13 January 2011).
[63] Joint announcement NEDO and NOW exchange memorandum of understanding. Essen, Germany: GmbH. 16 May 2010. http://www.nedo.go.jp/content/100080361.pdf (accessed 27 December 2011).
[64] Lin K-S, Pan C-Yu, Chowdhury S, et al. (2011) Hydrogen generation using a CuO/ZnO-ZrO$_2$ nanocatalyst for autothermal reforming of methanol in a microchannel reactor. *Molecules* 16(1): 348–366.
[65] Dritz T (2011) Oxford Catalysts Fuelling a Cleaner World. Oxfordshire, UK: Oxford Catalysts Limited. http://www.oxfordcatalysts.com/index.php (accessed 2 October 2011).
[66] Hyundai (2011) Hyundai second generation fuel cell bus launched at Seol motor show. Online report. Seoul, South Korea: Hyundai. http://worldwide.hyundai.com/web/News/View.aspx?idx=181&nCurPage=1&strSearchColunm=&strSearchWord=&ListNum=119 (accessed 2 October 2011).
[67] HydrogenCarsNow (2006) Audi A2H2 Car. Laguna Beach, CA: Hydrogencarsnow.com. http://www.hydrogencarsnow.com/audi-a2h2-hydrogen-car.htm (accessed 10 September 2010).
[68] Ballard Power Systems, Inc (2009) Ballard Reports Strong 2010 Results and Provides 2011 Outlook. Vancouver, BC: Ballard Power Systems, Inc. http://www.ballard.com/print/about-ballard/newsroom/news-releases/news02011101.aspx (accessed 27 December 2011).
[69] Daimler AG (2009) The vehicles. Stuttgart, Germany: Daimler AG. http://www.daimler.com/dccom/0-5-658451-1-1232162-1-0-0-0-0-0-11979-0-0-0-0-0-0-0-0.html (accessed 6 October 2009).
[70] FuelCellToday (2009) Daimler unveils new Citaro FuelCELL hybrid bus. Hertfordshire, UK: FuelCellToday. http://www.fuelcelltoday.com/news-events/news-archive/2009/june/daimler-unveils-new-citaro-fuelcell-hybrid-bus (accessed 27 December 2011).
[71] FuelCellToday (2009) Organisation-Fiat Group. Hertfordshire, UK: FuelCellToday. http://www.fuelcelltoday.com/industry/industry-directory/f/fiat-group (accessed 27 December 2011).
[72] Hydrogen Motor (2006) Fiat Panda Hydrogen. Istanbul, Turkey: Hydrogen Motor. http://www.hydrogen-motors.com/fiat-panda-hydrogen.html (accessed 6 October 2009).
[73] HydrogenCarsNow (2006) Fiat Panda Hydrogen concept car. Laguna Beach, CA: Hydrogencarsnow.com. http://www.hydrogencarsnow.com/fiat-panda-hydrogen-concept.htm (accessed 11 September 2009).
[74] Ford Motor Company (2008) Migration to alternative fuels. Dearborn, MI: Ford Motor Company. http://www.ford.com/microsites/sustainability-report-2008-09/issues-climate-technologies-migration-fcv (accessed 6 October 2009).
[75] General Motors (2009) Technology. Detroit, MI: General Motors. http://www.gm.com/experience/technology/fuel_cells/fact_sheets/index.jsp (accessed 6 October 2009).
[76] Honda Motor Co. (2009) Specifications. Tokyo, Japan: Honda Motor Co.. http://automobiles.honda.com/fcx-clarity/specifications.aspx (accessed 6 October 2009).
[77] American Honda Motor Co. (2009) How FCX clarity works. Torrance, CA: American Honda Motor Co. http://automobiles.honda.com/fcx-clarity/vflow.aspx (accessed 6 October 2009).
[78] American Honda Motor Co. (2009) Home energy station. Torrance, CA: American Honda Motor Co. http://automobiles.honda.com/fcx-clarity/home-energy-station.aspx (accessed 6 October 2009).
[79] Pettendy M (2010) Hyundai ready for fuel cell future. Go Auto, 9 November 2010. Sandringham VIC: John Mellor Pty Ltd. http://www.goauto.com.au/mellor/mellor.nsf/story2/A8BEF8C476DDBF75CA2577D600161BFD (accessed 10 January 2011).
[80] Hyundai Completes Development of ix35 Hydrogen Fuel-Cell Electric Vehicle (2010) Hyundai Media Release 23 December 2010. North Ryde, NSW: Hyundai Motor Company. http://www.hyundai.com.au/About-Hyundai/News/Articles/Hyundai-completes-development-of-ix35-Hydrogen-Fuel-Cell-Electric-Vehicle/default.aspx (accessed 10 January 2011).
[81] Hydrogen Motor (2008) The Morgan LIFECar (2008). Istanbul, Turkey: Hydrogen Motor. http://www.hydrogen-motors.com/morgan.html (accessed 6 October 2010).
[82] Nissan Motors (2009) In-house fuel cell stack. Tokyo, Japan: Nissan Motors. http://www.nissan-global.com/EN/TECHNOLOGY/INTRODUCTION/DETAILS/IFCS/ (accessed 27 December 2011).
[83] Toyota USA News Room (2009) Toyota advanced fuel cell vehicle completes government field evaluation. Torrance, CA: Toyota Motor Sales. http://pressroom.toyota.com/article_display.cfm?article_id=1726 (accessed 6 October 2010).

[84] Toyota Motor Sales (2009) Fuel cell hybrid vehicles. Torrance, CA: Toyota Motor Sales. http://www.toyota.com/about/environment/innovation/advanced_vehicle_technology/FCHV.html (accessed 6 October 2010).
[85] Volkswagen of America (2007) Clean drive revolution 'Made in Germany'. Herndon, VA: Volkswagen of America, Inc. http://blogs.vw.com/conceptcars/2010/09/29/a-clean-drive-revolution-made-in-germany/ (accessed 27 December 2011).
[86] Emmerson G (2009) Volkswagen fuel cell vehicles-future shock. Anaheim, CA: Eurotuner Magazine. http://www.eurotuner.com/features/eurp_0910_volkswagen_fuel_cell_vehicles/los_angeles_auto_show.html (accessed 6 October 2010).
[87] Volkswagen Group (2008) Entering the hot phase. Wolfsburg, Germany: Volkswagen AG. http://www.volkswagenag.com/vwag/vwcorp/content/en/innovation/fuel_and_propulsion/strategy/fuel_cell.html (accessed 6 October 2010).
[88] Callaghan-Jerram L, Dehamna A, and Adamson K-A (2010) Transport fuel cell analysis report, fuel cell today. Hertfordshire, UK: FuelCellToday. www.fuelcelltoday.com.
[89] Gangi J (2000) Specialty Vehicles Chart. Fuel Cells 2000. Washington DC, USA. http://www.fuelcells.org/info/charts.html#special (accessed 10 January 2011).
[90] Bergen A, Djilali N, Pitt L, *et al.* (2008) Transient electrolyser response in a renewable-regenerative energy system. *International Journal of Hydrogen Energy* 34(1): 64–70.
[91] Walter K (1997) The unitized regenerative fuel cell. *Science and Technology Review*. Livermore, CA: Lawrence Livermore National Laboratory. https://www.llnl.gov/str/Mitlit.html (accessed 8 October 2010).
[92] Doddathimmaiah P and Andrews J (2009) Theory, modelling and performance measurement of unitised regenerative fuel cells. *International Journal of Hydrogen Energy* 31(19): 8157–8170.
[93] Gray E, Mac A, Webb CJ, *et al.* (2011) Hydrogen storage for off-grid power supply. *International Journal of Hydrogen Energy* 36(1): 654–663.
[94] Harrison KW, Kramer WE, Martin GD, and Ramsden TG (2009) The wind-to-hydrogen project: Operational experience, performance testing, and systems integration. Golden, CO: National Renewable Energy laboratory. http://www.nrel.gov/hydrogen/pdfs/44082.pdf (accessed 11 October 2010).
[95] Shabani B, Andrews J, and Watkins S (2010) Energy and cost analysis of a solar-hydrogen combined heat and power system for remote power supply using a computer simulation. *Solar Energy* 84(1): 144–155.
[96] Paul B and Andrews J (2008) Optimal coupling of PV arrays to PEM electrolysers in solar–hydrogen systems for remote area power supply. *International Journal of Hydrogen Energy* 33(2): 490–498.
[97] Maeland A (1996) Hydrogen production-based on Russian hydropower. Oslo, Norway: Rosnor Energy. http://www.rosnor.com/index.php/en/reports_and_articles/reports/hydrogen_study (accessed 10 January 2011).

Further Reading

Stolten D (ed.) (2010) *Hydrogen and Fuel Cells: Fundamentals, Technologies and Applications*. Wiley-VCH Verlag GmbH & Co. KgaA. ISBN: 978-3-527-32711-9.
Vielstich W, Gasteiger HA, and Yokokawa H (eds.) (2009) *Handbook of Fuel Cells: Advances in Electrocatalysis, Materials, Diagnostics and Durability*. Hoboken, NJ: John Wiley & Sons.
Hoogers G (2003) *Fuel Cell Technology Handbook*. London, UK: CRC Press. ISBN-10: 0849308771
Larminie J and Dicks A (2003) *Fuel Cell Systems Explained*, 2nd edn. Chichester, UK: John Wiley & Sons.
Barbir F (2006) *PEM Fuel Cells: Theory and Practice*. Amsterdam, The Netherlands: Elsevier Academic Press. ISBN 0120781425.
EG&G Technical Services, Inc. (2004) *Fuel Cell Technology Handbook*, 7th edn. Morgantown, WV: US Department of Energy.
Mench MM (2008) *Fuel Cell Engines*. Hoboken, NJ: John Wiley & Sons, Inc.doi:10.1002/9780470209769.ch9.
Rand D and Dell R (2007) *Hydrogen Energy: Challenges and Prospects (RSC Energy Series)*. London, UK: Royal Society of Chemistry. ISBN: 978-0-85404-597-6.

Relevant Websites

www.fuelcells.org – Fuel Cells 2000.
www.fuelcellmarkets.com – Fuel Cell Markets.
www.fuelcelltoday.com – Fuel Cell Today.
www.hpath.com – Partnership for Advancing the Transition to Hydrogen.
www.usfcc.com – US Fuel Cell Council.

4.09 Molten Carbonate Fuel Cells: Theory and Application

T Leo, FuelCell Energy Inc., Danbury, CT, USA

© 2012 Elsevier Ltd. All rights reserved.

4.09.1	Introduction	227
4.09.2	Carbonate Fuel Cell Chemistry and System Configuration	228
4.09.3	Cell Stack and Power Plant Design	229
4.09.4	Advantages of MCFC Power Plants	231
4.09.5	Applications of MCFC Power Plants	232
4.09.5.1	Self-Generation Applications	233
4.09.5.2	Grid Support Applications	233
4.09.5.3	Renewable MCFC Power Plant Applications	235
4.09.6	Future Advanced MCFC Applications	238
4.09.6.1	Hydrogen Production – DFC-H2 Concept	238
4.09.6.2	Carbon Separation	238
4.09.7	Conclusions	239
References		239

Glossary

Anaerobic digester A system for disposing of organic waste materials which uses bacteria to break down the waste, producing methane and carbon dioxide byproducts. Anaerobic digesters are used to process waste at municipal wastewater treatment plants and at food processing plants. The gas byproduct can be used as a fuel in some systems, depending on the tolerance for the carbon dioxide diluent.

Anaerobic digester gas The gas produced as a byproduct of anaerobic digestion. The gas is typically 60 to 70% methane with the balance being carbon dioxide, plus traces of sulfur compounds and other impurities.

Anode An active fuel cell component functioning as a negative electrode, where oxidation of fuel occurs, producing electrons.

Cathode An active fuel cell component functioning as a positive electrode, where reduction of oxidant and consumption of electrons occurs.

Combined heat and power (CHP) An application of fuel cells (or other types of power plants) where waste heat produced during power production is used for applications such as heating water, producing steam, or driving an absorption chiller. This heat utilization avoids the use of fuel, providing cost and carbon emission savings.

Direct FuelCell (DFC) A trade name for molten carbonate fuel cell, which refers to the fact that hydrocarbon fuels are sent directly to the fuel cell stack, where they are reformed to hydrogen. In some other fuel cell systems the reforming reaction has been done in a pre-processor subsystem.

Distributed generation Electric power that is generated where it is needed (distributed throughout the power grid) rather than in a central location. Centrally generated power requires extensive transmission networks, while distributed generation does not.

Electrolyte A material which allows transport of ions from anode to cathode. In the molten carbonate fuel cell the electrolyte is a mix of alkali metal carbonates, and carbonate ions are transported from cathode to anode.

Fuel cell A device which converts the energy value of a fuel to electricity electrochemically, without combusting the fuel. The functional components of a fuel cell are the anode, the cathode, and the electrolyte matrix.

Matrix A thin porous layer between the anode and cathode which contains the fuel cell electrolyte.

Molten carbonate fuel cell A fuel cell which uses mixed alkali metal carbonates as the electrolyte. The fuel cell operates at a high enough temperature for the carbonates to become liquid and ionically conductive.

Reforming Catalytic conversion of hydrocarbon fuel (such as pipeline natural gas or digester gas) to hydrogen-rich gas. The hydrogen-rich gas serves as a fuel for the electrochemical reaction.

4.09.1 Introduction

One of the earliest fuel cells to be deployed commercially are the molten carbonate fuel cells (MCFCs), which are high-temperature fuel cells that operate with a variety of fuels with high efficiency and very low emissions. Research and development on the system has been conducted since the 1950s, and demonstration and commercialization activities were underway by the late 1990s. The current state of the technology is such that it is best used for baseload power generation in stationary power plant systems [1].

Commercial power plants based on MCFCs have been available since 2003, and there are currently more than 60 MW of commercial power plants operating at more than 50 sites around the world.

The success of the technology is due to key features related to the high temperature of operation. The cells operate at 600–650 °C, higher than phosphoric acid or PEM cells, but lower than SOFC fuel cells. At this temperature the reaction kinetics are such that the cells do not need noble metal catalysts to achieve good performance, but the temperature is not so high as to require exotic alloys or ceramics as materials of construction. The absence of noble metal catalysts reduces fuel cell stack cost and reduces sensitivity to fuel impurities and carbon monoxide, which allows a high degree of fuel flexibility. The operating temperature is also high enough to allow hydrocarbon fuels (e.g., natural gas or anaerobic digester gas (ADG)) to be used without an external reforming system. These fuels can be reformed to hydrogen within the fuel cell stack. This increases system efficiency and reduces cooling system cost, since the reforming reaction is driven by waste heat from the fuel cell reaction [2].

The following sections describe the operating principle of internal reforming MCFCs, followed by a discussion of actual power plant configuration and applications.

4.09.2 Carbonate Fuel Cell Chemistry and System Configuration

The operating principle is described schematically in **Figure 1**. When configured in 'internal-reforming' systems, the electrochemical cell stack is where hydrocarbon fuels are reformed into hydrogen. A mixture of fuel and water vapor is sent to the anode chambers of the cells in the stack. Reforming and shift reactions occur, which convert the hydrocarbon fuel to hydrogen:

$$\text{Reforming: } CH_4 + H_2O \rightarrow CO + 3H_2, \quad \Delta H_{650°C} = +53.68 \text{ kcal g mol}^{-1}$$

$$\text{Shift: } CO + H_2O \rightarrow CO_2 + H_2, \quad \Delta H_{650°C} = -8.5 \text{ kcal g mol}^{-1}$$

$$\text{Net: } CH_4 + 2H_2O \rightarrow CO_2 + 4H_2, \quad \Delta H_{650°C} = +45.18 \text{ kcal g mol}^{-1}$$

The overall conversion is endothermic, which helps provide thermal management to the fuel cell stacks. During power generation, more than half of the waste heat produced by the fuel cell reaction is consumed in the reforming reaction. Water produced in the fuel cell anode reaction provides additional reforming reactant, and since the hydrogen produced by the reaction is continuously consumed in the fuel cell, the reforming/shift reaction is driven to completion, converting virtually all of the hydrocarbon fuel to hydrogen. This complete conversion is obtained despite the fact that the fuel cell operates at significantly lower temperatures, and with less steam input, than would be used in a conventional external reformer system.

The electrochemical reactions occurring in carbonate fuel cells are as follows:

At the anode. The H_2 produced by the reforming reaction reacts with carbonate ion (CO_3^{2-}) and produces H_2O and CO_2 by the reaction:

$$H_2 + CO_3^{2-} \rightarrow H_2O + CO_2 + 2e^-$$

The CO_2 produced in this reaction is sent back to the fuel cell cathodes by the power plant process system (described below).

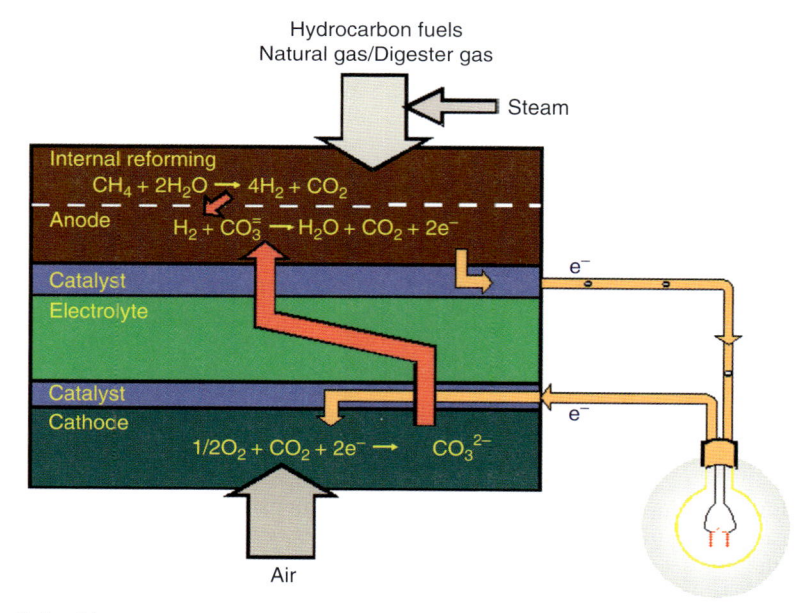

Figure 1 Carbonate fuel cell chemistry.

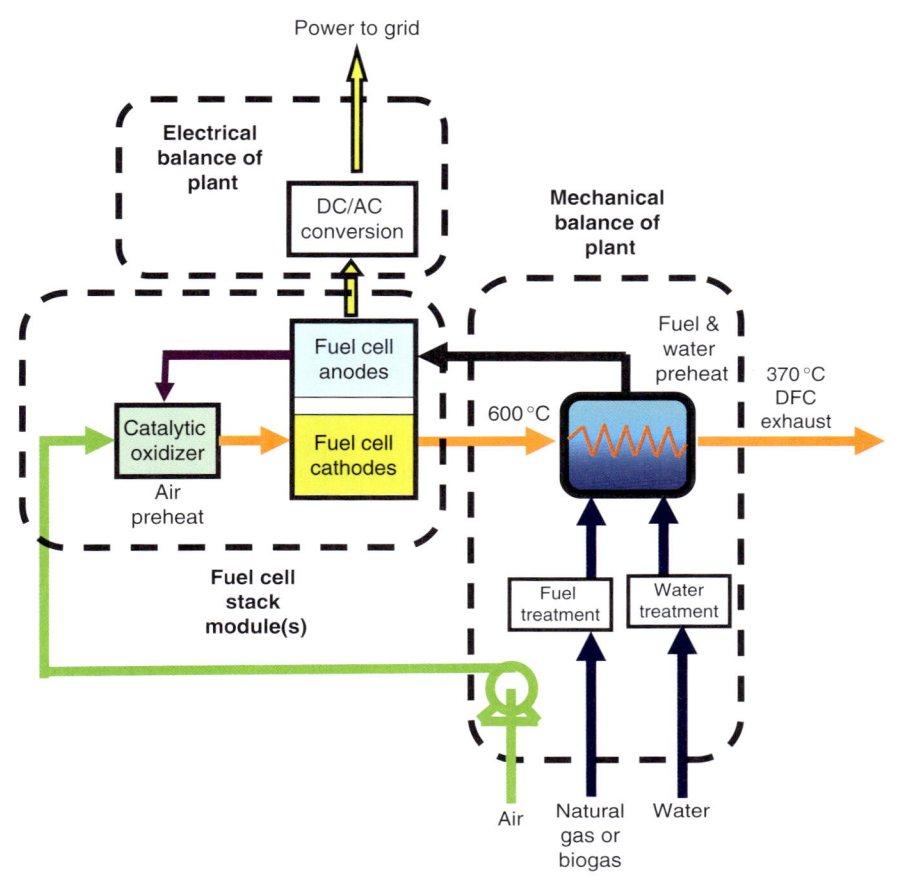

Figure 2 Carbonate fuel cell power plant simplified process diagram.

At the cathode. Oxygen from air and carbon dioxide from the anode reaction are reacted to form CO_3^{2-} as follows:

$$\tfrac{1}{2} O_2 + CO_2 + 2e^- \rightarrow CO_3^{2-}$$

The CO_3^{2-} ions formed on the cathode electrode are electrochemically transported to the anode, where they are consumed by the anode reaction.

These cell reactions require a process system that provides heated fuel and oxidant reactants to the fuel cells at a proper flow rate, and which provides a mechanism to deliver CO_2 produced by the anode reaction to the cathodes. A number of different system approaches are possible. FuelCell Energy (FCE) uses a system that leaves some fuel unutilized to serve as energy input to heat up incoming air. The overall power plant process is shown schematically in **Figure 2**.

Water and hydrocarbon fuel (typically, natural gas or methane biogas) are treated to remove sulfur and other impurities, heated to stack temperature, and sent to the fuel cell stacks. The reforming/shift reactions described above then convert the hydrocarbon fuel to hydrogen. The stack anodes consume about 70% of the hydrogen produced by the reforming reaction. The residual 30% hydrogen is used to preheat incoming air in a catalytic oxidizer. The heated air is then sent to the cathodes at a temperature of approximately 550 °C. Because the air was mixed with the anode exhaust stream in the catalytic oxidizer, the cathode inlet gas contains the CO_2 produced by the anodes, which is required for the cathode reaction. After the cathode reaction, the cathode exhaust gas exits the fuel cell stacks at approximately 600 °C, and it is used to provide the preheat to the incoming fuel and water streams, in the power plant heat recovery unit (HRU). The exhaust gases are cooled to 370 °C in the HRU, and can then be used for a variety of waste heat applications, as described below.

The theoretical operating temperature of MCFCs at 650 °C is 1.03 V [3]. In practice, the cells typically operate at approximately 0.8 V per cell under rated load conditions. This voltaic efficiency, combined with the 70% coulombic fuel utilization efficiency, gives a 54% DC power generation efficiency. After accounting for DC to AC power conversion losses and parasitic power requirements for balance-of-plant systems, typical power plant fuel to AC power efficiency is just under 50% on a lower heating value (LHV) basis.

4.09.3 Cell Stack and Power Plant Design

Figure 3 is an illustration of the repeating cell components of the fuel cell stack. The anode and cathode electrode structures are thin layers of porous nickel alloys. The electrodes are laminated on either side of a thin porous ceramic lithium aluminate substrate, which holds the molten carbonate electrolyte within its pores.

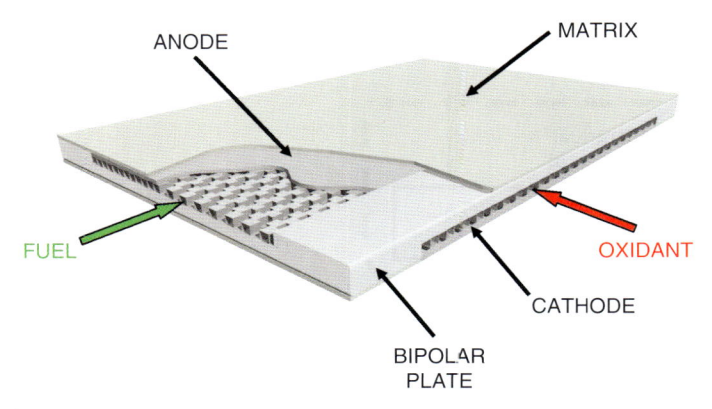

Figure 3 Carbonate fuel cell hardware.

The electrolyte is a mixture of alkali carbonates, which becomes liquid and ionically conductive at 450–510 °C. The pore structure of the ceramic matrix, Ni anode, and Ni cathode layers are strictly controlled in order to achieve the desired distribution of electrolyte between the three layers. Well-defined liquid–solid–gas interfaces in the cell structure provide the optimum amount of gas reaction sites and ionic mobility. Development efforts to extend cell life have focused in large part on maintaining the desired pore size distribution over time.

Corrugated flow layers, made of 300-series stainless steel, are placed on either side of the anode/matrix/cathode lamination to provide the required gas flow passages for anode fuel gases and cathode oxidant gases. Anode and cathode gases are separated by a stainless steel bipolar plate, which also provides the series electrical connection from each cell to the next.

In current commercial fuel cell products, a cell stack consists of approximately 400 of these cell package structures. When stacked together, the corrugations present gas inlet and exit passages on alternating faces of the stack. **Figure 4** shows a photograph of a commercial-scale stack, rated at 350 kW net AC output. When configured into a stack module, stainless steel manifolds are placed against the appropriate stack faces to direct inlet gases or collect exit gas flows.

The cell package and stack structures shown in **Figures 3** and **4** are typical of the MCFC technology commercialized by FCE in Danbury, CT, USA. FCE (along with their partner in South Korea, POSCO Power) is currently the only company offering commercial fuel cell power plants based on MCFC technology. FCE's fuel cell system utilizes internal reforming, and it is called the Direct FuelCell (DFC) in reference to the fact that hydrocarbon fuels are sent directly to the fuel cell stacks, without the need for an external reforming system.

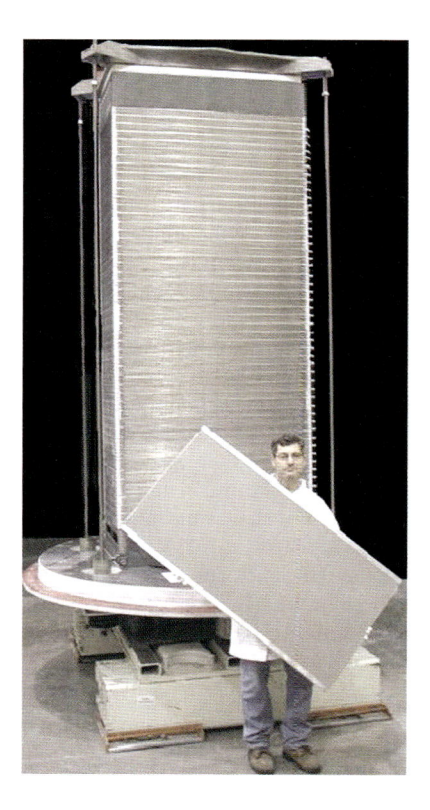

Figure 4 Carbonate fuel cell stack.

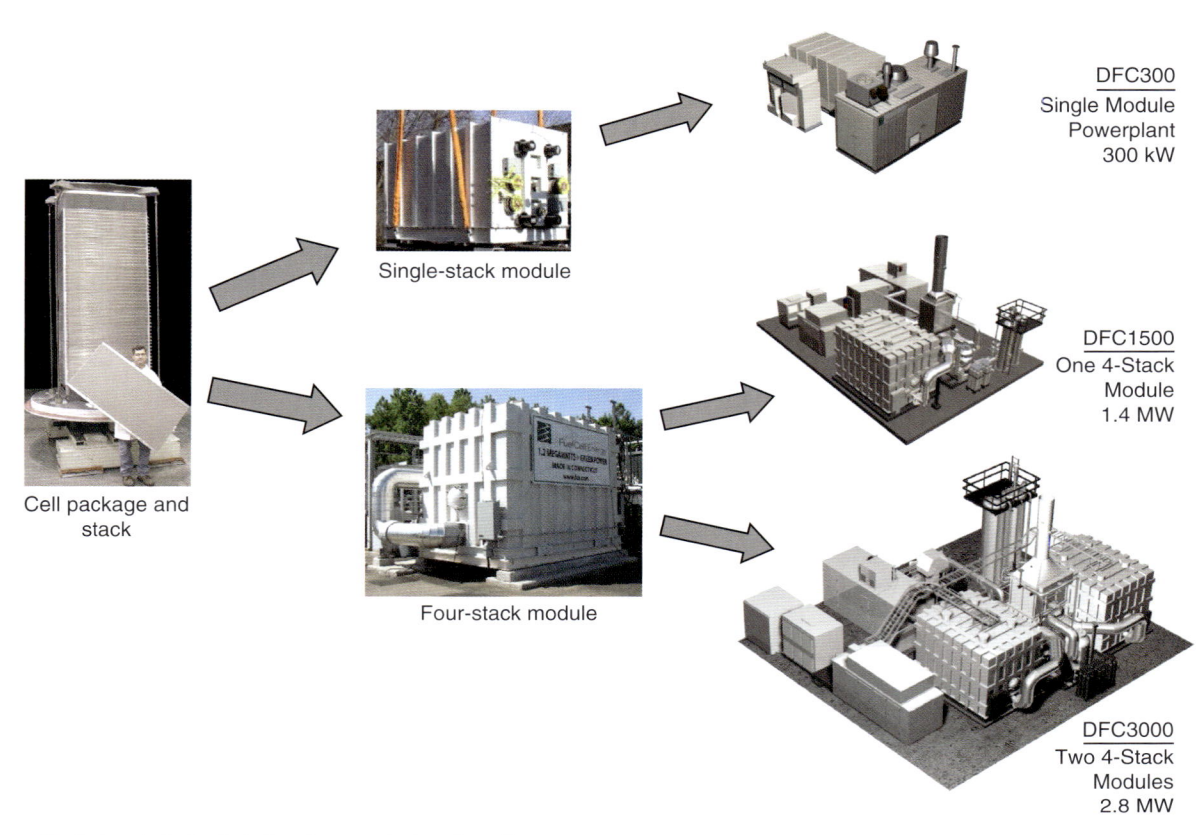

Figure 5 Carbonate fuel cell stack and power plant configurations.

FCE produces three standard power plant configurations based on the DFC design. The systems are designated DFC300, DFC1500, and DFC3000 and produce 300, 1400, and 2800 kW, respectively. As shown in **Figure 5**, the standard power plant systems utilize one of two modules: a single-stack module rated at 300 kW or a four-stack module rated at 1.4 MW. Both modules use the same basic cell package and stack as described above.

All of the systems operate at 47% LHV electrical efficiency with new fuel cell stack modules. Current DFC fuel cell stack life is 5 years. During this time, the power plant output declines to 90% of the initial rated output value, and the electrical efficiency declines by 10% (4.7 percentage points) to 42.3%. At the end of 5 years of operation, the stack modules are replaced with modules with new cells, and initial performance levels are restored.

In addition to the stack module, two other subsystems are used in each power plant system. The mechanical balance-of-plant section contains the process equipment that prepares air, fuel, and water for use in fuel cell stack modules. The electrical balance-of-plant section converts the DC power into high-quality AC power. Like other fuel cell systems, DFC power plants use solid-state static inverter systems, which provide additional benefits to local grid power quality beyond the power conversion function. Inverters have the ability to provide or absorb volt–ampere reactive power (VARs), have low frequency distortion, and low fault currents. These features make fuel cells more easily integrated into grid systems as distributed resources compared with power generation systems with rotating electric generators.

4.09.4 Advantages of MCFC Power Plants

DFC power plant systems compete against a wide variation of power generation technologies, including the default option: the electric grid. As a new technology, DFC systems are often more expensive than conventional power generation options, but they have key features which make them a good economic fit for many applications:

- High electrical efficiency, which results in reduced fuel costs and reduced carbon footprint per kilowatt-hour of generated power.
- High temperature waste heat, which can be used for a variety of purposes, improving economics and further reducing carbon footprint.
- Low emissions and low noise, which facilitate distributed generation installations on-site near power and heat users.

The high electrical efficiency is put into perspective in **Figure 6**, which compares electrical efficiency for a variety of power generation systems over a wide range of system sizes. No other commercially available power generation system can match the efficiency of fuel

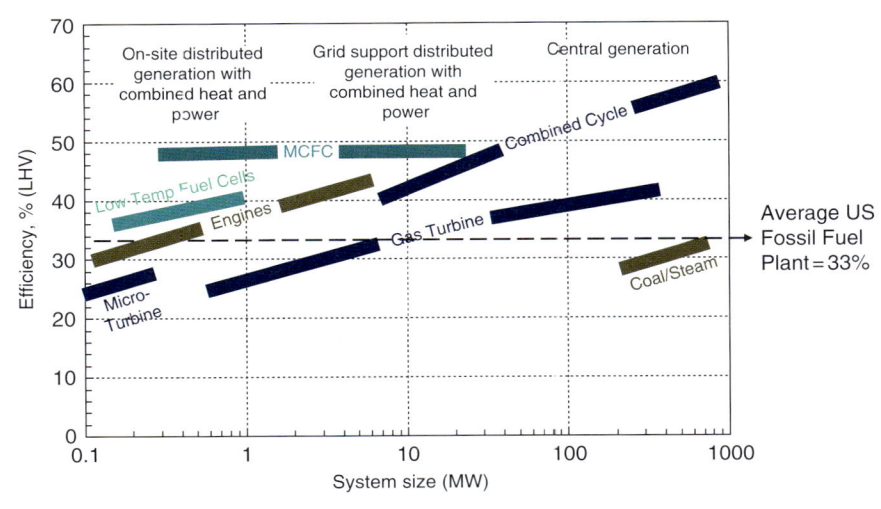

Figure 6 Comparison of MCFC electrical efficiency with alternative power generation technologies.

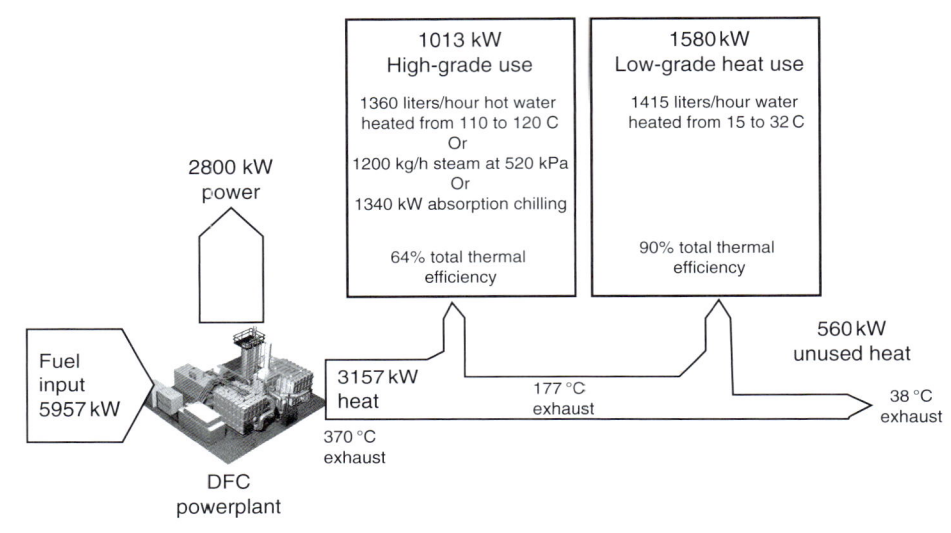

Figure 7 Thermal efficiency for typical combined heat and power options.

cells in distributed generation sizes. Combined-cycle power plants start to approach DFC efficiencies at sizes above 10 MW, but for typical on-site power generation applications, DFC systems will be more efficient.

Beyond electrical efficiency, DFC systems are almost always deployed in combined heat and power systems, where waste heat in the fuel cell exhaust is used to offset on-site thermal fuel use, further increasing efficiency and reducing carbon footprint. The 370 °C exhaust can be used in heat exchangers to produce hot water, steam, or to provide energy to absorption chilling systems. **Figure 7** illustrates the thermal balance for a number of heat recovery options that could be used with a DFC3000 2.8 MW system. High-grade heat uses include hot water, steam, or absorption chilling. Enough energy is often left over to provide for low-grade heat recovery to produce additional hot water or to provide other heating functions. In the examples shown in **Figure 7**, the high- and low-grade heat uses result in a total thermal efficiency of 90% [4].

In addition to high electrical efficiency and high-grade waste heat, the third major advantage of DFC fuel cells is very low emissions. **Table 1** compares the emissions of DFC fuel cell power plants to other distributed generation options and the average US fossil fuel plant. The fuel cell systems are orders of magnitude lower in NO_x and particulate emissions compared with conventional power generation systems. The high electrical efficiency also translates to low CO_2 emissions (which become zero when renewable biogas fuel is used).

4.09.5 Applications of MCFC Power Plants

DFC power plant systems are deployed in applications that produce clean power using natural gas fuel or applications that produce clean, renewable power using biogas-derived fuels. Applications can also be split into two other categories: on-site power generation to reduce grid power use and power generation for export to the grid.

Table 1 Comparison of DFC power plant emissions to conventional power generation sources

	NO_x (lb MWh^{-1})	SO_x (lb MWh^{-1})	PM-10 (lb MWh^{-1})	CO_2 (lb MWh^{-1})
Average US fossil fuel plant	5.06	11.6	0.27	2031
Microturbine (60 kW)	0.44	0.008	0.09	1596
Small gas turbine (250 kW)	1.15	0.008	0.08	1494
DFC fuel cell on natural gas	0.01	0.0001	0.00002	940
DFC fuel cell on natural gas with CHP	0.006	0.00006	0.00001	550
DFC fuel cell on biogas	0.006	0.00006	0.00001	0

Source: Emissions estimates for nonfuel cell sources are from 'Model Regulations for the Output of Specified Air Emissions from Smaller-Scale Electric Generation Resources', 15 October 2002, The Regulatory Assistance Project, for the National Renewable Energy Laboratory (NREL) [5].

4.09.5.1 Self-Generation Applications

DFC power plants have been used in on-site power applications to meet the baseload power requirements of a wide range of municipal, military, commercial, and industrial customers including wastewater treatment plants, manufacturing facilities, office buildings, hospitals, universities, and military bases. Many of the earlier self-generation projects used the smaller DFC300 product, but as the technology has been proven, the demand has been shifting to larger installations, which have a lower installed cost per kilowatt. **Figure 8** shows an example of a self-generation project at an industrial bakery in Connecticut. This early generation DFC1500 system, rated at 1.2 MW, provides more than half of the facility's power requirement, and excess heat from the power plant is used to support bakery processes, offsetting fuel use in plant boilers. After the fuel cell exhaust flows through the steam generator, it flows to another heat exchanger which is used to provide preheat to a facility gas stream. This two-level heat recovery gives the project a very high thermal efficiency, enhancing the economics and greenhouse gas reductions achieved by the system. The stack module can be seen in the right of the photograph, and the equipment on the left of the picture is the DC–AC power conversion system. The power plant exhaust (in the center of the photograph) exits vertically and is then directed down and behind the unit to the steam generation system.

Figure 9 shows another on-site combined heat and power (CHP) application, in this case a 1.4 MW DFC1500 at a university in California. In this view, the hot water heat recovery system can be seen just behind the power plant equipment.

These are two typical examples of combined heat and power installations in on-site self-generation projects. This type of project makes up about 40% of the 67 MW of MCFC power plants operating around the world. The remaining 60% are applications where power is exported to the utility grid instead of consumed on-site.

4.09.5.2 Grid Support Applications

In the grid support market, power is sold into the electric grid, at prices set by feed-in tariffs or by pricing mechanisms under Renewable Portfolio Standards (RPS) programs. These projects tend to be larger scale than the self-generation applications. The

Figure 8 DFC1500 power plant in combined heat and power application at industrial bakery in Connecticut.

Figure 9 DFC1500 power plant in combined heat and power application on California State University, East Bay campus.

Figure 10 11.2 MW DFC power plant in Daegu City, South Korea.

DFC3000 power plant is often being used in multiple-plant configurations for grid support systems. The most significant grid support market for fuel cells is in South Korea, where an RPS pricing mechanism provides favorable pricing for fuel cell power.

Figure 10 shows the largest fuel cell installation in the world, an 11.2 MW site with four DFC3000 power plants in Daegu City, South Korea. The system produces power for sale to the local utility under a long-term power purchase agreement, and provides heat to local neighborhood users. South Korea has supported fuel cell grid sales through a feed-in tariff mechanism which has now been transitioned to a renewable energy credit (REC)-based pricing scheme under their national RPS program. In South Korea, the high efficiency and very low emissions of fuel cell power plants qualify them for inclusion as renewable power, even when using natural gas fuel. The same is true for the state of Connecticut in the United States (and four other states), which has a feed-in tariff type program targeted at establishing 150 MW of renewable, clean generation in the state. The state of California is in the process of enacting feed-in tariffs for combined heat and power and renewable power sources, which could support additional grid support fuel cell installations.

Driven largely by the scale of the projects, the grid support application is the largest growing market segment for DFC fuel cell power plants. Unlike the self-generation application, it is not always possible to identify local users for waste heat from these grid-connected systems. Because of this, power plant developers have been evaluating approaches to converting waste heat from the systems into additional power. One of the most straightforward of these approaches is to use DFC waste heat to drive an organic Rankine cycle (ORC) system. An ORC is a power generation system similar to a steam turbine plant, except that it uses an organic working fluid with lower boiling point than water, to capitalize on lower-temperature heat sources. ORCs are used to

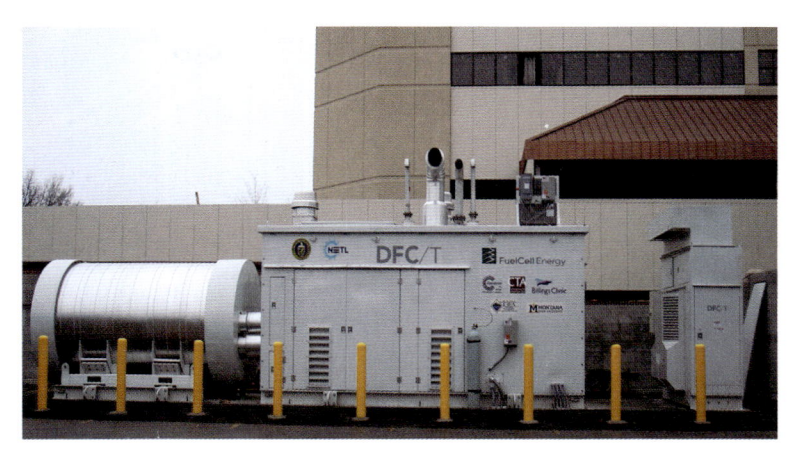

Figure 11 320 kW sub-MW DFC/T power plant during field test at Billings Clinic in Billings, MT.

recover industrial waste heat or to produce power from geothermal sources. When operated from the waste heat of a DFC power plant, the additional power from an ORC bottoming cycle can increase the electrical efficiency of the power plant from 47% to approximately 50%.

FCE has also developed a hybrid cycle in which a gas turbine generator is integrated into the fuel cell system at the point of highest temperature (after the anode gas oxidizer) in order to achieve even higher efficiencies. The gas turbine is unfired, and runs entirely on waste heat from the fuel cell process. The technology has been demonstrated at the sub-MW scale. **Figure 11** shows a prototype system that was based on the DFC300 product (rated 250 kW at the time) combined with a Capstone microturbine, for a combined rated output of 320 kW. The unit was tested at FCE's Connecticut test facility and then operated in the field at a hospital site in Billings, MT, USA. The maximum LHV electrical efficiency demonstrated was 58% [6]. The hybrid system, designated the DFC/T, achieves a higher efficiency than exhaust-based bottoming cycles (like the ORC) because it is driven by higher temperature heat in the fuel cell system. FCE is developing megawatt-scale DFC/T designs for commercialization in the near future.

A high-efficiency configuration that is commercially available today involves the use of waste heat from DFC fuel cell systems to support power generation from natural gas pressure letdown energy recovery. Natural gas is transmitted over long distances at high pressure, and then reduced in pressure for distribution in local markets. This pressure reduction is done at gate stations near major markets, and it is usually done with pressure reducing valves. Enbridge Inc., a major natural gas distribution company, and FCE have codeveloped a hybrid system in which the pressure reduction is done in an expansion turbine, which drives an electric generator. In order to prevent excess cooling of the expanding natural gas, waste heat from a DFC power plant is used to preheat the high-pressure gas before expansion. This system, called the DFC-ERG (for Energy Recovery Generation) has been demonstrated at Enbridge's headquarter, Toronto, Canada, in a 2.2 MW system consisting of 1.2 MW fuel cell generation and 1 MW expansion turbine generation. The maximum efficiency demonstrated by this system has been 70% on an LHV basis [7]. The power plant is shown in **Figure 12**. The fuel cell system, with four single-stack modules, is shown in the foreground of the photograph, and the turbine generation and heat transfer equipment is behind the fuel cell system.

4.09.5.3 Renewable MCFC Power Plant Applications

As described above, MCFC system currently available in the DFC configuration are designed for internal reforming of methane-based fuels, which makes them a good fit for biogas fuels which are predominantly methane, such as ADG. ADG differs from pipeline quality natural gas in that it has higher levels of contaminants, such as sulfur compounds and siloxanes, and the methane tends to be diluted with CO_2, another by-product of the anaerobic digestion process. ADG from municipal wastewater treatment processes consist of about 60% methane and 40% CO_2. ADG from brewery or food processing waste digestion has about 70% methane concentration [8].

MCFCs are particularly well suited for operation on these bio-derived fuels, due to its insensitivity to the CO_2 diluent. As described above, a unique aspect of the carbonate fuel cell chemistry is that CO_2 is produced in the anodes and consumed in the cathodes. Because of Nernst effects, the presence of CO_2 diluent in the fuel will reduce anode performance and improve cathode performance. In practice, the cathode gain is roughly equal to the anode penalty – the DFC power plants perform about the same in the presence of the CO_2 diluent, as long as methane content is above approximately 50%. **Figure 13** compares performance from a test stack operating on pure methane versus operation on methane diluted with CO_2. The results show that the CO_2 diluent had no impact on cell performance. This has been born out in many commercial projects at municipal wastewater treatment plants using ADG with 60% methane concentration. In fact, a small performance gain (vs. natural gas) has been observed at sites with 70% methane/30% CO_2 gas compositions, which suggests that at this concentration the cathode gain is slightly more than the anode performance loss.

Figure 12 2.2 MW DFC-ERG system in Toronto, Canada.

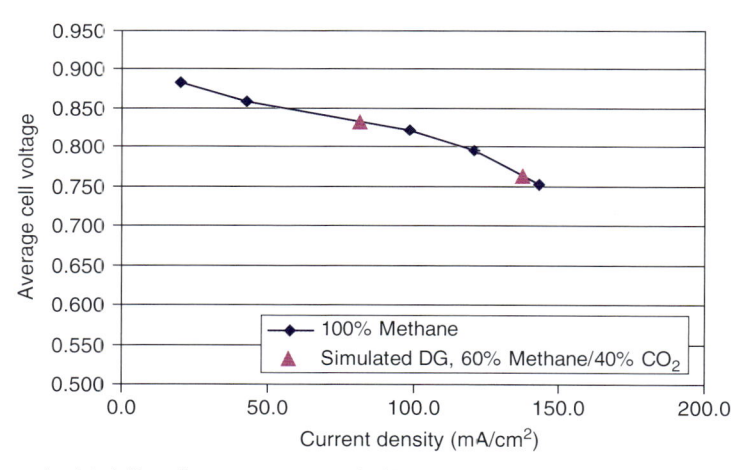

Figure 13 Stack performance on simulated dilute digester gas compared with pure methane fuel.

As of this writing, there are approximately 9 MW of DFC power plants operating on biogas at 11 sites around the world, mostly in California. Most systems are at municipal wastewater treatment sites, but systems are also installed at food processors and breweries. **Figure 14** shows a 1.4 MW DFC1500 system at a municipal wastewater treatment plant at Turlock Irrigation District in California. **Figure 15** shows a system at a wastewater treatment facility in Tulare, California, consisting of three sub-MW DFC300 systems. After several years of operating these systems, the municipality installed a fourth unit to utilize more ADG and increase the capacity of power generation at the site [9].

Figure 14 1.4 MW system at wastewater treatment site at Turlock Irrigation District, California.

Figure 15 900 kW system at wastewater treatment site in Tulare, California.

While executing the first biogas projects, FCE evolved a variety of control strategies and features to deal with the specific characteristics of biogas. Unlike pipeline natural gas, the production and composition of the biogas fluctuates over time. Systems have been developed to automatically respond to changes in composition by changing fuel utilization and air flow set points. A fuel blending option has been introduced, which can substitute natural gas for ADG if the biogas production falls off, allowing the power plant to continue operation at full power. Early biogas projects suffered from poor performance of the gas pretreatment systems which remove excess sulfur from the gas. These lessons learned have been incorporated into design guidance, which is given to customers who are specifying gas treatment systems for fuel cell power plants during the project development stage. This refinement of the renewable fuel application is a key factor in the growth of this market segment, as successful projects inspire other wastewater treatment plant or food processing operators to explore the technology. Agricultural-based biogas is a potentially large emerging market segment, which could benefit from fuel cell power generation. Municipal wastewater treatment, food and beverage processing, and agricultural operation all generate solid waste that can be reduced by digestion, and that digestion produces methane gas that must be disposed of. Using the methane gas for power generation eliminates on-site flaring, and if that power generation is in a fuel cell power plant, local generation of NO_x and particulates is also eliminated. The unique insensitivity of MCFC systems to the CO_2 dilution in these fuels makes them a good match for these applications.

4.09.6 Future Advanced MCFC Applications

Development programs are being conducted on future MCFC-based systems with additional features beyond generation of heat and power. The two concepts being evaluated involve using MCFC-based systems to produce hydrogen, and using MCFC as a carbon separation system for CO_2 capture from conventional fossil plants.

4.09.6.1 Hydrogen Production – DFC-H2 Concept

As discussed earlier, in the internal reforming DFC system, hydrocarbon fuels are converted to hydrogen in the fuel cell stacks. Most of the hydrogen is used in the electrochemical power generation reaction and the residual hydrogen is used to heat incoming cathode air. In the DFC-H2 concept, most of the residual hydrogen is separated from the anode exhaust, and purified for delivery to a hydrogen user. The user could be a hydrogen vehicle fueling station, an industrial hydrogen user, or a low-temperature hydrogen fuel cell that provides additional power. The preheat of incoming air is done with a heat exchanger, since the energy content of the residual fuel stream is no longer enough to heat up the air. DFC-H2 systems produce less usable waste heat than a conventional DFC system (because some of the thermal energy has been used for air preheat), but they do produce some waste heat, along with power and hydrogen. These tri-generation systems are sometimes referred to as combined heat, hydrogen, and power (CHHP) systems.

The first full-scale DFC-H2 system was built in 2009, based on the 300 kW DFC300 configuration. Some of the fuel cell power is used to power the hydrogen separation system, so the net output of the DFC-H2 system is 250 kW, and it produces up to 250 kg day^{-1} of hydrogen. The system was tested at FCE's Connecticut facilities in 2010, and then delivered to the Orange County Sanitation District (OCSD) wastewater treatment facility site in California for field testing and a 3-year operation test [10].

Figure 16 shows the system on test at the OCSD site. The DFC-H2 system can produce clean hydrogen from natural gas, with less carbon emissions than conventional hydrogen production from steam methane reforming, because the reforming heat is coming from fuel cell waste heat, not fuel burning. The system can also be operated on renewable fuel, as the OCSD system is, with no carbon impact. At the OCSD site, the renewable hydrogen produced by the system is used to fuel hydrogen vehicles at a filling station located nearby. The project is led by Air Products, which also operates the on-site vehicle fueling station. In addition to FCE and Air Products, this demonstration project is also supported by the National Fuel Cell Research Center at the University of California Irvine, California Air Resources Board (CARB), South Coast Air Quality Management District (SCAQMD), US Department of Energy (DOE), and Southern California Gas Company.

In the system shown in **Figure 16**, the fuel cell equipment can be seen to the left of the photograph, and the hydrogen separation and storage equipment is to the right. The system separating hydrogen from the anode exhaust is a pressure swing absorption (PSA) system, which is a modification of conventional separation technology. FCE is also developing an electrochemical separation system that could reduce the cost and energy requirements of the hydrogen separation section of the system.

4.09.6.2 Carbon Separation

The carbonate fuel cell chemistry includes the unique characteristic that CO_2 is produced at the anode electrodes and consumed at the cathode electrodes to support the transfer of carbonate ions through the electrolyte. This aspect of MCFC operation can be used as a carbon transfer mechanism to separate carbon from a dilute stream and transfer it to a more concentrated stream where it can be

Figure 16 DFC-H2 power plant producing 250 kW and over 250 kg day^{-1} of hydrogen and power derived from renewable ADG at Orange County Sanitation District, California.

more easily separated. Investigations are being conducted to determine if this concept can be used to efficiently capture CO_2 from fossil power plant exhaust.

Carbon capture and sequestration is of great interest in countries that depend on fossil fuels for a significant portion of the power generation mix. Conventional systems to extract CO_2 from power plant exhaust require a significant portion of the plant electrical output to operate. The MCFC carbon capture application involves sending the exhaust from a fossil plant to the oxidant inlet of an operating MCFC power plant. The CO_2 in the exhaust would be consumed by the cathode reaction, and an equivalent amount of CO_2 will be produced in the anodes. This effectively transfers CO_2 from the dilute power plant exhaust stream (where CO_2 concentration ranges from 5% to 15%, depending on the type of plant) to the anode exhaust stream. The CO_2 concentration in the anode exhaust stream is approximately 70%, and it can be more easily separated from this more concentrated stream.

Cell tests have been done to quantify the performance of operating cells with oxidant gases based on simulated composition of exhaust gas from various types of coal and natural gas power plants. These results are now being used in modeling studies to predict system performance as an input into economic evaluation of the concept.

4.09.7 Conclusions

MCFCs have achieved a high degree of success because of inherent aspects of the fuel cell chemistry: high efficiency, high-grade waste heat, and very low emissions. Market adoption is broadening as customers become familiar with the technology and comfortable with deploying large-scale systems. This trend, combined with the emergence of new advanced applications of the technology, should make the MCFC the first fuel cell technology to play a significant role in the stationary power generation mix.

References

[1] McPhail S, Bove R, and Moreno A (2008) 'International Status of Molten Carbonate Fuel Cell (MCFC) Technology'; *2008 ENEA Ente per le Nuove Tecnologie, l'Energia e l'Ambiente Lungotevere Thaon di Revel*, 76 00196 Roma.
[2] Farooque M and Maru HC (2006) Carbonate fuel cells: Milliwatts to megawatts. *Journal of Power Sources* 160(2): 827–834.
[3] DE-AM26-99FT40575 (2004) *Fuel Cell Handbook*, 7th edn. EG&G Technical Services, Inc., US Department of Energy, NETL, November 2004.
[4] Pais C and Leo A (2009) CHP applications of high temperature fuel cells. *World Energy Engineering Congress*. 4–6 November 2009. http://www.energycongress.com/
[5] National Renewable Energy Laboratory (NREL) (2002) Model regulations for the output of specified air emissions from smaller-scale electric generation resources, 15 October 2002. *The Regulatory Assistance Project*, for the National Renewable Energy Laboratory (NREL).
[6] Ghezel-Ayagh H (2008) Direct FuelCell/turbine power plant. *Final Technical Progress Report, DOE DE-FC26-00NT40798*. US Department of Energy, NETL.
[7] Enbar N and Jaffe S (2010) *Best Practices: Enbridge's Approach to Greening the Natural Gas T&D Network via Hybrid Fuel Cells*. Energy Insights No. EI221326.
[8] Mossinger T (2008) Cogeneration and fuel cells, water and wastewater. In: *Air, Water, Energy Conference*, California Water Environment Association. April 2008. http://www.cwea.org/sarbs/pdfs/AirWaterEnergyConf/TomMossingerFuelCellsCogeneration.pdf (last accessed 19 December 2011).
[9] Fuel Cells (2000) Fuel cell system turns waste into electricity at the Tulare wastewater treatment plant. www.fuelcells.org/info/TulareCaseStudy.pdf (last accessed 19 December 2011).
[10] Heydorn E (2011) Validation of an integrated Hydrogen Energy Station. Section VII.4 of US Department of Energy Hydrogen and Fuel Cell Program 2011 Annual Progress Report. Available at: http://www.hydrogen.energy.gov/pdfs/progress11/vii_4_heydorn_2011_pdf (accessed 20 December 2011).

4.10 Solid Oxide Fuel Cells: Theory and Materials

A Tesfai and JTS Irvine, University of St Andrews, St Andrews, UK

© 2012 Elsevier Ltd. All rights reserved.

4.10.1	Introduction	241
4.10.1.1	Fuel Cells	242
4.10.1.2	Thermodynamics	243
4.10.1.3	The Nernst Equation	245
4.10.1.4	The SOFC	246
4.10.1.4.1	Principles of operation	246
4.10.1.4.2	Advantages of SOFC over other types of fuel cell	246
4.10.1.5	SOFC Components	246
4.10.1.5.1	Electrolyte	246
4.10.1.5.2	Cathode	247
4.10.1.5.3	Anode	247
4.10.1.5.4	Interconnect	248
4.10.1.6	Example Systems	249
4.10.1.6.1	Introduction to CHP systems	249
4.10.1.6.2	Efficiency and efficiency limits	250
4.10.1.6.3	Heat and power load requirements for a typical UK home	251
4.10.1.6.4	Fuel cell-based micro-CHP systems	251
4.10.1.6.5	Performance characteristics	251
4.10.1.6.6	Fuel cell micro-CHP technical specifications and functional requirements	251
4.10.1.6.7	Efficiency	252
4.10.1.6.8	Durability	252
4.10.1.6.9	Fuel cell heat-to-power ratio and its advantages	253
4.10.1.6.10	Engineering methods to achieve a variable heat-to-power ratio	254
4.10.2	Conclusion	254
Acknowledgment		255
References		255

Glossary

Anode Where oxidation occurs, typically a fuel electrode.
Cathode Where reduction occurs, typically the air electrode.
Electrolyte Ion conducting membrane separating fuel and air electrodes.
Fugacity Equal to the pressure of an ideal gas which has the same chemical potential as the real gas.
Gibbs free energy Thermodynamic potential that measures the 'useful' work.
Interconnect Gastight electrical connection between anode and cathode.
PEMFC Polymer electrolyte membrane fuel cell.

4.10.1 Introduction

The increasing demand for energy due to economic growth particularly in developing countries on one hand and increasingly energy-intensive lifestyles and trends on the other hand is posing a serious environmental sustainability challenge. The problem of whether these competing demands for energy can be satisfied in a future of shrinking fossil fuel resources [1, 2] and global warming [3, 4] is causing a serious concern. In recent years, this has intensified the search for more reliable and sustainable energy sources.

Currently, due to rapid depletion of oil reserves, natural gas and coal have been increasingly used as alternatives. However, it is now widely accepted that long-term sustainable energy supply can only be achieved with the use of renewable energy sources (RESs). Some of the potential RESs are wind, solar, and tidal energy systems. Electrochemical devices such as fuel cells will play an important role both to provide clean hydrogen gas for mobile application and also for converting fuel to energy more efficiently than conventional systems.

International experts agree that the optimal strategy and principles for addressing the energy and greenhouse gas (GHG) emissions is first to minimize energy losses through efficient use of fossil fuels; second to introduce cost-effective RESs – solar wind, and geothermal energy; and third to use green fuels – hydrogen and biofuels. This strategy has led some to propose a move to the hydrogen economy.

The notion of a hydrogen economy involves a combination of RESs and H_2 technologies used for local and industrial energy production and consumption to simultaneously address the major energy and environmental challenges. Fuel cells have been proposed as the most efficient way to convert the hydrogen to heat and power at the point of use for decentralized stationary [5, 6] power systems and for transportation [7, 8]. The efficiency of fuel cells emanates from the fact that unlike the conventional fossil fuel power stations where there are many intermediate energy conversion steps, the conversion of the chemical energy takes place in a single step. Avoiding these intermediate steps reduces the irreversible losses of energy to the atmosphere and enables fuel cells to achieve efficiencies in the region of 40–60%.

The major advantage of fuel cell systems is that hydrogen, which is the main energy carrier [5, 9] generated from RESs, reacts with oxygen supplied from air to produce heat and electricity at the point of use. The only by-product from such a reaction is water. One of the main advantages of a fuel cell is that it produces negligible or undetectable emissions of nitrous oxides [10] compared to conventional generators. The other advantages include the following: (1) moving from centralized to decentralized energy supply systems, thereby ensuring the security of supply and better efficiency as the waste heat can be recycled for space or water heating [11]; (2) in the case of high-temperature fuel cells, the efficiency is increased further by utilizing the high-grade heat generated in a conventional downstream device such as a gas turbine system, generating more electricity, further improving efficiency, and also producing less noise pollution.

As mentioned above, to achieve fully sustainable RES, the three strategic principles have to be implemented in a step-by-step process. The capability of fuel cells to produce energy with high efficiency implies that even before the hydrogen economy is fully realized, fuel cells will play a major role in minimizing the emission of carbon dioxide and energy wastage, which is the first phase of achieving reliable and fully sustainable renewable energy systems. The general trend toward RES is visible worldwide; it is therefore clear that together with the solar, wind, and other renewable energies, fuel cells will play a vital role in achieving clean energy systems. However, though fuel cell technology may be nearly mature, failing to achieve the infrastructure for it could set back its development progress. It is therefore important to mention that in order to realize the full potential of fuel cells and the hydrogen economy, decentralized bottom-up hydrogen infrastructure needs to be established. New technology such as hydrogen fuel storage systems for portable, stationary, and transport use needs to be established.

One area where solid oxide fuel cell (SOFC) is expected to play a significant role is the building sector. Combined heat and power (CHP), also known as cogeneration, is the simultaneous production of electrical and useful thermal energy from the same primary energy source such as oil, coal, natural or liquefied gas, or solar [12, 13]. The CHP concept can be applied to small-scale residential buildings as well as for large-scale cogeneration systems for industrial purposes. CHP is suitable for residential building applications, provided that the heat energy produced is required for space heating or other applications. In comparison with conventional methods of generating heat and electricity separately, cogeneration systems can increase energy efficiency that can result in lower costs and reduction in GHG emissions [14]. In the case of single-family residential building applications, due to thermal and electrical load variations and requirements, the surplus thermal energy has to be stored in a thermal storage device such as a water tank or in phase change materials, while surplus electricity can be sold to the grid or stored in batteries or capacitors. Also any shortage can be purchased from other sources such as electrical grids. In the case of commercial or multifamily or institutional applications, benefits from the thermal/electrical (T/E) load diversity reduce the need for storage [14].

CHP system efficiency is determined by the system type, size, and the operating conditions of the prime mover. CHP units for building applications are required to achieve more than $4500\,h\,yr^{-1}$ utilization [15]. Cogeneration system efficiency is generally expressed in terms of both electrical and thermal efficiency [15].

4.10.1.1 Fuel Cells

A fuel cell is a device that converts the chemical energy of a fuel and oxidant into electrical energy and heat through an electrochemical process. The fuel and oxidant are typically stored outside of the fuel cell and transferred into the fuel cell as the reactants are consumed. A fuel cell consists of three main components: anode, cathode, and electrolyte, as shown schematically in **Figure 1** [16, 17].

The fuel, which is typically a hydrogen source, is fed to the anode. The oxidant, which is pure oxygen or air, is fed to the cathode. The hydrogen is split into electrons and protons as in eqn [1]. The electrons are transferred through the external circuit to the cathode to react with oxygen that produces oxygen ion, O^{2-}, as in eqn [2]. For an oxide electrolyte the oxygen ion moves thorough the electrolyte to the anode or for a proton conducting electrolyte the proton moves to the cathode to produce heat and water as in eqn [3]. As can be seen from eqn [3], the overall reaction yields water.

$$H_2 \rightarrow 2H^+ + 2e^- \qquad [1]$$

$$\tfrac{1}{2}O_2 + 2e^- \rightarrow O^{2-} \qquad [2]$$

$$H_2 + \tfrac{1}{2}O_2 \rightarrow H_2O \qquad [3]$$

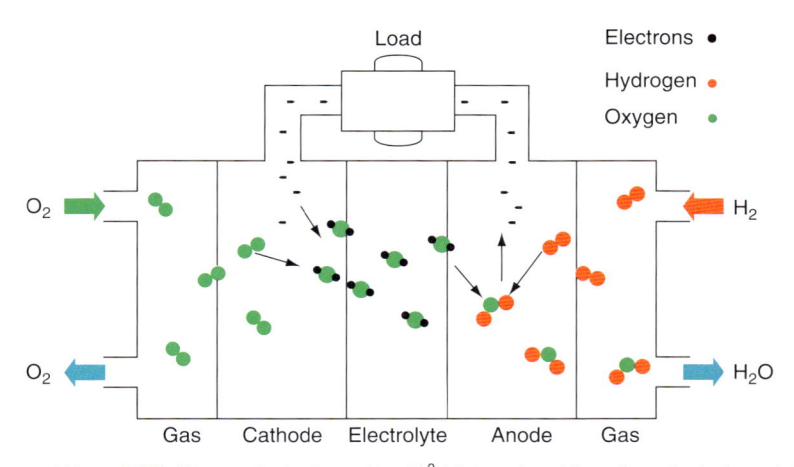

Figure 1 Transport processes within an SOFC. The negatively charged ion (O^{2-}) is transferred from the cathode through the electrolyte to the anode where it reacts with H^+ to generate water as a by-product.

Table 1 Comparison between fuel cell types

	PEFC	PAFC	AFC	MCFC	SOFC
Electrolyte	Polymer	H_3PO_4	KOH	Carbonate	Solid oxide
Operating temperature (°C)	80	200	100–250	650	800–1000
Efficiency (%)	40–50	40–80	70	60–80	65–85
Charge carrier	H^+	H^+	HO^-	CO_3^{2-}	$O^{2-}(H^+)$
Catalyst	Pt	Pt	Ni	Ni	Perovskites
Main cell components	C-based	Graphite-based	C-based	Stainless steel	Ceramic

There are different types of fuel cells, some of which are summarized in **Table 1**. Though these fuel cells have same basic operating principles, they differ mainly on the type of migrating ion through the electrolyte. The proton exchange membrane (PEM) electrolyte is a solid polymer in which protons migrate through the membrane to the cathode that then reacts with the O^{2-} to form H_2O. It runs at temperatures of around 70 °C, so the problem of slow reaction rates is addressed by using advanced catalysts and electrodes. Platinum is the catalyst, but developments in recent years mean that only minute amounts are used, and the cost of the platinum is a small part of the total price of a PEM fuel cell [17].

An alkaline fuel cell was used on the Apollo and Shuttle Orbiter craft. The problem of slow reaction was overcome by using high porous electrodes with a platinum catalyst and sometimes by operating at quiet high pressures. Usually operated below 100 °C, their main problem is that air and fuel supplies must be free from CO_2, otherwise pure oxygen and hydrogen must be used.

The phosphoric acid fuel cell (PAFC) is the first to be produced in commercial quantities and enjoys widespread terrestrial use. Porous electrodes, platinum catalysts, and a fairly high temperature (220 °C) are used to boost the reaction rate to a reasonable level. Hydrogen is supplied by reforming natural gas to hydrogen and carbon dioxide; the equipment required to do this adds to the total operational cost, complexity, and size of the fuel cell system. Nonetheless, PAFC is an exceptionally reliable and a maintenance-free power system.

The molten carbonate fuel cell (MCFC) comprises Li_2CO_3 and K_2CO_3 or Li_2CO_3 and Na_2CO_3 in an Li_2OAlO_2 matrix, where the matrix comprises 40 wt.% [17]. At the high operating temperatures of above 600 °C, the carbonates become a molten salt, with the CO_3^{2-} providing ionic conductivity.

Disadvantages of the MCFC are the corrosive nature of the electrolyte, which reduces the lifetime, and the requirement of CO_2 recycling in order to have a high enough CO_2 concentration at the cathode [16, 18]. In addition, carbon monoxide can be used as a fuel. Whether hydrogen or carbon monoxide is used as the fuel has a very small effect on the voltage of the fuel cell, with, respectively, 1.02 and 1.04 V produced [17].

4.10.1.2 Thermodynamics

As previously mentioned, an SOFC is a device that converts the chemical energy (enthalpy of combustion reaction) of a fuel and oxidant into electrical energy and heat through an electrochemical process. The electrical power available from an ideal cell is reduced mainly due to two effects: ohmic resistance that generates heat and the irreversible mixing of gases that causes a voltage drop. This means a fuel cell is not able to convert the complete fuel into useful energy.

In the case of fuel cells, the 'Gibbs free energy' can be defined as the "energy available to do external work, neglecting any work done by changes in pressure and/or volume" in a fuel cell; the 'external work' involves moving electrons around an external circuit

[17]. In a fuel cell, the change in Gibbs free energy (ΔG) due to electrochemical reaction at constant temperature and pressure gives the maximum electrical work (W) obtainable:

$$W = \Delta G = -nFE \quad [4]$$

where n is the number of electrons participating in the reaction, F is Faraday's constant (96 487 C g-mol^{-1} electron), and E is the ideal potential of the cell. The fundamental thermodynamic relationship that connects the Gibbs free energy, enthalpy, and entropy is also given by the following function [17]:

$$\Delta G = \Delta H - T\Delta S \quad [5]$$

where ΔH is the enthalpy change and ΔS is the entropy change. The total thermal energy available is ΔH. The available free energy is equal to the enthalpy change less the quantity $T\Delta S$ that represents the unavailable energy resulting from the entropy change within the system.

The amount of heat that is produced by a fuel cell operating reversibly is $T\Delta S$. Reactions in fuel cells that have negative entropy change generate heat (such as hydrogen oxidation), while those with positive entropy change (such as direct solid carbon oxidation) may extract heat from their surroundings if the irreversible generation of heat is smaller than the reversible absorption of heat. For the general cell reaction,

$$\alpha A + \beta B \rightarrow cC + \delta D \quad [6]$$

The standard state Gibbs free energy change of reaction is given by eqn [7]:

$$\Delta G^0 = c\underline{G}_C^0 + \delta \underline{G}_D^0 - \alpha \underline{G}_A^0 - \beta \underline{G}_B^0 \quad [7]$$

where G^0 is the partial molar Gibbs free energy for species i at temperature T. This potential can be computed from the heat capacities (C_p) of the species involved as a function of T and from values of both ΔS^0 and ΔH^0 at a reference temperature, usually 298 K. Empirically, the heat capacity of a species, as a function of T, can be expressed as

$$C_P = a + bT + cT^2 \quad [8]$$

where a, b, and c are empirical constants. The specific enthalpy for any species present during the reaction is given by eqn [9]:

$$\underline{H}_f = \underline{H}_f^0 + \int_{298}^{T} C_{pi} dT \quad [9]$$

And, at constant pressure, the specific entropy at temperature T is given by

$$\underline{S}_f = \underline{S}_f^0 + \int_{298}^{T} \frac{C_{pi}}{T} dT \quad [10]$$

It then follows that

$$\Delta H = \sum_i n_i \underline{H}_i |_{out} - \sum_i n_i \underline{H}_i |_{in} \quad [11]$$

and

$$\Delta S = \sum_i n_i \underline{S}_i |_{out} - \sum_i n_i \underline{S}_i |_{in} \quad [12]$$

The Gibbs free energy change of reaction can be expressed by eqn [13]:

$$\Delta G = \Delta G^0 + RT \ln \frac{f_C^c f_D^\delta}{f_A^\alpha f_B^\beta} \quad [13]$$

where ΔG^0 is the Gibbs free energy change of reaction at the standard state pressure (1 atm) and at temperature T, and f_i is the fugacity of species i. Substituting eqn [4] in eqn [13] gives the relation

$$E = E^0 + \frac{RT}{nF} \ln \frac{f_C^c f_D^\delta}{f_A^\alpha f_B^\beta} \quad [14]$$

Or, more generally,

$$E = E^0 + \frac{RT}{nF} \ln \frac{\prod [\text{reactant fugacity}]}{\prod [\text{product fugacity}]} \quad [15]$$

Equation [15] is the general form of the Nernst equation. Fuel cells generally operate at pressures low enough that the fugacity can be approximated by the partial pressure.

For pure H$_2$ and O$_2$ reactants (H$_2$ + ½O$_2$ → H$_2$O), the Nernst equation is given by eqn [16]:

$$E = E + \left(\frac{RT}{2}\right)\ln\left(\frac{P_H}{P_H}\right) + \left(\frac{RT}{2}\right)\ln[P] \qquad [16]$$

4.10.1.3 The Nernst Equation

The Nernst potential, E, gives the ideal open circuit cell potential. This potential sets the maximum performance achievable by a fuel cell, with respect to pressure of the reactants and the temperature of the reaction [17]. Provided there is no reactant crossover or external leak resulting in electrical short-circuiting, the open current voltage (OCV) that is measured between the anode and cathode of a cell while drawing a negligible current from it is equal to the Nernst voltage [17].

The ideal standard potential (E_o) at 298 K for a fuel cell in which H$_2$ and O$_2$ react is 1.229 V with liquid water product or 1.18 V with steam product. The potential is the change in Gibbs free energy resulting from the reaction between hydrogen and oxygen. The difference between 1.29 and 1.18 V represents the Gibbs free energy change of vaporization of water at standard conditions. **Figure 2** shows the relationship of E with the cell temperature. The figure shows the potential of higher temperature cells, the ideal potential corresponds to a reaction where the water product is in a gaseous state (i.e., E_o is 1.18 V).

The Nernst equation provides a relationship between the ideal standard potential (E^0) for the cell reaction and the ideal equilibrium potential (E) at other partial pressures of reactants and products. For the overall cell reaction, the cell potential increases with an increase in the partial pressure (concentration) of reactants and a decrease in the partial pressure of products.

The OCV of a fuel cell is also strongly influenced by the reactant concentrations. The maximum ideal potential occurs when the reactants at the anode and cathode are pure. In an air-fed system or if the feed to the anode is other than pure dry hydrogen, the cell potential will be reduced. Similarly, the concentration of reactants at the exit of the cell will be lower than at the entrance.

As current is drawn from the cell, the cell voltage drops below the OCV and this usually decreases further with increasing load. The difference between the reversible cell voltage and the actual cell voltage is called overpotential, overvoltage, or polarization and is denoted as η. The main reasons for this voltage drop are as follows:

Ohmic polarization η_Ω in the electrolyte as well as in the electron-conducting cell components

Activation or charge transfer polarization η_A that occurs when a charge transfer from an electrode to the electrolyte takes place or *vice versa*

Concentration polarization η_C that can be due to an insufficient supply of reactants to the reaction surface (diffusion polarization)

Reaction polarization η_R that is caused by other rate-determining reactions involved in the overall reaction (reaction polarization) and effectively leading to a reactant shortage at the electrode/electrolyte interface. For this reason, it is often included in the concentration polarization

The total overpotential can be written as a sum, namely

$$\eta = \eta_\Omega + \eta_A + \eta_C + \eta_R \qquad [17]$$

Since the different polarizations are mainly of an electrochemical nature and only the concentration polarization can be explained by purely thermodynamic considerations, they will all be looked at from an electrochemical perspective.

At low current density, the polarization is mainly due to activation polarization since ohmic losses are negligible and the supply with reactants is usually not critical. With increasing current, the ohmic losses increase and usually prevail over a wide range of current densities that can be identified by a nearly linear relationship between the current and voltage. Higher current densities

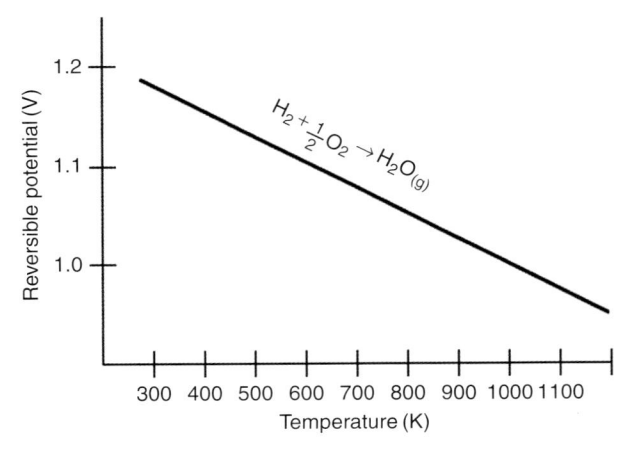

Figure 2 H$_2$/O$_2$ fuel cell ideal potential as a function of temperature.

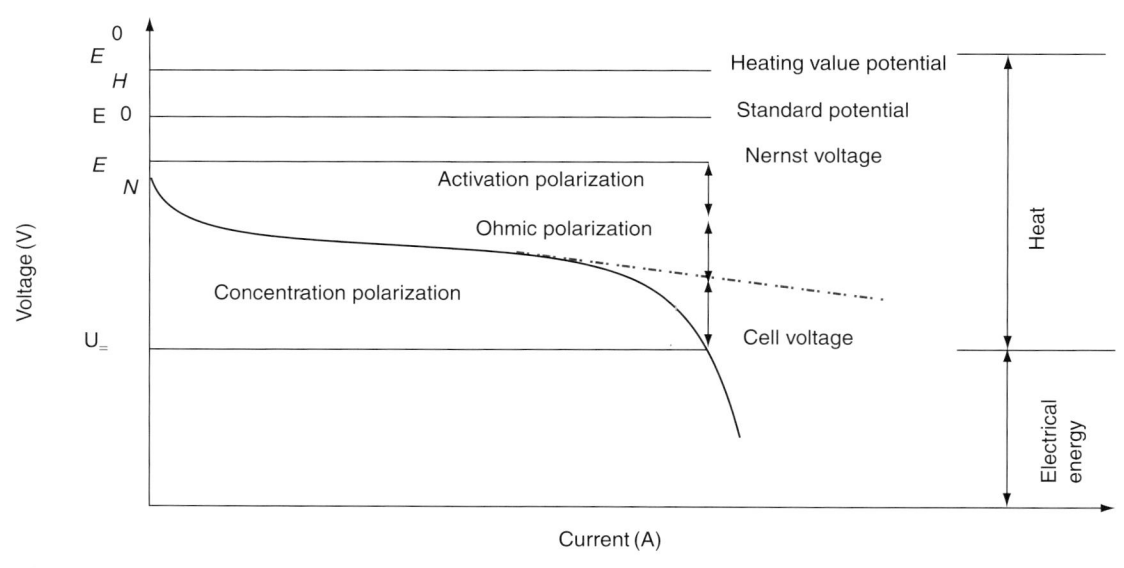

Figure 3 Schematic voltage–current diagrams.

imply an increasing species exchange rate from and to the reaction sites. If the exchange rate is not sufficient, then a marked reactant concentration gradient builds up and results in concentration polarization, as can be seen in **Figure 3**. Depending on the current density, different factors dominate the polarization – the kinetic, the ohmic, and the concentration polarizations.

4.10.1.4 The SOFC

4.10.1.4.1 Principles of operation

There are various different types of fuel cells as listed in **Table 1** along with some of their features. Depending on the type of electrolytes and electrodes, these fuel cells operate at different temperatures. The SOFC is a complete solid-state device that uses an oxide ion-conducting ceramic material as the electrolyte. It is therefore simpler in concept than all the other fuel cell systems described, as only two phases (gas and solid) are required [17]. The high operating temperatures imply that precious metal electrocatalysts are not needed, hence reducing the cost of cell components; it is also possible to use carbon-based fuels directly, removing the need for external reformers, further reducing the cost.

Yttria-stabilized zirconia (YSZ) is the most commonly used material for the electrolyte. It was first used as a fuel cell electrolyte by Baur and Preis in 1937 [20]. Nickel/YSZ cermet and lanthanum strontium manganite (LSM) are the materials commonly used for the anode and the cathode, respectively.

Typically, the conductivity of the fuel cell materials increases with temperature [21, 22]. The dominant losses in SOFCs tend to be due to the ohmic resistance losses; therefore, increasing the temperature enhances the efficiency. Considerable attempts to develop electrolytes that can operate at lower temperatures are ongoing. Lowering the operating temperature would reduce the cost of system components and improve cell longevity [23]; currently, typical SOFCs generally operate between 1073 and 1273 K.

4.10.1.4.2 Advantages of SOFC over other types of fuel cell

Having a solid electrolyte is an advantage for SOFCs as it eliminates the electrolyte management problems associated with PAFCs and MCFCs [21]. In contrast to PEM fuel cells in which high-purity hydrogen and an expensive platinum catalyst is used, the high operating temperature of SOFC enables relatively inexpensive electrode materials to be used. SOFC has high tolerance to impurities due to the catalytic properties of the nickel anode to reform hydrocarbons within the cell. This makes it more favorable than the low-temperature fuel cells, which require very high levels of purity that increase the cost. A further advantage of the high operating temperature of the SOFC is that the hot exhaust gases can be utilized in a downstream process such as a gas turbine to increase the overall system efficiency to in excess of 70% [24, 25].

SOFC has the highest operating temperature range of all fuel cells, which presents both challenges for the construction and durability and also opportunities, for example, in combined cycle (bottoming cycle) applications.

4.10.1.5 SOFC Components

4.10.1.5.1 Electrolyte

The ideal SOFC electrolyte, yttria doped zirconia (YSZ), is stable under reducing and oxidizing conditions. It is a pure ionic conductor, completely nonreactive with anode and cathode at both operating and production temperatures. Its thermal expansion has to be close to other fuel cell components and it must be gas tight to prevent direct combination of fuel and oxidant. Pure zirconia is not used, as its ionic conductivity is too low for fuel cell use [16].

For SOFC applications, there are various materials that have been explored as electrolyte, YSZ and gadolinium-doped ceria (GDC) are the most common materials used for the oxide-conducting electrolyte. Above 800 °C, YSZ becomes a conductor of oxygen ions (O^{2-}); zirconia-based SOFC operates between 800 and 1100 °C. The ionic conductivity of YSZ is 0.02 S m^{-1} at 800 °C and 0.1 S cm^{-1} at 1000 °C). A thin electrolyte (25–50 µm) ensures that the contribution of electrolyte to the ohmic loss in the SOFC is kept to a minimum.

4.10.1.5.2 Cathode

The cathode electrode operates in an oxidizing environment of air at 1000 °C, as shown in eqn [2]. Oxygen is reduced to oxide ions at the cathode surface, consuming two electrons in the process. The cathode electrode, like the anode, is a porous structure that allows mass transport of reactants and products.

Materials suitable for an SOFC cathode have to fulfill the following key requirements:

- high electronic conductivity;
- stability in oxidizing atmospheres at high temperature;
- thermal expansion match with other cell components;
- compatibility and minimum reactivity with different cell components;
- minimum reactivity and interdiffusion with the electrolyte and the interconnection with which air electrode comes into contact;
- sufficient porosity to allow transport of the fuel gas to the electrolyte/electrode interface; and
- minimal reactivity and interdiffusion among the electrolyte and the interconnection with which matching thermal expansion among different air electrode comes into contact.

LSM, ($La_{0.84}Sr_{0.16}$)MnO_3, a p-type semiconductor, is most commonly used for the cathode material. Although adequate for most SOFCs, other materials may be used, particularly attractive being p-type conducting perovskite structures that exhibit mixed ionic and electronic conductivity [17]. This is especially important for lower temperature operation since the polarization of the cathode increases significantly as the SOFC temperature is lowered. The advantages of using mixed conducting oxides become apparent in cells operating at around 650 °C. As well as the perovskites, lanthanum strontium ferrite, lanthanum strontium cobalite, and n-type semiconductors are better electrocatalysts than the state-of-the-art LSM, because they are mixed conductors [17].

Lanthanum manganite is a p-type perovskite oxide and shows reversible oxidation–reduction behavior. The material can have oxygen excess or deficiency depending upon the ambient oxygen partial pressure and temperature. The electronic conductivity of lanthanum manganite is due to hopping of an electron hole between the Mn^{3+} and the Mn^{4+}. This conductivity is enhanced by doping with divalent ions such as strontium to give $La_{1-x}Sr_xMnO_3$ (LSM); this causes some La^{3+} ions to be replaced by Sr^{2+} ions, which increases the Mn^{4+} content, decreases the activation energy (E_a), and increases the electronic conductivity [26].

The electronic conductivity is dependent on oxygen pressure, which was explained by oxygen vacancy formation due to the valence change of Mn ion in the lattice. The range of acceptable oxygen partial pressures allowing stability decreases with increasing strontium dopant levels; however, increasing the strontium content increases the electronic conductivity, giving a maximum at $La_{0.5}Sr_{0.5}MnO_3$ [16, 27]. The conductivity is stable at temperatures above 700 °C [26].

The thermal expansion coefficient (TEC) of the $LaMnO_3$ is higher than YSZ at 11.2×10^{-6} K^{-1} at $x = 0.3$ Sr content [26]. As with the anode, the difference in thermal expansion can be reduced by addition of YSZ into the cathode, which also serves to increase the triple phase boundary (TPB) [16, 28].

In its stoichiometric form, $LaMnO_3$ reacts with the YSZ electrolyte at temperatures in excess of 1200 °C [16], producing insulating phases of lanthanum zirconate [17] and hence hampering fuel cell performance. However, doping with strontium to produce $La_{0.43}Sr_{0.57}MnO_3$ reduces this effect, while also increasing the electronic conductivity of the cathode layer. YSZ is often added to the LSM cathode to increase the TPB and also to limit the TEC of the cathode to a level more similar to the electrolyte [16].

The TPB between the electrocatalyst/electrolyte particles is only active if the electrocatalyst particle is connected to an electronic conduction network that is in contact with the current collector and the electrolyte particle is connected to an ionically conducting network in contact with the electrolyte membrane. These types of networks or particles are defined as percolating. The nonpercolating particles and particle clusters are referred as being isolated [16, 29].

4.10.1.5.3 Anode

The key requirements for the anode are high conductivity, stability in reducing atmospheres, and sufficient porosity to allow good mass transport. The most common anode for SOFCs is the Ni/YSZ cermet; nickel is the active catalyst for the oxidation of hydrogen to water. The metallic component nickel is chosen among other components because of its high electronic conductivity and stability under reducing conditions. The addition of YSZ serves three main functions: to inhibit sintering of the nickel [16, 26], to provide TEC comparable with other fuel cell components (mainly the electrolyte), and to increase the TPB [30, 31]. Increased zirconia would improve thermal mismatch between the electrolyte and the electrode; however, electrochemical activity and conductivity would decrease. The conductivity of the Ni–YSZ composite has to pass the percolation threshold.

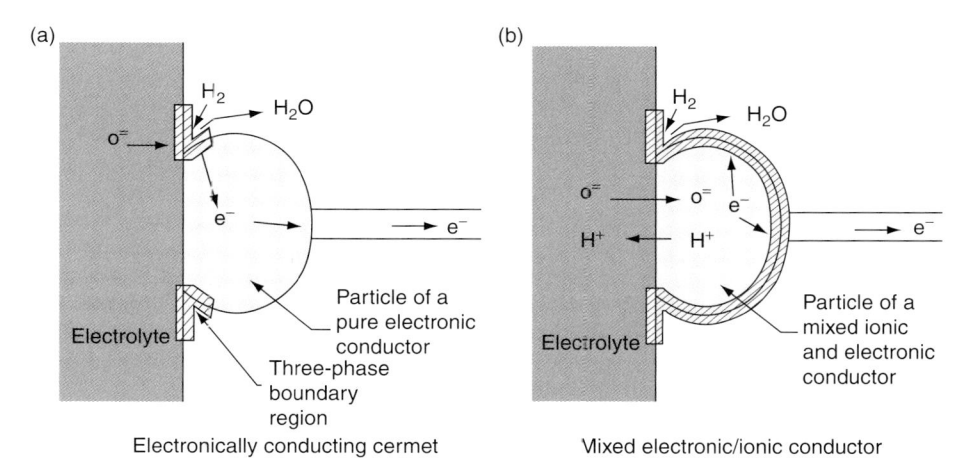

Figure 4 Illustration of the TPB regions of different SOFC anode materials [17].

The anode has sufficient porosity (20–40%) allowing good mass transport of reactants to the electrolyte/electrode interface while removing products away from the interface [16, 17]. It also improves the triple boundary by allowing O^{2-} ion movement within the anode electrode.

The presence of nickel on the anode provides electronic conductivity and catalytic activity, both for direct oxidation and for steam reforming of methane. A small amount of ceria is added to the anode cermet to improve ohmic polarization loss at the interface between the anode and the electrolyte. This also improves the tolerance of the anodes to temperature cycling and redox changes within the anode gas [16, 17] (**Figure 4**).

The TPB shown in **Figure 4** is a key area. It is at this point where all the reactants come together and are catalyzed to form the desired products. It is important to increase this surface area as this is where the oxygen ions and the hydrogen gas are brought together to react at the surface of the nickel site [16, 32]. It is also important to have Ni to Ni contact to improve conductivity to the external electrical circuit. A Ni to YSZ ratio of 3:7 by volume is close to the limit for percolation of the nickel particles, and as a result, the measured conductivities very significantly depend on the particle size and porosities [16, 33, 34].

4.10.1.5.4 Interconnect

A major material challenge in SOFC development is the interconnect material, which provides the conductive path for electrical current to pass from the anode of one cell to the cathode of the next cell in electrical series. Interconnect also separates the fuel gas from the oxidant in adjoining cells of a stack [35]. Thus, the interconnect material must be nonreactive with cathode and anode at both operating and production temperatures, stable in both the oxidizing and reducing atmosphere, gas tight to prevent direct combination of the fuel and oxidant, and nearly 100% conductive or >1 S cm^{-1} [29] to support electron flow at the operating conditions [29, 36, 37]. Since the SOFCs operate at high temperatures (600–1000 °C), the interconnect must be chemically and thermally compatible with the other cell components from room temperature to those operating temperatures and to even higher temperatures at which the fuel cell is fabricated [38].

Owing to its thermal and chemical stability and high electrical conductivity at both reducing and oxidizing atmospheres, $LaCrO_3$, a p-type perovskite, has been a widely investigated interconnect for SOFCs [39, 40]. Doped $LaCrO_3$ has good electronic conductivity and negligible ionic conductivity [16]. Dopants such as Ca, Mg, and Sr can be substituted on either the La or Cr sites, causing an increase in electronic conduction due to the charge compensations of the Cr as the Mn in the doped $LaMnO_3$ cathode [16].

Strontium is the most commonly used dopant [41], has a smaller effect on lattice expansion, and allows higher degree of doping and hence increased [29]. The thermal expansion of $La_{0.9}Sr_{0.1}CrO_3$ is 10.7×10^{-6} K^{-1} [26, 28, 29], which is very close to that of the electrolyte: 10.5×10^{-6} K^{-1}. The material possesses good properties as it is stable in both reducing and oxidizing environments and has TECs similar to other fuel cell components.

However, obtaining dense films is the greatest challenge with this material; Cr(VI) is volatile at high sintering temperatures in oxidizing atmospheres [26, 29], resulting in thin layers of Cr_2O_3 forming at the interparticle neck during the initial sintering stages [26, 29, 40].

Due to the difficulties described above in obtaining dense films of the doped $LaCrO_3$ material and because of the current research toward lower operating temperature fuel cells (500–800 °C), there has been an increased interest and research in high-temperature alloys [26, 29, 42, 43]. Although thermal expansion of metals is generally higher than that of YSZ [22], 10.5×10^{-6} K^{-1}, the metallic interconnects are of low cost and easy to manufacture. Furthermore, it is more flexible in accommodating stresses [44, 45] and also has greater tolerance to thermal expansion and the advantages of high electrical and thermal conductivity and stability [29, 43, 44]. Chromium-, iron-, and nickel-based alloys are the main metallic interconnect materials investigated [16, 43, 46]. Due to their lower cost and better long-term performance, iron- or nickel-based superalloys are preferred [16, 29, 45]. However, the oxidation behavior of metallic interconnects is a huge challenge. Essentially, the oxidation process involves the chemical reaction of a metal with gaseous oxygen in the atmosphere. The partial pressure of oxygen typically seen in the fuel atmosphere in the fuel cell ranges between 10^{-22} and 10^{-17} atm: orders of magnitude higher than the Cr/Cr_2O_3 equilibrium of oxygen partial pressure of 10^{-28} atm (at 800 °C) [16, 45, 46], causing the formation of Cr_2O_3. Depending on the degree of scaling, the formation of this protective and thermodynamically stable oxide increases the contact resistance of an oxidized metallic interconnect. While not fully understood, the degree of scaling seen on the anode side is greater than that on the cathode side [16, 43, 45]. This is thought to be due to the presence of water vapor on the anode side, causing a porous scale to be formed [45], thereby increasing the gas transport to the substrate.

The oxidation process on metal surfaces is a diffusion-controlled process that can be simplified by eqn [18], where x is the oxide-scale thickness or the weight gain per area, K_p is the parabolic rate factor, and t is time [45, 46]:

$$X^2 = K_p t \qquad [18]$$

The acceptable area-specific resistance (ASR) for the metallic interconnect during service, which is the product of the electrical resistivity of the studied layer and its thickness, is generally considered to be below $0.1\,\Omega\,cm^2$.

$$ASR = \tau_s l_s + 2\tau_0 l_0 \qquad [19]$$

The scale has a much lower conductivity than that of the alloy, increasing the ASR as determined by eqn [19] [45], where τ_0 and τ_s are the resistivity of the scale and alloy substrate and l_0 and l_s correspond to the scale and alloy substrate thickness, respectively. Hence the requirement for a slow oxide growth rate to prolong the lifetime of the interconnect material. The growth rate of Cr_2O_3 is quite fast [29]; however, by adding a small quantity of reactive elements such as Y, La, and Zr, it can be retarded [43, 45]. The addition of these elements also increased adherence of the scale to the substrate, thereby reducing the likelihood for spallation of the scale and changing the TEC [29].

The resistivity of the metallic substrate in comparison with the resistivity of the oxide layer is negligible. Therefore, the first term in eqn [19] can be neglected; the ASR of an oxidized metallic interconnect is overwhelmingly dominated by that of the oxide layer on both surfaces, so that

$$ASR = 2\tau_0 l_0 \qquad [20]$$

Considerable studies are ongoing to coat the metallic interconnect with an oxide that retards the chromium diffusion, while remaining electronically conductive and possessing all other necessary physical properties such as matching thermal expansion and stability. As with the ceramic interconnect described above, the metallic interconnects suffer from the high volatility of Cr(VI) in fuel cell operating conditions [29]. This can lead to poisoning of the cathode by deposits of Cr_2O_3 at the cathode–electrolyte interface and in the pores [45] and reaction with the LSM to form Cr_2MnO_4 spinels [16]. In addition, during fuel cell startup, the NiO in the anode can react to form Ni–Cr spinels, which are consequently reduced with the NiO; this can lead to deposits of large Cr_2O_3 crystals in the anode [45]. Coating Mn with a nickel-based superalloy Haynes 230, which had the effect of forming $MnCr_2O_4$, has shown positive results, improving the electrical conductivity of the scale [16, 47].

4.10.1.6 Example Systems

It is widely expected that fuel cell-based power systems will be used for a variety of applications. There are a few parameters for SOFCs that can be changed; these changes, such as operating temperature and pressure, affect the performance of the cell in fairly predictable ways. This review focusses on SOFC-based CHP systems to provide an overview of the advantages and challenges of SOFCs. The review discusses the state of development and the performance, environmental benefits, and costs of these technologies. In addition, this review will provide a comparative assessment of these technologies in terms of their advantages, disadvantages, costs, efficiency, emissions, and durability.

4.10.1.6.1 Introduction to CHP systems

CHP, also known as cogeneration, is the simultaneous production of electrical and useful thermal energy from the same primary energy source such as oil, coal, natural or liquefied gas, or solar [13, 48]. The CHP concept can be applied to small-scale residential buildings as well as for large-scale cogeneration systems for industrial purposes. CHP is suitable for residential building applications, provided that the heat energy produced is required for space heating or other applications. In comparison with conventional methods of generating heat and electricity separately, cogeneration systems can increase energy efficiency that can result in lower costs and reduction in GHG emissions [14].

CHP system efficiency is determined by the system type, size, and the operating conditions of the prime mover. CHP units for building applications are required to achieve more than $4500\,h\,yr^{-1}$ utilization [15]. Cogeneration system efficiency is generally expressed in terms of both electrical and thermal efficiency [15].

The key requirements for CHP feasibility are its durability, GHG savings, electrical and power efficiency, and also capital and installation costs. Cogeneration applications often involve the burning of fossil fuels, which gives rise to GHG emissions. The combustion products obtained from burning fossil fuels include carbon dioxide (CO_2), oxides of nitrogen (NOx), sulfur dioxide

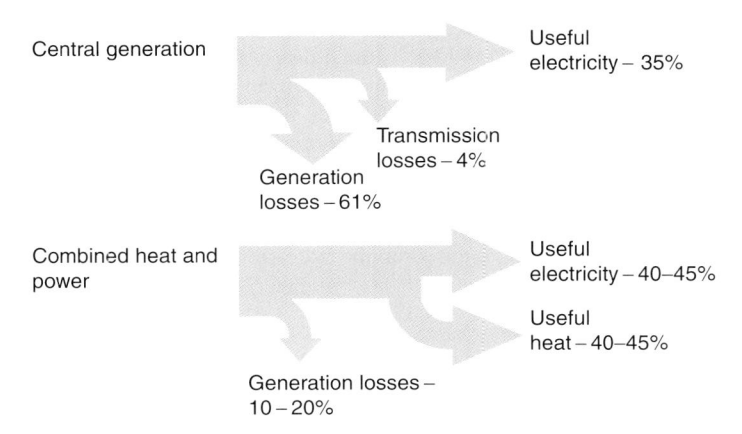

Figure 5 Comparison of energy flow for centrally generated and distributed (micro-CHP) generation [49].

(SO$_2$), carbon monoxide (CO), unburnt hydrocarbons, and particulates. The efficiency of fuel utilization in cogeneration systems (i.e., emissions per unit of useful energy produced from cogeneration systems) is lower than those with conventional systems [13].

A variety of cogeneration systems are commercially available, or under research and development, for the single-family and multifamily residential building market and small-scale commercial applications. These include steam turbines, reciprocating internal combustion engines, combustion turbines, microturbines, Stirling engines, and fuel cells. These technologies could replace the conventional boiler in a dwelling and provide both electricity and heating, possibly with the surplus electricity exported to the local grid or surplus heat stored in a thermal storage device [13] (**Figure 5**).

4.10.1.6.2 Efficiency and efficiency limits

The efficiency limit for heat engines such as steam and gas turbines to produce electricity is limited by Carnot's law from thermodynamics. If the maximum temperature of the heat engine is $T1$ in K, and the heated fluid is released at temperature $T2$, then Carnot showed that the maximum efficiency possible is given by eqn [21]:

$$\text{Carnot limit} = 1 - \frac{T2}{T1} \quad [21]$$

The optimum efficiencies of power stations using steam turbines are about 45% and diesel- and petrol-powered generators are 30% and 20%, respectively [16, 19]. Fuel cells are not subject to the Carnot efficiency limit. However, irreversibilities due to activation losses, fuel crossover and internal currents, ohmic losses, and mass transport or concentration losses reduce the fuel cell efficiency. If all the chemical energy (Gibbs free energy), ΔG, from the reaction of reactants and products would be converted into electrical energy, this would give 100% efficiency. In reality, the efficiency of fuel cells is limited. The maximum electrical energy available is equal to the change in Gibbs free energy [21] as determined by eqn [22] (**Table 2**).

$$\text{Maximum efficiency} = \frac{\Delta \bar{g}_f}{\Delta \bar{h}_f} \times 100 \quad [22]$$

The waste heat generated from operating fuel cells at elevated temperature is more useful than that from the lower temperature cells, and so by adding heat engine bottoming cycle, efficiency similar to the theoretical one for an ambient temperature fuel cell is achievable. A high-temperature fuel cell combined with, for example, a steam cycle, condensing close to room temperature, is a

Table 2 $\Delta \bar{g}_f$, maximum EMF (or reversible open circuit voltage), and efficiency limit (HHV basis) for hydrogen fuel cells [21]

Form of water product	Temperature (°C)	$\Delta \bar{g}_f$ (kJ mol^{-1})	Maximum EMF (V)	Efficiency limit (%)
Liquid	25	−237.2	1.23	83
Liquid	80	−228.2	1.18	80
Gas	100	−225.2	1.17	79
Gas	200	−220.4	1.14	77
Gas	400	−210.3	1.09	74
Gas	600	−199.6	1.04	70
Gas	800	−188.6	0.98	66
Gas	1000	−177.4	0.92	62

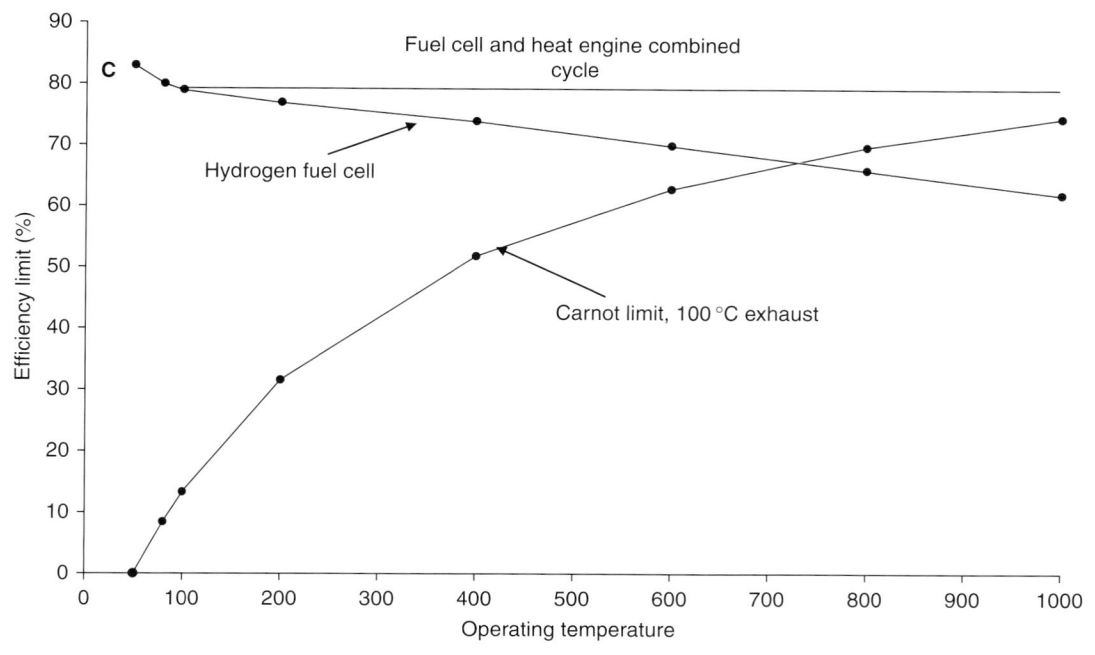

Figure 6 Efficiency limits for a heat engine, a hydrogen fuel cell, and a fuel cell/turbine combined cycle.

'perfect' thermodynamic engine [50]. For the heat engine and the combined cycle, the lower temperature is 100 °C, see **Figure 6**. The fuel cell efficiencies are referred to as the higher heating value [13] (**Figure 6**).

$$T_C = \frac{\Delta H}{\Delta S} \qquad [23]$$

4.10.1.6.3 Heat and power load requirements for a typical UK home

Typical energy demand for space heating and power load requirements for a typical family home in the United Kingdom over the course of 24 h is shown in **Figure 7**. As would be expected, heating demand varies considerably between the winter and summer months. The values presented in **Figure 7** are the average kilowatt for each 5-min period of a typical winter day. The average heat and electrical load is shown in **Figure 7**, which is 3.5 kW$_{th}$ and 0.6 kW$_e$, respectively (a heat-to-power ratio of 5.8: 1). An average residential dwelling has an annual heat-to-power ratio of ~5.5:1 [51].

4.10.1.6.4 Fuel cell-based micro-CHP systems

Fuel cell-based cogenerators are highly efficient and have the potential to offer the highest efficiency for small-scale applications [50]. As indicated by various researchers, for small-scale cogeneration applications in the 1–50 kW range, polymer electrolyte fuel cell (PEMFC)- and SOFC-based cogeneration systems promise the advantage of high efficiencies, reduced fuel use, reduced environmental impacts, and a good match for the residential T/E load ratio [53, 54].

4.10.1.6.5 Performance characteristics

The potential benefits of fuel cell-based micro-CHP units have been proven through various demonstration projects, such as the US Department of Defense fuel cell demonstration program [55], utility demonstration programs [55], and other programs [53]. Fuel cell-based cogeneration systems generate lower environmentally harmful emissions than combustion-based cogenerators and have the potential to achieve total efficiencies as high as 90%. Volatile organic compounds may be reduced by 93% [56], carbon dioxide emissions by up to 49%, carbon monoxide emissions by 68%, and nitrogen oxide (NOx) emissions by 91% [56]. Furthermore, due to their low noise outputs, fuel cell-based cogeneration systems are particularly suitable for residential, commercial, and institutional applications.

4.10.1.6.6 Fuel cell micro-CHP technical specifications and functional requirements

The main functional requirements for any micro-CHP technologies are its ability to meet the several technical and functional parameters [16]:

- The efficiency, both in terms of electrical generation and overall CHP efficiency
- The durability and maintenance requirement of the system

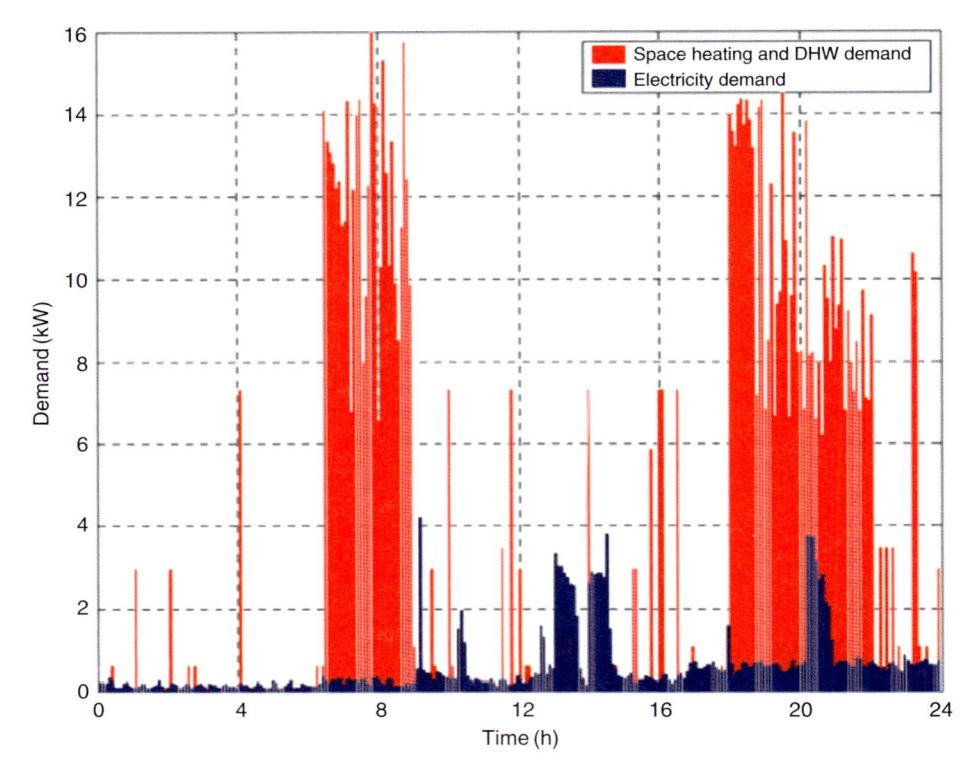

Figure 7 Heat-to-power ratio variation for a typical UK dwelling. Values are in (average) kilowatts for each 5-min period of a typical winter day [52].

- How well the heat and power generated by the system match the demand of a typical European home
- Capital and running costs

4.10.1.6.7 Efficiency

The performance of fuel cell systems is a function of the type of fuel cells and their capacity. Generally, fuel cell systems are a combination of chemical, electrochemical, and electronic subsystems; therefore, the optimization of electrical efficiency and the operational performance characteristics of fuel cell systems pose an engineering challenge [13].

Due to the performance losses incurred from fuel processing and other ancillary components, the electrical efficiency of a complete natural gas-fired system is one-fifth to one-third lower than that of the stack alone [57]. Despite these losses, fuel cell micro-CHP units still offer significantly higher electrical efficiency than engine-based technologies.

Japanese field trials have validated the performance of hundreds of PEMFC systems, which demonstrated 27–30% efficiency [68] compared with rated specifications of around 33% higher heating value (HHV) [61, 62]. Slightly lower performance is expected in real-world use due to suboptimal operation, as has been observed with other technologies [58].

Smaller trials of SOFC systems based on the Kyocera stack have demonstrated efficiencies ranging from 40 to 45% HHV when running on natural gas [57, 59]. Other SOFC designs from American companies typically have 30–35% HHV efficiency [60]. Total system efficiencies are generally lower than for engine-based CHP systems, averaging around 70–75% [61]. This is possibly due to the relative immaturity of fuel cell micro-CHP systems or because PEMFC stacks (which dominate the published data sets) produce lower temperature heat, which is more difficult to recover. With optimized stack cooling and a condensing heat exchanger, it is believed that the total efficiency could be increased to the levels of engine-based CHP and condensing boilers.

4.10.1.6.8 Durability

Lifetime and reliability are one of the main hurdles that must be overcome before fuel cells can become commercially viable for micro-CHP. Currently, both PEMFC and SOFC stacks lose power at a rate between 0% and 5% per 1000 h, depending on the design and materials used by each manufacturer [61, 62]. Reduced catalytic activity in the cells and reformer combined with increasing cell resistance causes a gradual drop in output voltage, and thus power output. This can shorten the stack lifetime, but mechanical deterioration of the cells is usually the limiting factor.

The widely held target for stationary system lifetime is 40 000 operating hours, giving approximately 10 years operation over a typical duty cycle where the unit is operated at regular intervals, but not continuously. Single-cell tests have demonstrated that this is possible with both PEMFC and SOFC under laboratory conditions. Top performing PEMFC stacks have demonstrated 20 000 h lifetimes in field trials [59], with 40 000 h expected for next-generation systems released in 2009 [60]. SOFC micro-CHP systems have not yet been demonstrated on such a scale, so only limited lifetime data have been reported beyond 5000–10 000 h of continuous operation [59].

Large-scale field trials have revealed that the reliability of micro-CHP systems falls short of expectations, and that the fuel cell stack no longer requires the greatest attention. These complex systems are currently filled with novel and relatively untried components, which has resulted in relatively simple problems causing numerous forced shutdowns. Analysis of nearly 1000 PEMFC systems installed in field trials has shown that only 7% experienced no faults in their first year of operation, while each system experienced an average of 2.5–3 failures per year [68]. However, the rate of failures almost halved between 2005 and 2007, and manufacturers are confident that they can be reduced to commercially acceptable levels.

4.10.1.6.9 Fuel cell heat-to-power ratio and its advantages

The fuel cell's heat-to-power ratio advantage over an engine is that at low temperatures, unlike the engine, it can achieve low heat-to-power ratio. **Figure 8** compares the minimum theoretical heat-to-power ratio of a fuel cell and an engine at various temperatures [63, 64]. For stationary power generation, a variable heat-to-power ratio has compelling advantages over a fixed one. First, the more closely a CHP unit can match the instantaneous supply of heat and electricity, the more fuel efficient it will be. Second, a variable heat-to-power ratio that leads to higher fuel efficiency also results in lower emissions. Finally, and most importantly, a variable heat-to-power ratio enables a power plant to achieve both [65] reliability (the ability to deliver electricity in a predictable manner) and [64] flexibility (the ability to rapidly change the amount of electricity delivered in response to rapid changes in demand). Reliability and flexibility are two of the most important technical characteristics for power generators.

On an individual power plant level, one of the main technical ways to achieve the functional requirements for such heat and power demand without significantly sacrificing overall (combined electrical and thermal) efficiency is to design a plant with a rapidly variable heat-to-power ratio [64]. The heat-to-power ratio is defined as the rate of useful thermal energy production to that of electrical energy production.

The ability to achieve a rapidly variable heat-to-power ratio over a large range is a relatively inimitable and unique technical and functional characteristic that fuel cells have over competing technologies. **Table 3** summarizes the results of a competitor analysis of power generation technologies that may be able to realistically achieve a rapidly varying heat-to-power ratio, data compiled from References 66 and 67.

Given the important financial, environmental, and competitive benefits, a rapidly variable heat-to-power ratio should be one of the primary technical goals that shape the design of fuel cell-based micro-CHP units.

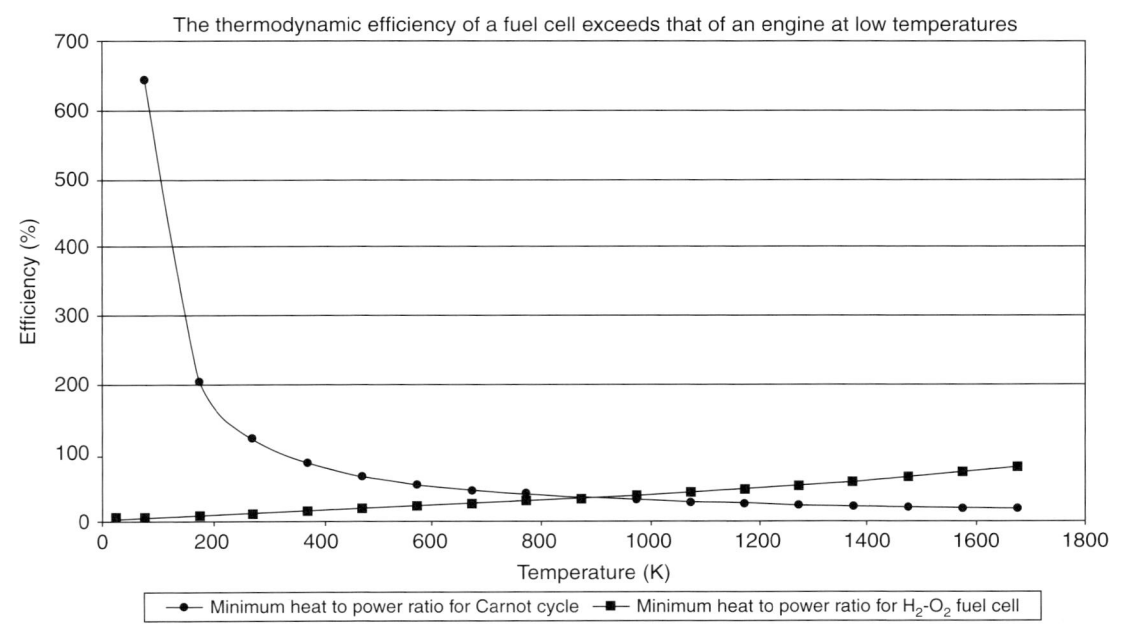

Figure 8 The fuel cell's heat-to-power ratio advantage over an engine is in achieving low heat-to-power ratios at low temperatures. The figure is based on the theoretical Carnot cycle efficiency of an engine operating between 30 and 1700 K and the maximum theoretical electrical efficiency of a hydrogen oxygen fuel cell [64].

Table 3 Comparison of CHP and conventional generation technologies against key success factors [64]

4.10.1.6.10 Engineering methods to achieve a variable heat-to-power ratio

Matching the heat-to-power ratio demanded from an individual building (and/or local network), a small-scale CHP system is a formidable task. On the demand side, the heat and power demanded in a house or office vary rapidly and sporadically. **Figure 7** illustrates the significant and rapid variation in the heat-to-power ratio of a detached house in the United Kingdom over a single day [52]. In order to achieve a flexible heat-to-power ratio, there are several design and operational options. In contrast to combustion engines, which have a maximum efficiency at their nominal operating point, fuel cell micro-CHP systems have excellent electrical load following efficiency characteristics. This enables fuel cells to be much more flexible to achieve a match between the heat-to-power ratio demanded. Although the typical fuel cell stack efficiency improves at lower loads, a fuel cell-based micro-CHP must incorporate several unique design features. Following are some of the techniques that can be used to achieve variable heat-to-power ratio [68]:

- vary the ratio of reactants, the temperature, and/or the pressure in the fuel processing subsystem to alter the amount of fuel flowing to the fuel cell and the enthalpy of the reforming reaction;
- vary the fuel flow rate to the anode offgas burner;
- vary the system's electrical configuration; and
- change the shape and/or position of the polarization curve during operation.

As shown in **Figure 9**, the heat output increases with the current load and the electrical efficiency increases with decreasing current load. How a fuel cell micro-CHP unit is sized and operated is a trade-off between system efficiency (fuel cost), unit size (capital cost), and the heat-to-power ratio. The voltage and stack efficiency increases as the power output of the fuel cell decreases. It is therefore often thought that fuel cells give improved efficiency with the intermittent and often low-level demand from domestic households.

4.10.2 Conclusion

The main functional requirements for any micro-CHP technology are the technology's ability to meet the several technical and economic parameters: a comprehensive review of technical and functional requirements of a micro-CHP system, in particular the

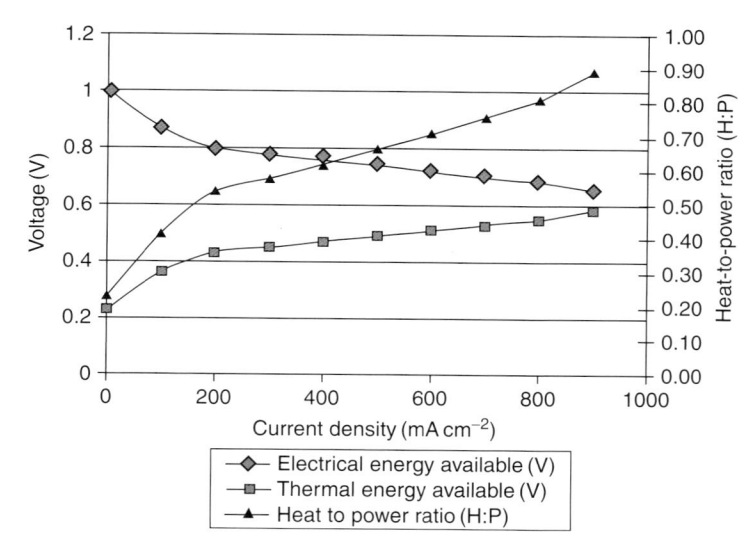

Figure 9 The polarization curve for a fuel cell, which indicates the electrical energy available from a fuel cell at any current draw. The heat available from the fuel cell is the mirror image of this curve. The heat-to-power ratio is the ratio of these curves [64].

SOFC- and PEMFC-based micro-CHP systems, was undertaken. Key technical functional requirements for a successful technology were identified as follows:

- Low heat-to-power ratio, to maximize the potential for year-round operation
- High electrical efficiency, to maximize the value of electricity generation

An extensive analysis of power generation markets concludes that one of the most important engineering characteristics of micro-CHP power generation technology is the system's flexibility to support the critical heat-to-power ratio that changes with time, sometimes abruptly. The ability to change the amount of electricity supplied rapidly in response to change in demand is crucial. Therefore, the optimal functional requirements for a successful micro-CHP system are its ability to achieve high electrical efficiency and a low heat-to-power ratio. Fuel cell-based systems were found to best match the key attributes and therefore offer the largest reduction in both carbon emissions and utility bills.

Micro-combined heat and power technology (μCHP) is an emerging technology for residential sector with the potential to provide high efficiency and the reduction of GHG emissions in the building sector to a sustainable level. Fuel cell-based micro-CHP systems have increased efficiency of energy conversion up to 90% as compared with an average of 30–35% for conventional fossil fuel-fired electricity generation systems. Though still on the brink of market entry, fuel cell cogeneration systems for residential and small commercial applications are the focus of interest as the prime technology for micro-CHP systems. These products are used or aim for meeting the electrical and thermal demands of a building for space and domestic hot water heating and, potentially, absorption cooling.

In comparison with all the other technologies, SOFC-based micro-CHP systems have a potentially superior performance. With its high electrical efficiency up to 45% and low heat-to-power ratio, it offers significant benefits, effectively supplying the total electrical demand of the homes throughout the year. Though the technology is still mainly at the developmental stage, SOFCs have the potential to meet these requirements.

Acknowledgment

The authors acknowledge the support of the European Commission through the European project H2Susbuild for funding research related to this chapter.

References

[1] Salameh MG (2003) Can renewable and unconventional energy sources bridge the global energy gap in the 21st century? *Applied Energy* 75: 33–42.
[2] Salameh MG (2000) Global oil outlook: Return to the absence of surplus and its implications. *Applied Energy* 65: 239–250.
[3] Leifeld J and Fuhrer J (2005) Greenhouse gas emissions from Swiss agriculture since 1990: Implications for environmental policies to mitigate global warming. *Energy policy* 8: 410–417.
[4] Lazare P (2001) Its time to tax global warming. *The Electricity Journal* 14: 62–68.
[5] Barreto L, Makihira A, and Riahi K (2003) The hydrogen economy in the 21st century. *International Journal of Hydrogen Energy* 28: 267–284.
[6] Sherif SA, Barbir F, and Veziroglu TN (2005) Wind energy and the hydrogen economy review of the technology. *Solar Energy* 78: 647–660.
[7] Ahluwalia RK and Wang X (2005) Direct hydrogen fuel cell systems for hybrid vehicles. *Journal of Power Sources* 139: 152–164.
[8] Chalk SG, Miller JF, and Wagner FW (2000) Challenges for fuel cells in transport applications. *Journal of Power Sources* 112: 307–321.

[9] Bockris J (2002) The origin of ideas on a hydrogen economy and its solution to the decay of the environment. *International Journal of Hydrogen Energy* 27: 731–740.
[10] Minh NQ and Takahashi T (eds.) (1995) *Science and Technology of Ceramic Fuel Cells*. Amsterdam: Elsevier.
[11] Drenckhahn W (1999) SOFC in power generation. *Journal of the European Ceramic Society* 19: 861–863.
[12] ASHRAE (2000) *Systems and Equipment*. ASHRAE Inc., Atlanta.
[13] Onovwiona HI and Ugursal VI (2006) Residential cogeneration systems: Review of the current technology. *Renewable and Sustainable Energy Reviews* 10: 389–431.
[14] Gilijamse W and Boonstra ME (1995) Energy efficiency in new houses – Heat demand reduction versus cogeneration. *Energy and Buildings* 23(1): 49–62.
[15] Major G (1995) *Small scale cogeneration*. Centre for the Analysis and Dissemination of Demonstrated Energy Technologies, The Netherlands. Editor. CADDET Energy Efficiency Analysis Series IEA/OECD.
[16] Jones FGE (2005) Tape Casting, Co-Firing and Electrical Characterisation of Novel Design Solid Oxide Fuel Cell SOFCROLL. PhD thesis, University of St Andrews.
[17] Larminie J and Dicks A (2000) *Fuel Cell Systems Explained*, 2nd edn. Chichester: Wiley.
[18] Kordesch KV and Simader GR (1995) Environmental-impact of fuel-cell technology. *Chemical Reviews* 95(1): 191–207.
[19] Vielstich W (1970) *Fuel Cells, Modern Processes for the Electrochemical Production of Energy*. Chichester, UK: Wiley-Interscience.
[20] Ishihara S and Yamamoto T (2003) In: *High temperature solid oxide fuel cells fundamentals, design and applications*. In: Singhal SC and Kendal K (eds.) Oxford: Elsevier.
[21] Larminie J and Dicks A (2001) *Fuel Cell Systems Explained*. Chichester, UK: Wiley.
[22] Yamamoto O (2000) Solid oxide fuel cells: Fundamental aspects and prospects. *Electrochimica Acta* 45(15–16): 2423–2435.
[23] Huijsmans JPP, van Berkel FPF, and Christie GM (1998) Intermediate temperature SOFC – A promise for the 21st century. *Journal of Power Sources* 71(1–2): 107–110.
[24] Singhal SC (2000) Advances in solid oxide fuel cell technology. *Solid State Ionics* 135(1–4): 305–313.
[25] Winkler W and Lorenz H (2002) The design of stationary and mobile solid oxide fuel cell-gas turbine systems. *Journal of Power Sources* 105(2): 222–227.
[26] Minh NQ (1993) Ceramic fuel-cells. *Journal of the American Ceramic Society* 76(3): 563–588.
[27] Lee HM (2003) Electrochemical characteristics of $La_{1-x}Sr_xMnO_3$ for solid oxide fuel cell. *Materials Chemistry and Physics* 77(3): 639–646.
[28] Wang SZ, et al. (1998) Promoting effect of YSZ on the electrochemical performance of YSZ+LSM composite electrodes. *Solid State Ionics* 115: 291–303.
[29] Zhu WZ and Deevi SC (2003) Development of interconnect materials for solid oxide fuel cells. *Materials Science and Engineering: A. Structural Materials Properties Microstructure and Processing* 348(1–2): 227–243.
[30] Tanner CW, Fung KZ, and Virkar AV (1997) The effect of porous composite electrode structure on solid oxide fuel cell performance. 1. Theoretical analysis. *Journal of the Electrochemical Society* 144(1): 21–30.
[31] Gorte RJ, et al. (2000) Anodes for direct oxidation of dry hydrocarbons in a solid-oxide fuel cell. *Advanced Materials* 12(19): 1465–1469.
[32] Ivers-Tiffee E, Weber A, and Herbstritt D (2001) Materials and technologies for SOFC-components. *Journal of the European Ceramic Society* 21(10–11): 1805–1811.
[33] Dees DW, et al. (1987) Conductivity of porous Ni/ZrO_2-Y_2O_3 cermets. *Journal of the Electrochemical Society* 134(9): 2141–2146.
[34] Jiang SP, Callus PJ, and Badwal SPS (2000) Fabrication and performance of Ni/3 mol% Y_2O_3-ZrO_2 cermet anodes for solid oxide fuel cells. *Solid State Ionics* 132(1–2): 1–14.
[35] Wang SL, et al. (2008) Influence of Cr deficiency on sintering character and properties of SOFC interconnect material $La_{0.7}Ca_{0.3}Cr_{1-x}O_3$-delta. *Materials Research Bulletin* 43(10): 2607–2616.
[36] Minh NQ (1993) Science and technology of zirconia V. In: Badwal SP, Bannister M, and Hannink RHJ(eds.) Lancaster, PA: Technomic Publishing Company, p. 652.
[37] Singhal SC (1999) Progress in tubular solid oxide fuel cell technology. In: Singhal SC and Dokiya M (eds.) *Proceedings of the Sixth International Symposium on Solid Oxide Fuel Cells*(SOFC-VI), Honolulu, HI, USA.
[38] Schneider LCR, et al. (2007) Percolation effects in functionally graded SOFC electrodes. *Electrochimica Acta* 52(9): 3190–3198.
[39] Chick LA, et al. (1997) Phase transitions and transient liquid-phase sintering in calcium-substituted lanthanum chromite. *Journal of the American Ceramic Society* 80(8): 2109–2120.
[40] Chakraborty A, Basu RN, and Maiti HS (2000) Low temperature sintering of $La(Ca)CrO_3$ prepared by an autoignition process. *Materials Letters* 45(3–4): 162–166.
[41] Simner SP, et al. (2000) Sintering of lanthanum chromite using strontium vanadate. *Solid State Ionics* 128(1–4): 53–63.
[42] Yokokawa H, et al. (1991) Chemical thermodynamic considerations in sintering of Lacro3-based perovskites. *Journal of the Electrochemical Society* 138(4): 1018–1027.
[43] England DM and Virkar AV (2001) Oxidation kinetics of some nickel-based superalloy foils in humidified hydrogen and electronic resistance of the oxide scale formed part II. *Journal of the Electrochemical Society* 148(4): A330–A338.
[44] Yang ZG, et al. (2003) Anomalous corrosion behavior of stainless steels under SOFC interconnect exposure conditions. *Electrochemical and Solid State Letters* 6(10): B35–B37.
[45] Zhu WZ and Deevi SC (2003) Opportunity of metallic interconnects for solid oxide fuel cells: A status on contact resistance. *Materials Research Bulletin* 38(6): 957–972.
[46] England DM and Virkar AV (1999) Oxidation kinetics of some nickel-based superalloy foils and electronic resistance of the oxide scale formed in air Part I. *Journal of the Electrochemical Society* 146(9): 3196–3202.
[47] Virkar AV and England DM. *Solid Oxide Fuel Cell INterconnector*, US Patent 6,053,231.
[48] ASHRAE (2000) *HVAC Systems and Equipment*, edn. I. ASHRAE, Inc., Atlanta.
[49] Morgan RE, Devriendt JM, and Flint B *Micro Chp: A Mass Market Opportunity*. Ceres Power White Paper.
[50] Resource Dynamic Corp (1999) *Industrial Application for Micropower: A Market Assessment*, Office of Industrial Technologies. and Oak Ridge National Laboratory, TN, USA: US Department of Energy, Editor.
[51] Cacciola G, Antonucci V, and Freni S (2001) Technology up date and new strategies on fuel cells. *Journal of Power Sources* 100(1–2): 67–79.
[52] International Energy Agency (IEA), *Annex 42-detailed load profiles*.
[53] Merida W (1998) Clean energy for today's world. *The Fuel Cell Seminar*. Palm Springs.
[54] Krist K and Jones W (1999) Solid oxide fuel cell residential cogeneration. *Joint DOE/EPRI/GR: FC Technology Review Conference*. Chicago, IL, USA, 1999.
[55] Wolk RH (1999) Fuel cells for homes and hospitals. *IEEE Spect1999* 36(5): 45–52.
[56] Demonstration (2008) *Report data from the Large Scale Residential Fuel Cell Demonstration Project in 2007*.
[57] Kyocere Corporation (2006) *Osaka Gas and Kyocera Announce the Results of the First Domestic Trial Operations of Solid Oxide Fuel Cell (SOFC) Cogeneration System for Household Use*.
[58] Carbon Trust (2007) *Micro-CHP Accelerator*. Interim Report. Carbon Trust, London, UK, 2007.
[59] Hawkes A, et al. (2009) Fuel cells for micro-combined heat and power generation. *Energy & Environmental Science* 2(7): 729–744.
[60] Singhal SC (2007) Innovative solid oxide fuel cell systems for small scale power generation. *Proceedings of the Tenth Grove Fuel Cell Symposium London*.
[61] Staffell I (2007) *Review of Solid Oxide Fuel Cell Performance. Methodology*, November.
[62] de Bruijn FA, Dam VAT, and Janssen GJM (2008) Durability and degradation issues of PEM fuel cell components. *Fuel Cells* 8(1): 3–22.
[63] Pilavachi PA (2002) Mini- and micro-gas turbines for combined heat and power. *Applied Thermal Engineering* 22(18): 2003–2014.
[64] Colella W (2002) Design options for achieving a rapidly variable heat-to-power ratio in a combined heat and power (CHP) fuel cell system (FCS). *Journal of Power Sources* 106(1–2): 388–396.
[65] Bauknecht D (2002) Market Analyst for the Electricity Industry in Germany, Switzerland, and Austria, Power Ink, plc, Brighton, UK.
[66] Gray P, Atuah K, Sun J, and Ahmadi M (1999) *Solid Polymer Fuel Cell Prototype System for Micro-CHP Phase 1: Market, Technical and Economic Study*. London, UK: Department of Trade and Industry, Editor.
[67] James SR (1993) *Stirling Engines 1993*. River Falls, WI: Moriya Press.
[68] www.fcdic.com/eng/news/200706.html (accessed 3 January 2012).

4.11 Biological and Microbial Fuel Cells

K Scott and EH Yu, Newcastle University, Newcastle upon Tyne, UK
MM Ghangrekar, Newcastle University, Newcastle upon Tyne, UK; Indian Institute of Technology, Kharagpur, India
B Erable, Newcastle University, Newcastle upon Tyne, UK; CNRS-Université de Toulouse, Toulouse, France
NM Duteanu, Newcastle University, Newcastle upon Tyne, UK; University 'POLITEHNICA' Timisoara, Timisoara, Romania

© 2012 Elsevier Ltd. All rights reserved.

4.11.1	Introduction	257
4.11.2	Fuel Cells and Biological Fuel Cells	258
4.11.2.1	Conventional Fuel Cells	258
4.11.2.2	Biological Fuel Cells	259
4.11.2.3	Enzymatic Fuel Cells	259
4.11.2.4	Types of Biofuel Cells and Enzymes	260
4.11.2.4.1	Types of enzymes based on electron transfer methods	260
4.11.2.4.2	Enzyme electrodes	261
4.11.2.4.3	Performance of enzymatic biofuel cells	264
4.11.3	Microbial Fuel Cells	265
4.11.3.1	Development of MFC	265
4.11.3.2	Electricity Generation Mechanism in MFC	265
4.11.3.3	Working Principles of MFC	266
4.11.3.4	Mediatorless MFC	267
4.11.3.5	Organic Matter Removal in MFC	267
4.11.3.6	MFC Operating Conditions and Material Aspects	268
4.11.3.6.1	Operating temperature	268
4.11.3.6.2	Operating pH	269
4.11.3.6.3	Organic loading rates and hydraulic retention time	269
4.11.3.6.4	MFC design	271
4.11.3.6.5	Inoculum in MFCs	273
4.11.3.7	Microbial Electrolysis	273
4.11.4	Conclusions	274
Acknowledgment		275
References		275

4.11.1 Introduction

The demand for energy is growing rapidly worldwide and with the increasing requirement to limit and control carbon emissions a major emphasis is being placed on providing sustainable sources of energy and more efficient use of that energy. Faced with this challenge, major efforts are being put into technologies based on renewables and in producing hydrogen as a fuel. Consequently, systems are under development that use, for example, wind or solar power to produce hydrogen by electrolysis [1–5]; hydrogen can also be produced by solar thermochemical processes [6]. The debate is still open on whether or not this is a viable means of storing energy (as hydrogen) or whether the new battery technology is more appropriate. Fermentation, photobiological methods, and use of algae [7] are alternative ways of producing hydrogen (or methane) from plant and biomass. As yet, none of these technologies can compete costwise with the generation of hydrogen from fossil fuels. Many of these processes have limitations in efficiency, for example, converting sugars to hydrogen, and it is unlikely that any single technology will solely satisfy the potential requirements for hydrogen (or electrical) energy. Thus, more efficient alternative methods are needed to develop and operate in parallel with other energy supply routes.

In parallel with research and technology development (R&TD) to produce hydrogen, there has been a significant growth in fuel cell R&TD due to the potential of fuel cells to provide a continuous supply of clean and efficient power from hydrogen. This research and development, while potentially very useful, fails to tackle the growing needs for sustainable energy generation because fuel cells mainly use hydrogen produced from hydrocarbon sources. However, the Earth has an abundant resource of 'renewable' carbon-based potential fuels that are both occurring naturally and produced via industrial processes in the form of wastes or by-products. While research is underway to indirectly use fuel cells to capitalize on some of these potential fuel sources, for example, through purification (and reforming) of biogas, many carbon sources are not immediate, viable fuels for current fuel cell technology. Most of these carbon materials are currently disposed of as waste. In comparison, biofuel cells (BioFC) have the potential to directly use a wide range of carbon sources, for example, urea, waste, and sludge, at low cost.

The fact that biofuel cells can convert readily available substrates (fuel type) from sustainable sources into hydrogen or electrical energy, presents an opportunity to make a major contribution to energy requirements. Such a process would also provide a means of simultaneously reducing the waste treatment costs currently associated with many of the waste carbon sources, which are the potential fuels for the biofuel cells, and their use would not likely to be affected by the cost, storage, and distribution of the fuel substrate, unlike conventional hydrogen fuel cells. However, biofuel cells are at an early stage of development compared to other fuel cell types and significant research and development is still needed to approach technology readiness.

4.11.2 Fuel Cells and Biological Fuel Cells

4.11.2.1 Conventional Fuel Cells

Fuel cells are electrochemical devices that convert the intrinsic chemical energy in fuels into electrical energy directly. The fuel cell was first demonstrated by William Grove in 1839 [8] using electrochemically generated hydrogen and oxygen in an acid electrolyte with platinum electrodes. The hydrogen and oxygen produced were then used to generate a small current (and voltage).

One simple way of considering how a fuel cell works is to say that the fuel is being combusted in a simple reaction without generation of heat. As the intermediate steps of producing heat and mechanical work, typical of most conventional power generation methods, are avoided, fuel cells are not limited by the thermodynamic limitations of conventional heat engines, defined by the Carnot efficiency [9]. As such, fuel cells promise power generation at high efficiency and low environmental impact. In addition, because combustion is avoided, fuel cells produce power with minimal pollutants. However, unlike batteries, the reductant (hydrogen) and oxidant (oxygen) in fuel cells must be continuously replenished to allow continuous operation. This is a significant attraction for the use of fuel cells – extended operation limited only by the storage capacity of the fuel tank. A schematic representation of a classical H_2/O_2 fuel cell is presented in **Figure 1**.

Fuel cells can, in principle, process a wide variety of fuels and oxidants, although of most interest today are common fuels, such as natural gas (and derivatives) or hydrogen, and using air as the oxidant.

In a typical fuel cell, fuel is fed continuously to the anode (negative electrode) and an oxidant (often oxygen in air) is fed continuously to the cathode (positive electrode). The electrochemical reactions take place at the electrodes to produce an electric current through the electrolyte, while driving a complementary electric current that performs work on the load. At the anode of say an acid electrolyte fuel cell using hydrogen fuel, the hydrogen gas ionizes (reaction [1]), releasing electrons, and creating H^+ ion (protons), thereby releasing energy [8, 9].

$$2 H_2 \rightarrow 4 H^+ + 4 e^- \quad E_a^0 = 0 V \quad [1]$$

At the cathode oxygen reacts with the protons that have migrated internally from the anode to cathode of the fuel cell, and electrons (reaction [2]) delivered from the anode via the external electrical circuit to form water [8, 9]

$$O_2 + 4 H^+ + 4 e^- \rightarrow 2 H_2O \quad E_a^0 = 1.229 V \quad [2]$$

For the reaction to proceed continuously, the electrons produced at the anode must pass through an external circuit and the H^+ ions must pass through the electrolyte. An acid is a fluid with free protons and thus serves as a good electrolyte for proton transfer. Proton conductivity [9] can also be achieved using solid electrolytes such as polymers and ceramics. Importantly, the electrolyte should only allow proton transfer and not electron transfer. Otherwise the electrons would not pass around the external circuit and thus would 'short-circuit' the cell and the function of the fuel cell would be lost.

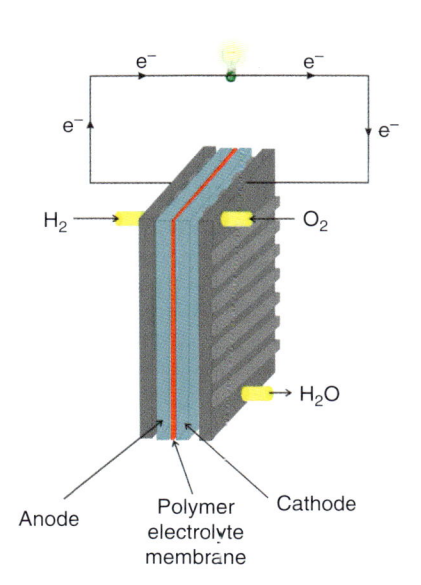

Figure 1 A hydrogen–oxygen fuel cell.

In theory, any substance capable of chemical oxidation (the reductant) that can be supplied continuously can be burned 'galvanically' as a fuel at the anode of a fuel cell. Similarly, the oxidant can be any fluid that can be reduced at a sufficient rate. For practical reasons, the most common oxidant is gaseous oxygen, which is readily available from air. Moreover, because of kinetic limitations in catalysts for fuel oxidation [9], the fuels typically used are ones with simple molecules such as hydrogen, methane, and methanol. It is the kinetic limitation in classic chemical fuel cells that has helped to stimulate greater interest in biological fuel cells to utilize a wider range of fuel feedstuffs.

4.11.2.2 Biological Fuel Cells

Biological fuel cells use biocatalysts for the conversion of chemical energy to electrical energy. Biological fuel cells work, in principle, in the same way as a chemical fuel cell: there is a constant supply of fuel into the anode and a constant supply of oxidant into the cathode however typically the fuel is a hydrocarbon compound. At the anode a fuel is oxidized, for example, glucose

$$C_6H_{12}O_6 + 6H_2O \rightarrow 6CO_2 + 24H^+ + 24e^- \quad E^0 = 0.014\,V \quad [3]$$

and at the cathode the oxidant is reduced, for example, oxygen

$$24H^+ + 24e^- + 6O_2 \rightarrow 12H_2O \quad E^0 = 1.2\,V \quad [4]$$

The resultant electrochemical reaction creates a current as a flow of electrons through the external electrical circuit, and protons internally within the cell are produced from the oxidation of the fuel. The theoretical cell potentials, quoted in reactions [3] and [4] for such reactions, are similar to those of conventional fuel cells, as can be seen in reactions [1] and [2]. The distinguishing feature, central to a biological fuel cell, is the use of biocatalysts.

There are two types of biological fuel cells, namely 'microbial' fuel cells and 'enzymatic' fuel cells, depending on the biocatalysts used. Microbial fuel cells (MFCs) use whole living organisms and enzymatic biofuel cells use isolated and purified enzymes as specific catalysts [10–16].

Biofuel cells function in one of two ways, using biocatalysts,

1. The biocatalyst generates the fuel substrate for the cell via a biocatalytic transformation or metabolic process.

   The biocatalysts in this type of fuel cell are not directly involved in energy generation, which is actually produced by a conventional fuel cell. For example, convert carbohydrate to hydrogen via a fermentation process using a multienzyme system and hydrogen-producing bacteria, then use a conventional H_2/O_2 fuel cell using metal catalysts, such as Pt [17], to connect to the bioreactor, and generate electricity from the biohydrogen. In this type of enzyme fuel cells, enzymes do not involved in direct energy generation, and the energy generation is realized by a conversional fuel cell. Enzymes generate the fuel substrate for fuel cell by a biocatalytic transformation or metabolic process. There have been several studies demonstrated using hydrogenase to produce hydrogen from glucose for conventional hydrogen–oxygen fuel cells [18, 19]. This type of biofuel cell is less common in enzymatic fuel cells.

2. The biocatalyst participates directly in the electron transfer reactions between the fuel and the anode.

   In this type of biofuel cells, biocatalysts are directly involved in the bioreactions for energy production. At the anode, microorganisms or enzymes oxidize organic matter and produce electrons, and on the cathode, either living organisms (microbes) or enzymes act as catalysts for oxidant reduction and accept electrons, the same principle as the conventional fuel cells. The performance of this type of biofuel cell is mainly dependent on the activity of the biocatalyst.

Compared with traditional chemical fuel cells, biological fuel cells are considered as potentially more 'environmental friendly'. Unlike conventional fuel cells, which typically use hydrogen as fuel and usually require extreme conditions of pH or high temperature, biological fuel cells use organic products produced by metabolic processes or use organic electron donors utilized in the growth processes as fuels for power generation. Biological fuel cells operate at ambient/room temperature and at neutral pH. In addition, microbes offer major advantages over enzymes; they can catalyze a greater extent of substrate oxidation of many fuels and can be less susceptible to poisoning and loss of activity under normal operating conditions.

4.11.2.3 Enzymatic Fuel Cells

Enzymes are known for their highly specific catalytic activities for bioreactions. The interest in developing enzyme-based bioelectronics, for example, for fuel cells and sensors, has arisen due to the increasing number of implantable medical devices for health care applications within the last decade. Many applications of the technology are proposed as biosensors for monitoring the changes in physiological substances, such as glucose sensing for diabetes patients [20, 21], and employing *in vivo* biofuel cells as the power sources for these implantable devices [22–24]. **Figure 2** shows a schematic diagram of a biofuel cell working in a blood vessel using glucose and dissolved oxygen as fuel and oxidant, respectively. Electrochemical glucose sensors are the most successful commercial biosensor devices for point-of-care and personal use because of the simplicity, flexibility, and low cost of electrochemical transduction instrumentation. Enzymes have also been used on environmental sensors to monitor some specific pollutants [25–27]. Portable electronic devices, such as laptops, mobile phones, and mp3 players, are new areas to explore the use of

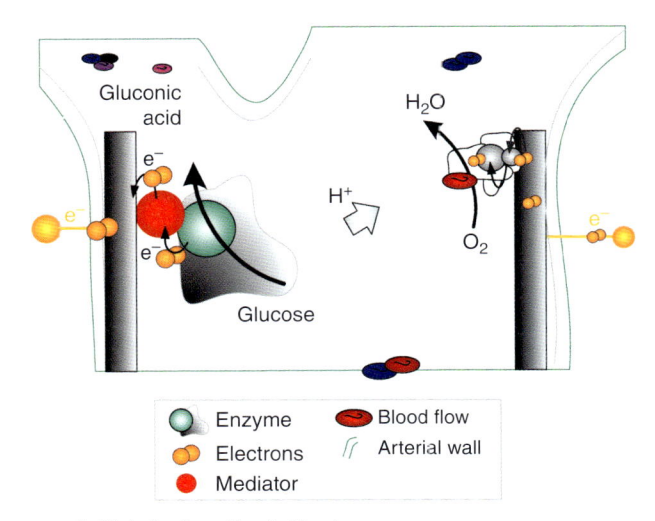

Figure 2 Schematic diagram of an enzymatic biofuel cell working in blood.

enzymatic biofuel cells [10–12], for example, Sony has developed a biofuel cell using sugar as the fuel and enzymes as catalysts to power a Walkman [28].

Enzyme-based fuel cells have been reported since the 1960s [29]. However, the development of enzymatic biofuel cells is still in its infancy, compared to conventional fuel cells, due to the low stability and low power outputs achieved. Electrodes biocatalytically modified with enzymes are the key for enhancing the performance of biofuel cells. Research in the development of enzyme electrodes for biofuel cell and biosensor applications has been carried out extensively in recent years. Studies on understanding the reaction mechanisms of enzyme catalytic reactions [30, 31] and developing new biomaterials [32–36] on enzyme modification [37–43], enzyme immobilization methods [44–50], and enzyme electrode structures [51] have been reported in the literature with the effort to improve the performance of enzyme electrodes.

4.11.2.4 Types of Biofuel Cells and Enzymes

4.11.2.4.1 Types of enzymes based on electron transfer methods

Redox enzymes can be divided into three groups (see **Figure 3**) based on the location of the enzyme active centers and methods of establishing electron transfer between enzymes and electrodes [52, 53].

1. Enzymes with nicotinamide adenine dinucleotide (NADH/NAD$^+$) or nicotinamide adenine dinucleotide phosphate (NADPH/NADP$^+$) redox centers, which are often weakly bound to the protein of the enzyme. Glucose dehydrogenase (GDH) and alcohol dehydrogenase belong to this group.
2. Enzymes where at least part of the redox center is conveniently located at, or near, the periphery of the protein shell, for example, peroxidases, laccase, and other multicopper enzymes fall into this category. Peroxidases, such as horseradish peroxidises and cytochrome c peroxidise, have been commonly used in enzyme reactions and immunoassay.

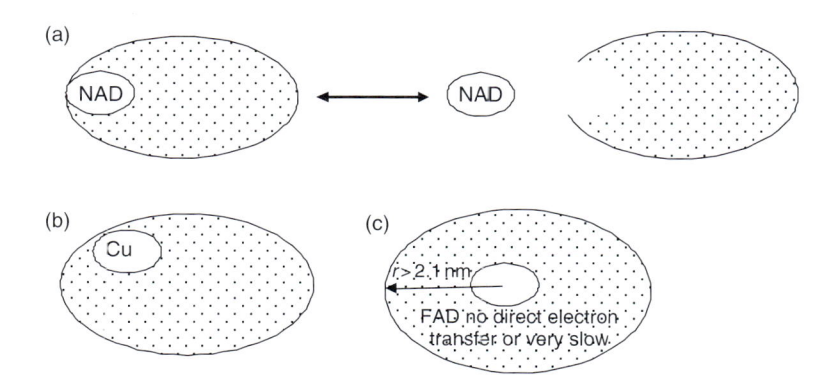

Figure 3 Three groups of enzymes based on location of enzyme active center. (a) Diffusive active center, (b) active center located on the periphery of the enzyme, and (c) strongly bound and deep-buried redox centers. Yu EH and Sundmacher K (2007) Enzyme electrodes for glucose oxidation prepared by electropolymerization of pyrrole. *Process Safety and Environmental Protection* 85(5): 489–493 [38]; Willner I, Blonder R, Katz E, *et al.* (1996) Reconstitution of apo-glucose oxidase with a nitrospiropyran-modified FAD cofactor yields a photoswitchable biocatalyst for amperometric transduction of recorded optical signals. *Journal of the American Chemical Society* 118(22): 5310–5311 [39].

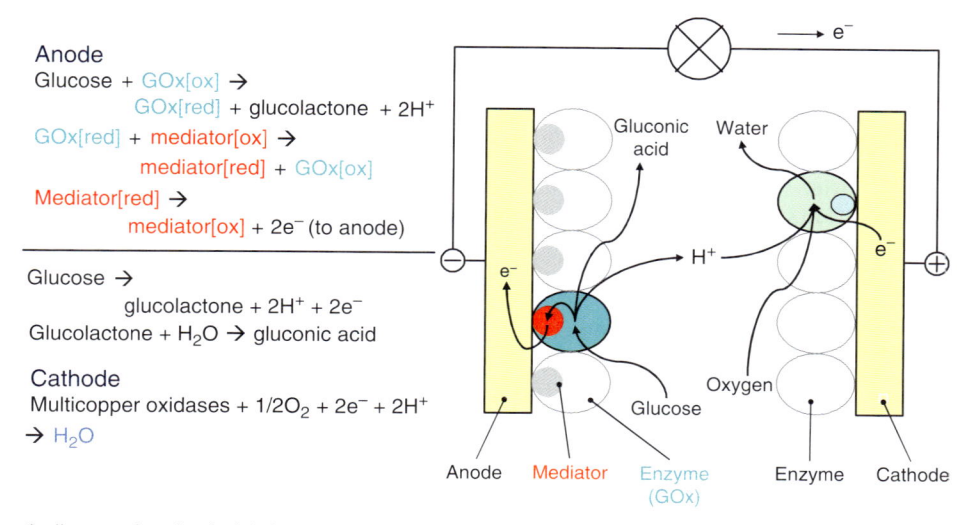

Anode
Glucose + GOx[ox] →
    GOx[red] + glucolactone + 2H⁺
GOx[red] + mediator[ox] →
    mediator[red] + GOx[ox]
Mediator[red] →
    mediator[ox] + 2e⁻ (to anode)

Glucose →
    glucolactone + 2H⁺ + 2e⁻
Glucolactone + H_2O → gluconic acid

Cathode
Multicopper oxidases + 1/2O_2 + 2e⁻ + 2H⁺
→ H_2O

Figure 4 Schematic diagram of work principle for mediated electron transfer in enzymatic biofuel cells.

3. Enzymes with a strongly bound redox center deeply bound in a protein or glycoprotein shell. Glucose oxidase is the most studied enzyme, example for this type of applications particularly on glucose sensors and biofuel cells [53].

The first two groups are able to carry out direct electron transfer (DET) between the enzyme active centers and the electrode surface. For the second group, the orientation of the enzyme on the electrode surface is the key factor affecting the activity of the enzyme. Enzymes in the third group are not able to have DET between the active centers and electrodes due to the large distance, >21 Å, between the enzyme active centers and the electrode surface [54]. In this case, for enzymes with the active center deeply buried inside the protein shell, direct electrical communication with electrodes can be established by using electron transfer mediators. These artificial electron donor or acceptor molecules (in case of reductive or oxidative enzymes, respectively) can be accepted by many redox enzymes in place of their natural oxidants or reductants. These enzymes have a varied range of structures and hence properties, including a range of redox potentials. **Figure 4** demonstrates the working principle of mediated electron transfer (MET) in enzymatic biofuel cells. It is clear that the performance of an enzymatic biofuel cell largely depends on the properties and activities of both the enzyme and mediator molecules.

Mediators that act as the electron transfer relay are based on a diffusional mechanism. Diffusional penetration of the oxidized or reduced relay into the protein can shorten the electron transfer distance between the enzyme active center and electrode [55]. Ferrocene derivatives are one of the most commonly used mediators for glucose oxidase. 'Wired' enzymes, which have a covalently binding mediator molecule to the enzyme to establish electron transfer, were first developed by Degani and Heller [56]. Benzoquinone [57, 58], hydroquinone [59], and pyrroloquinoline quinone (PQQ) [60, 61] have also been reported as mediator for glucose oxidase.

4.11.2.4.2 Enzyme electrodes

The proper functioning of an enzyme-based electrode relies on both the chemical and physical properties of the immobilized enzyme layer. Methods for immobilization of enzymes can be divided into physical and chemical methods.
  Physical methods include

1. Gel entrapment – Here the enzymes were entrapped in a gel matrix, such as gelatine and polyacrylamide, as well as dialysis tubing [62].
2. Adsorption – Adsorption of the enzyme to the electrode surface is simple and no additional reagents are required, as there is only weak bonding involved between the enzymes and electrode surface. Enzyme electrodes using Ni-Fe hydrogenase and laccase for use in a biofuel cell were prepared by adsorption of enzymes to a graphite surface by Vincent et al. [63]. Rapid electrocatalytic oxidation of hydrogen by the hydrogenase, which was completely unaffected by carbon monoxide, was obtained. The reaction was only partially inhibited by oxygen.

Chemical methods are the main methods used for fabricating enzyme electrodes for biofuel cell applications. The methods include covalent immobilization and immobilizing enzymes in polymer matrices.

4.11.2.4.2(i) Enzyme electrodes with layered structures

Covalent immobilization is the most irreversible and stable immobilization technique, with the most commonly used materials being noble metals and carbon. The enzyme electrodes typically have a layered structure based on covalent bindings, with the enzymes immobilized on the electrode surface either in self-assembled monolayers (SAMs) or in layer-by-layer structures binding mediators to transfer electrons from the site of fuel oxidation at the enzyme to the electrode surface.

Katz and Willner developed a method to establish DET between the active center of glucose oxidase and the electrode surface through a defined structured path by reconstitution of the enzyme with nitrospiropyran-modified and 2-aminoethyl-modified flavin adenine dinucleotide (FAD), cofactor [39, 40, 64–67]. They produced a fuel cell using enzymes on both anode and cathode where the electrode substrate was gold. The anodic reactions, defined reactions [5]–[7], were glucose oxidation using reconstituted glucose oxidase connecting with a monolayer of PQQ as the mediator, and the cathodic reaction was reduction of hydrogen peroxide by microperoxidase-11 (MP-11) [64]. The open-circuit voltage of the cell was ~310 mV, and the maximum power density was around 160 μW cm^{-2}.

$$\text{Electrode} - \text{PQQ} - \text{FAD} - \text{GOx} + \text{Glucose} \rightarrow \text{Electrode} - \text{PQQ} - \text{FADH2} - \text{GOx} + \text{Gluconic acid} \qquad [5]$$

$$\text{Electrode} - \text{PQQ} - \text{FADH2} - \text{GOx} \rightarrow \text{Electrode} - \text{PQQH2} - \text{FAD} - \text{GOx} \qquad [6]$$

$$\text{Electrode} - \text{PQQH2} - \text{FAD} - \text{GOx} \rightarrow \text{Electrode} - \text{PQQ} - \text{FAD} - \text{GOx} + 2\text{H}+ + 2e^- \qquad [7]$$

On the enzyme anode, glucose was first oxidized by the reconstitutioned glucose oxidase and produced gluconic acid and two electrons. The FAD cofactor in GOx accepts 2e$^-$ and simultaneously is reduced to FADH$_2$. These processes are described by reaction [5].

In reaction [6], FADH$_2$ was oxidized by PQQ, released 2e$^-$ and hydrogen, and recovered to oxidation form GOx. PQQ accepted 2e$^-$ and hydrogen, and was reduced to PQQH$_2$ in the mean time.

In the further reaction [7], the PQQH$_2$ was oxidized on the electrode and released the 2e$^-$ and hydrogen in the form of proton. Through a series of redox reaction from glucose, GOx (FAD) layer and PQQ mediator layer, the electrons produced from glucose oxidation were able to reach the electrode surface.

SAM enzymatic electrodes were fabricated using thio- [68–70] groups attaching to the gold electrode surface SAMs having biospecific affinity for lactate dehydrogenase for the electroenzymatic oxidation of lactate [71]. Gooding et al. [49], Sato and Mizutani [72], and Dong and Li [73] have covalently immobilized redox proteins, enzymes, and phospholipids to the SAMs of 3-mercaptopropionic acid on a gold electrode surface. The electrochemical characteristics of self-assembled octadecanethiol monolayers on polycrystalline gold electrodes were studied by means of cyclic voltammetry and by measuring the monolayer transient total capacitance, as well as the differential capacitance changes during the CV scan, in the presence of various redox probes placed in the bulk of the supporting electrolyte [74]. The results showed that the capacitance measurements are very sensitive to the changes in the structure of a monolayer in the course of the redox reaction.

Enzyme electrodes with multilayer structures have been studied with mono- and bienzymes for molecular recognition and generation of electrical signals [75–78]. Calvo et al. established enzyme electrodes using layer-by-layer supramolecular structures composed of alternate layers of negatively charged enzymes and cationic redox polyelectrolyte. Glucose oxidase (GOx), lactate oxidase (LOx), and soybean peroxidase (SBP) have been electrically wired to the underlying electrode by means of poly(allylamine) with Os(bpy)$_2$ClPyCOH+ covalently attached (PAA-Os) in organized structures having high spatial resolution. The concentration of redox mediator integrated into the multilayers, obtained from the voltammetric charge and an estimation of the layer thickness, exceeds by 100-fold the amount of deposited enzyme assessed by quartz crystal microbalance [79]. An electrode was fabricated by alternate layer-by-layer deposition of periodate-oxidized glucose oxidase (GOx) and poly(allylamine) (PAA) by Zhang et al. [48]. The covalent attachment process was followed and confirmed using electrochemical impedance spectroscopy (EIS). The gold electrodes modified with the GOx/PAA multilayers showed excellent electrocatalytical response to the oxidation of glucose with ferrocenemethanol as the mediator. From the analysis of the voltammetric signals, the coverage of active enzyme on the electrode surface had a linear relationship with the number of GOx/PAA bilayers suggesting that the analytical performance can be tunable by controlling the number of attached bilayers.

4.11.2.4.2(ii) Enzyme electrodes with polymer matrix

Although enzyme electrodes with layered structures have shown efficient electron transfer in various applications, there are some limitations. First, the amount of enzymes immobilized on the electrode is limited by the electrode surface due to a monolayer covalent binding scheme. Second, the more molecular layers immobilized on the electrode surface, the more electric resistance would be introduced to the electrode, which in turn will affect the electronic response of the electrode. Also, the electrode activity will be influenced by the orientation of the enzymes and mediator molecules.

Conducting redox polymers can be a solution to overcome these limitations. Conducting polymers, such as polypyrrole (PPy) and polyaniline (PANI), are very commonly used to immobilize enzymes and fabricating enzyme electrodes. PPy is one of the most extensively used conducting polymers in design of bioanalytical sensors and has some unique properties that prevent some undesirable electrochemical interactions and facilitation of electron transfer from some redox enzymes [80]. Enzyme electrodes with PPy are fabricated by electropolymerization and enzymes are entrapped in the polymer as a dopant during the polymerization process [38, 81–86]. PPy can also be functionalized by adding cationic pendant groups, such as the tris(bipyridyl)ruthenium (II) complex to the polymer films to introduce an electron relay [87]. A two-step method consisting of the adsorption of an aqueous amphiphilic pyrrole monomer-enzyme mixture on an electrode surface followed by the electropolymerization of the adsorbed monomers was developed by Cosnier [88]. A new biotin derivative functionalized by an electropolymerizable pyrrole group has been synthesized, and the electrooxidation of this biotin pyrrole has allowed the formation of biotinylated conducting

Figure 5 Au electrode coated with polypyrrole-FeFcGOx layer. Reproduced with permission from Larossa-Guerrero A, Scott K, Head IM, *et al.* (2010) Effect of temperature on the performance of microbial fuel cells. *Fuel* 89(12): 3985–3994. Copyright (2010) Elsevier [168].

PPy films in an organic electrolyte, which revealed an avidin-biotin-specific binding at the interface of the polymer solution. This provided a simple electrochemical approach to allow reagentless immobilization of enzymes on electrode surfaces [89, 90]. **Figure 5** shows the scanning electron microscopy (SEM) and atomic force microscope (AFM) images of the PPy film entrapped with ferrocene-modified glucose oxidase [38].

PANI is another extensively used polymer for enzyme immobilization. An enzyme-mediator-conducting polymer model using benzoquinone (Q)-PANI system was established by Cooper and Hall [72], which can produce enhanced current densities [91]. Raitman *et al.* integrated PANI/poly(acrylic acid) films and redox enzymes for the study of the bioelectrocatalyzed oxidation of glucose or lactate [92]. Improved selectivity and stability of a glucose biosensor was obtained based on *in situ* electropolymerized PANI-polyacrylonitrile composite film [93]. A novel method was developed by Willner's group to generate an integrated electrically contacted GDH electrode by the surface reconstitution of the apo-enzyme on a PQQ-modified PANI [94]. The same group also developed an integrated enzyme-electrode where the glucose oxidase reveals direct electrical contact with the electrode using poly(aniline–aniline boronic acid) wires generated on ds-DNA templates [95].

In order to establish electron transfer between the enzyme active centers and the electrode surface and provide the structure for enzyme immobilization, polymer mediators have been developed and applied to the enzyme electrodes. Osmium-based polymers are the most studied polymer. Current commercially available continuous glucose sensors have been using osmium-based polymers to fabricate enzyme electrodes. The advantages of these polymers include wide redox potential windows from different derivatives for various redox reactions, fast electron transfer rate, and good chemical stabilities [21, 96–105].

In 1991, Heller's group developed a redox epoxy, which was designed for use in enzyme electrodes and was formed by reacting two water-soluble components (a poly(vinylpyridine) complex of Os(bpy)$_2$Cl and a diepoxide) under near-physiological conditions. The binding simultaneously immobilizes the enzyme, glucose oxidase, and connects it electrically with the electrode. The catalytic 'reaction layer' in this case extends through the entire film [106, 107]. Since then they have developed various Os polymer derivatives used for enzymatic oxidation and oxygen reduction reactions, as well as biofuel cells with these enzyme electrodes [21, 96–105]. Micro enzyme electrodes were developed with 7 μm diameter carbon fibers using poly(vinylpyridine) Os(bipyridine)$_2$Cl derivative-based redox hydrogels to immobilize glucose oxidase [108]. A miniaturized biofuel cell with this carbon fiber electrode configuration was developed [109]. The power density of this device was 5 times greater than the previous best biofuel cells, which at 37 °C, a power output of 600 nW was obtained, which was enough to power small microelectronics.

For implantable applications, there is concern over possible leach out of Os compounds over the long term, due to their toxicity. Biocompatibility is another issue for implantable devices. Biopolymers based on phospholipid polymer mimicking the cell membrane were developed and these polymers have good biocompatibility and inhibit the adhesion and activation of blood cells, thus minimizing blood coagulation that could inhibit the device operation when it contacts blood [33, 35, 110]. The feasibility of introducing redox properties to phospholipid polymers was investigated and through modification of the polymer side chain, it is possible to use the biopolymers for enzyme electrodes for implantable applications [111]. A hydrophilic copolymer, poly(vinylferrocene-*co*-2-hydroxyethyl methacrylate) (poly(VFc-*co*-HEMA)), also a biopolymer, was prepared as a polymeric, electron transfer mediator for producing amperometric biosensors. The poly(VFc-*co*-HEMA) membrane is useful as an enzyme-immobilizing carrier matrix for fabricating glucose sensors as well as a polymeric, electron transfer mediator [112].

4.11.2.4.3 Performance of enzymatic biofuel cells

One of the first enzymatic biofuel cells reported by Willner and Katz used a PQQ monolayer-functionalized Au electrode as the anode and a microperoxidase-11 (MP-11)-modified Au electrode as the cathode [64]. In this system, H_2O_2 was the cathodic oxidizer, whereas the anodic fuel-substrate is 1,4-dihydronicotinamide adenine dinucleotide, NADH. The biofuel cell generates an open-circuit voltage of ~320 mV and a short-circuit current density of ~30 $\mu A\,cm^{-2}$. The maximum electrical power extracted from the cell was 8 μW at an external load of 3 kΩ.

Another biofuel cell developed by Willner and Katz was a novel glucose/O_2 biofuel cell without compartmentalization between anode and cathode. The anode consisted of a surface reconstituted glucose oxidase monolayer, whereas the cathode was the reconstituted cytochrome c/cytochrome oxidase couple. The biofuel cell was assembled by the engineering of layered bioelectrocatalytic electrodes. DET between enzyme and mediator, as well as mediator and the electrode surface was established. The enzyme active center, cofactor, was first removed to form apoenzyme. The mediator bound on the electrode surface was covalently bound to artificial active center before reconstitution of enzyme with artificial active center to establish an electron transfer pathway [113]. An open-circuit cell voltage of 0.11 V and peak power output of 4 μW were achieved. This system paves the way to tailoring implantable biofuel cells for generating electrical power [113].

Katz and Willner applied the property of conductivity change for oxidation and reduction status of Cu-poly(acrylic acid) polymer and developed an electroswitchable and tunable biofuel cell based on the biocatalyzed oxidation of glucose. By the cyclic electrochemical reduction and oxidation of the polymer films associated with the anode and cathode between the Cu-0-poly(acrylic acid) and Cu^{2+}poly(acrylic acid) states, the biofuel cell performance is reversibly switched between 'ON' and 'OFF' states, respectively. The open-circuit voltage of the cell was 120 mV and the short-circuit current density reached 550 $\mu A\,cm^{-2}$. The maximum extracted power from the cell was 4.3 μW with an external load resistance of 1 kΩ. The slow reduction of the Cu^{2+} polymer films allows for the control of the content of conductive domains in the films and the tuning of the output power of the biofuel cell [114].

An enzyme-based biofuel cell with a pH-switchable oxygen electrode, controlled by enzyme logic operations processing *in situ* biochemical input signals, was developed recently [115]. Two Boolean logic gates (AND/OR) were assembled from enzyme systems to process biochemical signals and to convert them logically into pH changes of the solution, as shown in **Figure 6**. The electrochemical activity of the modified electrode was switchable by alteration of the solution pH value. The electrode was electrochemically mute at pH > 5.5 and was activated for the bioelectrocatalytic oxygen reduction at pH < 4.5. The sharp transition between the inactive and active states was used to control the electrode activity by external enzymatic systems operating as logic switches in the system. When the biofuel cell was activated (through activating the biocatalytic cathodic process), an open-circuit voltage (V_{oc}) of 380 mV and short-circuit current density (I_{sc}) of 3 $\mu A\,cm^{-2}$ were obtained. The maximum power density was 700 $nW\,cm^{-2}$ [116].

The latest development from Mano *et al.* for a miniature, membraneless glucose-O_2 biofuel cell built with Os derivative polymer mediators for glucose and bilirubin oxidase on the anode and cathode, respectively was reported with a power density of 4.8 $\mu W\,mm^{-2}$ produced at a voltage of 0.60 V in a physiological buffer containing phosphate buffer saline at p. 7.0 at 37.5 °C [100].

Fruit juices, such as orange juice, grape juice, and banana juice, have all been studied as potential fuels for a membraneless biofuel cell. The cell was prepared based on glucose oxidase and laccase as anodic and cathodic catalyst, respectively, by using 1,1'-dicarboxyferrocene as the mediators on both anode and cathode. This research demonstrated the possibility of using easy access fruit juice to power portable electronics [10]. By adopting grape or banana juice instead of glucose as fuels in the biofuel cell, the V_{oc} (0.191 V) and I_{sc} (60 μA, current density ~146.3 $\mu A\,cm^{-2}$) for grape juice and V_{oc} (0.202 V) and I_{sc} (72 μA, current density ~175.6 $\mu A\,cm^{-2}$) for banana juice were achieved, which are similar to glucose. The V_{oc} and I_{sc} of the fuel cell by using the orange juice as fuels are approximately twofold and threefold higher than glucose. The maximum power density of 11.66 μW (power density ~28.4 $\mu W\,cm^{-2}$) at 0.216 V was achieved with orange juice [10].

For implantable medical devices, nontoxic mediators for enzyme electrodes are essential. In Kyoto University, a biofuel cell was developed using Vitamin K-3-modified poly-L-lysine (PLL-VK3) as the electron transfer mediator during catalytic oxidation of NADH by diaphorase (Dp) at the anode of the biofuel cell. PLL-VK3 and Dp were co-immobilized on an electrode and then coated with NAD(+)-dependent GDH. An oxidation current of ~2 $mA\,cm^{-2}$ was observed when the electrochemical cell contained a stirred

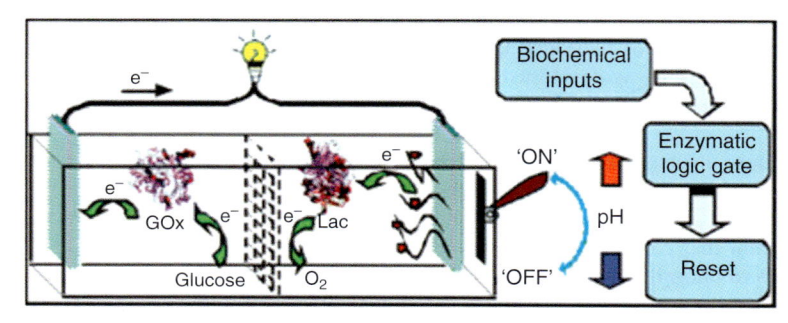

Figure 6 Schematic diagram of a biofuel cell with a pH-switchable oxygen electrode, controlled by enzyme logic operations processing *in situ* biochemical input signals. Reprinted with permission from Amir L, Tam TK, Pita M, *et al.* (2008) Biofuel cell controlled by enzyme logic systems. *Journal of the American Chemical Society* 131(2): 826–832 [115]. Copyright (2009) American Chemical Society.

30 mM glucose, 1.0 mM NAD(+), p. 7.0 phosphate-buffered electrolyte solution. The open-circuit voltage of a glucose/O_2 biofuel cell with the polydimethylsiloxane (PDMS)-coated Pt cathode was 0.55 V and its maximum power density was 32 $\mu W\,cm^{-2}$ at 0.29 V when a p. 7.0 buffered fuel containing 5.0 mM glucose and 1.0 mM NAD(+) was introduced into the cell at a flow rate of 1.0 ml min^{-1}. The cell's output current density declined by ~50% during 18 h of operation [117].

Apart from glucose, other organic fuels such as alcohol and glycerol have also been used in enzymatic biofuel cells. An enzymatic biofuel cell using ethanol and operated at ambient temperature has been developed. The anode of this biofuel cell was based on immobilized quinohemoprotein alcohol dehydrogenase (QH-ADH), while the cathode was based on co-immobilized alcohol oxidase (AOx) and microperoxidase (MP-8). The enzymes are able to have DET to the electrode surfaces. The maximal open-circuit potential of the biofuel cell was 240 mV and maximal power for completed biofuel cell was 1.5 $\mu W\,cm^{-2}$ [118].

Glycerol has attracted increasing interest because it is a by-product from biodiesel production. An enzymatic biofuel cell was developed by using glycerol as the fuel and employing a three-enzyme cascade on the anode that can accomplish the complete oxidation of glycerol [119]. The bioanode that was developed contained PQQ-dependent alcohol dehydrogenase (PQQ-ADH), PQQ-dependent aldehyde dehydrogenase (PQQ-AldDH), and oxalate oxidase immobilized within a tetrabutylammonium-modified Nafion membrane. This glycerol/air biofuel cell yielded power densities of up to 1.32 $mW\,cm^{-2}$ and has the ability to operate at 100 mM glycerol.

Nanocarbon materials, such as carbon fiber and carbon nanotubes, have also been applied in enzymatic biofuel cells because of their excellent electronic properties. A passive-type biofuel cell, which generated a power of over 100 mW with a cell volume of 80 cm^3, operated at a pH of 7, gave a maximum power density of ~1.45 ± 0.24 $mW\,cm^{-2}$ at 0.3 V. This performance was achieved by densely packed enzymes and mediator on carbon-fiber electrodes with the enzymatic activity retained. These cell units, with a multistacked structure, successfully operated a radio-controlled car and a memory-type walkman for more than 2 h [120].

Membraneless and mediator-free DET enzymatic biofuel cells with bioelectrodes comprised single-wall carbon nanotubes (SWCNTs) deposited on porous silicon substrates were reported. Anodic glucose oxidase (GOx) and cathodic laccase (Lac) were immobilized on the porous silicon/SWNT substrates used in the fuel cell, in a p. 7 phosphate buffer solution (PBS). A peak power density of 1.38 $\mu W\,cm^2$ (with a lifetime of 24 h) down to 0.3 $\mu W\,cm^2$ was obtained using a 4 mM glucose solution as fuel and air as an oxidant [121].

4.11.3 Microbial Fuel Cells

4.11.3.1 Development of MFC

A large amount of energy exists within various waste streams and can be degraded by microbes. At the turn of the nineteenth century, the idea of using microbial cells to produce electricity was first envisaged by Potter [13], who tried to generate electricity with *E. coli*. In 1931, Cohen created a number of microbial half fuel cells connected in series [122]. DelDuca et al. succeed in operating a hydrogen and air fuel cell using hydrogen production from fermentation of glucose by *Clostridium butyricum* at the anode [14]. Rohrback et al. [15] designed a biological fuel cell in which *C. butyricum* was also used to generate hydrogen by glucose fermentation. In 1969, Yao et al. showed that glucose could be used as a fuel in the presence of a platinum-black anode [16]. In the early 1980s, Bennetto studied MFCs in more detail and designed a fuel cell as a possible method for the generation of electricity for third world countries [123]. Bennetto showed that mediators could enhance the efficiency of electron- transfer and the reaction rate. Since then a large amount of research has examined various aspects of MFCs from materials, to bioelectrochemistry to microorganisms.

Tanisho et al. [124] studied an MFC with *Enterobacter aerogenes* and a stainless-steel net anode plated with platinum black. The main anode reactant for Tanisho was hydrogen, which was biochemically produced from glucose by the bacteria. An alternative strategy was direct conversion of the sugars to electrical power. Existing transition metal-catalyzed fuel cells cannot be effectively used to generate electric power from carbohydrates [12]; however biofuel cells, in which whole cells or isolated redox enzymes catalyze the oxidation of the sugar, have been developed [28–35].

4.11.3.2 Electricity Generation Mechanism in MFC

The mechanism by which electricity can be produced directly from the degradation of organic matter in an MFC is still not completely understood. Heterotrophic bacteria liberate energy from the oxidation of organic matter, the process called as catabolism. MFCs make use of the catabolic activity of living cells, that is, bacteria (biocatalysts), to convert chemical energy into electricity. When bacteria oxidize a chemical, they capture the electrons and transfer them to a series of respiratory enzymes used to store energy in the form of adenosine triphosphate (ATP) within the cell. Electrons are then released to an electron acceptor such as iron, nitrate, sulphate, or oxygen. The same bacteria that respire using iron have recently been found to be able to transfer electrons to an anode [125].

When microorganisms consume a substrate (e.g., glucose) in the presence of oxygen, they produce carbon dioxide and water through an oxidative metabolism, as defined in reaction [8]:

$$C_6H_{12}O_6 + 6O_2 \rightarrow 6CO_2 + 6H_2O \qquad [8]$$

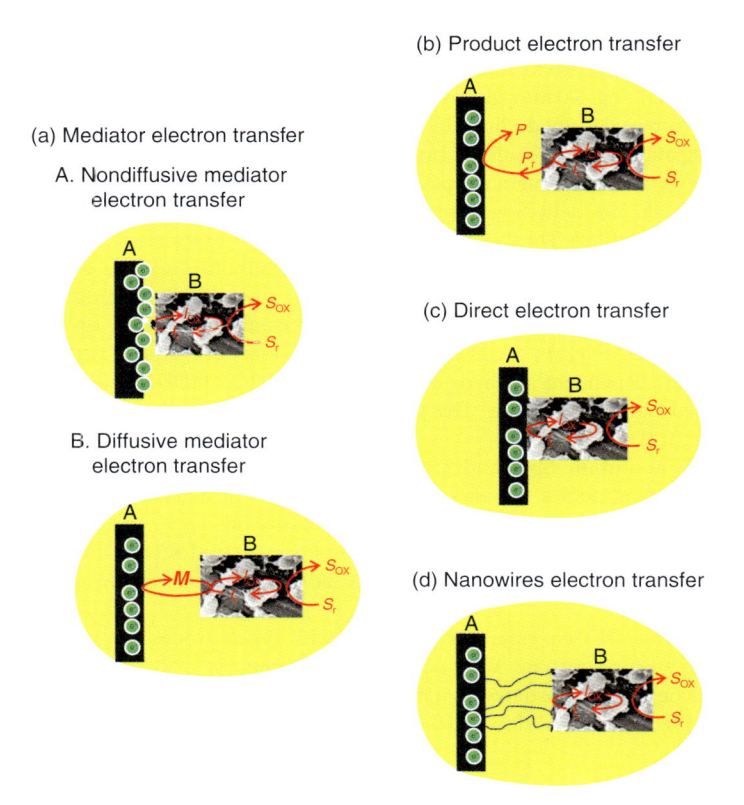

Figure 7 Mode of electron transfer mechanisms in an MFC. M, mediator; A, anode; B, bacteria; C, cytochromes; D, nanowires; S_{ox}, substrate oxidation; S_{red}, substrate reduction; I_{cx}, intermediate oxidation; I_{red}, intermediate reduction; P_{ox}, production oxidation; P_{red}, production reduction; and e−, electron.

However, when oxygen is not present, in an MFC, they produce carbon dioxide, protons, and electrons according to reactions [3] and [4]. Various mechanisms have been proposed by which electron transfer occurs in MFC between bacteria and the anode (**Figure 7**). A mechanism has been proposed describing DET, in which some outer-membrane bound proteins, such as cytochromes [126, 127], play the role of transferring electrons to the electrode.

$$\text{Substrate} \xrightarrow{\text{Microbial metabolism}} \text{Wastes} + (\text{membrane cytochrome}) - (\text{membrane cytochrome}) -$$
$$\xrightarrow{\text{anode}} (\text{membrane cytochrome}) + e- \qquad [9]$$

Another mechanism concerns the use of external or self-produced mediators:

$$\text{Substrate} + \text{Mediator} \xrightarrow{\text{Organism}} \text{Product} + \text{Mediator} \quad \text{Mediator} \xrightarrow{\text{Anode}} \text{Mediator} + e- \qquad [10]$$

It has also been suggested that bacteria are able to form 'nanowires' contacting the electrode, through which electrons are transferred [128].

4.11.3.3 Working Principles of MFC

The operation principle of the MFC is shown in **Figure 8**. An anode and cathode are placed in aqueous solutions in two chambers separated by a proton exchange membrane (PEM). The generation of current is due to the nature of microorganisms; they transfer electrons from a reduced electron donor to an electron acceptor at a higher electrochemical potential. Bacteria in an anode biofilm carry out oxidation of organic matter, producing electrons and protons: one proton for every electron, and dependent on fuel source, carbon dioxide may eventually be produced as an oxidation product. Electrons are transferred to the cathode through the external circuit, thereby powering an external electrical load, and protons are transferred through the membrane. Electrons and protons react on the cathode, reducing the oxidant (generally oxygen) to water, and generating electricity.

Unless the species in the anode chamber are anodophiles, the bacteria having ability to reduce inert electron acceptor, the microbes are incapable of transferring electrons directly to the anode [130]. Hence, to enhance power output of the device electron mediators (e.g., neutral red [131], methylene blue, thionine [132], and Fe(III)EDTA [133, 134]) can be used in the MFCs to accelerate the electron transfer. Mediators in an oxidized state are reduced by accepting electrons. These electrons

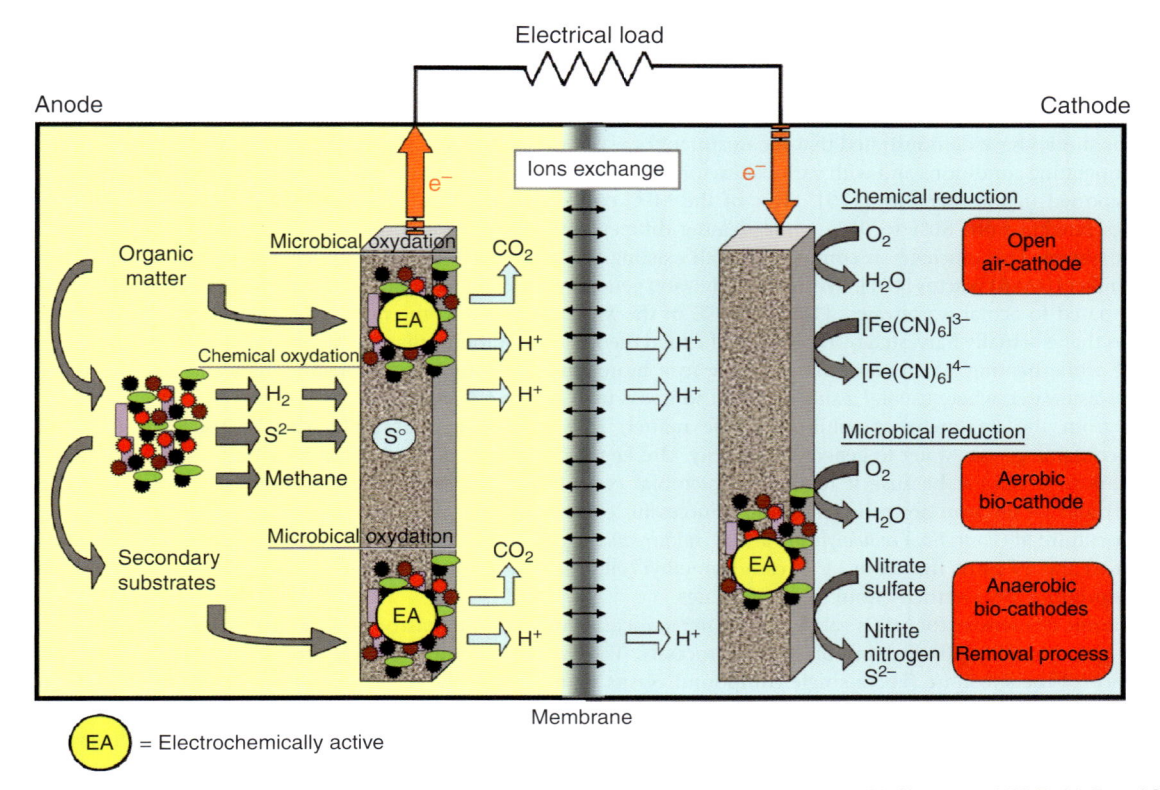

Figure 8 Schematic representation of microbial fuel cell operation. Reprinted with permission from Duteanu NM, Ghangrekar MM, Erable B, and Scott K (2010) *Microbial fuel cells – An option for wastewater treatment. Environmental Engineering and Management Journal* 9(8): 1069–1087. [129]. Copyright (2010) Environmental Engineering and Management Journal.

are released to the anode and mediators are oxidized again in the bulk solution in the anode chamber. This cyclic process can accelerate electron transfer and enhance power output of the MFC. However, the use of mediators causes several problems for practical devices and technology development is focused on mediatorless MFCs, that is, cells in which external chemical mediators are not used.

4.11.3.4 Mediatorless MFC

Recent studies [135, 136] showed that complex microbial communities in wastewater-fed MFCs produce soluble redox mediators, for example, pyocyanin [137]. It has been shown that certain metal-reducing bacteria, belonging primarily to the family *Geobacteraceae* can directly transfer electrons to electrodes using electrochemically active redox enzymes, such as cytochromes, on their outer membrane [136]. Furthermore, *Geobacter sulfurreducens* is known to transfer electrons beyond cell surfaces to electrodes through membrane proteins [138, 139] or nanowires [128]. The electron transfer between the electrode and *E. coli* cells is reported to be carried out by soluble compounds in the culture [140]. *E. coli* cells evolved under electrochemical tension in an MFC pose direct electrochemical behavior due to excretion of hydroquinone derivatives through a highly permeable outer membrane [141]. In addition to these species, metabolites produced by *Pseudomonas* species enable Gram-positive bacteria that can also achieve extracellular electron transfer [142]. Several other anodophilic bacteria have been identified in recent research, those are described in detail in Section 4.11.3.6. MFCs containing such electrochemically active bacteria (EAB) do not need mediators for electron transfer to electrodes and are called mediatorless MFCs.

4.11.3.5 Organic Matter Removal in MFC

Compared with the other fuel cells including enzymatic biofuel cells, MFCs may use a wider range of fuel sources (e.g., complex organic matter in wastewater), although the level of power achieved, as yet, is not high. Highest power per unit volume of 2.15 kW m^{-3} is reported using *G. sulfurreducens* in the anode [143]. Differences in power production and bacteria present on the anode suggest that substrate composition influences bacterial enrichment on the anode and in turn the current production efficiency. Extensive research on developing reliable MFCs has focused mostly on selecting suitable organic and inorganic substances that can be used as sources of energy. It now seems that electricity can be generated from any biodegradable material, ranging from pure compounds, such as acetate and glucose, to complex mixtures and wastes, such as glucose, acetate, butyrate [144], cysteine [145], proteins [146], and lignocellulose [147]. MFCs have generated electricity directly from complex organic mixtures in food processing [148, 149], brewery [149], domestic [150–153], chemical [154, 155], starch [156] wastewaters, swine manure slurry [157, 158], manure waste [159], landfill leachate [160], and meatpacking wastewater [146].

Various studies have demonstrated that the treatment of wastewater is one of the most promising applications of MFCs. Under different operating conditions and with various reactor types used, chemical oxygen demand (COD) removal ranging from 60% to 90% is reported in the literature [129]. Most of the MFC configurations are reported to be capable of giving COD removal efficiencies ranging from 80% to 95% while treating different wastewaters; demonstrating the utility of MFC as a wastewater treatment system. This efficiency is comparable with existing popularly used anaerobic processes, such as the upflow anaerobic sludge blanket (UASB) reactor [161]. Synthetic wastewater generally gives higher organic matter removal and Coulombic efficiency (CE) compared to actual wastewaters [153]. The CE of the MFC is defined as the ratio, expressed in percentage, of amount of Coulombs that is actually harvested by the MFC to the total theoretical Coulombs that can be generated from the substrate supplied. Lower CE while treating actual wastewaters is due to a more complex nature of the organic matter in actual wastewater than synthetic wastewater, where usually a single carbon source is used by the researchers.

Apart from the treatment of soluble organic matter, it is interesting that MFCs can be used for the treatment of cellulose-containing wastewater to generate electricity. Unlike typical soluble substrates that have been used as electron donors in MFC, cellulose is unique because it requires a microbial consortium that can metabolize both an insoluble electron donor (cellulose) and an electron acceptor (electrode). Successful electricity generation from cellulose-fed MFC was reported using a defined coculture of *Clostridium cellulolyticum* and *G. sulfurreducens* [162]. The coculture achieved a maximum power density of 143 (anode area) and 59.2 mW m^{-2} from 1 g l^{-1} carboxymethyl cellulose and MN301 cellulose, respectively [162]. A pure culture alone could not produce any electricity from these substrates.

Coulombic efficiencies for MFCs vary but, in general, increase with power density because there is less time for substrate to be lost through competing physical and biological processes. The maximum power density produced appears to be related to the 'complexity' of the substrate (i.e., a single compound versus many compounds). This trend of reduced power production has been observed in studies using the same system that power output was only 146 mW m^{-2} using domestic wastewater versus 494 mW m^{-2} using glucose [163]. Min and Logan [150] found in a flat-plate MFC that power output was 86% less when dextran was used instead of glucose in the feed. Thus, it appears that the effect of multiple substrates or polymers in the organic solution can reduce the maximum power output. Also nonfermentable substrates, such as acetate and butyrate, yielded Coulombic efficiencies of 50–65%, while fermentable substrates, such as glucose, dextran, and starch, produced Coulombic efficiencies of only 14–21%.

4.11.3.6 MFC Operating Conditions and Material Aspects

MFC performance is affected by several factors, which includes the inoculum, that is, the source of bacterial culture and bacterial strain(s) used at the anode, the fuel substrate and concentration, pH, conductivity, temperature and conditions of operation of the MFC, including hydraulic loading rate, as well as the reactor design and cell materials for anode, cathode, and anode-to-cathode separator.

4.11.3.6.1 Operating temperature

Temperature is one of the most important parameters in anaerobic digestion and methane production is strongly dependent on it. Most anaerobic digesters operate at the mesophilic range and the characteristics of this process have been widely studied and documented [164]. Most of the studies report a marked decrease in methane production as temperature decreased, with an optimum temperature for mesophilic bacteria known to be around 35–40 °C [165]. When the reactor temperature is lower, the mesophilic bacterial consortia goes through a long selection and adaptation process during which their activity slows down drastically and results in developing a group of mesophilic psychrotrophic bacteria. There is also a group of bacteria called psychrophilic bacteria that naturally prefer low-temperature environments [166]; they have more recently become the object of study [167, 168].

Similar to other biological wastewater treatment processes, performance of the anode in an MFC is affected by the temperature. However, just as in chemical fuel cells, increasing temperature also improves the kinetics of oxygen reduction and reduces the internal resistance of the cell, which can lead to greater current densities and greater CE; for example, 43% at 30 °C compared to 8% at 22 °C [169].

With an increase in temperature, the biochemical reaction rate can also increase and hence results in an increase of biomass growth rate due to increase in the substrate utilization rate. Higher growth rate would also result in faster microbial attachment on the electrode.

An operating temperature of 35 °C was reported to be optimum [170], although this is clearly dependent upon the bacterial strain used. Reductions in power density (70–43 mW m^{-2}), CE, and COD removal efficiency were reported with a reduction in temperature from 30 °C to 20/22 °C [171]. Conversely, thermophilic operation of an MFC at 55 °C for over 100 days was reported to produce a power density of 37 mW m^{-2} at a CE of 89% [172]. In MFC generating electricity from marine sediments, cell operation at 60 °C was reported to produce 10 times more power as compared to operation at 22 °C [173]. Successful current production is also reported in MFCs operated at 50 °C [174].

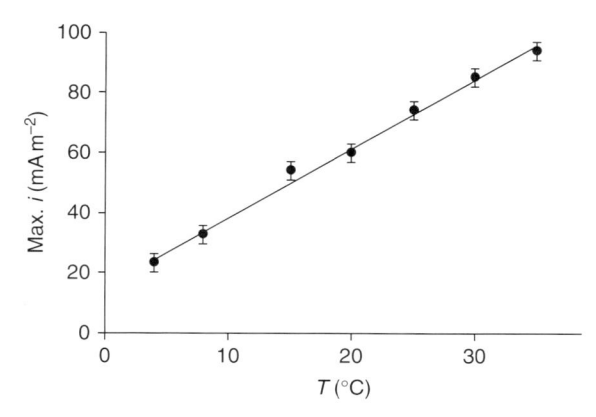

Figure 9 Variation of maximum current density single-chamber MFCs with carbon cloth cathodes, under 1 kΩ working at temperatures between 4 °C and 35 °C. Reproduced with permission from Larossa-Guerrero A, Scott K, Head IM, et al. (2010) Effect of temperature on the performance of microbial fuel cells. Fuel 89(12): 3985–3994. Copyright (2010) Elsevier [168].

Research in MFCs at different temperatures ranging from 4 °C to 35 °C has been performed with single-chamber MFCs (SCMFCs) and two-chamber MFCs. In one report, the reactor feed was brewery wastewater diluted in domestic wastewater [168]. These data showed that an increase in temperature increased COD removal, current densities, and cell voltages (**Figure 9**). Further, the power density increased by an order of magnitude over the temperature range studied, with results ranging from 58% final COD removal and maximum power of 15.1 mW m^{-3} reactor at 4 °C to 94% final COD removal and maximum power of 174.0 mW m^{-3} reactor at 35 °C for SCMFCs with carbon cloth-based cathodes. Bioelectrochemical processes in these MFCs were found to have a temperature coefficient, Q_{10}, of 1.6. Temperature coefficient in chemistry and biochemistry represents a measure of the processes rate of change of the system when the temperature is increasing with 10 °C. Thus, the temperature coefficient Q_{10} is defined as [168]

$$Q_{10} = (R_1/R_2)^{10/(T_2-T_1)}$$

where R is the rate and T is the temperature expressed in Celsius or Kelvin degrees.

4.11.3.6.2 Operating pH

MFCs are typically operated at pH values between 6 and 8 in the anode chamber and neutral (p. 7), or a little higher, in the cathode chamber (**Figure 10**). This is because the anodic microbial process performs well around neutral pH and microbial activity decreases at higher or lower pH: an anodic chamber pH between 7 and 8 is reported to produce maximum CE and current [135]. Such pH values are often inherent in the feed/waste stream being processed; however, reductions in current and CE were reported at p. 6 and above p. 9.0 [176]. Data presented so far suggest that a pH between 6 and 7 may give optimum power production from the MFC, although operation of MFC at feed pH up to 10 is possible. Higher pH in the anode chamber favors higher COD removal but reduces power, and a higher pH difference between the anode and cathode can improve power output of the MFC due to improvements in the kinetics of oxygen reduction [129, 135, 176].

4.11.3.6.3 Organic loading rates and hydraulic retention time

Organic loading rates (OLRs) and retention time (residence time) generally influence MFC performance, which is particularly dependent on the substrate being used as a fuel. Nonfermentable substrates, such as acetate, give higher power densities and energy conversion efficiencies as compared to fermentable substrates, such as glucose [177]. When using humic acid (HA) as a mediator in two-chamber MFCs, acetate produced higher power due to a simpler metabolism than glucose and xylose [178]. In the presence of HA, the power increased by 84% and 30% for glucose and xylose, respectively, due to the mediating effect of HA. No specific effect of HA addition was reported for acetate. External mediator addition increases power output during fermentable substrate degradation indicating limited electron transfer ability of the microbes developed in the cell.

Generally, there is an optimum range of OLR to obtain maximum COD removal efficiency and maximum power that depends on the configuration of the MFC used and the wastewater being treated. The OLRs used in MFCs are comparable with those used in activated sludge processes. However, these are only comparable with the OLRs adopted for sewage treatment in high-rate anaerobic processes, such as UASB reactor and anaerobic filters, and far less than the OLRs used in case of industrial wastewater treatment in UASB reactors.

The applied OLRs will have a marked influence on both power yield and substrate degradation rate in the MFC. Typically OLRs in the range of 0.05–2.0 kg COD m^{-3} day^{-1} are used by researchers to achieve maximum power from the MFC. It is reported that in treating wastewater a maximum power yield (274 mW g^{-1} COD) was obtained at an OLR of 0.574 kg COD m^{-3} day^{-1} [179]. Operation of the MFC at the higher OLR is reported to reduce the CE. While treating leachate, increasing OLR from 0.65 to 5.2 kg COD m^{-3} day^{-1} resulted in a decrease of overall CE from 14.4% to 1.2% [180].

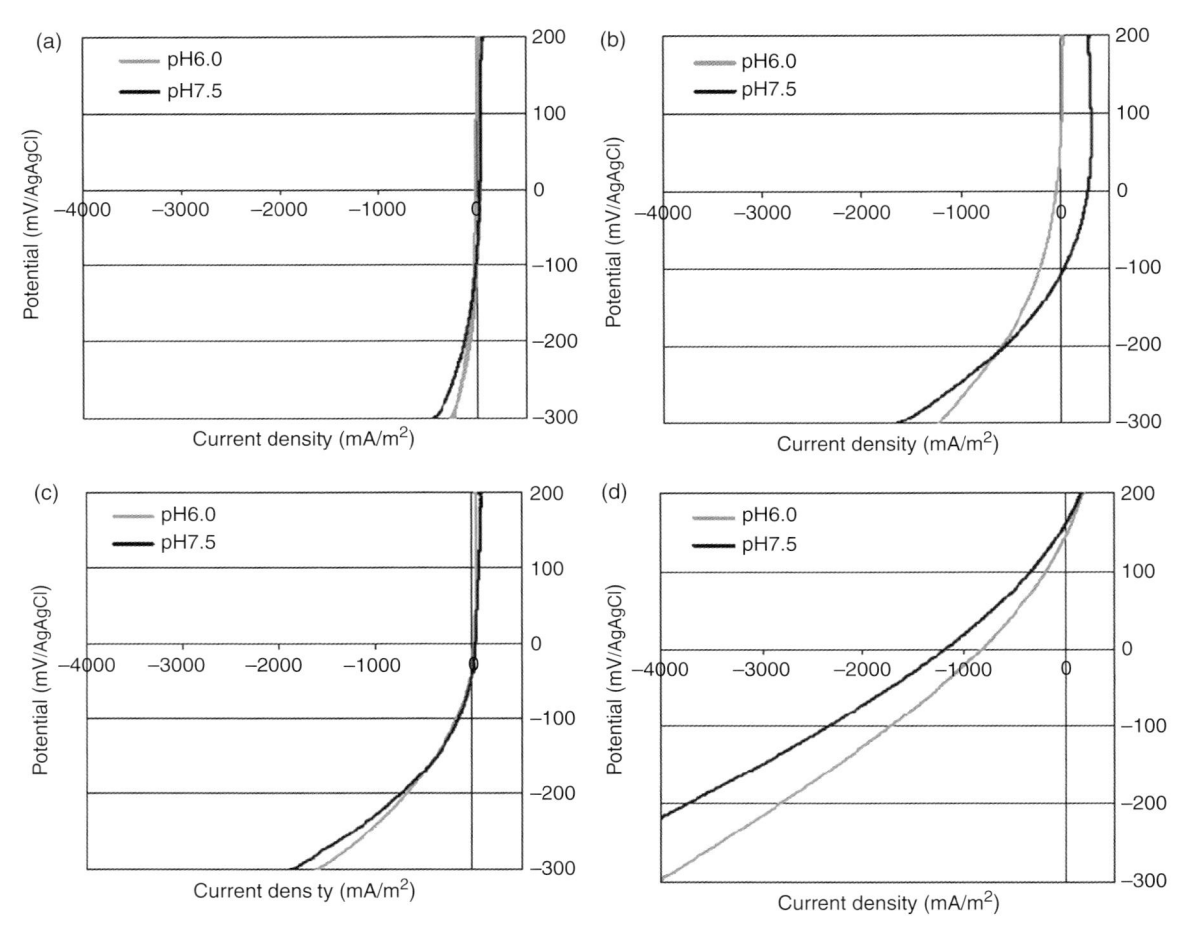

Figure 10 Effect of pH on noncatalyzed oxygen reduction – linear sweep of oxygen reduction with air-breathing cathode prepared from (a) untreated carbon Vulcan XC-72R, (b) H_2O_2-treated carbon Vulcan XC-72R, (c) HNO3-treated carbon Vulcan XC-72R, and (d) platinum supported on carbon Vulcan XC-72R. Reprinted with permission from Duteanu N, Erable B, Senthil Kumar SM, et al. (2010) Effect of chemically modified Vulcan XC-72R on the performance of air breathing cathode in a single chamber microbial fuel cell. *Bioresource Technology* 101: 5250–5255 [175]. Copyright (2010) Bioresource Technology – Elsevier.

The hydraulic retention time (HRT) affects the contact between the substrates and microorganisms. It is evident that higher HRT in the anode chamber favors higher treatment efficiency and higher power production [181]. The optimum HRT depends on the type of organic matter being treated, the reactor geometry, and the strength of the wastewater. The favorable HRTs reported in the literature are a little higher than the HRTs generally adopted for established wastewater treatment systems such as UASB reactor. Hence, to make the size of MFCs competitive with other already established treatment processes, it is required to modify the configuration of MFC to process higher OLR at lower HRTs.

SCMFC, with a high surface packed bed of irregular graphite granules as the anode, in batch and continuous mode operation, have been used to treat wastewater [182]. CEs varied from 30% to 74%, depending upon feed COD (**Table 1**). In continuous operation, the

Table 1 Effect of the COD loading rate in batch mode

Inlet COD (ppm)	Max current (mA)	Max volumetric power density (Wm^{-3})	Maximum power density (mWm^{-2})	COD removal (%)	Coulombic efficiency (%)	COD removed by non Faradaic reaction (%)
1000	0.450 ± 0.009	8.1	81	69 ± 1	30 ± 2	48
500	0.354 ± 0.007	4.9	49	62 ± 3	57 ± 5	27
200	0.331 ± 0.005	4.4	44	60 ± 5	76 ± 2	14
100	0.312 ± 0.009	3.8	38	68 ± 4	74 ± 1	18

Graphite granule bed depth: 3 cm. Fuel: AW. R_{ext}: 500 Ω

Table 2 Effect of the hydraulic retention time (HRT) on the SCMFC performance

Flow rate (cm³ min⁻¹)	HRT (min)	Current output at the steady state (mA)	Power output at the steady state (mW)	Coulombic efficiency (%)	COD removal (%)
0.028	446	0.413 ± 0.007	0.085 ± 0.004	63 ± 4.5	69 ± 5.2
0.1	125	0.478 ± 0.008	0.114 ± 0.005	44.3 ± 7	31.3 ± 4.6
1	12.5	0.55 ± 0.004	0.151 ± 0.003	7.4 ± 1.9	19.9 ± 4.1

Graphite granule bed depth: 3 cm. Fuel: AW with 200 ppm of COD. R_{ext}: 500 Ω

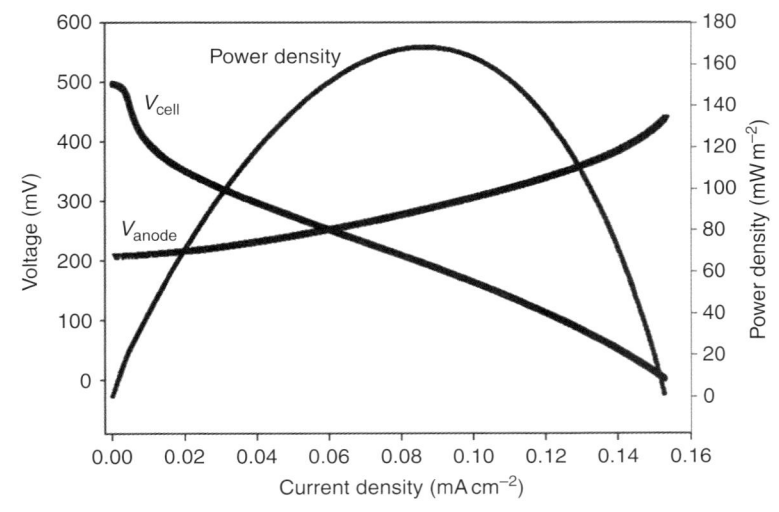

Figure 11 Polarization and power density curves for an MFC. Anode: graphite granules (3 cm layer). Power and current density refer to the anode area: 12.5 cm². The cells were fed with AW containing 1000 ppm as COD. Reproduced with permission from Yu FH and Sundmacher K (2007) Enzyme electrodes for glucose oxidation prepared by electropolymerization of pyrrole. *Process Safety and Environmental Protection* 85(5): 489–493. Copyright (2007) Elsevier [38].

COD removal of 89% and CE of 68% was reported with a feed COD of 1000 ppm and at a flow rate of 0.0028 cm³ min⁻¹. Power performance was a volumetric power density of 1.3 W m⁻³, with respect to the net anodic volume (12.5 cm³) (Figure 11).

Saturation-type relationships between substrate concentration and power or voltage generated are typically observed in MFCs at sufficiently high concentrations [157]. For example, when the effect of influent COD concentration in the wastewater, ranged from 129 to 1124 mg l⁻¹ was studied, the maximum power density was 164 mW m⁻², with a half-saturation concentration of 259 mg l⁻¹ [181]. At low COD concentration, electricity generation is limited by the anode due to kinetic limitations.

Conductivity of the wastewater in the anode chamber also affects the power output by reducing the internal resistance at higher conductivity and hence increasing the power [163]. An MFC used to treat paper recycling plant wastewater was reported to be limited by conductivity [183]. When only wastewater (conductivity 0.8 mS cm⁻¹) was used as a feed, a power density of 144 mW m⁻² was produced with total COD, soluble COD, and cellulose removals of approximately 29%, 51%, and 16%, respectively. When a 50 mM PBS (5.9 mS cm⁻¹) was added to the wastewater, power densities reached 501 mW m⁻² (CE of 16%), with removal of soluble COD of 73% and total COD removal of 76%. Cellulose was removed at levels up to 96% during treatment.

Nutrient requirement is also a factor that will influence MFC performance. Certain ratio of carbon source supplied as substrate to nitrogen and phosphorous is necessary to support the bacterial growth by avoiding nutrient limitation. The COD/N ratio required for the MFC-type wastewater treatment system is reported to be lower than the conventional treatment [184]. Nitrogen can be supplemented in the form of urea, ammonium sulfate, and ammonium nitrate producing equivalent power [185]. However, removal of nitrogen from the feed is reported to adversely affect power production. The effect of phosphorous concentration in the feed on performance of MFC is not available so far. In general, it appears that the 'P' requirement similar to anaerobic process satisfies the requirement of electrogenic, that is, anodophilic bacteria. The exact nutrient requirement of the MFC will depend on the type of microorganisms used in the anode for specific organic matter removal. Studies are required to establish exact macronutrient and micronutrient requirements of the electrogens to sustain their growth in the MFC.

4.11.3.6.4 MFC design

The geometrical design of the MFC, its dimensions and positioning of the electrode with respect to membrane, and the arrangement of influent and effluent for proper distribution of substrate to the anode chamber are among the parameters that will play an important role in MFC performance [186].

Oxygen in air is the obvious choice of oxidant for MFCs. Although other chemicals such as hydrogen peroxide, hexacyanoferrate $[Fe(CN)_6]^{3-}$, and permanganate can also be used as effective cathodic electron acceptors and give higher power density, they are not considered as sustainable because they still require continuous replacement. An alternative to oxygen is ferric ions which can be reduced to ferrous ions (Fe^{2+}) at the cathode. MFC with ferric iron reduction at the cathode and simultaneous biological ferrous iron oxidation of the catholyte was demonstrated using a bipolar membrane separating the anode and cathode [187]. The immobilized microorganism *Acidithiobacillus ferrooxidans* oxidized ferrous iron to ferric iron at a rate high enough to ensure an MFC power output of $1.2\,W\,m^{-2}$ and a current of $4.4\,A\,m^{-2}$.

In general, using air as an oxidant in MFCs is reliant on a suitable choice of catalyst material. A near neutral pH is not a preferred condition for good oxygen reduction kinetics [129]. Using dissolved oxygen in aqueous catholyte solutions will limit the cell voltage and power capabilities; hence air cathodes are frequently used to enhance the performance of MFCs. An air cathode MFC is an efficient configuration not requiring active aeration or addition of chemicals for cathodic reaction (**Figure 12**).

An alternative to oxygen reduction in MFCs is to use protons to form hydrogen gas. Such hydrogen can then be used as a fuel to generate energy by other power devices. However, such microbial electrolysis does not produce power in conjunction with hydrogen but requires a power input (some several hundred millivolts) to realize reasonable production rates. This is due to the difference of ~1.2 V in the standard potential for oxygen reduction and proton reduction.

The ideal material selected for the cell electrodes should offer a higher surface area per unit volume to maximize opportunity for direct growth of microorganisms on the anode surface. Graphite granules, felt, and carbon brush or fibers can be suitable alternatives for use as the electrodes. An electrode material offering very high surface area and very fine pore size may not be suitable as it may lead to the formation of dead pockets (area not used for direct growth of microorganism) and reduction in the MFC power output [188]. Graphite fiber brush anodes that have high surface areas and a porous structure can produce high power densities ($1430\,mW\,m^{-2}$, $2.3\,W\,m^{-3}$) as compared to other carbon forms [189]. A power density of as high as $2.01\,W\,m^{-2}$ has been reported for an MFC using a carbon brush anode [190]. Furthermore, it is required to explore the possibility of non-noble metal catalyst coating on the electrode surface to maximize power production with minimum cost for MFC construction.

The membrane used in MFCs to separate the anode from the cathode acts as an electrolyte and allows typically proton transfer. However, the use of membrane can limit the application of MFC for wastewater treatment. Proton transfer through the membrane may be a limiting factor especially due to membrane fouling expected due to suspended solids and soluble contaminants in large-scale wastewater treatment [191]. In addition, membranes are expensive and thus will limit acceptance of MFCs for large-scale wastewater treatment, due to higher production costs. Hence, to make MFC economically competitive, a low-cost alternative to the use of membranes or a design appraisal of the cell to eliminate the need for a membrane is needed. An issue with the membraneless design is to prevent large quantities of oxygen diffusing toward the anode chamber that would reduce the CE. A higher power density of $346\,mW\,m^{-2}$ was reported in mediatorless and membraneless MFC using plastic sieves rather than polymer electrolyte membrane (PEM) [170]. In another example, maximum power of $49\,W\,m^{-3}$ ($215\,A\,m^{-3}$) was reported for a membraneless MFC [192]. The use of porous fabrics such as J-Cloth, instead of PEM, was evaluated as a separator between the anode and the cathode. Due to the significant reduction of oxygen diffusion with two layers of J-Cloth, over a 100% increase in CE was demonstrated in comparison to cell without J-Cloth: power densities of $627\,W\,m^{-3}$ in fed-batch mode and $1010\,W\,m^{-3}$ in continuous-flow mode were reported [193]. Recently, Behera *et al.* [194] have demonstrated the performance of a low-cost MFC, with a relatively high volume of 400 ml, made from an earthen pot without using commercially available expensive membranes. This earthen pot MFC, with total production cost less than 1.0 US$, gave a maximum power output of $16.8\,W\,m^{-3}$, while treating synthetic wastewater, and demonstrated competitive performance compared to MFCs incorporating polymer membranes and expensive cathode catalysts.

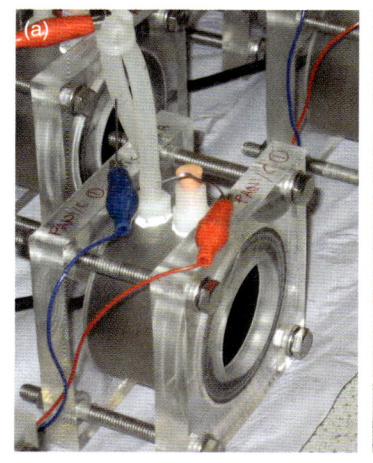

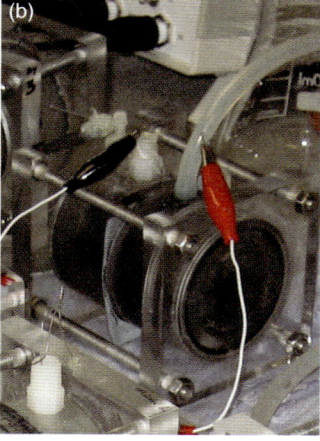

Figure 12 (a) Microbial fuel cell (MFC) with aqueous cathode, (b) MFC with aqueous cathode.

4.11.3.6.5 Inoculum in MFCs

Hydrolysis of complex polymers (transformation of complex polymers into substance that can be readily biodegraded by microbial consortium [195]) by hydrolytic organisms is the first and one of the most important steps in the bioconversion of organic waste. Despite the hydrolytic capabilities of many anaerobic bacteria by secretion of exocellular enzymes or attachment of the bacteria to the solid substrate, this step is considered to be the most rate-limiting in the fermentation of organic matter and is also usually yield-limiting in the biological conversion processes [196]. The lower efficiencies of anaerobic digestion are, in practice a result of the rigidly structured, slowly biodegradable compounds (e.g., plant waste lignocelluloses) in mixed waste streams. Efficiencies higher than 80% can be reached with high-quality biomass such as cellulolytic crops or carbohydrate-rich wastewaters from the food industry.

Pure cultures have frequently been used as inoculum of the MFC. Facultative anaerobic bacteria, *Aeromonas hydrophila* and *Enterobacter aerogenes*, were reported to be electrochemically active in the anode chamber of an MFC [124, 197]. The facultative anaerobe grows rapidly under aerobic conditions, consuming oxygen to oxidize organic substrates, and also grow under anaerobic conditions, degrading substrates into hydrogen and a residue. Due to the property of H_2 production and O_2 consumption, they are very suitable for an MFC [124]. *Ochrobactrum anthropi* YZ-1 has also demonstrated the ability to produce current using a wide range of substrates, including acetate, lactate, propionate, butyrate, glucose, sucrose, cellulose, glycerol, and ethanol [198]. A *Klebsiella pneumoniae* strain L17 biofilm also degraded starch and glucose to generate electricity [199] and *K. pneumoniae* biofilm cells showed DET from fuels to electrode.

Bacteria of the genus *Shewanella* are known for the diversity of terminal electron acceptors they can reduce and are one of the primary families of bacteria used in MFCs [200]. *Shewanella oneidensis* (originally known as *Shewanella putrefaciens*) is a nonfermenting, motile (self-propelled motion under appropriate circumstances), facultative anaerobic bacterium found in suboxic sediments (region where concentrations of oxygen is extremely low) [201]. *Shewanella oneidensis* MR-1 is the wild-type strain while *S. oneidensis* DSP10 is a spontaneous rifampin-resistant (a bactericidal antibiotic drug resistant) mutant more recently used in MFCs [202]. *S. oneidensis* grown with glucose in the presence of oxygen generates more power than under strictly anaerobic conditions, where the elimination of oxygen should typically increase the fuel cell efficiency and increase power output [203]. An increase in power with oxygen exposure is an indication that aerobic *S. oneidensis* can effectively utilize complex carbon sources as electron donors in MFCs.

G. sulfurreducens were reported to give higher power than when mixed anaerobic sludge is used as inoculum [143]. Phototrophic (the organisms that carry out photosynthesis to acquire energy) purple nonsulfur bacterium (*Rhodopseudomonas palustris* DX-1) can efficiently generate electricity by DET in MFCs using a wide range of substrates (volatile acids, yeast extract, and thiosulfate) making it another useful culture for high power generation (2720 $mW\,m^{-2}$) compared to mixed culture MFCs [204]. *Acidiphilium* sp. strain 3.2 Sup 5 cells, isolated from an extreme acidic environment, were reported to produce high currents, up to 3 $A\,m^{-2}$, by oxidizing glucose even with solution saturated in air and at very low pH [205]. Identification of such strains will be useful in the MFC for generation of higher current density as such strains are unaffected by the presence of oxygen, which will help in solving the problem of O_2 diffusion from the cathode and for developing MFC without membranes.

Metal-reducing bacteria *Rhodoferax ferrireducens* have been shown to play an important role in the anaerobic environment with sugars and that microbial electricity generation was attributed to the electrochemical and biological active cells attached to the electrode. Planktonic, that is, the cells grown in liquid suspension rather than attached to the electrode surface, cells showed limited/ no ability to catalyze electricity generation [206, 207].

The use of mixed cultures can develop higher current in MFCs due to wide acceptance of different forms of organic matter present in the real wastewaters as a substrate. Recent studies have shown that the MFC inoculated with mixed anaerobic sludge can also generate current densities comparable with selected pure cultures [186]. Domestic wastewater can also be used as an inoculum [170]. Heat treatment was reported to be effective for pretreatment of the inoculum to enhance power production in MFC [191]. Mild ultrasonication pretreatment to the mixed anaerobic sludge, used as inoculum, is also reported to be effective in improving MFC performance, and the performance reported was 2.5 times higher than that obtained without any pretreatment of the mixed anaerobic sludge [208].

Pretreatment of sludge is particularly important for suppressing the methanogens, the group of bacteria responsible for production of methane, present in the mixed anaerobic culture. Electrogenic bacteria have the ability to outcompete methanogens when nonfermentable substrate is used. However, typically when a fermentable substrate is used in MFCs, that is, in the case of real wastewater treatment, methane formation is reported in the MFC during longer operation times [209, 210]. Hence, a strategy is needed to suppress the methanogens during inoculation and also intermittently during reactor operation.

4.11.3.7 Microbial Electrolysis

An important spin-off from MFC research has been hydrogen production by 'microbial electrolysis cells' (MEC), which is particularly interesting because of the considerable international effort directed toward hydrogen's use as an energy carrier. Microbial electrolysis is effectively a biological analogue to chemical electrolysis in the same way that an MFC is a biological analogue to a chemical fuel cell. In MECs an organic substrate is oxidized microbially to generate protons that transfer to the cathode to be reduced to hydrogen gas (see **Figure 13**). In a MEC, the evolution of hydrogen at the cathode is the same as for traditional water electrolysis:

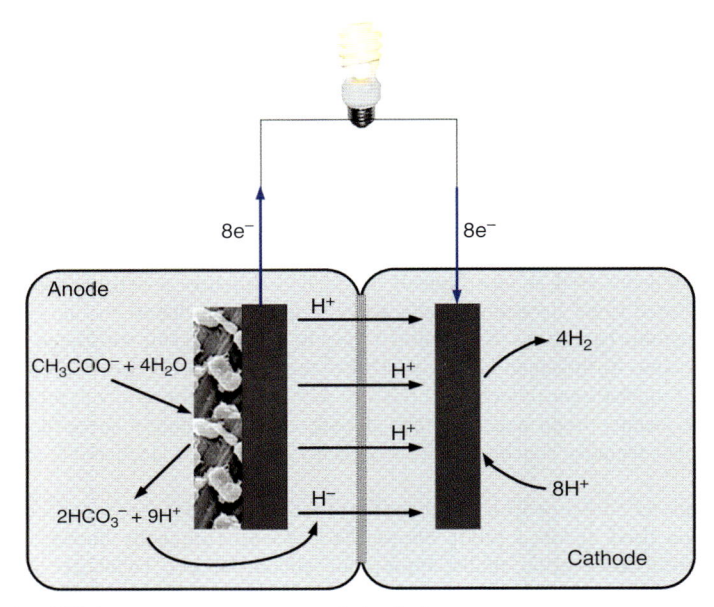

Figure 13 Schematic diagram of an MFC for wastewater treatment producing hydrogen.

$$2H^+ + 2e- \rightarrow H_2 \qquad [11]$$

while, at the anode, the oxidation of water is replaced by the oxidation of organic compounds, for example, acetate, which is converted to bicarbonate:

$$CH_3COO^- + 4H_2O \rightarrow 2HCO_3^- + 9H^+ + 8e- \qquad [12]$$

Comparing the thermodynamic equilibrium of this system, 0.236 V (at p. 7.0), to the 1.23 V required for water electrolysis indicates the promising potential of MEC technology. MEC technology has progressed rapidly in only a few years and production rates as high as 3.12 m^3 of H$_2$ m^{-3} day^{-1} have been reported [210, 211].

Overall the attractions of MECs are the very low energy requirements to produce hydrogen, for most substrates, and the ability to fully mineralize substrates to carbon dioxide, unlike most chemical electrolysis analogues. Furthermore, the selection of MECs over MFCs can be justified if hydrogen rather than electrical energy is required, but some technical reasons are equally compelling. Engineering cells for gas evolution is simpler and therefore less costly than for oxygen reduction; oxygen (air) reduction must overcome the mass transport limitations in gas diffusion electrodes as well as kinetic and catalytic limitations.

Two different functional MECs have been reported: first, using simple separators isolating anode and cathode solutions and second, a membraneless cell used to liberate hydrogen from a gas electrode [212, 213]. Using a substrate such as acetate is attractive as it offers a lower cost of operation in terms of energy and has considerable relevance to waste treatment. However, other more energetic substrates could deliver higher rates of hydrogen generation with associated lower capital cost per m^3 of hydrogen. Conventional electrolysis uses cell voltages of around 1.8 V and high current densities; orders of magnitude higher than in MECs, which dictates the energy cost. Thus, for MECs to compete with water electrolysis requires a major reduction in capital cost coupled to low-operating costs, which means operating at low cell voltages with low-cost cell design and materials. Thus, the vast majority of MEC research, which has demonstrated the concept, is not practical because of the use of high-cost materials such as Pt catalysts, gas diffusion electrodes, and Nafion membranes.

4.11.4 Conclusions

Rapid development on enzymatic biofuel cells has been achieved in the past decade. Much of the research has focused on establishing efficient electronic communications and interactions between enzyme and electrode using various approaches. With the demands for reliable power for medical devices for implantable applications, enzymatic biofuel cells have shown particular advantages over conventional energy devices because of the specific activity available from enzymes and the capability of miniaturization. In addition to medical applications, enzymatic biofuel cells can use renewable fuels with high energy density and safety for microelectronics.

However, there are great challenges for further advances in the technology. The most significant issues to achieve increased power output from biofuel cells include long-term stability of the enzyme electrodes; efficient electron transfer between enzymes and electrode surfaces; and improved enzyme biocatalytic activity. These are the main objectives for the next-generation enzyme electrodes for biofuel cells. In order to meet the challenges and achieve these goals, following areas are essential for pushing forward the technology for practical applications and commercialization:

1. Protein engineering of native enzyme molecules with desired properties tailored for specific applications.
2. New immobilization methods and biomaterials to improve the stability of enzymes.
3. Nanomaterials integrated in the enzyme electrode structure to improve the electron transfer and enzyme catalytic activity.
4. Novel fuel cell design configurations to improve the cell voltage and power output.

The development of MFCs is still in its infancy with the need for considerable improvements in power output from accessible substrates. Thus, most MFCs still require their fuel to be of low molecular nature. Abundant energy, stored primarily in the form of carbohydrates, can be found in waste biomass from agricultural, municipal, and industrial sources as well as in dedicated energy crops, such as corn and other grains. If a glucose molecule were to be completely oxidized to CO_2, there are potentially 24 electrons available, but there is no direct simple chemical method to harvest this process. Thus, exploitation of microorganisms that contain a range of enzymes to facilitate this transformation is of importance.

MFCs represent a promising technology for renewable energy production; their most likely near-term applications are as a method of simultaneous wastewater treatment and electricity production. They will be useful in other specialized applications as well – for example, as power sources for environmental sensors and environmental bioremediation. With modifications, MFC technologies could find applications ranging from hydrogen production to renewable energy production from biomass. Around 2 billion people worldwide do not have adequate sanitation, and a treatment system based on MFCs provides an opportunity to develop the technology, because the substrate is 'free' and wastewater must be treated.

Successful development of biofuel cell technology relies on the joint efforts from different disciplines: biology to understand biomolecules; chemistry for knowledge on biochemical reactions and electron transfer mechanisms; material science to develop novel materials with high biocompatibility and maintain activity from biomolecues; and chemical engineering to design and establish the system. This innovative technology will encourage energy production from renewable sources and will have major impacts and benefits for medical science, clinical research, and health care management. The cost of materials used to construct MFCs will be a key factor for the successful application of the technology at large scales.

Acknowledgment

The author thanks EPSRC for research fellowship (EP/C535456/1) to carry out this work.

References

[1] Zhang X-R, Yamaguchi H, and Cao Y (2010) Hydrogen production from solar energy powered supercritical cycle using carbon dioxide. *International Journal of Hydrogen Energy* 35(10): 4925–4932.
[2] Fischer M (1986) Review of hydrogen production with photovoltaic electrolysis systems. *International Journal of Hydrogen Energy* 11(8): 495–501.
[3] Steeb H, Mehrmann A, Seeger W, and Schnurnberger W (1985) Solar hydrogen production: Photovoltaic/electrolyzer system with active power conditioning. *International Journal of Hydrogen Energy* 10(6): 353–358.
[4] Joshi AS, Dincer I, and Reddy BV (2011) Solar hydrogen production: A comparative performance assessment. *International Journal of Hydrogen Energy* 36(17): 11246–11257.
[5] Derbal-Mokrane H, Benzaoui A, M'Raoui A, and Belhamel M (2011) Feasibility study for hydrogen production using hybrid solar power in Algeria. *International Journal of Hydrogen Energy* 36(6): 4198–4207.
[6] Aldo S (2005) Solar thermochemical production of hydrogen review. *Solar Energy* 78(5): 603–615.
[7] Burgess SJ, Tamburic B, Zemichael F, *et al.* (2011) Solar-Driven Hydrogen Production in Green Algae. In: Laskin A, Gadd G, and Sariaslani S (eds.) *Advances in Applied Microbiology*, pp. 71–110. Academic Press.
[8] EG&G Technical Services, I., ed. (2004) *Fuel cell handbook*, 7th edn. US Department of Energy, Morgantown, West Virginia.
[9] Duteanu N (2008) *Pile de combustie directa a metanolului echipate cu electrolit polimer solid*. Timisoara, Romania: Editura 'POLITEHNICA'.
[10] Liu Y and Dong SJ (2007) A biofuel cell harvesting energy from glucose-air and fruit juice-air. *Biosensors & Bioelectronics* 23: 593–597.
[11] Cracknell JA, Vincent KA, and Armstrong FA (2008) Enzymes as working or inspirational electrocatalysts for fuel cells and electrolysis. *Chemical Reviews* 108(7): 2439–2461.
[12] Ramanavicius A, Kausaite A, and Ramanaviciene A (2005) Biofuel cell based on direct bioelectrocatalysis. *Biosensors & Bioelectronics* 20(10): 1962–1967.
[13] Potter MC (1911) Electrical effects accompanying the decomposition of organic compounds. *Proceedings of the Royal Society of London (Series B, Containing Papers of a Biological Character)*. 84(571): 260–276.
[14] DelDuca MG, Friscoe JM, and Zurilla RW (1963) Developments in industrial microbiology. *American Institute of Biological Science* 4: 81–84.
[15] Rohrback GH, Scott WR, and Canfield JH (1962) Biochemical fuel cells. In: *Proceedings of the 16th Annual Power Sources Conference*, Fort Monmouth, NJ, 22–24 May. Defense Technical Information Center.
[16] Yao SJ, Appleby AJ, Geise A, *et al.* (1969) Anodic oxidation of carbohydrates and their derivatives in neutral saline solution. *Nature* 224: 921–922.
[17] USA (2004) Microbial fuel cell research continues. *Chemical Engineer* 762–763: 11.
[18] Woodward J, Mattingly SM, Danson M, *et al.* (1996) In vitro hydrogen production by glucose dehydrogenase and hydrogenase. *Nature Biotechnology* 14(7): 872–874.
[19] Mertens R and Liese A (2004) Biotechnological applications of hydrogenases. *Current Opinion in Biotechnology* 15(4): 343–348.
[20] Rigla M, Hernando ME, Gomez EJ, *et al.* (2008) Real-time continuous glucose monitoring together with telemedical assistance improves glycemic control and glucose stability in pump-treated patients. *Diabetes Technology & Therapeutics* 10(3): 194–199.
[21] Heller A (1999) Implanted electrochemical glucose sensors for the management of diabetes. *Annual Review of Biomedical Engineering* 1: 153–175.
[22] Calabrese Barton S, Gallaway J, and Atanassov P (2004) Enzymatic biofuel cells for implantable and microscale devices. *Chemical Reviews* 104(10): 4867–4886.
[23] Heller A (2004) Miniature biofuel cells. *Physical Chemistry Chemical Physics* 6(2): 209–216.

[24] Itamar W (2009) Biofuel cells: Harnessing biomass or body fluids for the generation of electrical power. *Fuel Cells* 9(1): 5.
[25] Suwansa-Ard S, Kanatharana P, Asawatreratanakul P, *et al.* (2005) Semi disposable reactor biosensors for detecting carbamate pesticides in water. *Biosensors & Bioelectronics* 21(3): 445–454.
[26] Tizzard AC and Lloyd-Jones G (2007) Bacterial oxygenases: *In vivo* enzyme biosensors for organic pollutants. *Biosensors & Bioelectronics* 22(11): 2400–2407.
[27] Liu LJ, Chen ZC, Yang SN, *et al.* (2008) A novel inhibition biosensor constructed by layer-by-layer technique based on biospecific affinity for the determination of sulfide. *Sensors and Actuators B-Chemical* 129(1): 218–224.
[28] The bioeconomy at work: Sony develops most efficient biofuel cell ever, powered by sugar (2007) Available from: http://news.mongabay.com/bioenergy/2007/08/bioeconomy-at-work-sony-develops-most-efficient.html.
[29] Yahiro AT, Lee SM, and Kimble DO (1964) Bioelectrochemistry: I. Enzyme utilizing bio-fuel cell studies. *Biochimica et Biophysica Acta (BBA) – Specialized Section on Biophysical Subjects* 88(2): 375–383.
[30] Rusling JF and Ito K (1991) Voltammetric determination of electron-transfer rate between an enzyme and a mediator. *Analytica Chimica Acta* 252(1–2): 23–27.
[31] Gallaway JW and Calabrese Barton SA (2008) Kinetics of redox polymer-mediated enzyme electrodes. *Journal of the American Chemical Society* 130(26): 8527–8536.
[32] Katz E, Lioubashevsky O, and Willner I (2004) Electromechanics of a redox-active rotaxane in a monolayer assembly on an electrode. *Journal of the American Chemical Society* 126(47): 15520–15532.
[33] Ishihara K, Oshida H, Endo Y, *et al.* (1992) Hemocompatibility of human whole blood on polymers with a phospholipid polar group and its mechanism. *Journal of Biomedical Materials Research* 26(12): 1543–1552.
[34] Ishihara K, Iwasaki Y, and Nakabayashi N (1998) Novel biomedical polymers for regulating serious biological reactions. *Materials Science & Engineering C-Biomimetic and Supramolecular Systems* 6(4): 253–259.
[35] Konno T, Watanabe J, and Ishihara K (2004) Conjugation of enzymes on polymer nanoparticles covered with phosphorylcholine groups. *Biomacromolecules* 5(2): 342–347.
[36] Nishizawa K, Konno T, Takai M, and Ishihara K (2008) Bioconjugated phospholipid polymer biointerface for enzyme-linked immunosorbent assay. *Biomacromolecules* 9(1): 403–407.
[37] Zhu Z, Wang M, Gautam A, *et al.* (2007) Directed evolution of glucose oxidase from Aspergillus niger for ferrocenemethanol-mediated electron transfer. *Biotechnology Journal* 2(2): 241–248.
[38] Yu EH and Sundmacher K (2007) Enzyme electrodes for glucose oxidation prepared by electropolymerization of pyrrole. *Process Safety and Environmental Protection* 85(5): 489–493.
[39] Willner I, Blonder R, Katz E, *et al.* (1996) Reconstitution of apo-glucose oxidase with a nitrospiropyran-modified FAD cofactor yields a photoswitchable biocatalyst for amperometric transduction of recorded optical signals. *Journal of the American Chemical Society* 118(22): 5310–5311.
[40] Xiao Y, Patolsky F, Katz E, *et al.* (2003) 'Plugging into enzymes': Nanowiring of redox enzymes by a gold nanoparticle. *Science* 299(5614): 1877–1881.
[41] Degani Y and Heller A (1988) Direct electrical communication between chemically modified enzymes and metal-electrodes.2. Methods for bonding electron-transfer relays to glucose-oxidase and d-amino-acid oxidase. *Journal of the American Chemical Society* 110(8): 2615–2620.
[42] Chen Q, de LumleyWoodyear T, Kenausis G, *et al.* (1997). Developments in 'wired' enzyme sensors. *Abstracts of Papers of the American Chemical Society* 213: 183-ANYL.
[43] Zhu ZW, Momeu C, Zakhartsev M, and Schwaneberg U (2006) Making glucose oxidase fit for biofuel cell applications by directed protein evolution. *Biosensors & Bioelectronics* 21(11): 2046–2051.
[44] Gooding JJ, Mearns F, Yang WR, and Liu JQ (2003) Self-assembled monolayers into the 21(st) century: Recent advances and applications. *Electroanalysis* 15(2): 81–96.
[45] Dieter T and Rennebergb R (2003) Encapsulation of glucose oxidase microparticles within a nanoscale layer-by-layer film: immobilization and biosensor applications. *Biosensors and Bioelectronics* 18(12): 1491–1499.
[46] Kudo H, Yagi T, Chu M, *et al.* (2008) Glucose sensor using a phospholipid polymer-based enzyme immobilization method. *Analytical and Bioanalytical Chemistry* 391(4): 1269–1274.
[47] Raitman OA, Katz E, Buckmann AF, and Willner I (2002) Integration of polyaniline/poly(acrylic acid) films and redox enzymes on electrode supports: An *in situ* electrochemical/surface plasmon resonance study of the bioelectrocatalyzed oxidation of glucose or lactate in the integrated bioelectrocatalytic systems. *Journal of American Chemical Society* 124(22): 6487–6496.
[48] Zhang S, Yang W, Niu Y, and Sun C (2004) Multilayered construction of glucose oxidase on gold electrodes based on layer-by-layer covalent attachment. *Analytica Chimica Acta* 523(2): 209–217.
[49] Gooding JJ, Erokhin P, Losic D, *et al.* (2001) Parameters important in fabricating enzyme electrodes using self-assembled monolayers of alkanethiols. *Analytical Sciences* 17(1): 3.
[50] Moehlenbrock MJ and Minteer SD (2008) Extended lifetime biofuel cells. *Chemical Society Reviews* 37: 1188–1196.
[51] Cooney MJ, Lau VSC, Martin G, and Minteer SD (2008) Enzyme catalysed biofuel cells. *Energy & Environmental Science* 1: 320–337.
[52] Heller A (1992) Electrical connection of enzyme redox centers to electrodes. *The Journal of Physical Chemistry* 96(9): 3579–3587.
[53] Bullen RA, Arnot TC, Lakeman JB, and Walsh FC (2006) Biofuel cells and their development. *Biosensors & Bioelectronics* 21(11): 2015–2045.
[54] Heller A (1990) Electrical wiring of redox enzymes. *Accounts of Chemical Research* 23: 128–134.
[55] Katz E, Shipway AN, and Willner I (2003) *Handbook of fuel cells*. In: Vielstich W, Gasteriger, HA, Lamm, A (eds.). London, UK: Wiley.
[56] Degani Y and Heller A (1987) Direct electrical communication between chemically modified enzymes and metal-electrodes.1. Electron-transfer from glucose-oxidase to metal-electrodes via electron relays, bound covalently to the enzyme. *Journal of Physical Chemistry* 91(6): 1285–1289.
[57] Bohmhammel K, Huttl R, Pritzkat K, and Wolf G (1993) Calorimetric investigations into enzyme catalysed glucose oxidation. *Thermochimica Acta* 217: 1–7.
[58] Bohmhammel K, Huttl R, Pritzkat K, and Wolf G (1993) Thermokinetic investigations into enzyme catalysed glucose oxidation. *Thermochimica Acta* 217: 9–18.
[59] Tamaki T, Ito T, and Yamaguchi T (2007) Immobilization of hydroquinone through a spacer to polymer grafted on carbon black for a high-surface-area biofuel cell electrode. *Journal of Physical Chemistry B* 111(34): 10312–10319.
[60] Katz E, Schlereth DD, Schmidt H-L, and Olsthoorn AJJ (1994) Reconstitution of the quinoprotein glucose dehydrogenase from its apoenzyme on a gold electrode surface modified with a monolayer of pyrroloquinoline q. *Journal of Electroanalytical Chemistry* 368(1–2): 165–171.
[61] Katz E, Schlereth DD, and Schmidt H-L (1994) Electrochemical study of pyrroloquinoline quinone covalently immobilized as a monolayer onto a cystamine-modified gold electrode. *Journal of Electroanalytical Chemistry* 367(1–2): 59–70.
[62] Schumacher D, Vogel J, and Lerche U (1994) Construction and applications of an enzyme electrode for determination of galactose and galactose-containing saccharides. *Biosensors & Bioelectronics* 9(2): 85–90.
[63] Vincent KA, Lenz JACO, Zebger I, *et al.* (2005) Electrocatalytic hydrogen oxidation by an enzyme at high carbon monoxide or oxygen levels. *Proceedings of the National Academy of Sciences of the United States of America* 102(47): 16951–16954.
[64] Willner I, Arad G, and Katz E (1998) A biofuel cell based on pyrroloquinoline quinone and microperoxidase-11 monolayer-functionalized electrodes. *Bioelectrochemistry and Bioenergetics* 44(2): 209–214.
[65] Willner I, HelegShabtai V, Blonder R, *et al.* (1996) Electrical wiring of glucose oxidase by reconstitution of FAD-modified monolayers assembled onto Au-electrodes. *Journal of the American Chemical Society* 118(42): 10321–10322.
[66] Katz E, Riklin A, Heleg-Shabtai V, *et al.* (1999) Glucose oxidase electrodes via reconstitution of the apo-enzyme: tailoring of novel glucose biosensors. *Analytica Chimica Acta* 385(1–3): 45–58.
[67] Willner I, Vered H-S, Blonder R, *et al.* (1996) Electrical wiring of glucose oxidase by reconstitution of FAD-modified monolayers assembled onto Au-electrodes. *Journal of American Chemical Society* 118(42): 10321.

[68] Li D, Zhang Y, and Li J (2003) Electrochemical study of 4-ferrocene thiophenol monolayers assembled on gold nanoparticles. *Microelectronic Engineering* 66(1–4): 91–94.
[69] Kawaguchi T, Tada K, and Shimazu K (2003) Redox and mass transport characteristics of domain-free mixed ferrocenyloctanethiol/alkanethiol monolayers on gold. *Journal of Electroanalytical Chemistry* 543(1): 41–49.
[70] Felgenhauer T, Rong H-T, and Buck M (2003) Electrochemical and exchange studies of self-assembled monolayers of biphenyl based thiols on gold. *Journal of Electroanalytical Chemistry* 550–551: 309–319.
[71] Schlereth DD and Kooyman RPH (1997) Self-assembled monolayers with biospecific affinity for lactate dehydrogenase for the electroenzymatic oxidation of lactate. *Journal of Electroanalytical Chemistry* 431(2): 285–295.
[72] Sato Y and Mizutani F (1997) Electrochemical responses of cytochrome c on a gold electrode modified with mixed monolayers of 3-mercaptopropionic acid and n-alkanethiol. *Journal of Electroanalytical Chemistry* 438(1–2): 99–104.
[73] Dong S and Li J (1997) Self-assembled monolayers of thiols on gold electrodes for bioelectrochemistry and biosensors. *Bioelectrochemistry and Bioenergetics* 42(1): 7–13.
[74] Krysinski P and Brzostowska-Smolska M (1998) Capacitance characteristics of self-assembled monolayers on gold electrode. *Bioelectrochemistry and Bioenergetics* 44(2): 163–168.
[75] Bourdillon C, Demaille C, Moiroux J, and Saveant JM (1994) Step-by-step immunological construction of a fully active multilayer enzyme electrode. *Journal of the American Chemical Society* 116(22): 10328–10329.
[76] Shoham B, Migron Y, Riklin A, *et al.* (1995) A bilirubin biosensor based on a multilayer network enzyme electrode. *Biosensors and Bioelectronics* 10(3–4): 341–352.
[77] Lowy DA and Finklea HO (1997) Gold electrodes with polyion multilayers and electrostatically bound redox couples. *Electrochimica Acta* 42(9): 1325–1335.
[78] Yoon HC and Kim HS (2000) Multilayered assembly of dendrimers with enzymes on gold: Thickness-controlled biosensing interface. *Analytical Chemistry* 72(5): 922–926.
[79] Calvo EJ, Battaglini F, Danilowicz C, *et al.* (2000) Layer-by-layer electrostatic deposition of biomolecules on surfaces for molecular recognition, redox mediation and signal generation. *Faraday Discussions* 116: 47–65.
[80] Ramanavicius A, Ramanaviciene A, and Malinauskas A (2006) Electrochemical sensors based on conducting polymer-polypyrrole. *Electrochimica Acta* 51(27): 6025–6037.
[81] Sung WJ and Bae YH (2000) A glucose oxidase electrode based on electropolymerized conducting polymer with polyanion-enzyme conjugated dopant. *Analytical Chemistry* 72(9): 2177–2181.
[82] Cosnier Serge CG and Watelet J-C (2001) A polypyrrole-bienzyme electrode (salicylate hydroxylase-polyphenol oxidase) for the interference-free determination of salicylate. *Electroanalysis* 13(11): 906–910.
[83] Yasuzawa M, Nieda T, Hirano T, and Kunugi A (2000) Properties of glucose sensors based on the immobilization of glucose oxidase in N-substituted polypyrrole film. *Sensors and Actuators B: Chemical* 66(1–3): 77–79.
[84] Cosnier S and Gondran CH (1999) Fabrication of biosensors by attachment of biological macromolecules to electropolymerized conducting films. *Analusis* 27(7): 558.
[85] Cosnier S, Senillou A, Gratzel M, *et al.* (1999) A glucose biosensor based on enzyme entrapment within polypyrrole films electrodeposited on mesoporous titanium dioxide. *Journal of Electroanalytical Chemistry* 469(2): 176–181.
[86] Trojanowicz M, Matuszewski W, and Podsiadla M (1990) Enzyme entrapped polypyrrole modified electrode for flow-injection determination of glucose. *Biosensors and Bioelectronics* 5(2): 149–156.
[87] Cosnier S, Deronzier A, and Roland JF (1992) Electrocatlatic oxidation of alcohols on carbon electrodes modified by functionalised polypyrrole RuO2 f lms. *Journal of Molecular Catalysis* 71(3): 303–315.
[88] Cosnier S (1998) Fabrication of amperometric biosensors by entrapment of enzymes in functionalized polypyrrole films. *Canadian Journal of Chemical Engineering* 76(6): 1000–1007.
[89] Cosnier S, Stoytcheva M, Senillou A, *et al.* (1999) A biotinylated conducting polypyrrole for the spatially controlled construction of an amperometric biosensor. *Analytical Chemistry* 71(17): 3692–3697.
[90] Ouerghi C, Touhami A, Jaffrezic-Renault N, *et al.* (2004) Electrodeposited biotinylated polypyrrole as an immobilization method for impedimetric immunosensors. *Ieee Sensors Journal* 4(5): 559–567.
[91] Cooper JC and Hall EAH (1993) Catalytic reduction of benzoquinone at polyaniline and polyaniline enzyme films. *Electroanalysis* 5(5–6): 385–397.
[92] Raitman OA, Eugenii K, Buckmann AF, and Willner I (2002) Integration of polyaniline/poly(acrylic acid) films and redox enzymes on electrode supports: An *in situ* electrochemical/surface plasmon resonance study of the bioelectrocatalyzed oxidation of glucose or lactate in the integrated bioelectrocatalytic systems. *Journal of American Chemical Society* 124(22): 6487.
[93] Xue HG, Shen ZQ, and Li CM (2005) Improved selectivity and stability of glucose biosensor based on *in situ* electropolymerized polyaniline-polyacrylonitrile composite film. *Biosensors & Bioelectronics* 20(11): 2330–2334.
[94] Raitman OA, Patolsky F, Katz E, and Willner I (2002) Electrical contacting of glucose dehydrogenase by the reconstitution of a pyrroloquinoline quinone-functionalized polyaniline film associated with an Au-electrode: An *in situ* electrochemical SPR study. *Chemical Communications* 8(17): 1936–1937.
[95] Shi LX, Xiao Y, and Willner I (2004) Electrical contacting of glucose oxidase by DNA-templated polyaniline wires on surfaces. *Electrochemistry Communications* 6(10): 1057–1060.
[96] Barton SC, Kim HH, Binyamin G, *et al.* (2001) The 'wired' laccase cathode: High current density electroreduction of O-2 to water at+0.7 V (NHE) at p. 5. *Journal of the American Chemical Society* 123(24): 5802–5803.
[97] Barton SC, Kim HH, Binyamin G, *et al.* (2001) Electroreduction of O-2 to water on the 'Wired' laccase cathode. *Journal of Physical Chemistry B* 105(47): 11917–11921.
[98] Kang C, Shin H, and Heller A (2006) On the stability of the 'wired' bilirubin oxidase oxygen cathode in serum. *Bioelectrochemistry* 68(1): 22–26.
[99] Soukharev V, Mano N, and Heller A (2004) A four-electron O-2-electroreduction biocatalyst superior to platinum and a biofuel cell operating at 0.88 V. *Journal of the American Chemical Society* 126(27): 8368–8369.
[100] Mano N, Mao F, and Heller A (2004) A miniature membrane-less biofuel cell operating at +0.60 V under physiological conditions. *ChemBioChem* 5(12): 1703–1705.
[101] Kim HH, Zhang YC, and Heller A (2004) Bilirubin oxidase label for an enzyme-linked affinity assay with O-2 as substrate in a neutral pH NaCl solution. *Analytical Chemistry* 76(8): 2411–2414.
[102] Mano N, Mao F, Shin W, *et al.* (2003) A miniature biofuel cell operating at 0.78 V. *Chemical Communications* 9(4): 518–519.
[103] Mano N, Fernandez JL, Kim Y, *et al.* (2003) Oxygen is electroreduced to water on a 'wired' enzyme electrode at a lesser overpotential than on platinum. *Journal of the American Chemical Society* 125(50): 15290–15291.
[104] Mano N, Kim HH, Zhang YC, and Heller A (2002) An oxygen cathode operating in a physiological solution. *Journal of the American Chemical Society* 124(22): 6480–6486.
[105] Barton SC, Pickard M, Vazquez-Duhalt R, and Heller A (2002) Electroreduction of O-2 to water at 0.6 V (SHE) at p. 7 on the 'wired' Pleurotus ostreatus laccase cathode. *Biosensors & Bioelectronics* 17(11–12): 1071–1074.
[106] Gregg BA and Heller A (1991) Redox polymer-films containing enzymes.2. Glucose-oxidase containing enzyme electrodes. *Journal of Physical Chemistry* 95(15): 5976–5980.
[107] Gregg BA and Heller A (1991) Redox polymer-films containing enzymes.1. A redox-conducting epoxy cement – Synthesis, characterization, and electrocatalytic oxidation of hydroquinone. *Journal of Physical Chemistry* 95(15): 5970–5975.
[108] Pishko MV, Michael AC, and Heller A (1991) Amperometric glucose microelectrodes prepared through immobilisation of glucose-oxidase in redox hydrogels. *Analytical Chemistry* 63(20): 2268–2272.
[109] Chen T, Barton SC, Binyamin G, *et al.* (2001) A miniature biofuel cell. *Journal of the American Chemical Society* 123(35): 8630–8631.
[110] Nakabayashi N and Williams DF (2003) Preparation of non-thrombogenic materials using 2-methacryloyloxyethyl phosphorylcholine. *Biomaterials* 24(13): 2431–2435.
[111] Yu E, Himuro Y, Takai M, and Ishihara K (2009) Feasibility study of introducing redox property by modification of PMBN polymer for biofuel cell applications. *Applied Biochemistry and Biotechnology* 160(4): 1094–1101.

[112] Himuro Y, Takai M, and Ishihara K (2009) Poly(vinylferrocene-co-2-hydroxyethyl methacrylate) mediator as immobilized enzyme membrane for the fabrication of amperometric glucose sensor. *Sensors and Actuators B-Chemical* 136(1): 122–127.
[113] Katz E, Willner I, and Kotlyar AB (1999) A non-compartmentalized glucose/O2 biofuel cell by bioengineered electrode surfaces. *Journal of Electroanalytical Chemistry* 479(1): 64–68.
[114] Katz E and Willner I (2003) A biofuel cell with electrochemically switchable and tunable power output. *Journal of the American Chemical Society* 125(22): 6803–6813.
[115] Amir L, Tam TK, Pita M, et al. (2008) Biofuel cell controlled by enzyme logic systems. *Journal of the American Chemical Society* 131(2): 826–832.
[116] Amir L, Tam TK, Pita M, et al. (2008) Biofuel cell controlled by enzyme logic systems. *Journal of the American Chemical Society* 131(2): 826–832.
[117] Togo M, Takamura A, Asai T, et al. (2007) An enzyme-based microfluidic biofuel cell using vitamin K-3-mediated glucose oxidation. *Electrochimica Acta* 52(14): 4669–4674.
[118] Ramanavicius A, Kausaite A, and Ramanaviciene A (2008) Enzymatic biofuel cell based on anode and cathode powered by ethanol. *Biosensors & Bioelectronics* 24(4): 761–766.
[119] Arechederra RL and Minteer SD (2009) Complete oxidation of glycerol in an enzymatic biofuel cell. *Fuel Cells* 9(1): 63–69.
[120] Sakai H, Nakagawa T, Tokita Y, et al. (2009) A high-power glucose/oxygen biofuel cell operating under quiescent conditions. *Energy & Environmental Science* 2(1): 133–138.
[121] Wang SC, Yang F, Silva M, et al. (2009) Membrane-less and mediator-free enzymatic biofuel cell using carbon nanotube/porous silicon electrodes. *Electrochemistry Communications* 11(1): 34–37.
[122] Cohen B (1931) The bacterial culture as an electrical half-cell. *Journal of bacteriology* 21: 18–19.
[123] Bennetto HP, Stirling JL, Tanaka K, and Vega CA (1983) Anodic reactions in microbial fuel cells. *Biotechnology and Bioengineering* 25(2): 559–568.
[124] Tanisho S, Kamiya N, and Wakao N (1989) Microbial fuel cell using *Enterobacter aerogenes*. *Bioelectrochemistry and Bioenergetics* 21(1): 25–32.
[125] McKinlay JB and Zeikus JG (2004) Extracellular iron reduction is mediated in part by neutral red and hydrogenase in *Escherichia coli*. *Applied and Environmental Microbiology* 70(6): 3467–3474.
[126] Bond DR and Lovley DR (2003) Electricity production by *Geobacter sulfurreducens* attached to electrodes. *Applied and Environmental Microbiology* 69(3): 1548–1555.
[127] Kim HJ, Hyun MS, Chang IS, and Kim BH (1999) A microbial fuel cell type lactate biosensor using a metal-reducing bacterium, *Shewanella putrefaciens*. *Journal of Microbiology and Biotechnology* 9(3): 365–367.
[128] Reguera G, Mccarthy KD, Mehta T, et al. (2005) Extracellular electron transfer via microbial nanowires. *Nature* 435(7045): 1098–1101.
[129] Duteanu NM, Ghangrekar MM, Erable B, and Scott K (2010) Microbial fuel cells – An option for wastewater treatment. *Environmental Engineering and Management Journal* 9(8): 1069–1087.
[130] Du Z, Li H, and Gu T (2007) A state of the art review on microbial fuel cells: A promising technology for wastewater treatment and bioenergy. *Biotechnology Advances* 25(5): 464–482.
[131] Park DH and Zeikus JG (2000) Electricity generation in microbial fuel cells using neutral red as an electronophore. *Applied and Environmental Microbiology* 66(4): 1292–1297.
[132] Wilkinson S, Klar J, and Applegarth S (2006) Optimizing biofuel cell performance using a targeted mixed mediator combination. *Electroanalysis* 18(19–20): 2001–2007.
[133] Vega CA and Fernandez I (1987) Mediating effect of ferric chelate compounds in microbial fuel cells with Lactobacillus plantarum, Streptococcus lactis, and Erwinia dissolvens. *Bioelectrochemistry and Bioenergetics* 17(2): 217–222.
[134] Davis F and Higson SPJ (2007) Biofuel cells-Recent advances and applications. *Biosensors and Bioelectronics* 22(7): 1224–1235.
[135] Gil GC, Chang IS, Kim BH, et al. (2003) Operational parameters affecting the performance of a mediator-less microbial fuel cell. *Biosensors & Bioelectronics* 18(4): 327–334.
[136] Kaufmann F and Lovely R (2001) Isolation and characterization of a soluble NADPH-independent Fe(III) reductase from *Geobacteria sulphurreducens*. *Journal of Bacteriology* 185(15): 4468–4476.
[137] Rabaey K, Boon N, Siciliano SD, et al. (2004) Biofuel cells select for microbial consortia that self-mediate electron transfer. *Applied and Environmental Microbiology* 70(9): 5373–5382.
[138] Bond DR and Lovley DR (2003) Electricity production by *Geobacter sulfurreducens* attached to electrodes. *Applied Environmental Microbiology* 69: 1548–1555.
[139] Chaudhuri SK and Lovely DR (2003) Electricity generation by direct oxidation of glucose in mediator-less microbial fuel cells. *Nature Biotechnology* 21(10): 1129–1232.
[140] Zhang T, Cui C, Chen S, et al. (2008) The direct electrocatalysis of *Escherichia coli* through electroactivated excretion in microbial fuel cell. *Electrochemistry Communications* 10(2): 293–297.
[141] Qiao Y, Li CM, Bao SJ, et al. (2008) Direct electrochemistry and electrocatalytic mechanism of evolved *Escherichia coli* cells in microbial fuel cells. *Chemical Communications* 21(11): 1290–1292.
[142] Pham TH, Boon N, Aelterman P, et al. (2008) Metabolites produced by *Pseudomonas* sp. enable a Gram-positive bacterium to achieve extracellular electron transfer. *Applied Microbiology and Biotechnology* 77(5): 1119–1129.
[143] Nevin KP, Richter H, Covalla SF, et al. (2008) Power output and columbic efficiencies from biofilms of *Geobacter sulfurreducens* comparable to mixed community microbial fuel cells. *Environmental Microbiology* 10(10): 2505–2514.
[144] Liu H, Cheng S, and Logan BE (2005) Power generation in fed-batch microbial fuel cells as a function of ionic strength, temperature, and reactor configuration. *Environmental Science and Technology* 39(14): 5488–5493.
[145] Logan BE, Murano C, Scott K, et al. (2005) Electricity generation from cysteine in a microbial fuel cell. *Water Research* 39(5): 942–952.
[146] Heilmann J and Logan BE (2006) Production of electricity from proteins using a microbial fuel cell. *Water Environment Research* 78(5): 531–537.
[147] Rismani-Yazdi H, Christy AD, Dehority BA, et al. (2007) Electricity generation from cellulose by rumen microorganisms in microbial fuel cells. *Biotechnology and Bioengineering* 97(6): 1398–1407.
[148] Oh S and Logan BE (2005) Hydrogen and electricity production from a food processing wastewater using fermentation and microbial fuel cell technologies. *Water Research* 39(19): 4673–4682.
[149] Wang X, Feng YJ, and Lee H (2008) Electricity production from beer brewery wastewater using single chamber microbial fuel cell. *Water Science and Technology* 57(7): 1117–1121.
[150] Min B and Logan BE (2004) Continuous electricity generation from domestic wastewater and organic substrates in a flat plate microbial fuel cell. *Environmental Science and Technology* 38(21): 5809–5814.
[151] You SJ, Zhao QL, Jiang JQ, and Zhang JN (2006) Treatment of domestic wastewater with simultaneous electricity generation in microbial fuel cell under continuous operation. *Chemical and Biochemical Engineering Quarterly* 20(4): 407–412.
[152] Rodrigo MA, Cañizares P, Lobato J, et al. (2007) Production of electricity from the treatment of urban waste water using a microbial fuel cell. *Journal of Power Sources* 169(1): 198–204.
[153] Ghangrekar MM and Shinde VB (2008) Simultaneous sewage treatment and electricity generation in membrane-less microbial fuel cell. *Water Science and Technology* 58(1): 37–43.
[154] Venkata Mohan S, Mohanakrishna G, Reddy BP, et al. (2008) Bioelectricity generation from chemical wastewater treatment in mediatorless (anode) microbial fuel cell (MFC) using selectively enriched hydrogen producing mixed culture under acidophilic microenvironment. *Biochemical Engineering Journal* 39(1): 121–130.
[155] Venkata Mohan S, Mohanakrishna G, Srikanth S, and Sarma PN (2008) Harnessing of bioelectricity in microbial fuel cell (MFC) employing aerated cathode through anaerobic treatment of chemical wastewater using selectively enriched hydrogen producing mixed consortia. *Fuel* 87(12): 2667–2676.
[156] Lu N, Zhou SG, Zhuang L, et al. (2009) Electricity generation from starch processing wastewater using microbial fuel cell technology. *Biochemical Engineering Journal* 43(3): 246–251.
[157] Min B, Kim J, Oh S, et al. (2005) Electricity generation from swine wastewater using microbial fuel cells. *Water Research* 39(20): 4961–4968.
[158] Jung RK, Dec J, Bruns MA, and Logan BE (2008) Removal of odors from swine wastewater by using microbial fuel cells. *Applied and Environmental Microbiology* 74(8): 2540–2543.

[159] Scott K and Murano C (2007) A study of a microbial fuel cell battery using manure sludge waste. *Journal of Chemical Technology and Biotechnology* 82(9): 809–817.
[160] You SJ, Zhao QL, Jiang JQ, et al. (2006) Sustainable approach for leachate treatment: Electricity generation in microbial fuel cell. *Journal of Environmental Science and Health – Part A Toxic/Hazardous Substances and Environmental Engineering* 41(12): 2721–2734.
[161] Latif MA, Ghufran R, Wahid ZA, and Ahmad A (2011) Integrated application of upflow anaerobic sludge blanket reactor for the treatment of wastewaters. *Water Research* 45(16): 4683–4699.
[162] Ren Z, Ward TE, and Regan JM (2007) Electricity production from cellulose in a microbial fuel cell using a defined binary culture. *Environmental Science and Technology* 41(13): 4781–4786.
[163] Liu H and Logan BE (2004) Electricity generation using an air-cathode single chamber microbial fuel cell in the presence and absence of a proton exchange membrane. *Environmental Science and Technology* 38(14): 4040–4046.
[164] Gavala HN, Angelidaki I, and Ahring BK (2003) Kinetics and modeling of anaerobic digestion process. *Advances in Biochemical Engineering/Biotechnology* 81: 57–93.
[165] Bohn I, Bjornsson L, and Mattiasson B (2007) Effect of temperature decrease on the microbial population and process performance of a mesophilic anaerobic bioreactor. *Environmental Technology* 28(8): 943–952.
[166] Aguayo J, Barra R, Becerra J, and Mart Á-nez M (2009) Degradation of 2,4,6-tribromophenol and 2,4,6-trichlorophenol by aerobic heterotrophic bacteria present in psychrophilic lakes. *World Journal of Microbiology and Biotechnology* 25(4): 553–560.
[167] Cheng S, Xing D, and Logan BE (2011) Electricity generation of single-chamber microbial fuel cells at low temperatures. *Biosensors and Bioelectronics* 26(5): 1913–1917.
[168] Larrosa-Guerrero A, Scott K, Head IM, et al. (2010) Effect of temperature on the performance of microbial fuel cells. *Fuel* 89(12): 3985–3994.
[169] Min B, Roman OB, and Angelidaki I (2008) Importance of temperature and anodic medium composition on microbial fuel cell (MFC) performance. *Biotechnology Letters* 30(7): 1213–1218.
[170] Zhan YL, Zhang PP, Yan GX, and Guo SH (2008) Constructing and operating of mediator- and membrane-less microbial fuel cell. *Gao Xiao Hua Xue Gong Cheng Xue Bao/Journal of Chemical Engineering of Chinese Universities* 22(1): 177–181.
[171] Feng Y, Wang X, Logan BE, and Lee H (2008) Brewery wastewater treatment using air-cathode microbial fuel cells. *Applied Microbiology and Biotechnology* 78(5): 873–880.
[172] Wrighton KC, Agbo P, Warnecke F, et al. (2008) A novel ecological role of the Firmicutes identified in thermophilic microbial fuel cells. *ISME Journal* 2: 1146–1156.
[173] Mathis BJ, Marshall CW, Milliken CE, et al. (2008) Electricity generation by thermophilic microorganisms from marine sediment. *Applied Microbiology and Biotechnology* 78(1): 147–155.
[174] Jong BC, Kim BH, Chang IS, et al. (2006) Enrichment, performance, and microbial diversity of a thermophilic mediatorless microbial fuel cell. *Environmental Science and Technology* 40(20): 6449–6454.
[175] Duteanu N, Erable B, Senthil Kumar SM, et al. (2010) Effect of chemically modified Vulcan XC-72R on the performance of air breathing cathode in a single chamber microbial fuel cell. *Bioresource Technology* 101: 5250–5255.
[176] Timur S, Anik U, Odaci D, and Lo Gorton L (2007) Development of a microbial biosensor based on carbon nanotube (CNT) modified electrodes. *Electrochemistry Communications* 9(7): 1810–1815.
[177] Lee HS, Parameswaran P, Kato-Marcus A, et al. (2008) Evaluation of energy-conversion efficiencies in microbial fuel cells (MFCs) utilizing fermentable and non-fermentable substrates. *Water Research* 42(6–7): 1501–1510.
[178] Thygesen A, Poulsen FW, Min B, et al. (2009) The effect of different substrates and humic acid on power generation in microbial fuel cell operation. *Bioresource Technology* 100(3): 1186–1191.
[179] Venkata Mohan S, Veer Raghavulu S, Srikanth S, and Sarma PN (2007) Bioelectricity production by mediatorless microbial fuel cell under acidophilic condition using wastewater as substrate: Influence of substrate loading rate. *Current Science* 92(12): 1720–1726.
[180] Zhang JN, Zhao QL, You SJ, et al. (2008) Continuous electricity production from leachate in a novel upflow air-cathode membrane-free microbial fuel cell. *Water Science and Technology* 57(7): 1017–1021.
[181] Li Z, Yao L, Kong L, and Liu H (2008) Electricity generation using a baffled microbial fuel cell convenient for stacking. *Bioresource Technology* 99(6): 1650–1655.
[182] Di Lorenzo M, Scott K, Curtis TP, and Head IM (2010) Effect of increasing anode surface area on the performance of a single chamber microbial fuel cell. *Chemical Engineering Journal* 156(1): 40–48.
[183] Huang L and Logan BE (2008) Electricity generation and treatment of paper recycling wastewater using a microbial fuel cell. *Applied Microbiology and Biotechnology* 80(2): 349–355.
[184] Virdis B, Rabaey K, Yuan Z, and Keller J (2008) Microbial fuel cells for simultaneous carbon and nitrogen removal. *Water Research* 42(12): 3013–3024.
[185] Tiwari KL, Jadhav SK, and Shukla P (2008) Effect of nitrogen sources on production capacity of microbial fuel cell. *Research Journal of Biotechnology* 3(2): 55–56.
[186] Jadhav GS and Ghangrekar MM (2008) Improving performance of MFC by design alteration and adding cathodic electrolytes. *Applied Biochemistry and Biotechnology* 151(2–3): 319–332.
[187] Ter Heijne A, Hamelers HVM, and Buisman CJN (2007) Microbial fuel cell operation with continuous biological ferrous iron oxidation of the catholyte. *Environmental Science and Technology* 41(11): 4130–4134.
[188] Aelterman P, Versichele M, Marzorati M, et al. (2008) Loading rate and external resistance control the electricity generation of microbial fuel cells with different three-dimensional anodes. *Bioresource Technology* 99(18): 8895–8902.
[189] Logan B, Cheng S, Watson V, and Estadt G (2007) Graphite fiber brush anodes for increased power production in air-cathode microbial fuel cells. *Environmental Science and Technology* 41(9): 3341–3346.
[190] HaoYu E, Cheng S, Scott K, and Logan B (2007) Microbial fuel cell performance with non-Pt cathode catalysts. *Journal of Power Sources* 171: 275–281.
[191] Ghangrekar MM and Shinde VB (2007) Performance of membrane-less microbial fuel cell treating wastewater and effect of electrode distance and area on electricity production. *Bioresource Technology* 98(15): 2879–2885.
[192] You S, Zhao Q, Zhang J, et al. (2008) Increased sustainable electricity generation in up-flow air-cathode microbial fuel cells. *Biosensors and Bioelectronics* 23(7): 1157–1160.
[193] Fan Y, Hu H, and Liu H (2007) Enhanced Coulombic efficiency and power density of air-cathode microbial fuel cells with an improved cell configuration. *Journal of Power Sources* 171(2): 348–354.
[194] Behera M, Jana PS, and Ghangrekar MM (2010) Performance evaluation of low cost microbial fuel cell fabricated using earthen pot with biotic and abictic cathode. *Bioresource Technology* 101(4): 1183–1189.
[195] Cammarota MC and Freire DMG (2006) A review on hydrolytic enzymes in the treatment of wastewater with high oil and grease content. *Bioresource Technology* 97(17): 2195–2210.
[196] Mata-Alvarez J, Mace S, and Llabres P (2000) Anaerobic digestion of organic solid wastes. An overview of research achievements and perspectives. *Bioresource Technology* 74(1): 3–16.
[197] Pham CA, Jung SJ, Phung NT, et al. (2003) A novel electrochemically active and Fe(III)-reducing bacterium phylogenetically related to *Aeromonas hydrophila*, isolated from a microbial fuel cell. *FEMS Microbiology Letters* 223(1): 129–134.
[198] Zuo Y, Xing D, Regan JM, and Logan BE (2008) Isolation of the exoelectrogenic bacterium *Ochrobactrum anthropi* YZ-1 by using a U-tube microbial fuel cell. *Applied and Environmental Microbiology* 74(10): 3130–3137.
[199] Zhang L, Zhou S, Zhuang L, et al. (2008) Microbial fuel cell based on *Klebsiella pneumoniae* biofilm. *Electrochemistry Communications* 10(10): 1641–1643.
[200] Logan BE, Hamelers B, Rozendal R, et al. (2006) Microbial fuel cells: Methodology and technology. *Environmental Science and Technology* 40(17): 5181–5192.
[201] Biffinger JC, Pietron J, Bretschger O, et al. (2008) The influence of acidity on microbial fuel cells containing *Shewanella oneidensis*. *Biosensors and Bioelectronics* 24(4): 906–911.

[202] Ringeisen BR, Henderson E, Wu PK, *et al.* (2006) High power density from a miniature microbial fuel cell using *Shewanella oneidensis* DSP10. *Environmental Science & Technology* 40(8): 2629–2634.

[203] Biffinger JC, Byrd JN, Dudley BL, and Ringeisen BR (2008) Oxygen exposure promotes fuel diversity for *Shewanella oneidensis* microbial fuel cells. *Biosensors & Bioelectronics* 23(6): 820–826.

[204] Xing D, Zuo Y, Cheng S, *et al.* (2008) Electricity generation by *Rhodopseudomonas palustris* DX-1. *Environmental Science and Technology* 42(11): 4146–4151.

[205] Malki M, De Lacey AL, Rodriguez N, *et al.* (2008) Preferential use of an anode as an electron acceptor by an acidophilic bacterium in the presence of oxygen. *Applied and Environmental Microbiology* 74(14): 4472–4476.

[206] Liu JL, Lowy DA, Baumann RG, and Tender LM (2007) Influence of anode pretreatment on its microbial colonization. *Journal of Applied Microbiology* 102(1): 177–183.

[207] Liu ZD, Lian J, Du ZW, and Li HR (2006) Construction of sugar-based microbial fuel cells by dissimilatory metal reduction bacteria. *Chinese Journal of Biotechnology* 22(1): 131–137.

[208] More TT and Ghangrekar MM (2010) Improving performance of microbial fuel cell with ultrasonication pre-treatment of mixed anaerobic inoculum sludge. *Bioresource Technology* 101(2): 562–567.

[209] Clauwaert P and Verstraete W (2008) Methanogenesis in membraneless microbial electrolysis cells. *Applied Microbiology and Biotechnology* 82: 829–836.

[210] Logan BE, Call D, Cheng S, *et al.* (2008) Microbial electrolysis cells for high yield hydrogen gas production from organic matter. *Environmental Science and Technology* 42(23): 8630–8640.

[211] Logan BE and Regan JM (2006) Electricity-producing bacterial communities in microbial fuel cells. *Trends in Microbiology* 14(12): 512–518.

[212] Tartakovsky B, Manuel MF, Wang H, and Guiot SR (2009) High rate membrane-less microbial electrolysis cell for continuous hydrogen production. *International Journal of Hydrogen Energy* 34(2): 672–677.

[213] Call D and Logan BE (2008) Hydrogen production in a single chamber microbial electrolysis cell lacking a membrane. *Environmental Science & Technology* 42(9): 3401–3406.

4.12 Hydrogen and Fuel Cells in Transport

K Kendall and BG Pollet, University of Birmingham, Birmingham, UK

© 2012 Elsevier Ltd. All rights reserved.

4.12.1	Introduction	281
4.12.2	Choice of Fuel Cell Technology	282
4.12.3	Hydrogen Production, Usage, and Infrastructure	283
4.12.4	Hydrogen Vehicles	284
4.12.4.1	Forklifts	284
4.12.4.2	Other Early Markets	285
4.12.4.3	Buses	286
4.12.4.4	Cars	287
4.12.4.5	Ships	289
4.12.4.6	Aircraft	290
4.12.5	Legislation	291
4.12.6	Conclusions	292
References		292

4.12.1 Introduction

Decarbonizing transport is proving to be one of the largest R&D projects of the early twenty-first century. There are around 800 million vehicles in use worldwide and the motor industry is therefore one of the largest global forces, employing millions of people, and generating about 60 million cars and 20 million trucks each year, a value chain in excess of $3 trillion per annum and 4.6 billion tons of CO_2 per annum worldwide (ca. 17% of mankind's greenhouse gas emissions) [1]. This ever increasing demand for personal mobility and near total dependence on liquid hydrocarbons means that emission reductions from this sector will be a great challenge. Since hydrogen and fuel cells offer zero emissions and doubling of efficiency (similar to battery electric drives) when compared to conventional internal combustion engines (ICEs), there should be a large impact of these technologies on the transportation sector.

The development of alternate fuels to petrol and diesel has been ongoing since the 1970s, initially in response to the oil shocks and concerns over urban air pollution. Efforts have gained momentum more recently as the volatility of oil prices and stability of supplies, not to mention the consequences of global climate change, have risen up political agendas the world over. Low-carbon technologies are therefore rapidly advancing, with biofuel, petrol and diesel hybrids, battery electric, and hydrogen fuel cell cars being developed by nearly every major manufacturer. It seems likely that a number of technologies will move forward together, gradually evolving into an optimum low-carbon solution, with hydrogen as the accepted long-term prospect.

Projections estimate that the world fuel cell market is expected to reach nearly $19.2 billion by 2020 [2], including transport, buildings, and portable applications. In the United Kingdom, targets for hydrogen and fuel cells in transport have been set by the Department of Energy and Climate Change (DECC) and the Technology Strategy Board (TSB), with durability of fuel cells up to 8000 h and cost targets for longer term sustainable hydrogen production below €5 kg^{-1}. It is hoped that breakthroughs will allow the industry to achieve commercial cost and performance targets of €45 kW^{-1} for a fuel cell with membrane power densities above 1 W cm^{-2} for transport.

However, there are two major problems in hydrogen and fuel cells for transport: hydrogen is rarely available to the consumer, while fuel cell cars are too expensive. Both hydrogen availability at filling stations and cheap fuel cell vehicles are needed if breakthroughs are to be achieved. The two main incentives for change, efficiency and zero emission, have not been sufficiently valued to date. Zero Emission Vehicle (ZEV) legislation initiated in the 1990s has since stalled [3], and the overall efficiency of the new vehicles has been disappointing when compared with pure battery and hybrid combustion vehicles [4], suggesting that the tank-to-wheels efficiency of fuel cell cars might be only about 22% rather than the figures of around 40% suggested by enthusiasts and available from battery electric cars.

Offsetting these problems, there have been many successful demonstration projects around the world [5] with hundreds of fuel cell vehicles and dozens of hydrogen refueling stations. All major vehicle manufacturers have created prototype vehicles and shown interesting performance data, but the date for commercialization is still some years away, typically 2015 [4]. By 2050, it has been estimated using an optimistic scenario that there will be around 50% penetration of the car market by hydrogen vehicles, with most of those in China. But such predictions are prone to error [6]. **Figure 1** suggests a likely future in which trucks and other long distance vehicles will still operate largely on diesel, probably biofuel, perhaps with some hybridization, but city cars will move almost totally to electric drives, with hydrogen storage as a common option for extended range and rapid refilling. So battery electric drives will be very common as cities progressively ban hydrocarbon emissions, with hybridization using hydrogen fuel cells a key feature. Since half the world population will live in cities, they will prefer battery commuter cars, whereas the other half need longer

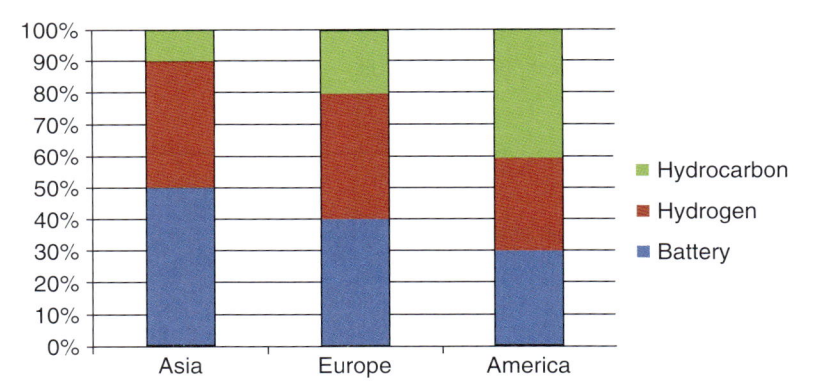

Figure 1 Chart predicting penetration of hydrogen in vehicles by 2050.

range hydrogen vehicles for rural driving. Therefore, our conclusion is that vehicles will be around 50/50 battery electric or battery/fuel cell hybrids in 2050, with some still running on hydrocarbons, particularly biofuel, especially in the Americas.

The purpose of this chapter is to review the progress in accepting hydrogen and fuel cell transport, starting with the most successful demonstrations today in forklifts and illustrating the competition from conventional fuels in early markets. Then, bus and car demonstrations are considered, putting the case for hydrogen fuel cell/battery hybrids, followed by specialized long-term boat and aircraft applications.

4.12.2 Choice of Fuel Cell Technology

When oil, one of the most important energy sources in the history of mankind, was first discovered in Pennsylvania almost 150 years ago, the fuel cell had already been known for 20 years, invented by Sir William Grove 'father of the fuel cell' in 1839. Back then it was an idea that was far ahead of its time. Today, however, it is the most important development in the history of decentralized electricity supply [7].

- A fuel cell is an 'electrochemical' device, operating at various temperatures, that transforms the chemical energy of a fuel (hydrogen, methanol, natural gas, etc.) into electrical energy, when reacting with an oxidant (air or oxygen) in the presence of a catalyst (also so-called electrocatalyst (EC)), producing water, heat, and electricity. There are currently five main fuel cells available on the market [7]. Alkaline fuel cells (AFCs), also known as the Bacon fuel cell after its British inventor, are the most developed fuel cells in terms of history. NASA has used AFCs since the mid-1960s in Apollo-series missions and on the Space Shuttle (it is this fuel cell that flew man to the Moon!). AFCs consume hydrogen and pure oxygen producing water, heat, and electricity and they operate below 80 °C. They are among the most efficient fuel cells, with the potential to reach up to 70% efficiency.
- Phosphoric acid fuel cells (PAFCs) use liquid phosphoric acid as the electrolyte. PAFCs consume hydrogen and oxygen or air producing water, heat, and electricity with an efficiency of up to 50%. The primary manufacturer of PAFC technology is UTC Power in the United States (also known as UTC Fuel Cells). As of 2005, there were close to 300 'PureCell' 200 kW units by UTC Power in service globally.
- Solid oxide fuel cells (SOFCs) are high-temperature fuel cells, operating typically between 700 and 1000 °C with efficiencies of up to 60%. An SOFC is made up of four layers, three of which are made of ceramics. SOFCs have so far been operated on methane, propane, and butane as fuels.
- Molten-carbonate fuel cells (MCFCs) operate at temperatures of up to 650 °C. They were initially developed for natural gas and coal-based power plants for electrical utility, industrial, and military applications.
- Proton exchange membrane fuel cells (PEMFCs), also known as polymer electrolyte membrane fuel cells, are currently being developed for transport applications as well as stationary and portable applications (**Figure 2**). There are two types of PEMFCs: one uses hydrogen as fuel – hydrogen PEMFC – and the other uses alcohol (e.g., ethanol, methanol) – direct alcohol fuel cell (DAFC) and direct methanol fuel cell (DMFC). Both types of PEMFCs use membrane electrode assemblies (MEAs), which are the heart of the fuel cell. Hydrogen PEMFCs consume hydrogen and oxygen/air producing water, heat, and electricity with an efficiency of up to 60% and operating at up to 150 °C. A DMFC consumes methanol in water and oxygen producing water, heat, and electricity with an efficiency of up to 40% and operating at up to 80 °C.

PEMFC is a technology that was initially developed for military and spacecraft applications at GE (General Electric, USA) in the 1960s but was abandoned in the 1970s due to high cost and poor durability issues. From the 1980s, a revival in PEMFC R&D was noticeable, mainly in the portable and vehicular applications, in several companies such as the Canadian company Ballard Power Systems. To date, PEMFC technology has been extended to wider applications, with the potential to power a portfolio of devices and

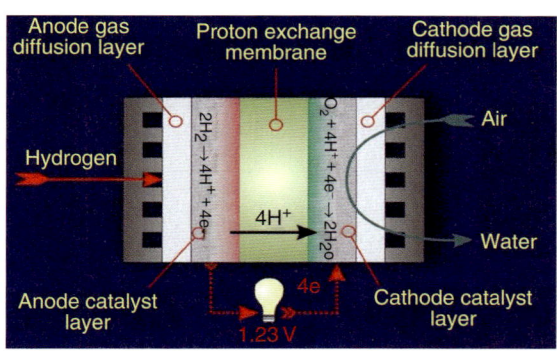

Figure 2 Proton exchange membrane fuel cell (PEMFC) diagram, a 1 kW PEMFC stack, and a 1.2 kW PEMFC Ballard Nexa power supply.

services, for example, mobile phones, personal electronic devices (PDAs) laptops, cars, buses, boats, houses, telecommunication stations, and space shuttles. In recent years, the PEMFC has been extensively demonstrated worldwide [8] in many application fields and is now being commercialized in early markets by Ballard, Hydrogenics, Intelligent Energy, and other companies.

However, cost and durability are still the two major barriers for large-scale manufacturing and full commercialization of this technology. For example, the EC is the main contributor to the PEMFC's limited performance, high cost, and poor durability. Currently, only Pt or Pt-based catalysts (e.g., Pt-Co) are practical for driving the electrochemical reactions in a PEMFC environment. Platinum comprises a large portion of the PEMFC cost due to its high price and limited supply. In a state-of-the-art PEMFC stack, the EC accounts for ca. 60% of the total cost, which is much higher than the cost of any other single component, for example, the polymeric proton exchange membrane (PEM) (10%), bipolar plate (BPP) (10%), and gas diffusion layer (GDL) (10%). Furthermore, catalyst stability is one of the major limitations on PEMFC durability, which is an important step in achieving the commercialization of PEMFC. Thus, developing high-performance, low-cost, and highly durable catalysts is the number one set of priorities for PEMFC research.

4.12.3 Hydrogen Production, Usage, and Infrastructure

Hydrogen has a very good energy content by weight: around 3 times that of gasoline and almost 7 times that of coal (hydrogen has the highest oxidation energy content of all fuels on a weight basis – 143 kJ g^{-1} [8]). However, the energy density of hydrogen per unit volume is quite low. Given that 5 kg of hydrogen is equivalent to about 5 gallons or 22 l of petrol [7, 8], to store it under ambient conditions would require a 5 m diameter vessel, which is impractical for most applications. Its volumetric energy density can be increased by storing the hydrogen under either increased pressure, at extremely low temperatures as a liquid, or in metal-hydride (M-H) systems. So hydrogen fuel storage for transport use remains a key issue.

Fifty million tons of hydrogen are produced globally, mainly through the reformation of fossil fuels, and almost 1 million tons of hydrogen are produced in the United Kingdom annually [8]. Recent worldwide hydrogen production totals show that 48% of hydrogen is produced from natural gas, 30% from oil, 18% from coal, and only 4% from renewables, mainly by electrolysis. Hydrogen is currently used in the chemical processing and petroleum industries, for the production of fats, oils, metals, and electronics, and as a fuel in space flight. Consequently, hydrogen is available in chemical plants but is not 'green' at present; in other words, it is not normally produced from renewable resources.

There is currently little hydrogen infrastructure in the United Kingdom. There are around 10 functional hydrogen refueling stations in Britain with 3 located in the Midlands at the University of Birmingham (**Figure 3**), Loughborough University, and

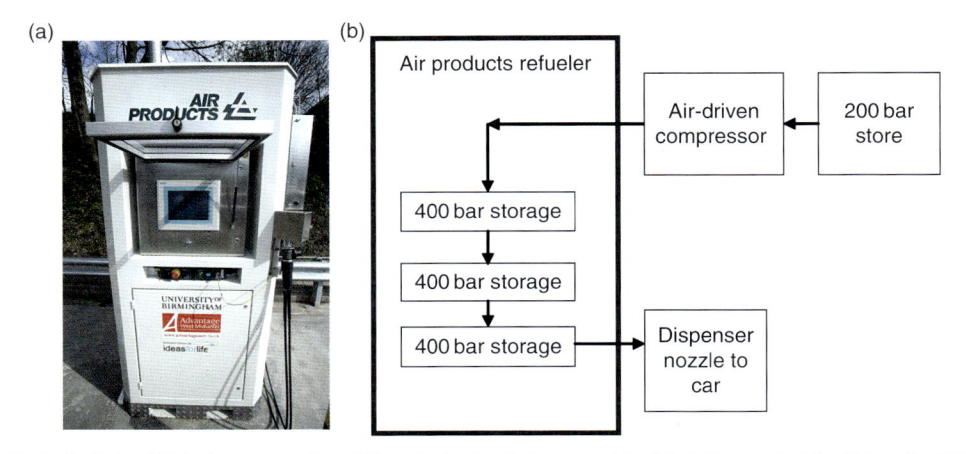

Figure 3 (a) Air Products Series 100 hydrogen refueling station, Centre for Hydrogen and Fuel Cells Research at the University of Birmingham. (b) Schematic showing the storage within the station, the remote storage, and the remote compressor.

Coventry University. However, plans are under way to implement a further series of hydrogen refueling stations in the Midlands, later spreading to the rest of the United Kingdom, giving more investment in infrastructure.

The refueler shown in **Figure 3(a)** was installed to fuel campus vehicles, with a capacity of 10–12 kg day^{-1} (1.8–2 kg per fill at 350 bar), sufficient for the five vehicle fleet. For such a small number of fillings, the refueler cost was $3 per filling, but the cost of green hydrogen, delivered by road from a waste food plant, was much more, that is, $15 per filling. **Figure 3(b)** shows the three 400 bar composite hydrogen storage tanks in the refueler. These were pumped up from the remote 200 bar steel cylinder store using an air-driven compressor located in the nearby building. The installation fitted the standard regulations for refueling 350 bar hydrogen vehicles defined in 2006 [9] and dispensed hydrogen into the vehicle storage tank at 350 bar by cascading from the three 400 bar tanks in the refueler. Using this standard [9] ensures that higher pressure hydrogen cannot be plugged in, nor can other gases like compressed natural gas.

4.12.4 Hydrogen Vehicles

4.12.4.1 Forklifts

Once the hydrogen refueler has been installed, the use of a vehicle fleet on a campus or a factory site becomes attractive. This has been proven particularly for hydrogen forklifts in warehouses. Considering the 2009 world market for fuel cells, about $330 million comprising around 24 000 units shipped, mainly in telecoms and other stationary applications [10], the major emerging market is forklifts for use in the multibillion dollar warehousing and distribution business. At present, battery and hydrocarbon combustion forklifts dominate, but hydrogen has advantages of greater range, quicker charging, less downtime, and steadier voltages, taking up less space and with fewer recycling issues. In the United States, around 1000 fuel cell forklifts [11] are now operating because they are significantly more efficient than battery vehicles. The Department of Energy and Department of Defense have recently been promoting this technology with five new projects to deploy 300 forklifts at large companies such as FedEx, Genco, and Sysco. In Europe, Linde have been following a similar path using Hydrogenics fuel cells to replace batteries, with 1.6 kg of hydrogen stored in composite cylinders at 350 bar [11, 12]. Supercapacitors provide pulse power to the electric motor while batteries are completely eliminated.

A recent installation on a greenfield site took place at Joliet, Illinois, for Central Grocers where 220 Plug Power fuel cell forklifts were fueled by hydrogen stored outside in a liquid storage and pumping facility shown in **Figure 4**. Multiple indoor gaseous hydrogen fueling points could fill each forklift in less than 2 min. The subsidy encouraging the installation was a tax credit of $3000 per kW up to 30% of unit price.

Figure 4 Hydrogen forklift in a warehouse and outside the liquid hydrogen installation.

Naturally, there has been some skepticism from the existing battery and truck providers, who claim that the investment costs are up to 50% higher and that new batteries such as lithium ion can provide solutions to the rapid charging and durability issues [12]. Two-year payback is the claim made by fuel cell manufacturers. The debate will run on for the next decade before the full results become available, and it may be that the answer is neither a pure battery nor a pure hydrogen solution. A combination of both, for example, fuel cell/lithium battery hybrid drive, may be a realistic solution as reviewed later in Section 4.12.4.4. The other option is using methanol as fuel by inserting DMFC battery chargers in conventional battery forklifts as demonstrated by Oorja [13].

4.12.4.2 Other Early Markets

The original early markets postulated 5 years ago, such as bicycles and trains, have not seen the success originally estimated [14]. Instead, in 2007, a large increase in fuel cell auxiliary power units (APUs) was observed, with the main application being APUs for recreational vehicles (RVs) in the United States and Europe. These were mainly polymer electrolyte membrane (PEM) generators built in Germany using DMFC technology. Typically 4000 units per year were supplied by Smart Fuel Cell (SFC AG) and were installed in camper vans and other leisure vehicles (Figure 5) and operated in national parks and areas where conventional combustion engine generators were restricted because of noise, fire risk, and other problems. The product EFOY (energy for you) was certified by TUV Sud in 2005 and began to sell significantly in 2007 [15, 16]. It is available from 48 RV manufacturers in Europe and there are 1400 consumer outlets for the 5 or 10 l methanol cartridges which can last for weeks.

Methanol was relatively easy to package in plastic cartridges, but hydrogen has not proved so easy to distribute to consumers, although a number of companies have attempted to make hydride storage cartridges available across the counter in shops. Instead, methanol has proved to be the most readily available fuel for PEM cells. Similarly, propane and camping gas are widely available for SOFCs, which have also been suggested for the RV markets. From the mobile home market, there are possible entries into the motorbike, the invalid carriage, and other small battery fuel cell hybrid applications [17]. Since the first fuel cell bike was shown by Karl Kordesch in 1967 [18], there has been steady development, with more than 30 companies posting information about their potential products [17]. However, the pure battery electric bike has dominated over the fuel cell, especially in China where 30 million battery electric bikes and scooters are made by 150 companies each year. The problem with a pure battery energy storage is the limited range of the bike, depending on the battery technology, whether lead-acid, NiCd, or lithium ion. The benefit of the fuel cell is that it raises the power and gives extended range, as in the experimental model developed at Loughborough shown in Figure 6, which increased the range from 25 miles on the four lead-acid batteries to 100 miles with the 2.4 kWh of hydrogen stored. In this design, the hydrogen was stored as pressurized gas at 350 bar. M-H stores have also been attempted but are not satisfactory

Figure 5 EFOY fuel cell generating 90 W_e and Motorhome Globe 4 containing an SFC fuel cell running on methanol.

Figure 6 Fuel cell hybrid bike developed by Intelligent Energy at Loughborough University.

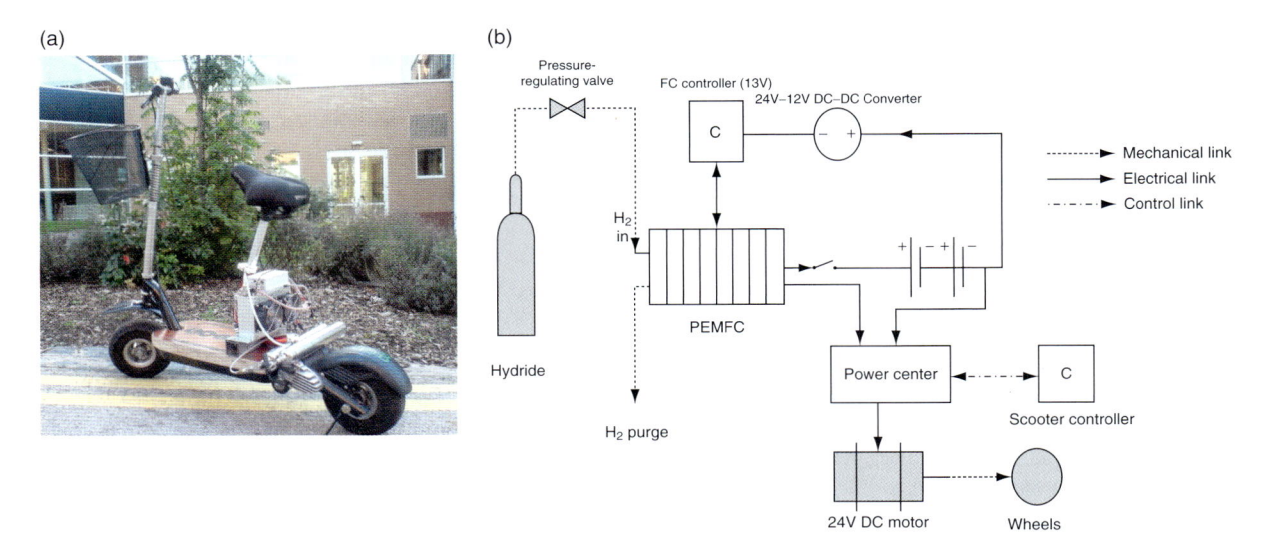

Figure 7 (a) Hydrogen fuel cell hybrid scooter (HFCHS) and (b) component diagram of the HFCHS showing all components and electrical drive system layout.

Table 1 Characteristics and comparison of the electric, petrol, and hybrid scooter

	GoPed FC Plug-in	GoPed Plug-in	GoPed (29 cc)
Vehicle cost	£3000	£1200	£800
mpg equivalent	500 mpg (H_2)	383 mpg	100 mpg
Energy efficiency	37–75%	75%	20%
Tail-pipe emission	None/H_2O	None	Harmful air pollutions
Well-to-wheel CO_2	9.37–40.95 g CO_2 km^{-1}	24.07 g CO_2 km^{-1}	90–120 g CO_2 km^{-1}
Running cost on fuel	£0.01–£0.11 mile^{-1}	£0.01 mile^{-1}	£0.06 mile^{-1}
Refueling time	15 min – 5 h	5 h	1 min
Range	15 miles	8 miles	32 miles
Top speed	25.8 mph	20 mph	24 mph
Noise level	55 db	55 db	75 db

mpg, miles per gallon.

owing to the large weight and thermal problems, while refilling is inconvenient because the hydride distribution system is not yet established. It appears therefore that larger vehicles such as buses are more appropriate for hydrogen application.

Recently, Shang and Pollet [19] showed that it is possible to develop and commission a hydrogen fuel cell hybrid scooter (HFCHS) with plug-in features (**Figure 7**). A commercially available 'pure' lead-acid battery electric scooter (GoPed) was converted to an HFCHS so as to investigate the effect of hybridization on driving duty cycles, range, performance, recharging times, well-to-wheel CO_2 footprint, and overall running costs. The HFCHS with plug-in features consisted mainly of a 500 W hydrogen PEMFC stack connected to four 12 V 9 Ah lead-acid batteries (576 Wh) and two hydrogen M-H canisters (54 kg of mass equivalent to 1.8 kWh of energy) supplying pure hydrogen (99.999%) and also acting as heat sink (due to endothermic hydrogen desorption process). In this study, the HFCHS urban driving cycle was compared with that of a conventional petrol and 'pure' battery electric scooter. The energy consumed by the HFCHS was 0.11 kWh km^{-1}, with an associated running cost of £0.01 km^{-1}, a well-to-wheel CO_2 of 9.37 g CO_2 km^{-1}, and a maximum range of 15 miles. It was shown that the HFCHS gave better energy efficiencies and speeds compared to battery- and petrol-powered GoPed scooters alone (**Table 1**).

4.12.4.3 Buses

Buses have been a focus for fuel cell development since 1995 when Geoffrey Ballard first demonstrated his early design in Vancouver [7]. This led to the propagation of fuel cell bus projects around the world, the most significant being the European-funded CUTE project [20], which started services in 2003 and ran 3 buses in each of 10 capital cities like London, Paris, and Madrid over a 2-year commercial period. These Citaro vehicles were built by Mercedes-Benz in Germany using a 250 kW Ballard PEMFC running on 44 kg pure hydrogen stored in 350 bar cylinders on the roof. Each city installed a hydrogen refueling station and these stations were designed and built by a number of companies including BP, Shell, and Air Products to test a number of technologies ranging from natural gas reforming to on-site electrolysis.

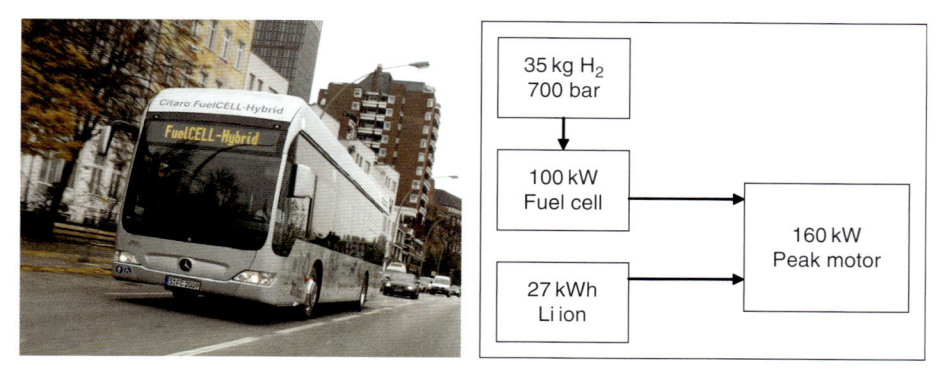

Figure 8 Citaro hybrid fuel cell bus supplied by Evobus to CHIC project, showing the hybrid system.

The problem with Ballard was his refusal to combine batteries with the fuel cells to form a hybrid, because he claimed that the batteries obscured the fuel cell performance. This may have been true, but there is little doubt that a combination of battery and fuel cell in the drivetrain, giving the hybrid fuel cell electric vehicle, has many advantages over the individual technologies. The hybrid drive beats the battery bus by having longer range and shorter refueling times. It also beats the fuel cell bus by providing high power peaks, allowing regenerative braking, increasing efficiency, extending fuel cell life, and reducing costs. This trend to hybridization has similarly been observed in diesel engine buses largely because it reduces emissions such that many bus suppliers now offer hybrid bus products which are used in cities such as London and Hamburg [21] to promote higher air quality.

Figure 8 shows the modern hybrid fuel cell bus made by EvoBus and supplied in 2010 to several German cities in the CHIC (Clean Hydrogen In European Cities) project [22]. This is a EU-funded project with 10 buses from three manufacturers deployed in several cities to test their performance and consumer response. The fuel cell was reduced in power to 100 kW while a 27 kWh lithium-ion battery was inserted to give 120 kW of cruise power and storage for regenerative braking and acceleration at 160 kW peak. Seven hydrogen cylinders on the roof allowed 35 kg of 700 bar gas to give a vehicle range about 250 km.

Recently, London has announced [23] that it will operate five hydrogen buses (RV1), running from Tower Gateway to Covent Garden, fueled by London's first permanent hydrogen refueling station. The station was officially opened in December 2010 by Kit Malthouse, Deputy Mayor of London. This not only marks London's progress in low-carbon transport innovation but means the city now has one of the largest fleets of hydrogen buses in Europe.

The main key achievements by Air Products under this program are the innovative station design and operation of a dual-phase hydrogen tanker, designed to deliver high-purity gaseous or liquid hydrogen. These represent major steps forward in infrastructure development and are key to the deployment of low-cost stations in the future. Air Products will also install a second hydrogen refueling station in London as part of the Joint Technology Initiative (JTI)-funded CHIC project [22].

4.12.4.4 Cars

The design of fuel cell cars has followed the bus narrative in moving from pure fuel cell toward fuel cell/battery hybrid. The difference is that there are very few bus manufacturers, whereas every major car company has produced fuel cell prototypes, together with plans to produce large numbers by 2015 [24]. Initially, the first cars produced by Daimler, the F-cell introduced in 2002 and the B class initiated in 2005, were based on a pure fuel cell drivetrain [25] which could be fitted into designs produced to satisfy the original 1993 ZEV legislation in California. The ultimate example of this was the 2008 Honda FCX Clarity, which used a 100 kW PEMFC to provide excellent performance [26]. This much-praised design suffered from a large mass and an excessive hydrogen tank but was otherwise thoughtfully conceived. The performance was fine with good acceleration, a top speed of 100 mph, and a range of 280 miles on 4.1 kg of hydrogen, and the consumer acceptance was superb. Although the 3-year leasing arrangement was $600 per month in the US trials which began in 2007, this price was heavily subsidized and the true individual vehicle cost for the initial run of 100 cars was approximately $500k. However, the battery was too small for regenerative braking and the fuel cell was too expensive. The rational solution is to downsize the fuel cell and increase the battery. Halving the mass would also be a way to double the efficiency.

This philosophy was the one pursued in Birmingham during the past few years. The first prototype shown in **Figure 9** was designed and built in 2005 by Professor John Jostins of Microcab Industries Ltd, who started a small company to deliver a novel hybrid solution [27]. The design criteria were

- fuel cell to provide cruise speed,
- larger battery to provide acceleration, regenerative braking, and plug-in capacity,
- mass around 500 kg to give maximum efficiency,
- four-seat city cab with excellent access through three doors, and
- many standard components to lower costs.

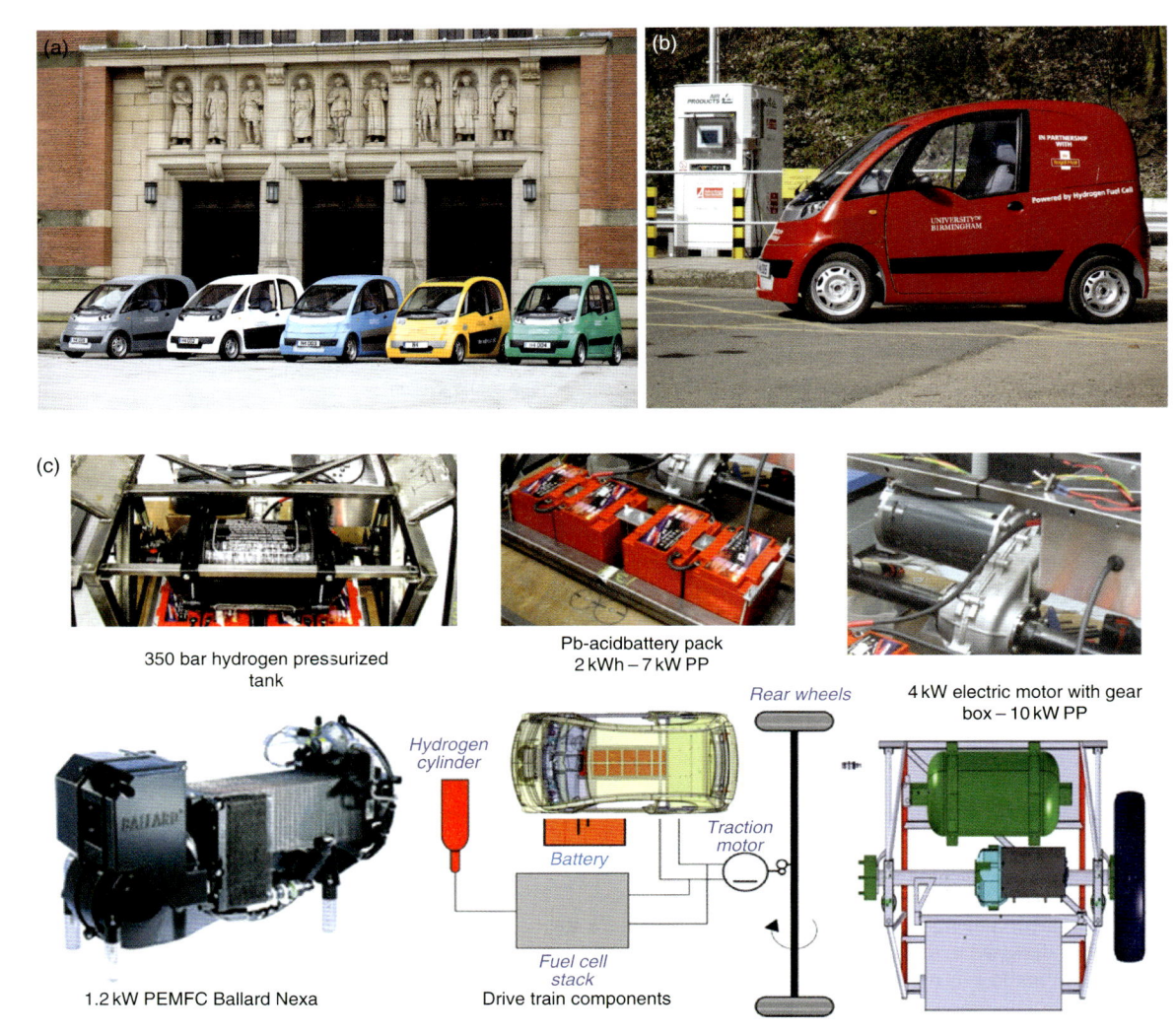

Figure 9 (a) Five hydrogen fuel cell–battery electric vehicles on the University of Birmingham campus, (b) hydrogen refueling station and the Royal Mail hydrogen fuel cell vehicle at the University of Birmingham, and (c) complete drivetrain components.

In 2006, Professor Kevin Kendall received support from Advantage West Midlands to buy the prototype plus four improved vehicles, which could then be trialed using the University campus as a test track. The Air Products refueler was opened at the School of Chemical Engineering in April 2008 and the five cars were then used to test the design calculations over a 2-year test program undertaken by a consortium of West Midlands suppliers part-funded by the UK government department BERR. The results [27, 28] showed that the initial campus design gave the desired acceleration, top speed of 20 mph, and a range of 60 miles on a campus drive cycle, but could not achieve the ECE15 urban cycle. This was not surprising because the fuel cell used was a 1.2 kW Ballard Nexa PEMFC stack (less than 1 g of Pt is used compared with 60 g for a 100 kW system), the hydrogen tank was 0.6 kg at 350 bar, and the battery was 2 kWh lead-acid. The main problem was the battery capacity, which was insufficient to give regenerative braking and plug-in range. Other issues such as the need for a lightweight aluminum chassis, the space requirements for fleet vehicles, the performance of lightweight body panels, and better heat management for window and cab temperature control were addressed in 2011 when the next batch of eight cars was assembled.

So far, Microcab Industries, in collaboration with the University of Birmingham, have made very good progress in new hydrogen hybrid fuel cell vehicle (**Figure 10**) [29], for example,

1. the range of the vehicle has been extended up to 200 miles (the range for a current state-of-the-art lithium-ion battery vehicle is only 60 miles),
2. refueling time of the vehicle is reduced to 3 min (battery vehicles have a domestic charging time of 5–8 h), and
3. the lifetime of the fuel cell stack has been increased up to 5000 h with a high-temperature PEMFC.

Economically, if 500 000 hydrogen hybrid vehicles were produced per annum, less than 0.5 ton of platinum would be required assuming a platinum loading of 0.6 g kW^{-1}. Of course, the main key issues are cost, lifetime, and reliability in both start-up and duty cycles, which

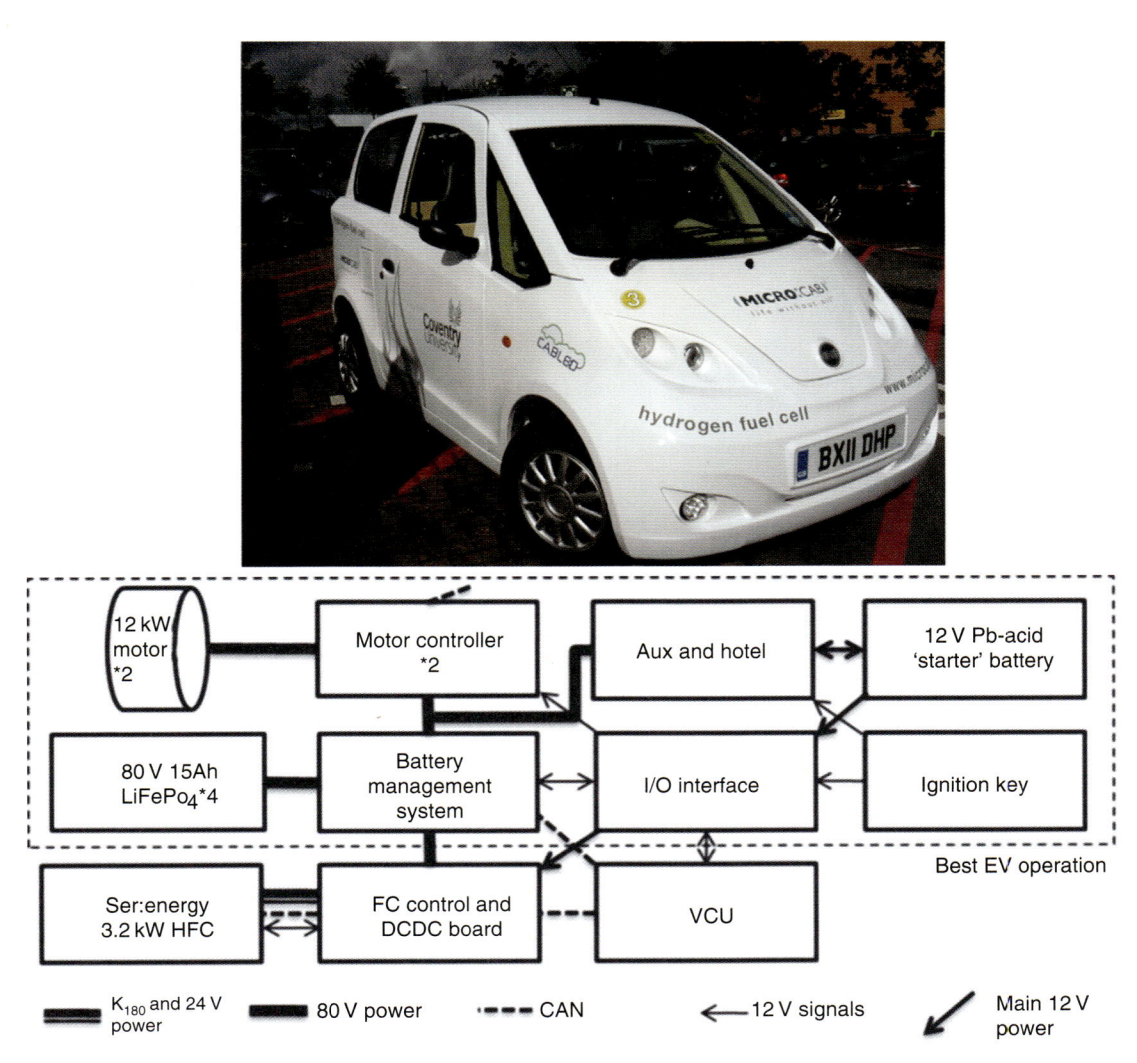

Figure 10 New Microcab vehicle showing the drivetrain components.

still require some attention. Based on a PEMFC stack production cost of $225 kW^{-1} (mainly attributed to Pt and membrane cost) with a DoE target of ~$30 kW^{-1} by 2015, fuel cell–electric hybrids become a very attractive option for commercial deployment.

Of course, another option is to convert a conventional petrol combustion hybrid car to run on hydrogen in order to test the filling station infrastructure and the performance/costs of the new systems. In 2006, Statoil did this in Norway by opening the first of its HyNor fueling stations in Stavanger with 15 modified Toyota Prius hybrids running on hydrogen gas. By 2009, there were seven hydrogen stations connecting the 600 km from Oslo to Stavanger and the number of hydrogen vehicles had increased to 50 with manufacturers Mazda, Think, and Toyota [30]. In addition, 10 Daimler B class fuel cell vehicles were planned to arrive in 2011. The advantages of demonstrating this technology in Norway were substantial:

- car taxes are high and can be reduced to incentivize consumers;
- hydrogen cars can drive in bus lanes and are exempt from road tolls;
- hydrogen is readily available from the Statoil plants; and
- hydrogen can be produced from renewables such as hydropower to give green energy.

4.12.4.5 Ships

Norway has also been the first to apply fuel cell technology to drive ships. **Figure 11** shows the Viking Lady [31], which was fitted with a 320 kW MCFC as one of the main power supplies. Hydrogen and carbon dioxide are stored in pressurized tanks to get the MCFC warmed up to 650 °C, and then liquefied natural gas is internally reformed on the anode. The ship's four Wartsila 2 MW engines also run on natural gas, generating additional power to drive the electric propulsion system. The fuel cell built by MTU costs

Figure 11 The 5900 te ship Viking Lady, which has an MCFC to supplement its gas turbine electrical drive system.

€12 million, but the cost was offset by the fall in tax due to 90% reduction in nitrogen oxide emissions. After delivery and testing in 2009, the ship was then chartered to the French oil company Total.

A recent report [32] has predicted a market of 160 GW worldwide for ship-based fuel cells. The main aim is to provide clean auxiliary power in harbors where diesel emissions are banned. The first entry should be cruise vessels, ferry vessels, and megayachts, but ultimately container ships will also be penetrated.

Although fuel cells are predicted to have a significant application on ships, the main market until now has been small APUs for leisure yachts [33]. Typically a DMFC provides 65 W of clean, silent power to drive navigation and other systems. The plastic container of methanol is sufficient to give power for weeks at sea. For example, Arcona Yachts, the second largest sailboat manufacturer in Sweden, has specified the Smart Fuel Cell EFOY system to provide around 2.2 kWh per day from methanol packs. By 2010, more than 18 000 of these units had been delivered to early markets including boats and mobile homes.

4.12.4.6 Aircraft

Hydrogen as an aircraft fuel, because of its buoyancy, had been suggested as long ago as 1783 when Jacques Charles and Nicolas Robert made their first ascent in a hydrogen-filled balloon in front of half the population of Paris, just 2 weeks after the Montgolfier brothers made their famous hot air journey [34]. Because hydrogen also gives 3 times lower weight than kerosene for the equivalent combustion energy, it began to be used in aircraft engines during the twentieth century [35], especially in gas turbines and rocket motors during the 1930s. For example, a Heinkel experimental turbojet was tested on hydrogen in 1937 [35]. It became clear in the last decades that large jets with cryogenic tanks of liquid hydrogen could be used as passenger airliners.

Another innovative idea for unmanned air vehicles (UAVs) was that solar photovoltaic-powered planes could produce hydrogen by electrolysis during the day and then fly at night using a fuel cell propulsion system. The Helios mission was funded by NASA and the UAV was built by Aerovironment Inc. in California, as shown in **Figure 12**. The design was remarkable because it was extremely light, had many electric propellers, and flew slowly at less than 100 mph to reach high altitudes well above the clouds. In 1999 the prototype first flew and then in 2001 it attained a record high altitude of 96 863 ft for a propeller plane. Unfortunately, it fell into the sea near Hawaii in 2003 as the hydrogen system was about to be tested to prove the idea that flights of several months duration were plausible. The report [36] suggested that turbulence was the cause of unstable wing oscillations.

The original project had been conceived in 1994 as a partnership between Government and Industry. Aerovironment had produced the first all-wing design, called the Pathfinder with six motors, from 1981 to 1997. This tripled in size from 30 m to almost 80 m wingspan by the fifth generation built in 2003 with 10 propellers. One of the key problems was developing the reversible fuel cell stack that would electrolyze during the day and consume hydrogen at night. The fuel cell pod in the center was heavy, with a mass of 230 kg, while two hydrogen storage pods with pressurized cylinders weighed 70 kg each. The crash appears to have slowed the project considerably.

Smaller UAVs for surveying farmland or studying traffic congestion have been powered by lithium-ion batteries, typically with a 1 h flight time [36]. To increase this mission time to 3 or even 6 h, a fuel cell range extender has been used. Hydrogen cylinders are too heavy for this duty, so propane has been preferred, with microtubular SOFCs producing about 100 W of cruise power, saving the batteries for take-off. The record for endurance is 15 h for SOFC-powered UAVs [38]. Small propane canisters are readily available and can be simply inserted into the plane after each flight.

Figure 12 The NASA Helios unmanned air vehicle combining photovoltaic cells by day and fuel cells for hydrogen power at night.

Figure 13 Boeing manned plane flying on proton exchange membrane fuel cell running on compressed hydrogen.

It was not until 2008 that a manned aircraft powered by an electric motor driven by a PEMFC with pressurized hydrogen fuel took off [39]. Boeing built a two-seat electric aircraft using an Intelligent Energy fuel cell stack and lithium-ion batteries to provide climbing power. It was a modified Dimona motor glider with a 16 m wingspan built by Diamond Aircraft Industries of Austria (**Figure 13**). Once at 1000 m altitude, the fuel cell itself drove the aircraft for about 20 min over Ocana in Spain.

4.12.5 Legislation

Legislation takes two forms: the first relates to safety standards and the second to longer term regulation of carbon emissions.

The safety standards are already being implemented in terms of designs for hydrogen production, transport, storage, and refueling nozzles [9].

Longer term legislation has been reviewed by the Committee on Climate Change (CCC), which released a report entitled 'Fourth Carbon Budget: Reducing Emissions through the 2020s' [40]. The report sees a need to produce hydrogen from low-carbon processes, including

- electrolysis using low-carbon electricity (the CCC recognizes thermodynamic efficiency, but envisages the benefit of hydrogen generation lying in the application of underutilized low-carbon generating capacity),
- direct production from fossil fuels with 'precombustion carbon capture and storage' (production of hydrogen for transport at 'off-peak' times), and
- production from bioenergy (though hydrogen would need to compete with other bioenergy uses for this resource).

The report considers the use of hydrogen vehicles relatively expensive due to
- the fact that many ways of supplying hydrogen involve significant losses when compared to electricity and its use in electric cars,
- significant infrastructure costs, and
- hydrogen vehicle costs.

This results in an estimated hydrogen abatement cost of around £220 per ton CO_2 for cars in 2030.

If experience toward 2030 suggests limits on the penetration of electric vehicles, the CCC believes that there could be a scope for increased penetration of hydrogen cars and vans. The report sees the principal advantage of hydrogen over electric vehicle batteries being in applications for which pure battery electric vehicles are unsuitable (e.g., vehicles requiring longer range). Therefore, if challenges in hydrogen infrastructure development can be addressed, there may be a useful role in niche markets, in which battery electric vehicles do not fulfill current promise:

- Buses provide a good opportunity for hydrogen given depot fueling.
- Hydrogen could be used in trucks with depot fueling and fueling stations along motorways and main roads.
- High-mileage fleet vans could use hydrogen based on depot fueling.

The CCC observes that widespread uptake of hydrogen cars and vans would require major investment in a national network of hydrogen fueling stations, at a scale close to that for petrol and diesel today, together with an accompanying infrastructure for hydrogen production and distribution.

4.12.6 Conclusions

Hydrogen and fuel cells are finding a number of applications in transport. Although the predicted markets for hydrogen bikes did not deliver, fleet vehicles like forklift trucks have proved more interesting. A single hydrogen store and refueling station can provide fuel for a large number of vehicles, which offers significant advantages over both battery and combustion engines in a central location such as a warehouse. A key feature is that hybrid drives combining PEMFCs with lithium-ion batteries or supercapacitors can give advantages. This is especially true for buses which have now moved away from the Ballard concept of a pure fuel cell vehicle to a hybrid electric design where a battery assists with braking and with pulse power.

For smaller vehicles, hydrogen is not readily accessible, so methanol-powered PEMFCs have been used as auxiliary power supplies on RVs for application in national parks where combustion engines are restricted. Delivery fleets and taxis are different because centralized hydrogen storage and dispensing is feasible. Lightweight cabs at the University of Birmingham have shown the benefits of improved efficiency and reduced emissions. Again the hybrid design works best, with about 40 miles range available from the plug-in lithium-ion battery and 160 miles from the hydrogen PEMFC, running on a 350 bar hydrogen cylinder which is recharged in 3–4 min.

Ships are also turning to electric drives where fuel cells can easily be added in, especially to provide clean power in ports where pollution is costly. Natural gas is the most likely fuel in the short term. Aircraft will use kerosene for the foreseeable future but unmanned aircraft can benefit from fuel cells to extend range. Propane is used with microtubular SOFCs in some small applications to add to the lithium-ion batteries. Hydrogen has been used on solar photovoltaic aircraft.

The conclusion is that fuel cells work best in transport when used to supplement and improve battery electric drives. Hydrogen is a suitable fuel for PEMFCs used in fleets. Methanol is more readily available to consumers needing auxiliary power for leisure activities. Fuels such as natural gas and propane are more useful in ships and UAVs.

References

[1] Plunkett JW (2010) *Plunkett's Automobile Industry Almanac 2011*. Houston, TX: Plunkett Research Ltd.
[2] Freedonia Group Inc (2011) World Fuel Cells. July 1; Tollefson J (2009) US congress revives hydrogen vehicle research. *Nature* 460: 442–443.
[3] State of California Air Resources Board (2009) Summary of Staff's preliminary assessment of the need for revisions to the Zero Emission Vehicle Regulation. November 25, pp. 1–24.
[4] Bossel U (2003) Efficiency of hydrogen fuel cell, diesel–SOFC-hybrid and battery electric vehicles. *European Fuel Cell Forum, Oberrohrdorf* 2003: 1–4.
[5] Wipke K, Sprik S, Kurtz J, and Ramsden T (2010) US Fuel Cell Electric Vehicle demonstration Project 2010 status update. *Fuel Cell Seminar*. San Antonio, Texas, October.
[6] Zhang F and Cooke P (2010) Hydrogen and fuel cell development in China: A review. *European Planning Studies* 18: 1153–1168.
[7] Larminie J (2003) *A Dicks, Fuel Cell Systems Explained*. New York: Wiley.
[8] Sorensen B (2012) *Hydrogen and Fuel Cells*. New York: Academic Press.
[9] ISO 17268:2006 (2006) Compressed hydrogen surface vehicle refuelling connection devices.
[10] Fuel Cell Today Industry Review 2010 (2010) Fuel cells sustainability. *Platinum Metals Review* 54: 125–126.
[11] Fuel Cell today (2010) Linde adds fuel cel forklift to its product range. 5 February.
[12] Hydrogen forklifts still a long way to go (2010) Forkliftaction.com.
[13] Gaines LL, Elgowainy A, and Wang MQ (2008) Full fuel cycle comparison of forklift propulsion systems. *Argonne National Lab Report ANL/ESD/08-3*, 5 November.
[14] Adamson KA and Jerram LC (2009) Niche transport survey. *Fuel Cell Today*, 1–14 August.
[15] Podesser P and Mueller J (2010) Smart Fuel Cell annual report. *Brunnthal*, 22 March.
[16] Olah GA, Goeppert A, and Prakash GKS (2009) *Beyond Oil and Gas: The Methanol Economy*. London: Wiley VCH.

[17] Roads2hycom (2011) Hydrogen and fuel cell scooters, electric bicycles, wheelchairs. Document 6114; Lin B (1999) Conceptual Design and Modelling of a Fuel Cell Scooter for Urban Asia. Master's Thesis, Princeton University.
[18] Crawley G (2006) Alkaline fuel cells. *Fuel Cell Today*, March.
[19] Shang JL and Pollet BG (2010) Hydrogen fuel cells and batteries hybrid scooter with plug-in integration. *International Journal of Hydrogen Energy* 35(23): 12709.
[20] HyFLEET: CUTE project (2009) Final Report. European Commission, Brussels.
[21] Bradley MJ (2000) *Engine Certification Recommendations Report, Northeast Advanced Vehicle Consortium, NAVC0599-AVP009903*, September.
[22] CHIC project kick-off 4 November 2010, European Union.
[23] McIvor A (2010) Fuel cells in urban transport: An Olympic challenge. *CleanTech Magazine*, September.
[24] Vine M Will fuel cells replace battery-powered cars? Seekingalpha.com/article/294466.
[25] Friedrich J (2004) First experiences with fuel cell vehicles in fleet operation. *Proceedings of F-Cell Symposium*. Stuttgart.
[26] Cunningham W (2010) Honda's fuel cell vehicle gets free energy. CarTechBlog, 27 January.
[27] Kendall K, Pollet BG, Dhir A, *et al.* (2011) Hydrogen fuel cell hybrid vehicles (HFCHVs) for Birmingham campus. *Journal of Power Sources* 196: 325–330.
[28] Kendall K, Pollet BG, and Jostins J (2008) *HEVC08 Conference*. Warwick, 8 December.
[29] Fisher P, Hillmansen S, Kendall K, and Jostins J (submitted) Electronic integration of fuel cell and battery system in novel hybrid vehicle. *Journal of Power Sources*.
[30] Norwegian Statement (2010) 13th Joint meeting of the ILC & SC. Essen, Germany, May.
[31] Biello D (2009) World's first fuel cell ship docks in Copenhagen. *Scientific American*, December.
[32] Wursig GM (2010) *Report for Germanischer Lloyd*.
[33] Fuel Cell Today (2010) Fuel cell yacht wins race. 7 January.
[34] Daniel Brewer G (1990) *Hydrogen Aircraft Technology*. Boca Raton, FL: CRC Press.
[35] Faas R (2001) Cryoplane. Airbus, Hamburg.
[36] Noll TE, Brown JM, Perez-Davis ME, *et al.* (2004) Investigation of the Helios prototype aircraft mishap. *NASA Report*.
[37] Frost & Sullivan, 2007 (2007) Study analysing the current activities in the field of UAV. Enterprise and Industry Directorate-General, European Commission. EU, Brussels.
[38] Crumm A (2011) Solid oxide fuel cell powerpacks running on propane. *7th Annual Conference on Hydrogen and Fuel Cells*. National Exhibition Centre, Birmingham, 30 March.
[39] MSNBC (2008) Aviation First: Plane flies on hydrogen fuel cells. 3 April.
[40] Committee on Climate Change (2010) The 4th Carbon Budget. 27 Carlisle Place, London, December.

4.13 H₂ and Fuel Cells as Controlled Renewables: FC Power Electronics

N Schofield, University of Manchester, Manchester, UK

© 2012 Elsevier Ltd.

4.13.1	Terrestrial Applications	296
4.13.1.1	Low Carbon Energy Conversion	296
4.13.2	Traditional Inverter Safe Operating Area	297
4.13.2.1	General Approach	297
4.13.2.2	Extending the Inverter SOA	297
4.13.3	Enabling Poor Voltage Regulation Systems	299
4.13.3.1	Multiswitch Voltage Source Inverter	299
4.13.4	Analysis for 250 kW Grid-Connected Fuel Cell	300
4.13.4.1	A 250 kW Grid-Connected Solid Oxide Fuel Cell	300
4.13.4.2	Inverter Power Loss Analysis	300
4.13.4.3	Buck Converter Power Loss Analysis	301
4.13.4.4	Operating Point Power Loss Analysis	302
4.13.5	Experimental Study of a Two-Switch MS-VSI	303
4.13.5.1	Static Voltage Balancing	303
4.13.5.2	Dynamic Voltage Balancing	303
4.13.5.3	Laboratory Test Environment	303
4.13.5.4	Implementation of Switch Voltage Balance and Gate-Drive Circuitry	304
4.13.5.5	Commission of Voltage Balance Circuit	305
4.13.5.6	H-Bridge Operation	305
4.13.6	Summary	305
4.13.7	Test Characterization of a H₂ PEM Fuel Cell for Road Vehicle Applications	307
4.13.7.1	Introduction	307
4.13.7.2	MES-DEA PEMFCs	308
4.13.7.2.1	General	308
4.13.7.2.2	Water Management	310
4.13.7.3	Fuel Cell Test Facility	310
4.13.7.4	Fuel Cell Test Characterization	311
4.13.7.4.1	Conditioning	311
4.13.7.4.2	Inlet H₂ Pressure	314
4.13.7.4.3	Fuel Cell Short-Circuit and Purging Routines	314
4.13.8	Summary	315
4.13.9	A H₂ PEM Fuel Cell and High Energy Dense Battery Hybrid Energy Source for an Urban Electric Vehicle	317
4.13.9.1	Introduction	317
4.13.9.2	Vehicle Energy and Power Requirements	318
4.13.9.3	Fuel Cells for Transportation	320
4.13.9.3.1	Background	320
4.13.9.4	Fuel Cell Modeling	320
4.13.9.4.1	Fuel Cell Operation	322
4.13.9.5	Vehicle Traction Battery	322
4.13.9.5.1	Background	322
4.13.9.5.2	Zebra battery simulation model	322
4.13.9.5.3	Lead–acid battery simulation model	323
4.13.9.6	Vehicle Performance Evaluation	324
4.13.9.6.1	Pure battery electric mode	325
4.13.9.6.2	Fuel Cell and Battery Hybrid Source	325
4.13.10	Summary	325
Acknowledgments		328
References		328

4.13.1 Terrestrial Applications

4.13.1.1 Low Carbon Energy Conversion

The desirability to achieve low carbon emissions from energy conversion processes is recognized worldwide as having a positive impact on decreasing the impact of climate change – and considered as a key global challenge for the twenty-first century. The drive to accommodate renewable and sustainable low emission power generation on terrestrial electrical networks is at the forefront of many government policies [1]. In the United Kingdom, the present carbon emission mix can predominantly be assigned to electrical power generation, industrial processes/heating, and transportation.

The transportation sector contributes a considerable portion of carbon emissions, 36% [1], and consumers demand direct replacement of vehicles with little if any sacrifice in performance, price, and range. Transportation has a significant role in carbon emission reduction as product lifecycles are shorter than those of existing sources. However, to achieve reductions in carbon emissions from electrical power generation, renewable resources must be harvested, for example, wind, wave, solar energy, and bio- and multimix carbon neutral fuels, the latter being potentially enabled via fuel cell (FC) systems. It is generally envisaged [2] that these technologies will generate energy into electrical networks at the low-voltage (LV) distribution level, as illustrated in **Figure 1** showing possible distributed energy resource options and the schematic of a 250 kW solid-oxide fuel cell-to-grid system that forms the base specification requirements for the study discussed in this section.

In order to substantially reduce carbon emissions, alternative technologies such as FCs and renewable energy sources such as wind, wave, and solar energy must be effectively harnessed so that their benefits can be exploited. Efficient and cost-effective electrical integration of such systems is typically implemented with traditional power inverter topologies such as the voltage source inverter (VSI). However, for such systems, the sizing of key system components is difficult due to the varying input voltage characteristic, or regulation, of the energy source inherent in these technologies. Thus, design of power inverter operational characteristics is generally prudently tailored to favor system safety; often resulting in the reduction of reliability, efficiency, and performance. Furthermore, the design procedure must be reapplied to each application.

The varying intensity of renewable energy sources, for example, sun intensity and wind speed, causes electrical output to vary considerably. Further, the principal energy conversion mechanisms are inherently susceptible to other external factors. For instance, energy conversion from sunlight in photovoltaic cells is adversely affected by environmental temperature [3]. Similarly, FC performance also varies with operating conditions in tandem with its operating point and associated loss mechanisms (i.e., polarization, ohmic, and concentration losses). Thus, power conversion systems such as converters and inverters are required to accommodate a wide operating area, necessitating relatively large safe operating areas (SOAs) to accommodate the variance in electrical input than may be encountered in more traditional industrial applications.

This section details the design of a series, multiswitch voltage source inverter (MS-VSI) that can actively modify the SOA of power inverters to optimize the silicon device rating during active power control and reduce power losses. Hence, the design can enable a wide operating envelope with greater efficiency and robustness over inverters having fixed SOA designs. Further, the design can be exploited in traditional applications by allowing faster switching, thus decreasing output harmonic content and reducing large/expensive filters, components that are often required to meet electrical grid standards. The section assesses the potential efficiency gains from an optimized MS-VSI based on a 250 kW solid oxide fuel cell (SOFC) system the V-I characteristic for which is provided by Rolls-Royce Fuel Cell Systems Ltd., as illustrated in **Figure 2** showing the characteristic and defining key aspects of the inverter SOA. MS-VSI operational issues such as voltage and current share are discussed and experimental results presented from a representative laboratory-based H-bridge test system.

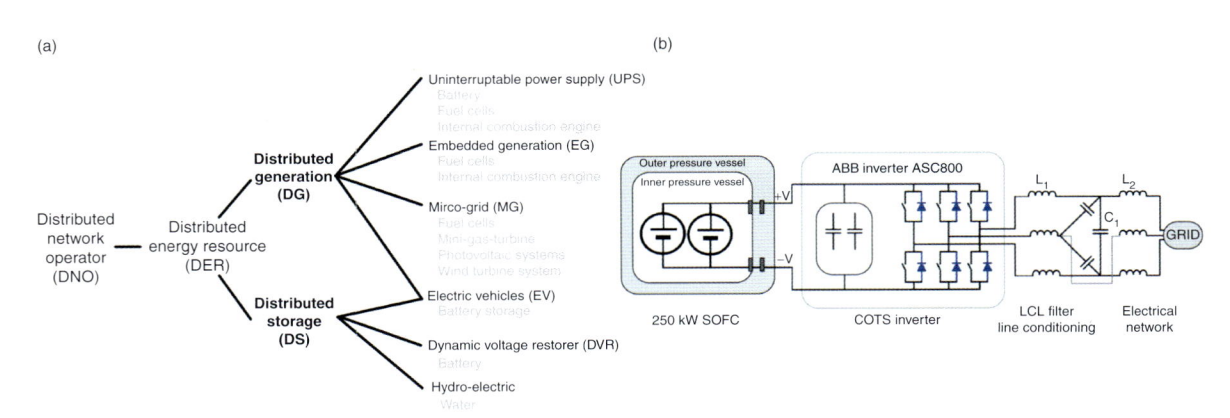

Figure 1 Distributed generation scheme of SOFC-to-grid power conversion. (a) Scheme of distributed energy resources. (b) Schematic of SOFC, grid interface inverter, and filter components.

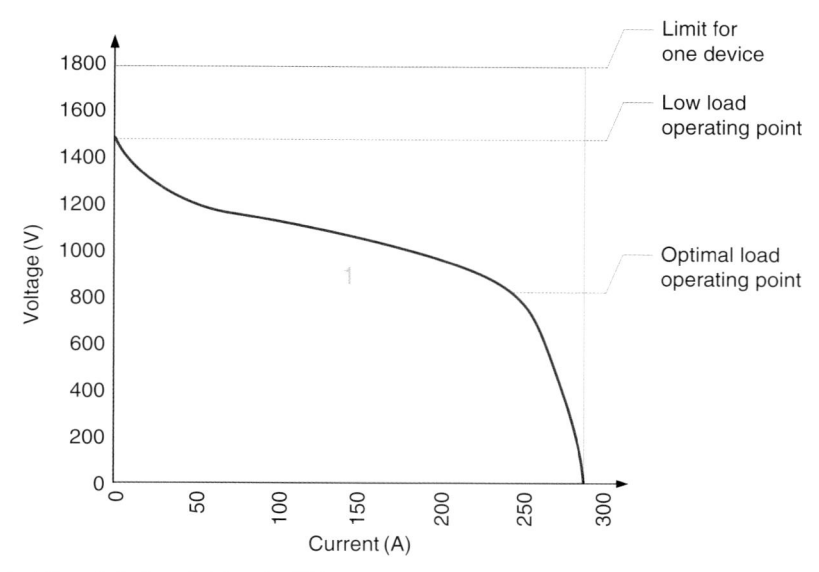

Figure 2 SOFC V-I characteristic and single-switch inverter SOA.

4.13.2 Traditional Inverter Safe Operating Area

4.13.2.1 General Approach

Traditional approaches to designing power inverters that are connected to energy sources having poor voltage regulation can sometimes warrant the use of multiple stages rather than operating a fully rated single SOA inverter. There are, however, instances when applications can demand additional power conversion stages. A renewable wind power inverter comprising AC–DC–AC or back-to-back inverters is studied in Reference [3]. The topology is suggested in order to achieve a variable speed operation, decoupling turbine rotation, and grid frequency, thus increasing the system efficiency [3]. Additional stages for DC sources such as batteries and FCs can warrant DC–DC–AC topologies to allow coupling at voltage levels that benefit a VSI [4, 5]. However, each of these additional stages, while sometimes justified, can increase component count, cost, and reliability issues.

Typically, these systems have their point of common coupling (PCC) at the low and medium voltage networks. Connection is readily achieved with a single switching power device in each arm of a three-phase, three-leg, two-level, six-switch VSI. However, challenges arise when considering the input voltage regulation and converter efficiency.

The traditional three-phase VSI, typically used in motor drives, is implemented with three-phase legs; each leg containing two power devices – an upper and a lower device. Additional legs can be implemented for star connected systems allowing measurement and control of zero-sequence currents [6]. The power switch device configuration is determined from the electrical input supply and an output SOA defined by the designer depending on the DC link range, switching algorithms, and consideration of load and stray inductance, for example, circuit elements. The reliability of the devices is critical to most applications and component suppliers recommend safety margins to take account of stray inductances and other circuit parasitic elements, for example, ABB Switzerland Ltd recommends a safety margin of 60% in LV installations [7].

As applications dictate the SOA, selection of devices is typically predetermined. However, in systems subject to poor supply regulation, such as renewable energy and FCs, the DC link can vary by as much as 2:1 leaving the device rating on the boundary between two technology levels or necessitate significant device overrating. Thus, if the standard two-level VSI topology is applied, the power switches must be rated for the worst-case DC link voltage at open circuit. This consequently makes them inefficient when operating at design point or heavily loaded. Of course, the designer also has to consider the duration in which the inverter will have to operate in this area. For safety and reliability reasons, a higher voltage device technology is typically selected. However, this can mean losing device performance because lower-voltage devices typically have better performance and switching speed.

4.13.2.2 Extending the Inverter SOA

The inverter design process is greatly influenced by the finite choice of power switch technology and voltage and current levels. In order to extend the current rating for a switching element, multiple devices can be placed in parallel. However, some derating is then necessary to allow for device characteristic variation and circuit parasitic elements. Further, careful consideration should be given to the on-state and switching losses and thermal stability [8]. Thermal stability can be aided by mounting parallel devices on the same heat sink [8], and using devices from the same production batch can help reduce mismatches in characteristics [9]. Increasing the SOA voltage limit requires the series stacking of multiple devices. This is challenging as the devices are no longer rated for the DC link voltage and mismatch in switching can lead to device failure.

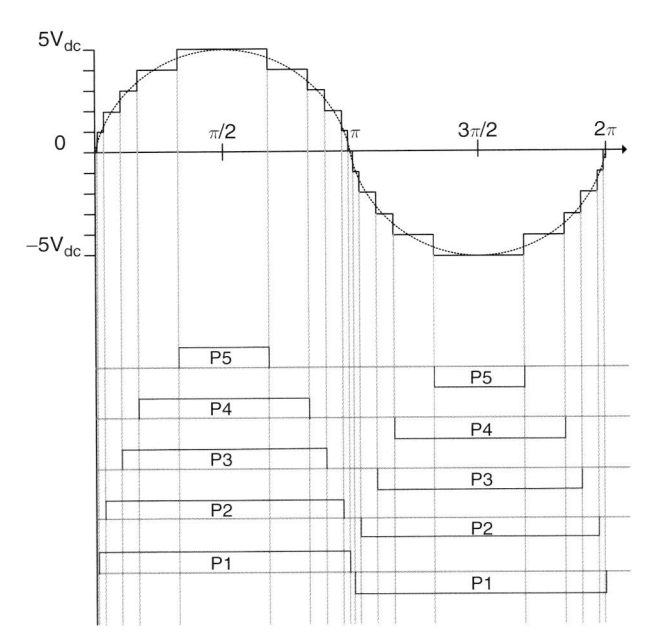

Figure 3 Cascaded five-stage multilevel inverter switch pattern. Adapted from Tolbert LM and Peng FZ, (2000) Multilevel converters as a utility interface for renewable energy systems. In: *Power Engineering Society Summer Meeting, 2000*, vol. 2, pp. 1271–1274. IEEE [10].

Increasing the SOA for a power stage is particularly desirable in high-voltage and traction applications. Multilevel inverters are an example for circuit topology that can achieve power conversion by emulating smaller DC sources [10]. The switching algorithms must accommodate the separate sources and ensure that devices do not switch together. Figure 3 shows the synthesized AC output from a five-stage cascaded system assuming each level represents 1.0 per unit voltage. Note that some of the switches must operate at a higher frequency than others unless switching algorithms swap the DC sources cyclically [10]. The multilevel inverter offers a number of advantages for DC–AC conversion. The configuration is modular, helping to reduce costs, and improve system security. However, the number of devices used is large and the different level switching frequencies introduce harmonics, which need subsequent output filtering. Further, control algorithms must be implemented for each switching level.

In order to provide the higher frequency of operation desirable for variable speed drives with reduced harmonic components, direct serial switching is being researched. An additional advantage of such implementation is the ability to use well-established control schemes [11]. Although adding complexity to circuit design, the series configuration of power semiconductor devices can have several advantages as follows:

- higher operating voltage and improved SOA
- increased switching speeds
- reduced power losses
- reduction in weight, volume, and cost.

Much attention has been given to achieve higher operating voltages [12–17] using series-connected semiconductor devices capable of operating at higher switching speeds, thus reducing output harmonics. Further, the implementation through series configuration allows well-established control techniques, such as sinusoidal pulse width modulation (SPWM) and space vector SVPWM [11]. The benefits of replacing a single insulated gate bipolar transistor (IGBT) switch with multiple lower-rated devices have been analyzed and simulated by Shammas *et al.* [18] who concluded that at higher operational frequencies, significant power savings can be made when using multiple series switches consisting of lower-voltage devices, for example, replacing a 6.5 kV switch with six 1.2 kV switches operating at 5 kHz produces a power saving of 42%. This work was undertaken using a specialist semiconductor program (ISE TCAD) that allowed comparison with modern trench IGBT devices, often implemented at lower-rated technology levels, with Punch-Through (PT) and Non-Punch-Through devices – an older technology not viable for higher-voltage-level devices. Abbate *et al.* [19] also modeled and experimentally validated the reduced power losses of series device combinations. Other work by Abbate has shown that series-switched devices offer similar robustness to single device operation [20]. Thus, the implementation can reduce weight, volume, and cost of components. Furthermore, switching at higher frequencies, typically above 3 kHz, reduces output harmonics and hence the sizing of passive inductive filters and the DC link capacitance.

The primary challenge in implementing series-connected semiconductor power devices is ensuring that the device voltage during static and dynamic operations is balanced. In multilevel inverters, the power semiconductor devices are switched at different time points during the cycle and not at the same time. Hence, voltage balance is not an issue. However, for the application being reported in this section, which is essentially a two-level system, the power semiconductor devices must switch at the same time or alternatively be rated for the full extreme of the DC link voltage. Achieving synchronized operation between the multiple series devices (that make one effective switch) is difficult due to tolerances in semiconductor fabrication, differences between the device gate-drive characteristics, circuit parasitic elements, and device leakage current. Additionally, consideration must be given to gate-drive delays, isolation circuitry, and control platform. In this section, a DSP dSpace™ system from Mathworks® is used for the development and implementation of the switching algorithm.

4.13.3 Enabling Poor Voltage Regulation Systems

As renewable energy sources, FCs, and modern battery technologies have inherent poor voltage regulation, an inverter with a flexible SOA is desirable, as illustrated schematically in **Figure 4** showing the SOA zones of a two-level or two-switch MS-VSI system. As optimization of SOA to match the DC link voltage and would increase power conversion efficiency. In terms of design, this could be achieved with the use of an additional power inverter. As the DC link begins to operate in an area outside of the initial inverter design, a second system could be used to convert the additional voltage. This could be achieved with a buck converter. However, such a system is not useful as the buck switch would be left in the circuit majority of time when the inverter handles the DC link without support. Further, a second inverter could be used, but again there are additional isolation components that are left latched.

4.13.3.1 Multiswitch Voltage Source Inverter

To increase switch voltage capability, mixed rating devices connected in series could be considered, as illustrated in **Figure 5**. Since FC voltage regulation is typically 2:1, two IGBT switches of the same voltage rating could potentially satisfy such operation. Thus, a lower ratio 3:2 could have mixed device level of 1.0 and 0.5 (**Figure 4**). During periods in which only one IGBT was required to

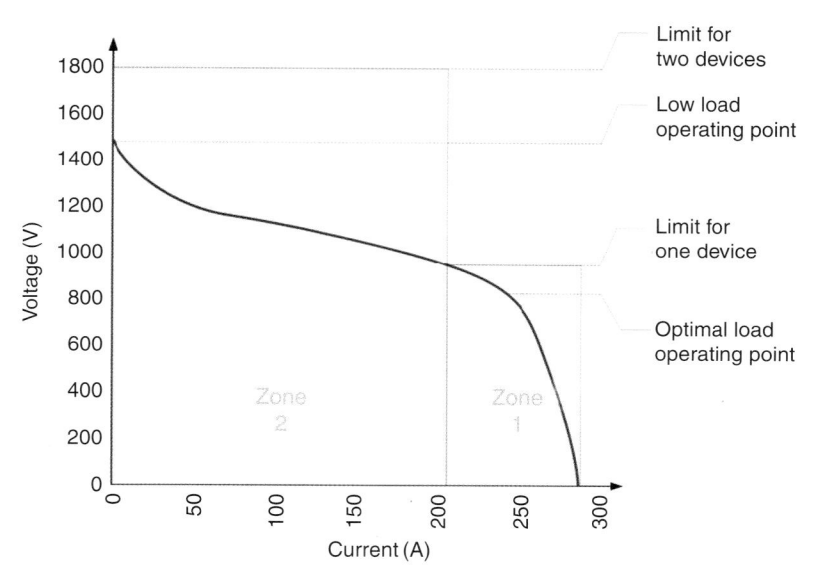

Figure 4 The active SOA for a two-switch MS-VSI.

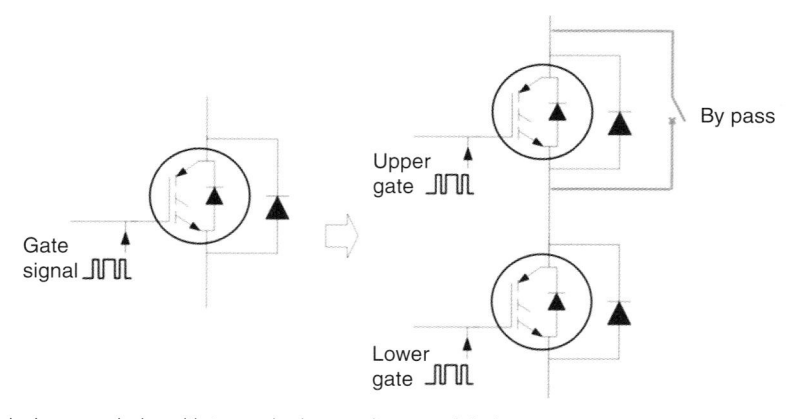

Figure 5 Replacement of single power device with two series lower voltage-rated devices.

switch the link voltage (i.e., at full load), one switch, for instance, the closest to the positive rail would need to be electrically bypassed or operate with the device latched in the closed position.

Consideration of a bypass switch reveals two possibilities: either a mechanical relay or transistor. The implementation of a mechanical relay switch, as an IGBT bypass, would provide large power loss savings since relays have a relatively low on-state resistance. However, the physical size and operation of a mechanical switch pose problems with the inverter power system layout. When building power electronic systems, it is important to reduce the spacing between components and minimize the circuital pathways to reduce stray fields and electromagnetic coupling. Further, integrating relays close to fast-acting IGBT power switches results in an increase in electrical noise due to large inductive loops associated with the relay package design.

An alternative to a mechanical switch is to use a semiconductor device as the bypass component. Here, metal oxide semiconductor field effect transistor (MOSFET) and IGBT are compared for suitability. MOSFETs have the advantage of lower on-state resistance and no internal voltage drop from drain to source. However, the device technology is not efficient for applications of above 600 V without a considerable increase in on-state resistance. For comparison, if a 600 V IGBT was to be used, the MOSEFT bypass switch would also have to be rated to 600 V. A device of 600 V rating and a maximum continuous current of 20 A, such as the INFINEON, SPP20N60S5 MOSFET, N, and TO-220, has a typical on-state resistance, $R_{DS\text{-on-hot}}$ of 190 mΩ. The MOSFET continuous power losses can be calculated using the following equation [21]:

$$\text{MOSFET\_PD}_{cond} = I_m^2 R_{DS\_on\_hot} \qquad [1]$$

where the IGBT device studied was an International Rectifier – IRGB4056DPBF – IGBT, COPAK, TO-220, rated at 600 V and 24 A continuous and having a V_{CE} of 0.812 V and R_{CE} of 5 mΩ. IGBT continuous power losses (latch closed) is calculated using

$$\text{IGBT\_PD}_{cond} = V_{CE}I + I^2 R_{CE} \qquad [2]$$

The two switches are similar in electrical rating and will provide a comparison suitable for the intended application. However, analysis has shown that for operation above 6 A the MOSFET has exhibits greater power losses than that of a latched IGBT. Therefore, the upper device of the two-switch MS-VSI concept will be a latched IGBT. Thus, considerations must now be given to the power losses of the series switch design options. **Figure 5** illustrates the traditional single switch that can be rated for all power conversion and its direct replacement of lower-rated multiple series switches that can be rated for multiple operating points. **Figure 4** illustrates the operating area for this proposed multiswitch, flexible SOA topology that allows the inverter to have an SOA that better matches the poor voltage regulation. Zone 1 has only a single switching device optimizing its active SOA to that at the full-load operating point. At low load, the DC link voltage is higher, thus requiring additional voltage rating facilitated by two series-connected devices.

4.13.4 Analysis for 250 kW Grid-Connected Fuel Cell

4.13.4.1 A 250 kW Grid-Connected Solid Oxide Fuel Cell

To investigate the suitability of the two-switch MS-VSI over power converter options discussed earlier, loss analysis was carried out for the full-rated inverter, the buck converter, and the MS-VSI. The suitability of a buck converter for power conversion from poorly regulated sources such as FCs has been examined [22]. However, previous work in this area has involved the addition of multiple power conversion systems. For this study, the DC link is based on an SOFC characteristic provided by Rolls-Royce Fuel Cells Limited. The SOFC technology offers high-efficiency power conversion, ~75%, when implemented as combined cycle. However, it requires a high-temperature environment, typically over 800 °C, and thus thermal cycling can take a considerable number of hours. Thus, the SOFC V-I curve has a typical FC 2:1 voltage ratio but can spend a significant period of time in the high-voltage, low-load operating area. If purely electrical techniques are used, that is, no fuel-mix modification or environmental change is made, then the inverter must have a fully rated SOA. This obviously leads to large inefficiencies when the system is operating between close to full load and low load.

The SOFC performance reduces over its lifetime and as such a higher percentage of the IGBT switch rating can be applied. Thus, Rolls-Royce Fuel Cell Systems use a device limit of 72.5%. During 80–100% loading, which is a long-term operating point, a 1700 V IGBT would be adequate and result in fewer losses. As the low-load voltage limit is so high, the MS-VSI approach is to implement two 1200 V devices, in the same way four 600 V devices could be used but for experimental simplicity a two-stage MS-VSI is realized. In regard to lower ratio V-I curves, like that of batteries, mixed rated devices may achieve a better-matched SOA, that is, a 1200 V and a 600 V device in series.

4.13.4.2 Inverter Power Loss Analysis

For a two-switch VSI, power losses were calculated using data for 1200 V IGBTs based on the Mitsubishi CM400DY-24NF [23]. Power silicon losses with sinusoidal current control are calculated from a model produced by Casanellas [24] that has been verified via calorimetric test and is considered to give accurate results with 5–10% [25]. Power silicon losses with sinusoidal current control can thus be calculated from the turn-on losses that are estimated using the following equation [24]:

$$P_{SWon} = \frac{1}{8} t_{rN} F_s V_{cc} \left(\frac{I_{cm}^2}{I_{cn}} \right) \qquad [3]$$

the conduction losses are estimated using

$$P_{\text{IGBT}} = \left(\frac{1}{8} + \frac{2\sqrt{3}}{9\pi}M\cos\theta - \frac{\sqrt{3}}{45\pi}M\cos 3\theta\right)\left(\frac{V_{\text{cen}} - V_{\text{co}}}{I_{\text{cn}}}\right)I_{\text{cn}}^2 \qquad [4]$$

the diode conduction losses are estimated using

$$P_{\text{DIODE}} = \left(\frac{1}{8} - \frac{2\sqrt{3}}{9\pi}M\cos\theta + \frac{\sqrt{3}}{45\pi}M\cos 3\theta\right)\left(\frac{V_{\text{cen}} - V_{\text{co}}}{I_{\text{cn}}}\right)I_{\text{cn}}^2 \qquad [5]$$

the turn-off losses are estimated using

$$P_{\text{SWoff}} = I_{\text{cm}}t_{\text{fN}}F_s V_{\text{cc}}\left(\frac{1}{3\pi} + \frac{I_{\text{cm}}}{24 I_{\text{cn}}}\right) \qquad [6]$$

and the diode reverse recovery losses are estimated using

$$P_{\text{RR}} = F_s V_{\text{cc}}\left\{\left[0.28 + \frac{0.38}{\pi}\frac{I_{\text{cm}}}{I_{\text{cn}}} + 0.015\left(\frac{I_{\text{cm}}}{I_{\text{cn}}}\right)^2\right] + Q_{\text{rrN}} + \left[\left(\frac{0.8}{\pi} + 0.05\frac{I_{\text{cm}}}{I_{\text{cn}}}\right) \cdot I_{\text{cm}}t_{\text{rrN}}\right]\right\} \qquad [7]$$

The parameters V_{cc}, t_{rn}, F_s, I_{cm}, I_{cn}, M, $\cos\theta$, V_{cen}, V_{co}, t_{fn} and their typical values are defined in **Table 1**. Power losses are calculated at the limit of the RRFCS working voltage range for a 1700 V IGBT, 1232 V 40 A – this equates to a power rating of 49 280 W. **Figure 6** compares the power losses for the 1700 V (877 W) and 2500 V IGBT (1932 W).

4.13.4.3 Buck Converter Power Loss Analysis

The DC–DC Buck converter, shown in **Figure 6**, along with a standard VSI would require a possible bypass switch to remove the IGBT and inductor during operating regions where the FC DC link voltage is higher than that of the SOA VSI. While this technique will be examined as part of the loss comparison with the two-switch MS-VSI and a fully rated SOA VSI, it adds significant cost, volume, complexity, control, and maintenance – should it be used in commercial applications. Furthermore, the additional harmonics from the buck converter would have an impact on the VSI power quality which must meet grid standards and apply additional harmonics onto the FC stack where it is anticipated that the lifetime impact of harmonics on the FC stack is unknown although it is assumed to be detrimental to SOFC chemistry over time. Therefore, for the purpose of this study and to provide mitigation against large electrical variance, a buck converter with a voltage ripple of less than 5% and current ripple of less than 1% will be considered.

In **Figure 6**, the switching device will require a working voltage of 1404 V and so a 2500 V IGBT will be considered. The traditional VSI will be modeled on Mitsubishi power devices and a DC link capacitance of 4000 μF. Thus, the same value will be used for the buck DC–DC converter capacitance. A switching frequency of 12 kHz and a inductance of 20 mH is chosen. The voltage ripple of the buck in continuous current mode is estimated using [26]

$$\Delta v = \frac{V_s D(1-D)}{8 f_s^2 L C} \qquad [8]$$

where V_s is the DC link voltage, D the switch duty cycle, f_s the switching frequency, L the inductance, and C the capacitance. The current ripple, continuous mode is estimated using [26]

Table 1 Parameter definitions and typical values for semi-conductor loss calculations

Parameter	Definition	Units	1200 V	1700 V
V_{cen}	Rated Collector-Emitter forward voltage drop	V	2.00	2.45
V_{co}	Rated Collector-Emitter forward voltage drop	V	1.00	1.10
I_{cn}	IGBT and diode rated current	A	400	400
Q_{rrn}		C	1.60 n	40 μ
t_{fn}	IGBT rated fall time at rated current	ns	350	350
T_{rrn}	Diode recovery fall time at rated current (I_{cn})	ns	250	450

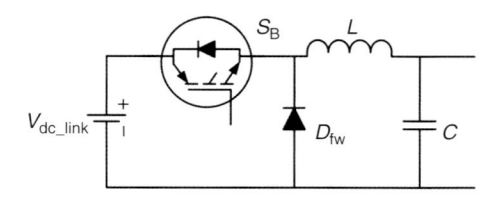

Figure 6 Buck circuit schematic.

302 H₂ and Fuel Cells as Controlled Renewables: FC Power Electronics

$$\Delta I = \frac{V_s D (1-D)}{f_s L} \qquad [9]$$

The free-wheel diode losses are estimated using [26]

$$P_{Dfw} = V_{Dfw} I \left(1 - \frac{t_{on}}{T}\right) \qquad [10]$$

(buck converter free-wheel diode losses can be calculated using eqn [5])where V_{Dfw} is the diode forward voltage drop, t_{on} the conduction duration, and T the time period.

4.13.4.4 Operating Point Power Loss Analysis

Four operating points, defined as 'a', 'd', 'c', and 'd' in **Figure 7**, will be considered for comparison purposes. Load point a (1300 V, 25 A) equates to a SOFC load of 10%, considered a warm-up stage. The system can spend ~8 h warming-up for operation or cooling for maintenance. Load point b (1100 V, 125 A) is the 50% load condition. Load point c (900 V, 225 A) represents the 90% load condition and load point d (850 V, 250 A) represents the 100% full-load condition, as illustrated in **Figure 7**.

Each point was assessed to map the loss profile from zero to full load for each candidate topology. **Figure 8** illustrates the power losses for each of the proposed power stages while **Table 2** shows that the two-switch series IGBT VSI provides an efficient operation

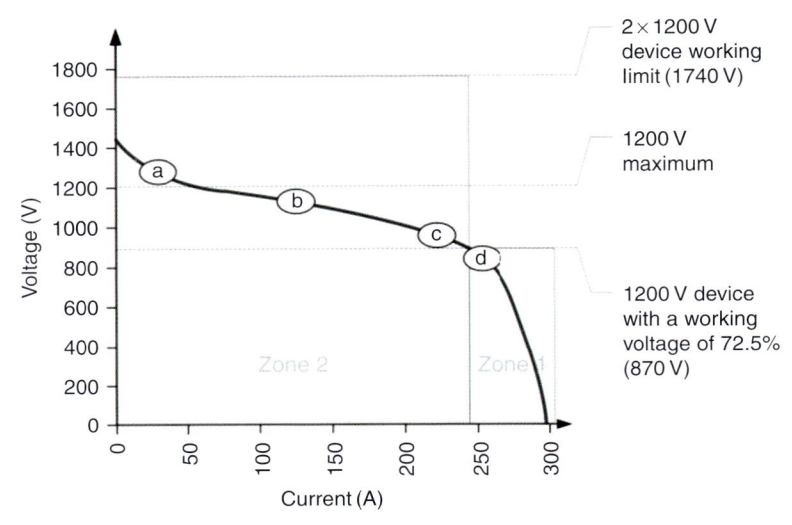

Figure 7 Replacement of single power device with two-series lower-voltage-rated devices.

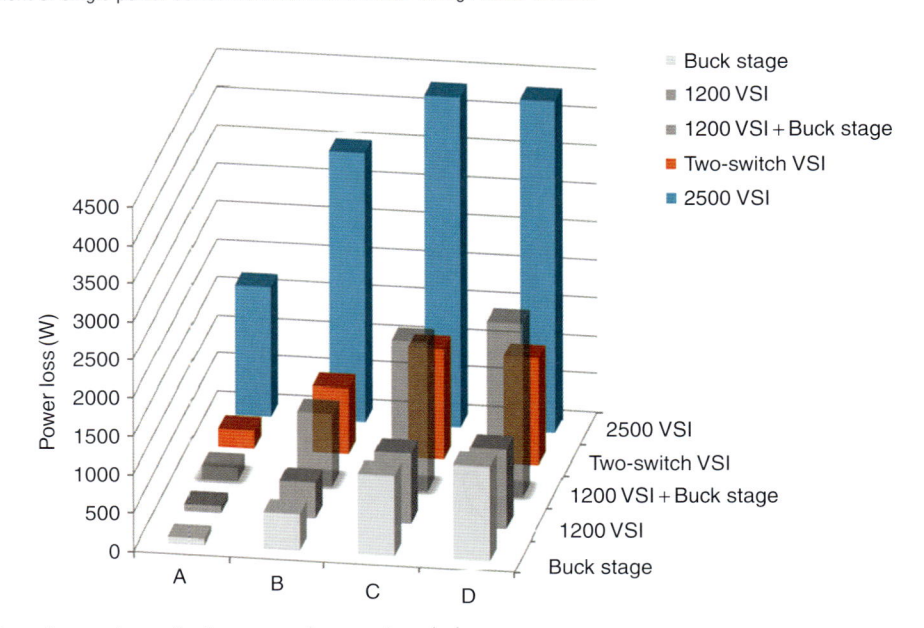

Figure 8 Comparison of power losses for the proposed power stage designs.

Table 2 Power losses for proposed load points and configurations

Load Point	Buck Stage (W)	1200 VSI (W)	1200 VSI + Buck Stage (W)	two-switch MS-VSI (W)	2500 VSI (W)
A, 1300 V, 25 A	83.2	96.2	179.4	242.8	1701.1
B, 1100 V, 125 A	476.1	470.5	946.7	864.1	3531.3
C, 900 V, 225 A	1045.5	916.0	1961.5	1452.2	4336.5
D, 850 V, 250 A	1235.0	1038.4	2273.4	1395.2	4352.2

when compared with both the rated 2500 V device VSI and the 1200 V IGBT plus buck DC–DC stage. Operating at point B, the two-switch VSI saves 82 W and is ~10% more efficient. However, the FC system will generally be operated loaded between 50% and 100% with significant periods of operation close to 80% and 90% load. Operating at point C, the two-switch VSI has 509 W less loss and is 25% more efficient than the buck stage. At point D, the two-switch system has a switching loss of 173 W in the lower IGBT devices and latched losses of 59 W in the upper IGBT devices. Thus, the two-switch MS-VSI implementation appears to show clear technical advantages over those of the other topologies considered – if the configuration can be achieved with the additional latching of the other series switch devices. It is noteworthy that this will take time to settle as the charge on the gates will vary and thus a number of switching cycles maybe required before the system stabilizes. This is difficult to model due to the unknown differences in power device characteristics; therefore, computer modeling may not adequate in justifying its design. Thus, a low-power, two-switch MS-VSI will be built for experimental validation.

4.13.5 Experimental Study of a Two-Switch MS-VSI

The advantages of a two-switch MS-VSI power semiconductor stage can be heavily exploited with applications where power sources have poor regulation. Alternatively, the lower-rated devices operated in series allow the inverter to achieve higher switching speeds while allowing well-established control schemes to be implemented. However, this can only be achieved if latching of the upper IGBT can be accomplished and voltage shared across the series devices. It has been reported by Baek [27] that the voltage balance circuit can, undesirably, self-activate if the DC link voltage is rapidly changed. While FC voltage regulation is poor, its chemistry inherently prohibits large and rapid changes in voltage. Thus, the latched state IGBT of a two-switch circuit may be sensitive to system transients. Further, as stray inductances from circuit layout have a large impact on circuit characteristics [27] and circuit stability could not be demonstrated by Saber simulations, it was decided to design and build a prototype inverter. This would allow investigation of the latching operation and voltage sharing between devices to be explored.

4.13.5.1 Static Voltage Balancing

Static voltage balancing of the two-switch devices is achieved by connecting resistors in parallel with the devices as demonstrated by Baek [12] at the cost of additional power loss. However, the steady-state response is reduced by decreasing the resistance of this network.

4.13.5.2 Dynamic Voltage Balancing

Dynamic voltage balancing can be achieved by the addition of components on either the gate side or the device side. A device-side snubber circuit can be implemented using either passive or active circuitry. Passive device-side snubber circuits consisting of devices such as capacitors, resistors, and inductors were proposed by Dongsheng and Braun [28]. Active device-side snubber circuits are explored in References 29 and 30, which utilize zero voltage switching to force the voltage across the device to zero before changing state. However, since the snubber devices are located on the device side, they must be rated for high voltages and currents and are therefore large in size, expensive, and have significant losses [12]. To benefit from the advantages of IGBT devices – cost, size, and speed – a gate-side circuitry is preferential and an implementation is discussed and demonstrated in Reference 31. However, the tuning of the snubber circuit depends on many factors including the variances between devices. The section provides a 'rules of thumb' and ratio of ratings based on an empirical study. A simple magnetically coupled gate-drive circuit was explored and validated in Reference 16. However, the additional circuitry is unfavorable due to its expense and size.

4.13.5.3 Laboratory Test Environment

In any test system, a large amount of instrumentation is required to measure IGBT and system performance. To reduce the amount of instrumentation required, only two IGBT switches were instrumented on the experimental circuit. This reduces the number of differential voltage transducers to six and requires only two current transducers. To test the IGBT two-switch configuration, V_{ge1}, V_{ce1}, V_{ge2}, V_{ce2}, V_{DC}, V_L, and I_L must be measured, as defined in **Figure 9** where V_{ge} is the gate voltage, V_{ce} the collector–emitter voltage, V_{DC} the DC link voltage, I_{DC} the DC link current, and I_L the load current. Further, the voltage and current measurements of the load and supply must be taken on both the control system and the data acquisition system. In order to ensure rigor in testing, identical systems were used.

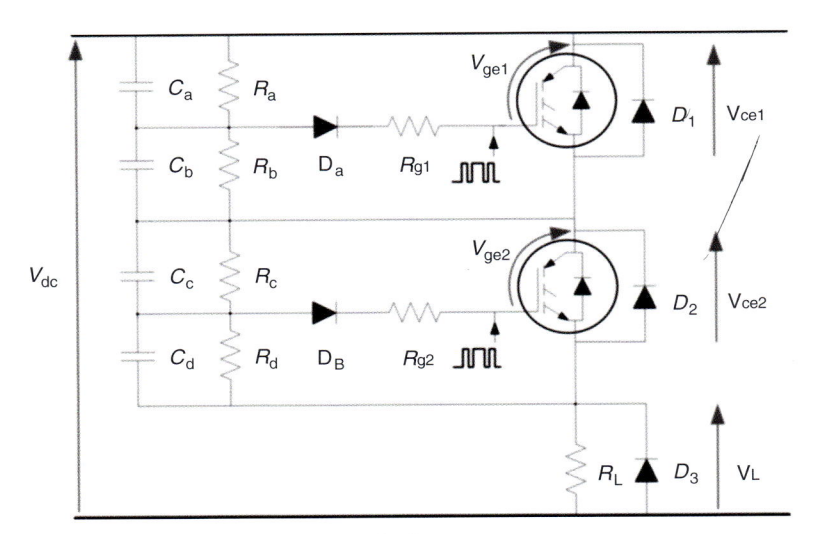

Figure 9 Schematic of two-switch test circuit connected to a resistive load.

The laboratory apparatus included two 400 MHz Lecroy oscilloscopes along with four 200 MHz differential voltage probes – high resolution is needed for the analysis of the system and to mitigate against mismatches in transducer performance. **Figure 10** illustrates the inverter setup: (a) is the differential voltage measurements connected to Lecroy oscilloscopes; (b) the H-Bridge two-switch MS-VSI installed in a protective plastic case; (c) the optical isolation for gate-drive signals from dSpace; and (d) a two-channel oscilloscope used to confirm leg commutation signals and confirm deadbanding. The switch control algorithm is implemented in Mathworks Simulink and ported on a RT1103 dSpace system. This provided digital control at a resolution of 12 kHz and has sufficient channels for independent gate-drive signals and feedback measurements. For rapid development and flexibility in control, each IGBT has a dedicated gate-drive signal. Thus, all gates can be independently controlled via the dSpace system. This removed the requirement for additional hardware to be installed on the gate drive to override the upper switch when latching is necessary.

4.13.5.4 Implementation of Switch Voltage Balance and Gate-Drive Circuitry

The IGBT voltage balance circuit was implemented as described in Reference 19 and then tuned to provide critically damped operation. **Figure 9** is a schematic of the test circuit used to verify implementation. The resistor network $R_a + R_b + R_c + R_d$ values were selected to provide a current twice that of the IGBT leakage current [19]. The device under test was an IRGB4056DPbF having a leakage current of 100 nA. Testing of the inverter would be nondestructive and carried out at a voltage of 100 V with a purely resistive load of 60 ohm – thus limiting the current to 1.667 A. Previous empirical work had led to an approximation that $R_a = 10 R_b$ and $R_c = 10 R_d$. Values used in Reference 19 did vary but were used as a benchmark that $R_a = R_d = 80$ kΩ and $R_b = R_c = 3$ kΩ. The capacitors C_a and C_c provide a voltage reference and should be larger than C_b and C_d that provide additional energy for passively driving the gate. The selection of these components should be made carefully; however, no procedure is defined. Thus, careful analysis of the

Figure 10 Experimental set-up for two-switch MS-VSI test validation.

circuit was required to optimize the component values. For the IRGB4056DPbF, the gate-emitter capacitance is 11 nF and so a value of 100 nF was used for C_a and C_c while C_b and C_d are estimated to be much smaller, therefore, a capacitor of 10 nF is employed. R_g is a feedback resistor whose value dictates the turnoff energy dissipated [14], recommends a value 10 times larger than the gate resistance and a value of 50 Ω is used. The diodes D_a and D_b are used to block gate-drive signals during normal operation.

4.13.5.5 Commission of Voltage Balance Circuit

On preliminary testing of serial operation of a two-switch system, it was found that the voltage balance circuit had a long response time of over 12 ms. The purpose of this inverter was to switch at 2 kHz as a proof of concept. In order to refine the steady-state response, a second set of measurements were taken and trend extrapolated to provide a predicted settle time of 20% of the switching period at 2 kHz. The closest physical resistors to the calculated values were $R_a = R_c = 680$ ohm, $R_b = R_d = 33$ ohm, this provided a settle time of 20 μs.

The values and ratios based on a previous work [19] were found via empirical tests due to the complexity of the nonideal IGBT characteristic, the paralleled gate-drive circuit, and the DC link characteristics. Upon examination, the capacitor chain in parallel with the voltage balance circuit was not providing the desired effect. The circuit suffered from a number of dynamic instabilities. Hence, the resistors were replaced allowing for a current of 70 mA and a settle time within that of the expected switching frequency.

The dynamic response of the circuit suffered from overshoot and ringing before it reached a steady state. This state then decayed into the static voltage balance after 10 μs. The DC level of the ringing is close to 100% of the DC link with an overshoot of around 1.3 per unit (p.u.). The circuits' response should be to settle at 0.5 p.u to ensure that the underrated devices are not be subjected to any overvoltage. The effects of decreasing C_b and C_d to 82 pF reduced the settle time but increased the peak voltage to 1.5 p.u. Correspondingly, having C_a and C_c smaller than C_b and C_d will lead to a very LV reference and a very slow voltage balance.

Reducing the lower-discharge capacitor reduced the ringing, although it increased the voltage overshoot to 1.5 p.u. Matching both the upper and lower capacitors provided a steady-state voltage close to the 0.5 p.u. design point. However, there was significant ringing of the IGBT gate potential. Reducing the voltage balance resistance led to reduced ringing, however this implied large losses. Thus, it was found that choosing C_b and C_d of 10 times that of the IGBT capacitance provided sufficient energy for switching operation and for a stable voltage reference; this led to critical dampening during switch off.

4.13.5.6 H-Bridge Operation

A second Simulink control model was created to allow software-based deadbanding and latching switch control. The latch state was copied to a secondary channel to allow for oscilloscope triggering and switching signals A and A′ were monitored on a third oscilloscope. DC link voltage was measured and a latching voltage of 60 V was implemented for test purposes, that is, for a DC link above 60 V both switches would be commutated and below 60 V the upper switches of the two-switch combination would be latched on and only the lower switches commutated. This test was performed to ensure that the control system functions appropriately and that the power circuit shares voltages equally across the devices after being latched while not operating the devices at a destructive level to aid development. **Figure 11** shows a schematic of the H-bridge balancing and power IGBT circuit layout, while **Figure 12** illustrates the laboratory layout schematic. **Figure 13(a)** is an oscilloscope screen shot of unlatching (turn-on) of the second power device without a voltage balance circuit. It can be seen that the full DC link voltage is across the upper power device. **Figure 13(b)** shows the same operation with the voltage balance circuit enabled, and thus, equal sharing of the DC link voltage.

The latching transition from zone 2 to zone 1 is seen in **Figure 14(a)** and switching from zone 1 to zone 2 is seen in **Figure 14(b)**. The voltage across both the upper and lower switches stabilize from both latched zone 1 and unlatched zone 2 states within 8 ms. Thus, if the DC link voltage was to increase from the threshold voltage to beyond the rated voltage within this time. the devices may fail as the DC link voltage may not balance during this period. However, when the DC link has a low value of dv/dt, the application would be suited. SOFC technology has a slow response to load changes and thus such a response time would be acceptable. Additionally, the DC link capacitance could play a role in reducing the likelihood of transients during this transition. Alternatively, mixed rated devices could be used so that the threshold voltage is suitably placed before a critical voltage balance level is reached.

4.13.6 Summary

Three power stages suitable for DC–AC conversion from a FC DC link have been examined. The power loss study has shown that a series-connected two-switch VSI with latching upper IGBT can provide power conversion from a poorly regulated voltage source with lower power losses than traditional single switch techniques. The reduction in power losses has been shown to be possible over a wide range of SOFC loading, that is, between 50% and 90% of full load. The excitation of the IGBT devices and inverter topology allows implementation using traditional modulation techniques while reducing the inverter cost, weight, volume, and power losses. The two-switch strategy will also reduce the electrical impact of the inverter on the FC since higher switching speeds will also be achieved though this has not been quantified and no additional DC link capacitance or power stage is required with the two-switch topology.

A H-bridge employing the two-switch IGBT design has been built and tested in the laboratory. A passive gate-side voltage balancing circuit has been tuned and proved to be sufficient for laboratory testing. However, the choice of passive components requires further work to formalize the design procedure. Also, there is potential to use active balancing and further reduce power losses, though this is outside the scope of this section.

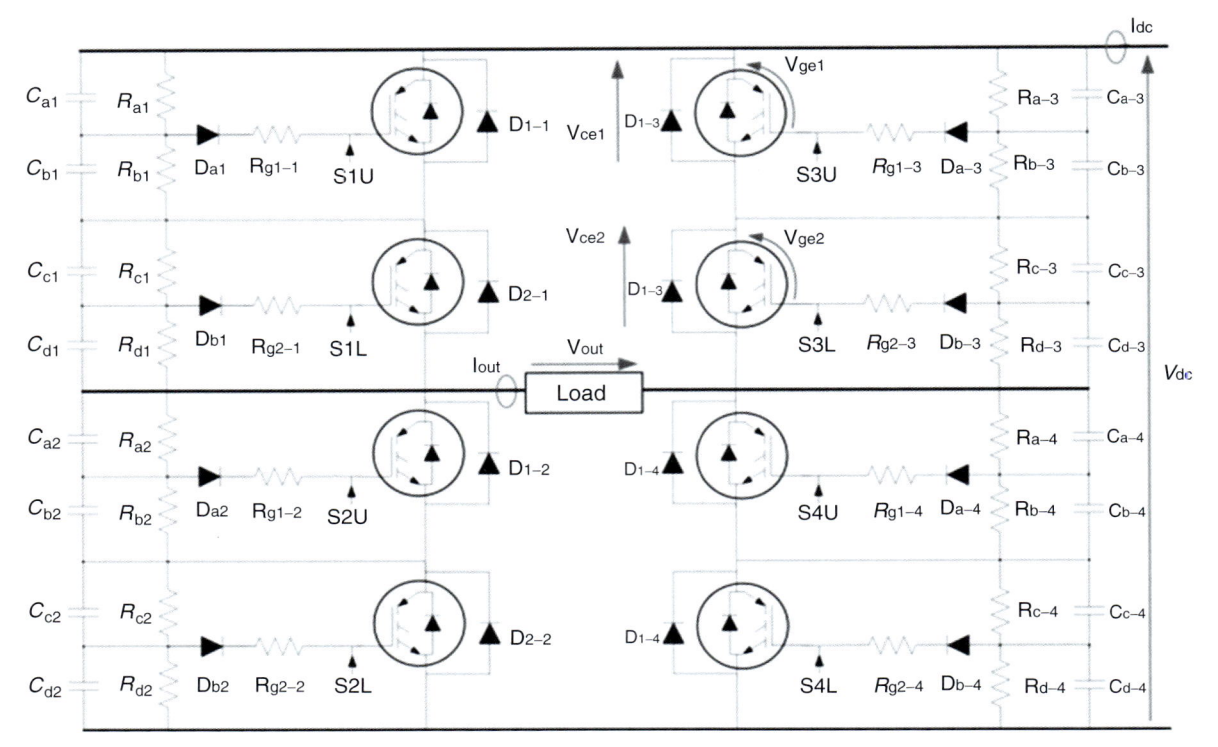

Figure 11 Schematic of two-switch MS-VSI with voltage balance circuit.

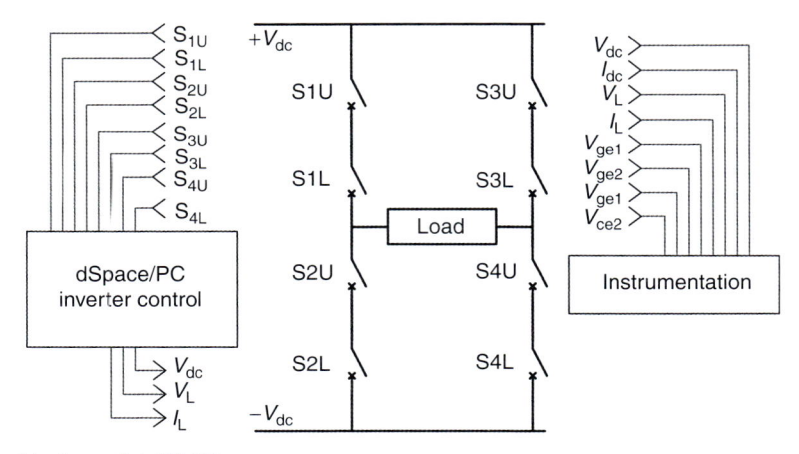

Figure 12 Laboratory layout for two-switch MS-VSI.

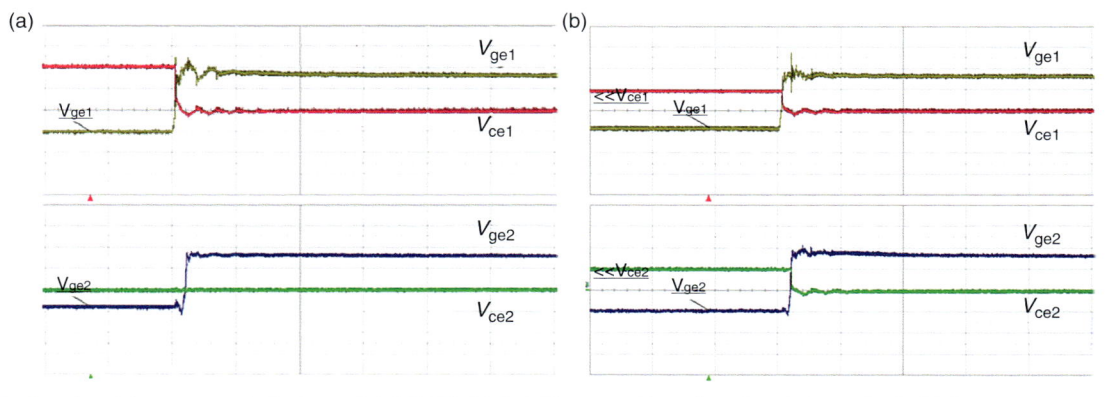

Figure 13 Experimental measurements for two-switch MS-VSI. (a) Switching, on, without the voltage balance circuit, DC link is not shared between devices. (100% V_{ce1}, 0% V_{ce2}) (b) Switching, on, with the voltage balance circuit, DC link is shared between devices (50% V_{ce1}, 50% V_{ce2}).

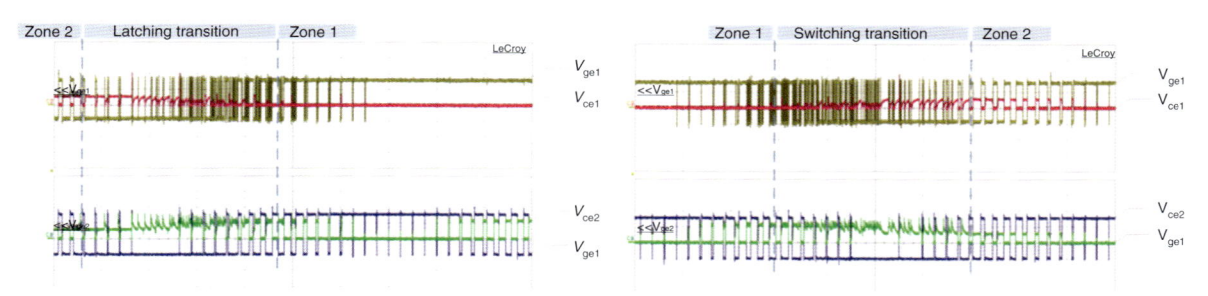

Figure 14 Experimental measurements for two-switch MS-VSI. (a) Switching transition from active to upper device latched. (b) Switching transition from latched to active.

Latching of the upper devices from a switching state and vice versa has shown to stabilize within 8 ms. It is understood that the success of the voltage balancing and short settle time would warrant that this approach is a feasible, efficient alternative to other power conversion techniques.

Further study is required to show that the configuration operates effectively at destructive voltage levels. Further analysis should also be considered for power losses with multiple series latching and merits of a even, closer matching SOA.

4.13.7 Test Characterization of a H_2 PEM Fuel Cell for Road Vehicle Applications

4.13.7.1 Introduction

This section discusses test characterization results for a H_2 PEMFC system developed for electric vehicle applications. An outline of the system design, construction, and operation is presented, including the electronic implementation of cell water management. For the chosen FC system, the section will discuss the importance of stack conditioning to improve output performance, in particular, after periods of inactivity. A laboratory-based test facility is discussed and characterization results presented to illustrate the FC system performance for various inlet fuel pressures and steady and dynamic loads.

In recent years, the security of energy resource and the sociological and environmental impacts of an increasing road transport population has motivated research and development into road vehicles utilizing alternative energy conversion technologies to the petroleum-based internal combustion engine (ICE). As such, FC systems have received considerable interest as potential energy converters for road vehicle power trains, and the most promising technology likely to displace petroleum-based systems in the future [32].

The FC is an electrochemical device that converts chemical energy into electrical energy via an electrochemical reaction process. As an energy converter, the FC is not a new concept, having a similar 150 year pedigree to electrochemical energy storage batteries. Historically, FCs have not been serious contenders for energy conversion in road transportation applications due to their relatively poor power density and high manufacturing costs, being restricted to higher value applications, for example, the US Gemini, Apollo, and, more recently, Shuttle Orbiter space programs [32, 33].

To address power density, cost, and application issues, FC research and development is being supported by various governments in Europe, North America, and the Far East, as well as by major automobile manufacturers worldwide. In Europe, there has been a steady increase in public funding for hydrogen and FC-related research via the various Framework Programs (FPs) of the European Community, as illustrated in **Figure 15** showing public funding to projects over the last 20 years [34]. Note that the EC funding is 40–60% of the total project budget. The main research subject areas for FP6 projects and their respective percentage budget share are detailed in **Table 3** [34], highlighting the broad spectrum of research to support this emerging sector of the road transportation market. Further information on the individual FP projects is available in the form of project overviews via public dissemination documents [34, 35].

The electrical output of an FC makes it an ideal energy source for integration into the power train of electric vehicles. The main FC technologies currently being considered for road transportation are

- the PEMFC,
- the direct methanol fuel cell (DMFC),
- the alkaline fuel cell (AFC), and
- the phosphoric acid fuel cell (PAFC).

Two other higher temperature technologies that are more appropriate to static higher power (above 500 kW) industrial and power utility applications are

- the SOFC and
- the molten carbonate fuel cell (MCFC).

Technical details of these six technologies are summarized in Reference 32. Of the above technologies, the PEMFC is one of the most suitable candidates for road vehicle applications, having an operating temperature of around 60–80 °C, good power density (0.4–0.8 kW l^{-1}), and potential for low cost in high volume manufacture [32]. An important advantage of FC-powered vehicles is the development of cleaner, more energy efficient cars, trucks, and buses that can initially operate on conventional fuels via local

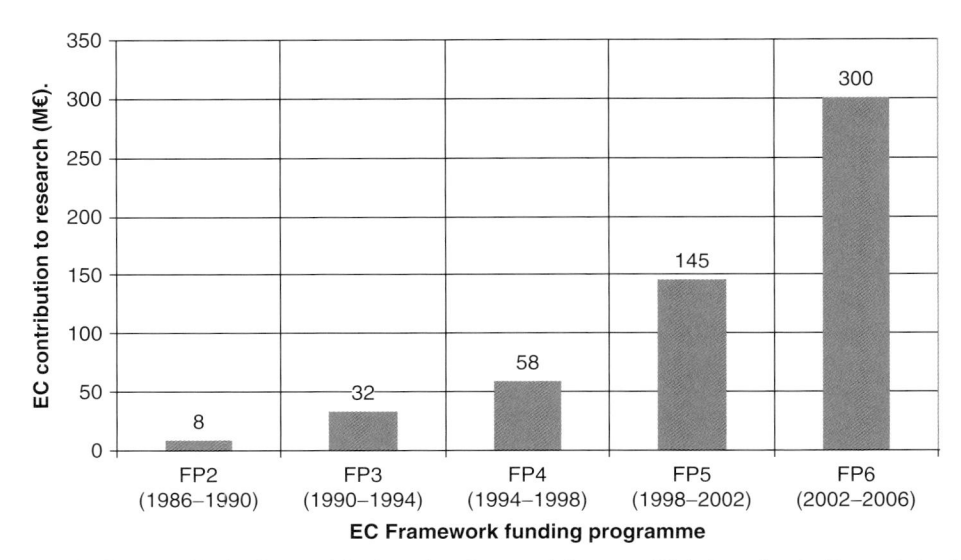

Figure 15 EC funding to hydrogen and fuel cell research in the various Framework Programs (FPs). Reproduced with permission from European Commission funded Fuel Cell and Hydrogen Research and Technical Development Projects (2002-2006) European Commission, http://ec.europa.eu/index_en.htm, Direct link: http://ec.europa.eu/research/energy/pdf/hydrogen_synopses_en.pdf, last visited July 2007 [34].

Table 3 EC Budget share per research area for FP6 projects [34]

Project subject area	Budget (%)
Fuel cell basic research (low temperature)	8.1
Fuel cell basic research (high temperature)	6.5
Transport applications (including fuel cell hybrid vehicles)	19.3
Stationary and portable applications	8.0
Validation and demonstration	18.6
H_2 production and distribution	19.3
H_2 storage	8.1
Safety, regulations, codes and standards	4.9
Pathways and socio-economic analysis	8.8

reformation, that is, gasoline and diesel. Such an intermediate step would enable the technology platform for a future move to renewable and alternative fuels, that is, methanol, ethanol, natural gas, and other hydrocarbons, and ultimately hydrogen, a particularly significant issue when considering the infrastructure and support logistics of a modern transportation network.

The integration and operation of an FC system in an electric vehicle power train requires a detailed understanding of the FC performance characteristics for both steady and dynamic loading. This section will present results from the test characterization of a 3 kW PEMFC system designed for low-cost automotive applications. The FC system rating was chosen to provide a range extension function for a 2.5 ton, zero emission taxi powered by two high peak power, high temperature, ZEBRA batteries, and two 3 kW hydrogen PEMFC systems [36]. The vehicle operational constraint was that it could be charged during evenings and had, therefore, to operate without refueling during the day. This constraint primarily arises from the lack of a hydrogen refueling and battery recharging infrastructure. It is envisaged that in the future this will change with the increasing uptake of more and all-electric vehicles, and thus the make-up of the vehicle on-board energy source ratings will also change according to their energy and power contributions to the overall vehicle energy management. The FC systems for the taxi provided a range extension function improving range for urban duty cycle driving from 119 to 242 km or 3.4 to 6.9 h [36]. Prior to vehicle testing, the FC systems were tested in the laboratory. This section is based on these test results.

4.13.7.2 MES-DEA PEMFCs

4.13.7.2.1 General

A typical FC consists of two electrodes with an electrolyte sandwiched in the middle. It will produce energy in the form of electricity and heat as long as fuel is supplied. In the basic PEMFC, hydrogen and oxygen are supplied to the FC, passing over the electrodes generating electricity, water, and heat. Hydrogen is fed into the anode of the FC and oxygen (or air) enters at the cathode. Encouraged by a catalyst, the hydrogen atom splits into a proton and an electron, each taking different paths to the cathode. The proton passes through the electrolyte while the electrons create a separate electrical current flow providing an external conducting path (load) is provided before returning to the cathode to be recombined with the hydrogen and oxygen to produce a molecule of water.

The MES-DEA PEMFC [37] is designed to be a compact, lightweight, and simple FC system. The FC system is comprised of two stacks of 60 series-connected cells. Each stack has separate forced air cooling and reaction air supply, and operates close to ambient pressure on the cathode for seal integrity.

Just as in a combustion engine, a steady ratio between the reactant and oxygen is necessary to keep the FC operating efficiently. Additionally, the FC membrane temperature must be managed throughout the cell in order to prevent degradation of the cell due to thermal loading. Hence, a microprocessor-based electronic control unit (ECU) manages the associated cooling and airflow fans, steering electronics for membrane hydration (to be discussed later), main, and purge valves. The microprocessor is also programmed to limit the maximum stack temperature (69 °C), upper DC output current (70 A) and lower stack voltage (60 V) limits, closing down the FC system when it is operated outside of these limits. An RS232 port is included on the ECU to provide readings of stack load current, terminal voltage, power demand, temperatures, and operating hours. **Figure 16(a)** illustrates the MES-DEA prototype 3 kW FC stacks, hydrogen and air supplies, and ECU, the main specification details of which are given in **Table 4** [37].

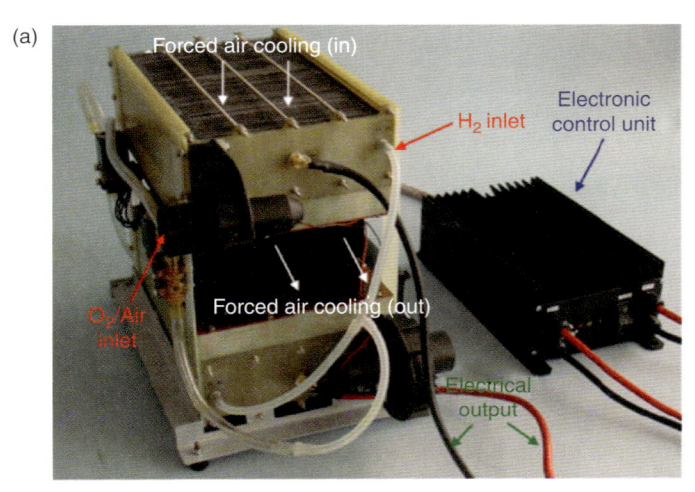

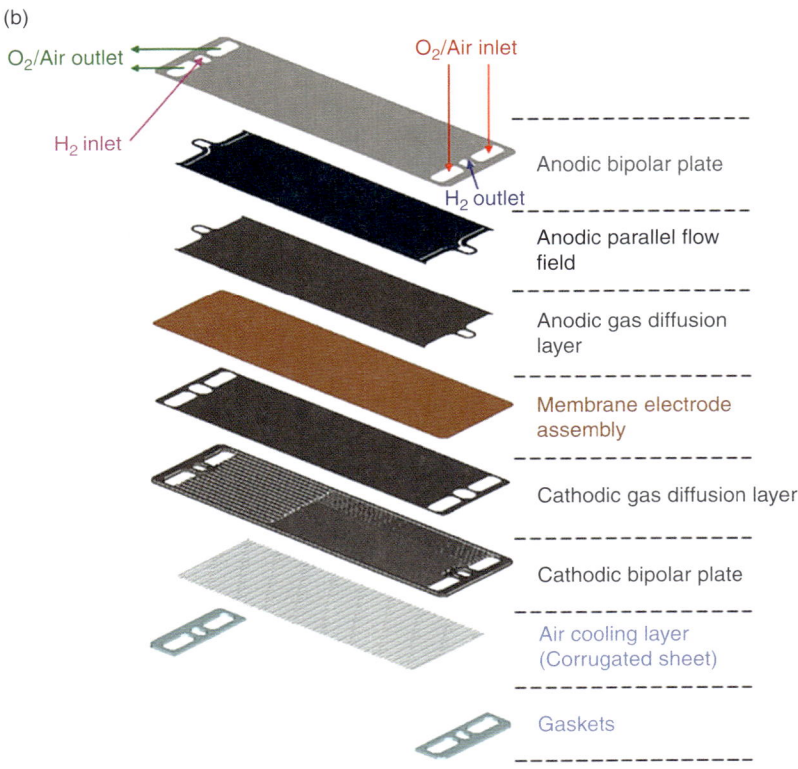

Figure 16 MES-DEA 3.0 kW H_2 fuel cell system. (a) Fuel cell and ECU. (b) Fuel cell composition. Reproduced with permission from MES-DEA (2007), *Fuel Cell Systems*, Switzerland, Direct link. http://www.mes-dea.ch/, last visited July 2007 [37].

Table 4 MES-DEA 3.0-kW prototype fuel cell system [37]

Performance data	
Unregulated output voltage range	72–114 Vdc
H$_2$ consumption at full-load	39 l$_n$ min^{-1}. (0.2 kg h^{-1})
Max. rated power output	3 kW
Total number of cells	120 (2 × 60 per stack)
Active cell area	61 cm^2
Operating conditions	
Stack temperature	Max. 69 °C
Hydrogen pressure	0.4–0.7 bar (gauge)
Air pressure	Ambient
Fuel supply	Pure hydrogen (0.9999)
ECU requirement	12 V, 25 W
Ambient temperature	0 to +35 °C
Gas humidification	None
Working cycle	Continuous
Cooling	Force air cooled
Total fuel cell volume	410 × 305 × 235 mm
Control unit volume	295 × 155 × 95 mm
Fuel cell weight	9 kg
Total system weight	11 kg

Each cell is composed of seven layers, as shown in **Figure 16(b)**, the first layer is the anode bipolar plate, a compressed expended graphite foil. The second layer is a carbon fiber plate for anodic parallel flow field. The third and fifth layers are the fine (µm) carbon anodic and cathodic fiber section diffusion layers. A German company, SGL Carbon AG, manufactures these four layers. The fourth layer is the prototype membrane electrode assembly manufactured by W. L. Gore & Associates. This layer can be further split into three, with the catalyst layers (top and bottom) containing platinum and carbon sandwiching the polymer electrolyte membrane. The sixth and seventh layers are manufactured in-house by MES-DEA and comprised a cathodic bipolar plate composite of graphite polymer and a corrugated silver-plated copper foil that forms the air-cooling layer, the bipolar plates sealing the gas reaction area. The last layer is a simple silicon-rubber gasket, to seal the reaction gases, that is, oxygen and hydrogen, between the cells. The typical cell active area is 61 cm^3.

4.13.7.2.2 Water Management

The MES-DEA FC system has a modular layout but, most significantly, has no auxiliary hydration plant. Generally, FC membranes must be hydrated otherwise the effectiveness of the reaction process is progressively reduced. Hence, excess water must be evaporated from the FC membranes at precisely the same rate that it is produced. If water is removed too quickly, the membrane dries out resulting in an increase in membrane resistance, eventually leading to damage or failure due to the creation of gas 'short-circuits', that is, hydrogen and oxygen combining across the membrane, generating heat that will progressively damage the FC. If the water removal is too slow the electrodes will flood preventing the reactants from reaching the catalyst and either stopping or reducing the reaction rate, impacting on the cell polarization characteristic [38] and conversion efficiency. Many methods are being investigated and developed to manage FC hydration, the hydration plant adding significantly to FC system mass, volume, and cost [38–40].

For the MES-DEA FC system, the stack is periodically purged via the ECU opening a valve thus supplying fresh H$_2$ and, at the same time, draining excess water that has accumulated in the reaction chambers. This purging routine is performed every 20 s for 0.5 s.

To hydrate the FC membranes, the stack is electronically short-circuited for 50 ms every 20 s. This function is also activated by the ECU when the stack voltage is below 95 V (~12 A) and is implemented via opening of the load switches and closing of the short-circuit switch, as detailed in the schematic of **Figure 17**. The switches, in this case, are MOSFET devices located in the ECU. This procedure results in the release of sufficient water in the stack membranes to maintain their moisture level. The hydration energy loss, in terms of unspent hydrogen and electronic losses, is lower than losses associated with other techniques and, more importantly, the system is significantly simplified, a commercial feature of the MEA-DEA technology. The impact of the purging and cell hydration routines on FC output will be highlighted in the results of Section 4.13.7.4.

4.13.7.3 Fuel Cell Test Facility

Three hydrogen PEMFC systems, one 0.5 kW and two 3.0 kW units, were purchased from MES-DEA as part of the UK DTi and EPSRC funded research project ZESTFUL, investigating the utility of a low-power (2 × 3 kW) FC system providing a range extension function for a battery electric vehicle [36]. As part of the project, a laboratory-based FC test facility was assembled to test characterize the FCs prior to their installation on the electric vehicle and as a continuing facility for FC test evaluation. The MES-DEA FC systems require near pure (0.999) hydrogen (H$_2$) gas at a typical gauge pressure of 0.50 bar (max. 0.70 bar) and maximum peak flow rate of

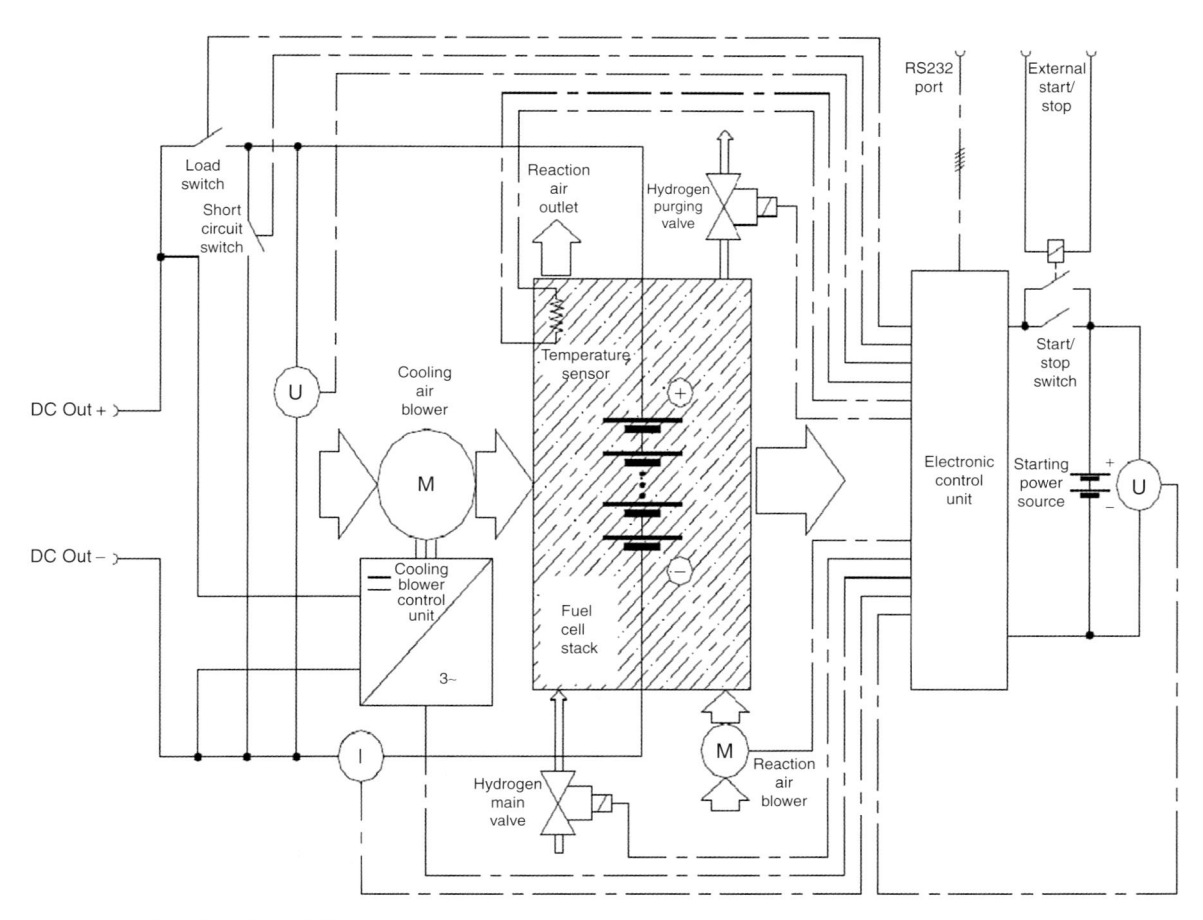

Figure 17 Schematic of fuel cell and ECU system.

60 l min^{-1} during purging. The low-pressure hydrogen supply is derived from compressed, 175 bar, H$_2$ gas stored in cylinders located in laboratory Room A3, as illustrated in **Figure 18(a)** showing a schematic of the FC test facility equipment layout.

Pressure regulators reduce the H$_2$ gas in two stages, from 175 bar (cylinder) to 3.0 bar, and then to 0.80 bar (manually set), to allow for the pressure drops along the feed pipe from Room A3, to the Fuel Cell Test Chamber in laboratory Room A2. These controls, overpressure safety vents, purge, and drain points are all installed on a manifold assembly in Room A3 as illustrated in **Figure 18(b)**. A ventilation fan also maintains a regular airflow for dilution of any gas leakage.

A Bronkhorst pressure transducer with an integrated controllable valve is used to give finer regulation of the FC hydrogen inlet pressure from 0.0 to 1.0 bar, control flow, and give a measurement of inlet pressure to the test facility data acquisition and control system. A Bronkhorst mass-flow transducer measures the H$_2$ flow rate, which is also logged via the data acquisition system. Additionally, the FC control system microprocessor helps maintain the hydrogen pressure and thus resolves pressure drop problems, in particular during fluctuations of the FC output load power. Two current and two voltage transducers measure the FC stack and load currents and voltages, respectively, that is, either side of the ECU. The gas and electrical instruments are mounted inside the FC test chamber, while a load bank with controllable switched resistive elements provides load increments at the FC output, **Figure 18(c)**. MST Technology H$_2$ detection systems monitor the background H$_2$ levels in Room A3 and the FC test chamber for safety. The detection of gas leaks has to be monitored carefully and not confused with short bursts of waste gas encountered during cell purging. The gas management therefore cross-checks gas supply (pressure and flow) and electrical output to instigate a safe operating regime.

A PC, installed with National Instruments (NI) PCI-6229, M Series data acquisition card (DAQ) and Labview 7.1 controls the FC test facility implementing start-up, safety checks and gas monitoring routines, and initiates predefined loading profiles. The PC also provides the data acquisition functions and displays the FC measurements and alarm status.

4.13.7.4 Fuel Cell Test Characterization

4.13.7.4.1 Conditioning

One operational issue experienced with the MES-DEA FC systems is the potential for reduced output performance if the systems are not used, or stored, for a period of time (months) due to dehydration of the stack membranes. The loss in performance is not permanent and can be recovered by a reconditioning procedure. However, this procedure is not currently implemented via the

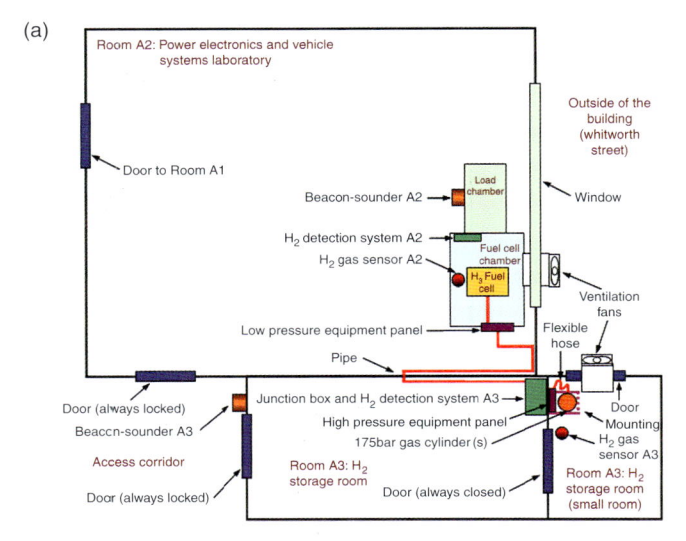

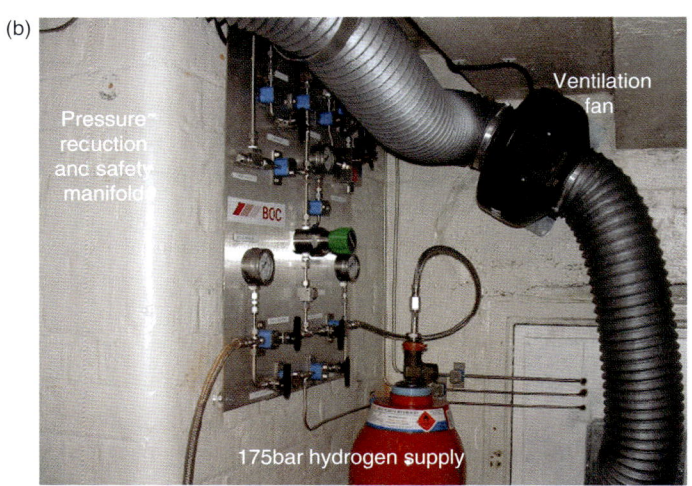

Figure 18 Fuel cell test facility. (a) Laboratory schematic layout. (b) High to low pressure manifold, Room A3. (c) Load and fuel cell chambers, Room A2.

existing FC hardware which thus requires further development. For laboratory purposes, the FC was reconditioned manually. Here, the FC membrane chambers are soaked with deionized water for ~30 min, and then completely drained out. Then the FC system is electrically loaded for a short period of time, 1–3 min. This procedure is repeated until the FC system capacity increases back to rated maximum output power at, or near, the specified terminal voltage.

By way of example, **Figure 19** illustrates results for the MES-DEA 3 kW FC system showing the improvement in performance for progressive reconditions (tests 10–17). The results clearly show that the FC system performance, in terms of fuel-to-electrical output conversion efficiency (**Figure 19(a)**), terminal voltage regulation or polarization (**Figure 19(b)**), and power output (**Figure 19(c)**), is gradually recovered after repetitive reconditioning.

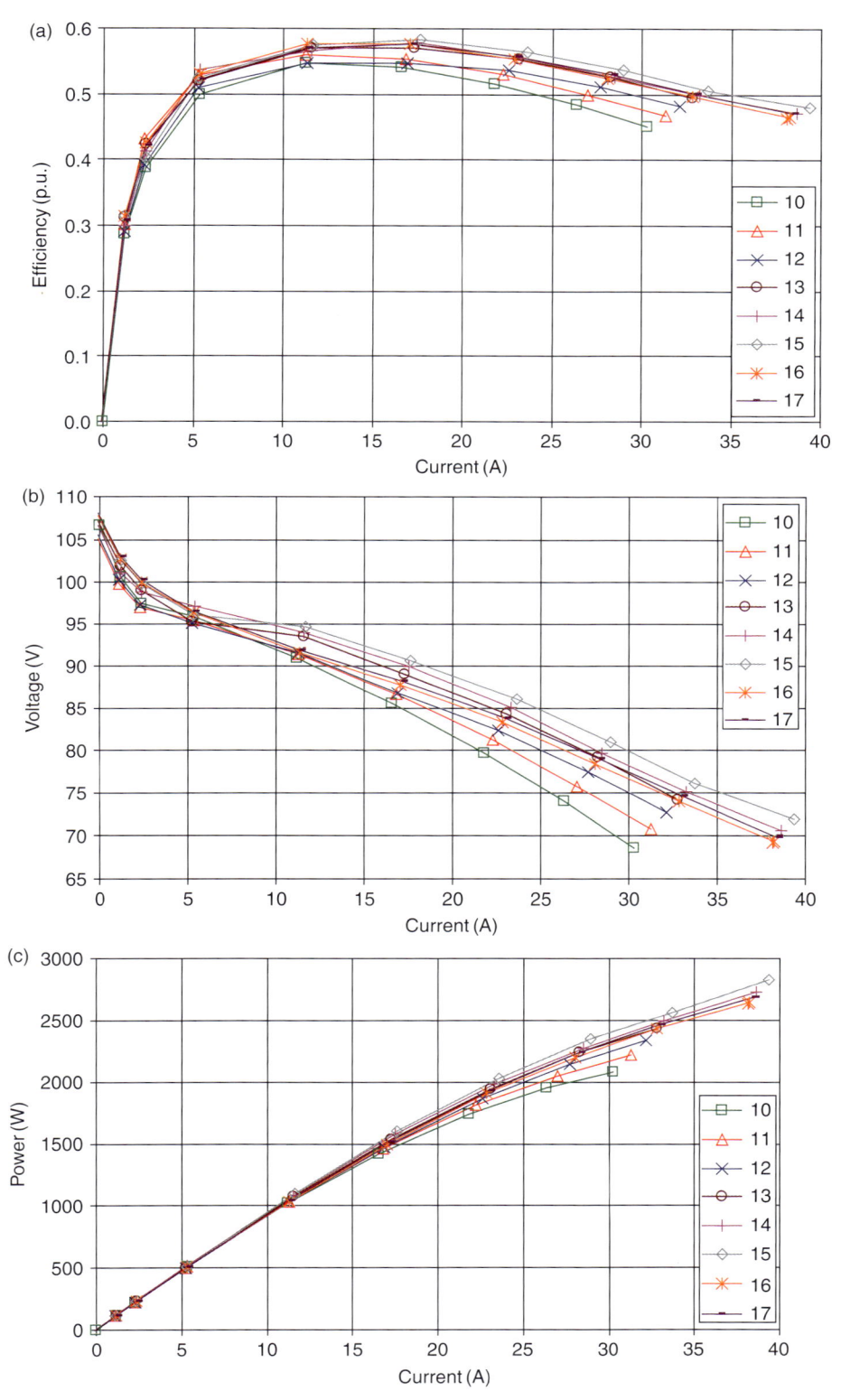

Figure 19 Improvement in fuel cell performance. (a) Fuel-to-electrical output efficiency. (b) System terminal voltage regulation, or polarization characteristic. (c) Fuel cell output power.

In application, the conditioning procedure could be implemented via modifications to the FC short-circuit and purging routines (to be discussed later) and with an acceptance of a reduced power output for an initial period of operation of about 30 min. During test evaluation, it was found that conditioning was not required if the FC had only been inactive for 1–2 weeks; this was depending on how prevailing environmental conditions are effected cell hydration.

A procedure is now executed by the test facility controller whereby a high (over) load is automatically switched for a short duration of 1–2 s to the FC output and the FC output voltage and capacity measured. This being repeated until the FC is at, or near, the nameplate ratings.

4.13.7.4.2 Inlet H_2 Pressure

After being reconditioned to rated performance and polarization conditions, the effect of inlet H_2 pressure was investigated via control of the Bronkhorst pressure transducer. The H_2 pressure to the FC system was set from 0.10 bar to 0.50 bar in 0.10 bar steps and polarization characteristics measured. **Figure 20** summaries the FC system performance for varying inlet H_2 pressures, clearly showing that the terminal voltage and maximum power output of the 3 kW FC system decreases with decreasing H_2 gas inlet pressure. However, the fuel-to-electrical output conversion efficiency was higher at lower pressure for load powers below 1.5 kW (below 15 A load current). This feature should form part of a FC management scheme optimizing fuel conversion at light loads.

During the test, the auxiliary power or parasitic losses vary, due to the energy required for the cooling fans, H_2 inlet valve, air inlet fans, and ECU, with load output power or decreasing H_2 fuel inlet pressure (**Figure 20(d)**). It was observed that the reasons which contribute to higher parasitic losses are the increase in speed of cooling fans and air inlet fans. The parasitic losses do not include the external power source for the ECU. This loss is negligible since during operation, needing an average 12.5 W for 9 s during the FC system starting procedure, 91 mW when the short-circuit routine is not activated, and an average 165 mW when the short-circuit routine is activated. Note that a peak power output from the FC system of 3.3 kW was recorded.

4.13.7.4.3 Fuel Cell Short-Circuit and Purging Routines

As discussed in Section 4.13.7.2, the MES-DEA FC system is periodically short-circuited and purged via the ECU to hydrate the cell membranes and release excess water, respectively. **Figure 21(a)** shows the FC terminal voltages and currents during progressively increasing stepped loads, showing that the short-circuit control strategy is only implemented when the FC terminal voltage falls below ~95 V. Note that, as shown in **Figure 21**, 'stack' refers to the measurements at the terminals of the FC stacks and before the ECU, while 'sys' refers to the load terminals after the ECU, that is, the output of the FC system. The short-circuit duration is captured by **Figure 21(b)**, although the signal resolution is limited by the bandwidth of the data acquisition system which was set low to capture the full-period events of **Figure 21(a)**.

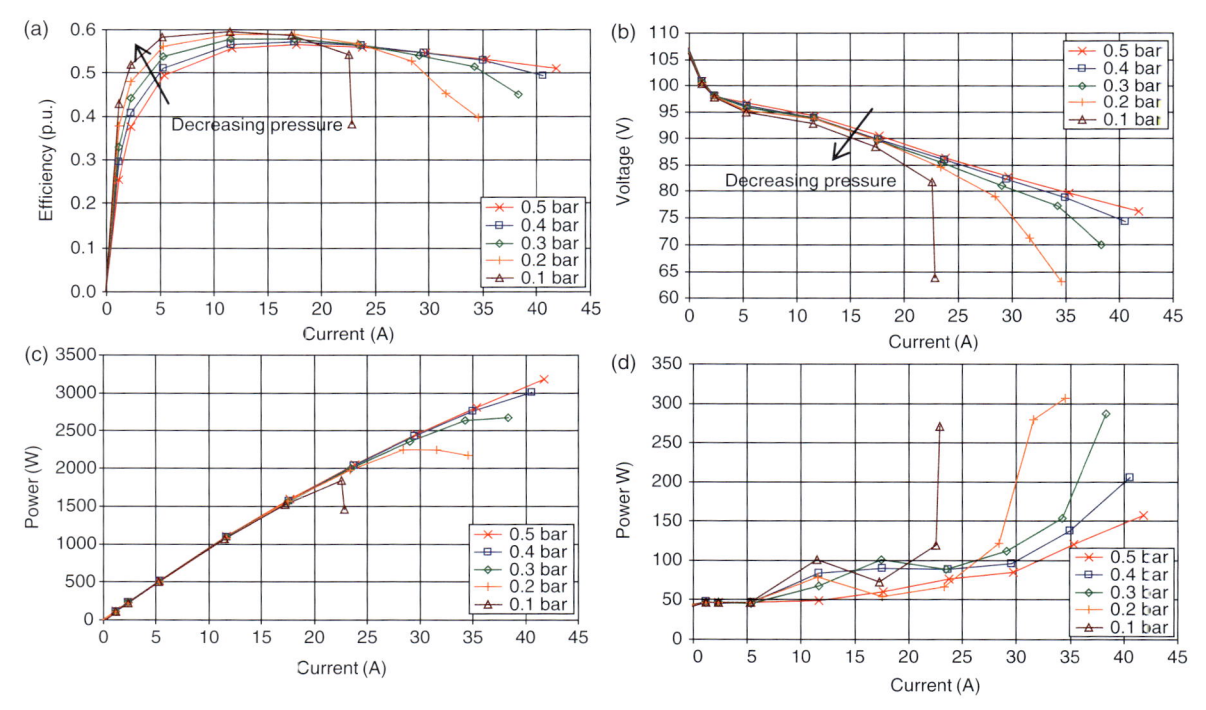

Figure 20 MES-DEA 3 kW fuel cell performance with inlet H_2 pressure varied from 0.10 bar to 0.50 bar. (a) Fuel-to-electrical output efficiency. (b) System terminal voltage regulation, or polarization characteristic. (c) Fuel cell output power. (d) Auxiliary power.

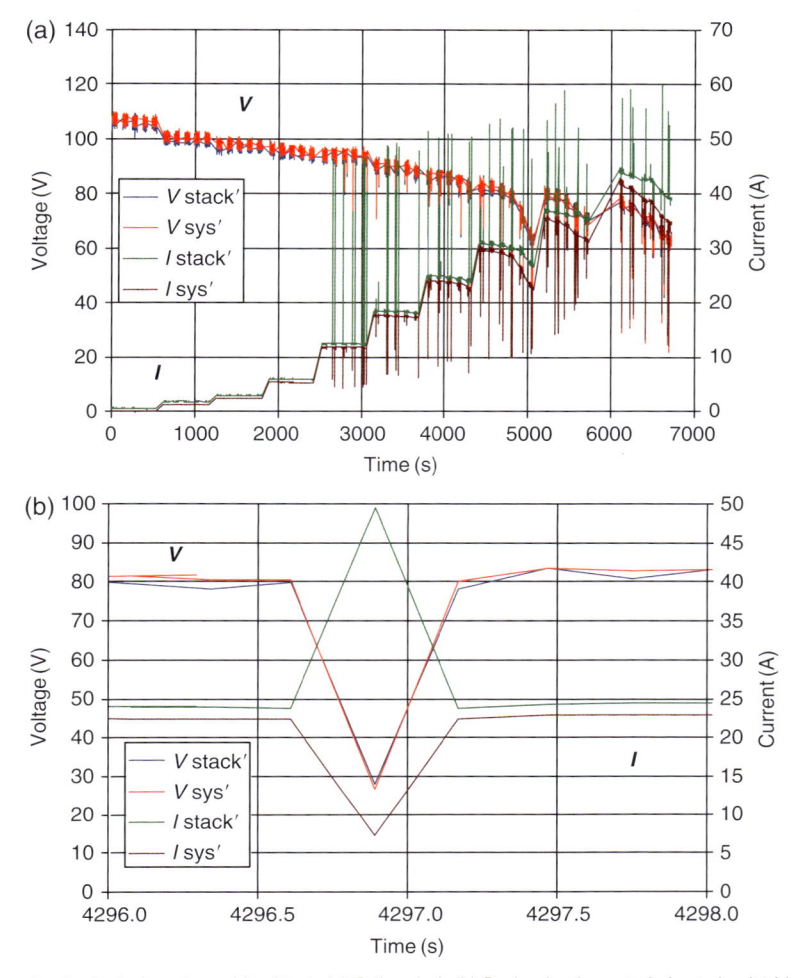

Figure 21 Fuel cell inputs and outputs during stepped load test. (a) Full period. (b) During implemented short-circuited by ECU.

Figure 22(a–d) illustrates test measurements for the 3 kW FC system, showing the system output voltage and current, output power, H_2 inlet gas pressure, and the H_2 inlet gas flow rate, respectively. The results confirm that the short-circuit and purging strategies implemented by ECU were 10 s apart, and each routine is repeated every 20 s. During short-circuit, the FC system output voltage and current are dropped to zero. At the same time, the H_2 fuel inlet pressure is reduced and the flow rate increased due to the increased energy conversion. Note the improvement in power output immediately after the hydration procedure. During purging, the H_2 fuel inlet pressure reduces with an increased flow rate, although this manifests itself as a small perturbation on the output power of the FC system.

Figure 23 shows the FC response time from no-load to 3 kW (full-load). The results show that the FC system output power, voltage, and current stabilize after 25 s of load change. **Figure 24** shows the FC response time from 3 kW (full-load) to no-load. The response time of this load change only took 30 ms for the output power and current, but the settling time for system voltage was about 1.5 s due to the response time of the inlet H_2 pressure controller. The inlet H_2 fuel pressure will decrease to around 0.5 bar (the limit set on pressure controller) when the next consecutive purging routine takes place.

4.13.8 Summary

This section has presented some laboratory test characterization results for the 3.0 kW H_2 PEM FC system developed by MES-DEA. The effects of fuel pressure and membrane hydration and the importance of reconditioning have been discussed.

The results clearly show that the FC output power increases with the increasing fuel pressure. At the recommended fuel pressure, the FC system achieved peak efficiency at around half of the rated power, that is, 10.5 kW. Below this output power, the FC efficiency was higher at lower fuel pressure, mainly due to a reduction in of the H_2 purging implemented in the ECU. This observation could be utilized by improved control algorithms in the FC EMU or vehicle interface controller.

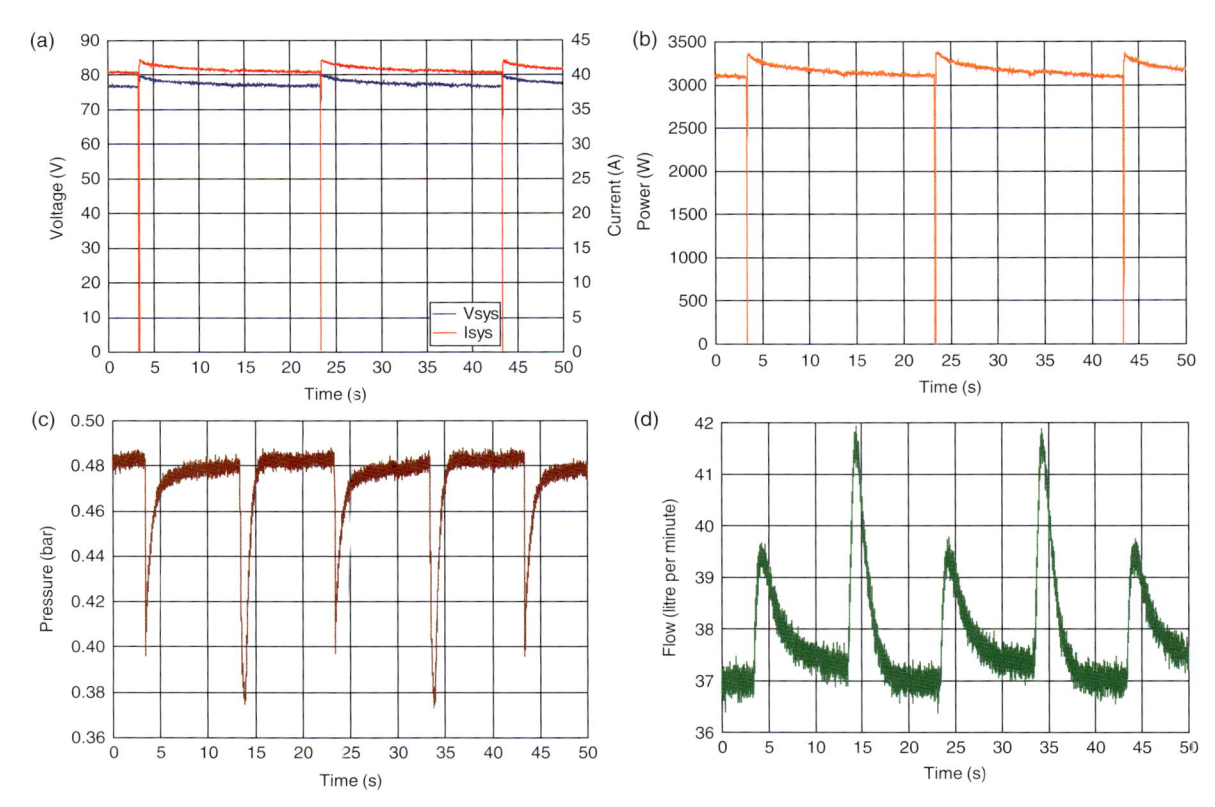

Figure 22 Fuel cell performance during 3 kW load test. (a) System voltage and current. (b) Output power. (c) H_2 inlet fuel pressure. (d) H_2 inlet fuel flowrate.

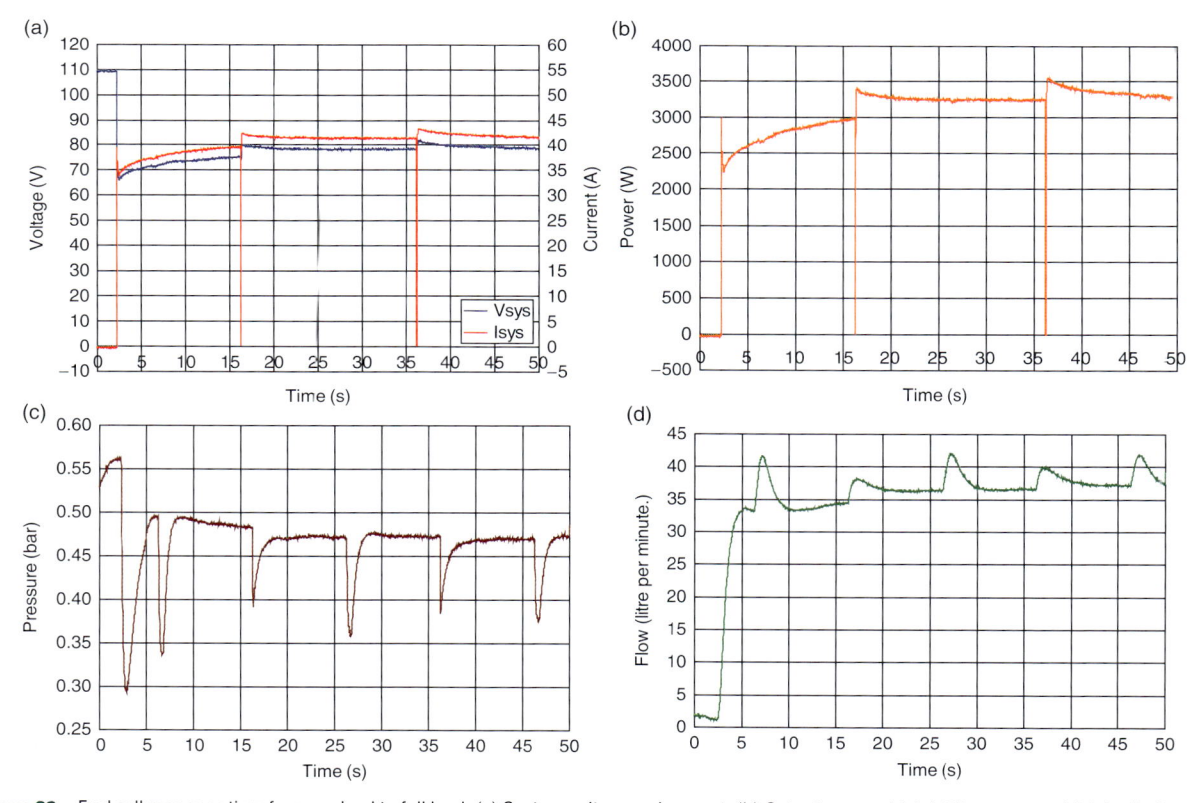

Figure 23 Fuel cell response time from no-load to full load. (a) System voltage and current. (b) Output power. (c) Inlet H_2 pressure. (d) Inlet H_2 flow rate.

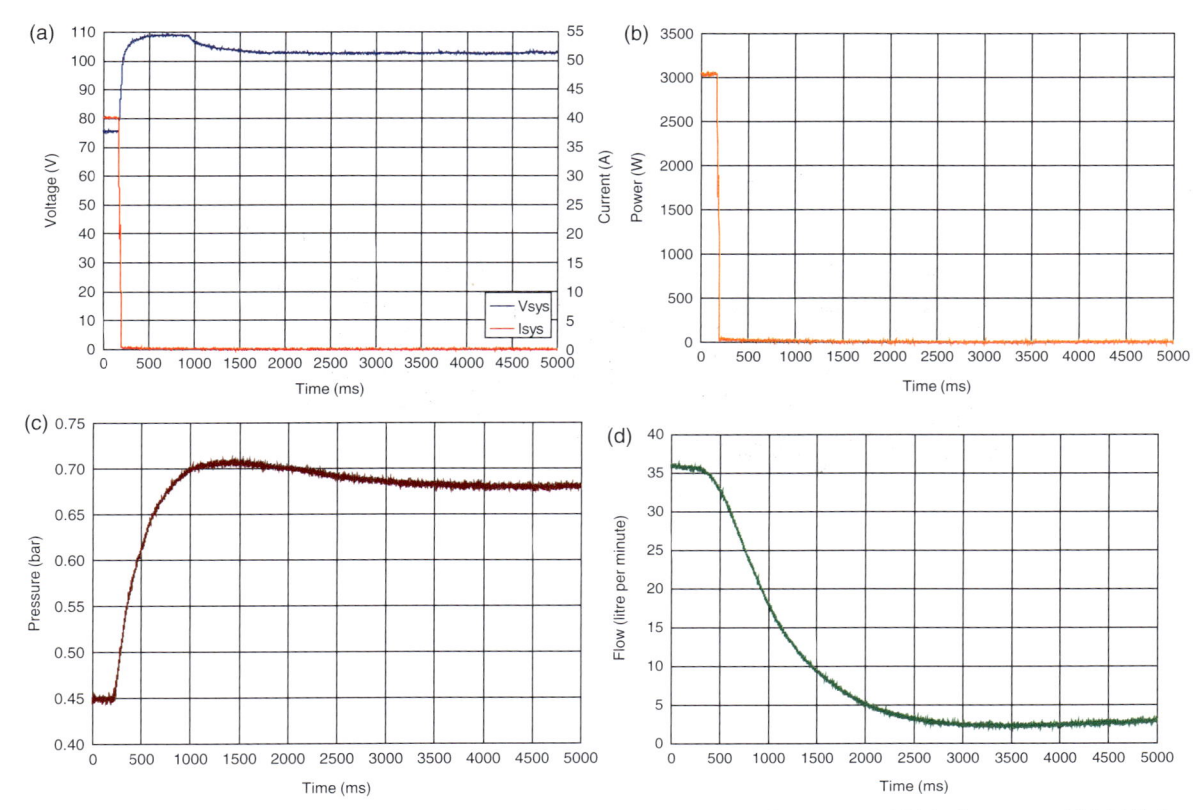

Figure 24 Fuel cell response time from full load to no-load. (a) System voltage and current. (b) Output power. (c) Inlet H_2 pressure. (d) Inlet H_2 flow rate.

The purging or 'short-circuit' routine for membrane hydration is only activated by the ECU when the FC output voltage falls below a threshold of ~94 V. It is important to point out that when the 3 kW FC system is operated above 1.5 kW, the parasitic power losses increase, thus the system efficiency is reduced.

Thus, all of the above FC characteristics must be taken into consideration when specifying the size of the FC for a vehicle energy system.

Proposed future work includes an investigation of the effect of air inlet flow rate and ambient temperature on FC performance, as well as the time response for system start-up, shut down, and load change.

4.13.9 A H_2 PEM Fuel Cell and High Energy Dense Battery Hybrid Energy Source for an Urban Electric Vehicle

4.13.9.1 Introduction

Electric vehicles are set to play a prominent role in addressing the energy and environmental impact of an increasing road transport population by offering a more energy-efficient and less-polluting drivetrain alternative to conventional ICE vehicles. Given the energy (and hence range) and performance limitations of electrochemical battery storage systems, hybrid systems combining energy and power dense storage technologies have been proposed for vehicle applications. This section will discuss the application of a hydrogen FC as a range extender for an urban electric vehicle for which the primary energy source is provided by a high energy dense battery. A review of FC systems and automotive drivetrain application issues are discussed, together with an overview of the battery technology. The prototype FC and battery component simulation models are presented and their performance as a combined energy/power source assessed for typical urban and suburban driving scenarios.

The impetus for more environmentally friendly road vehicles and alternative road vehicle energy conversion has fostered research and development in electrically powered vehicles for road transport applications since the late 1980s. This is particularly the case for medium- to heavy-duty vehicles where some additional propulsion system mass is not as critical as for smaller passenger vehicles. Further, in recent years, FC systems have also been proposed as a potential energy carrier, and the most suitable alternative likely to displace petroleum-based fuels during the first half of this century [32, 41]. While there are many technical and resource management issues associated with the displacement of petroleum fuels for transportation, and the commensurate supply infrastructure requirements, this section will discuss some of the application issues associated with the implementation of hybrid energy sources for electric and FC vehicles. Specifically, the section will report on initial drivetrain design results from a research program investigating the utility of an electric London Taxi supplied via a high energy dense electrochemical battery and hydrogen FC range extender for inner city operation.

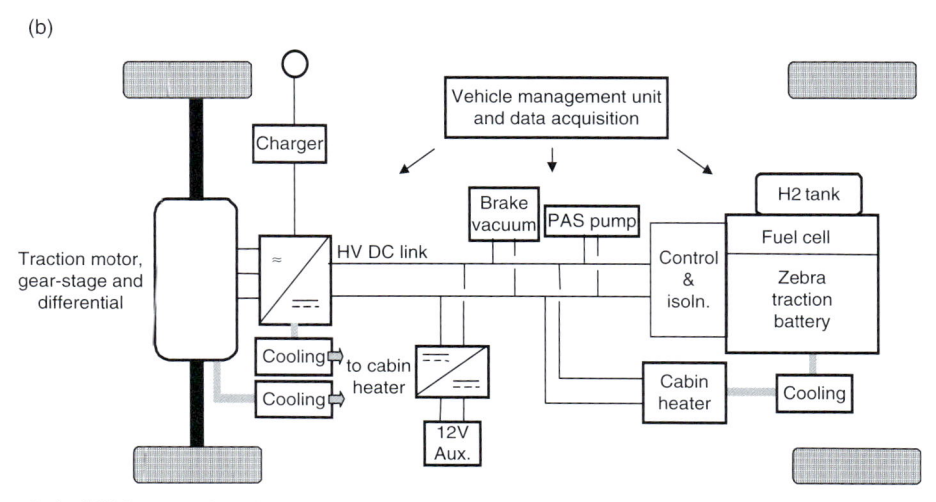

Figure 25 Hydrogen fuel cell-high energy dense battery electric London Taxi and drivetrain layout schematic. (a) London Taxi. (b) Drivetrain schematic.

The aims of the research program are to investigate and address the principal technical difficulties associated with the future commercial application of FC technologies in electric vehicle traction drivetrains. As such, a zero emission London Taxi powered via two high peak power (32 kW), high temperature, ZEBRA batteries and a 6 kW, hydrogen, PEMFC system, is being developed for vehicle power train test evaluation, as illustrated in **Figure 25** showing the vehicle and drivetrain layout schematic. The prime mover for the taxi is a brushless permanent magnet (PM) machine and integrated gear reduction and differential drive to the vehicle back axle. The PM machine is controlled via a three-phase voltage source converter, the DC supply to which is provided by the traction battery and FC via a DC–DC converter. The vehicle on-board hybrid energy source will allow the PEMFC to operate predominantly at a steady power, and at power levels associated with optimal fuel energy conversion efficiency, with the battery acting to buffer peak loads, recover vehicle braking energy and provide the bulk energy demand. Hence, the FC operates primarily in a range extension function.

The section will review FC systems and discuss automotive drivetrain application issues, together with an overview of the battery technology. The regulation of the traction battery and FC when subject to the dynamic power loading illustrated in **Figure 26(b)**, necessitates detailed modeling to assess the functionality of the individual components once interconnected with the drivetrain. Hence, the prototype FC and battery component simulation models are presented and their performance as a combined hybrid energy source assessed for typical dynamic urban and suburban driving duty cycle scenarios. It is shown that the FC and battery combination are complementary for such duty loading, extending the vehicle range while minimizing the installed FC power.

4.13.9.2 Vehicle Energy and Power Requirements

For road vehicle applications, the on-board energy and power sources must satisfy the load demand of the vehicle traction drivetrain. The decision as to whether the energy storage medium supplies all of the vehicle load or simply the average power requirements can significantly influence the sizing of the vehicle energy/power systems and hence system cost. The difficulty in

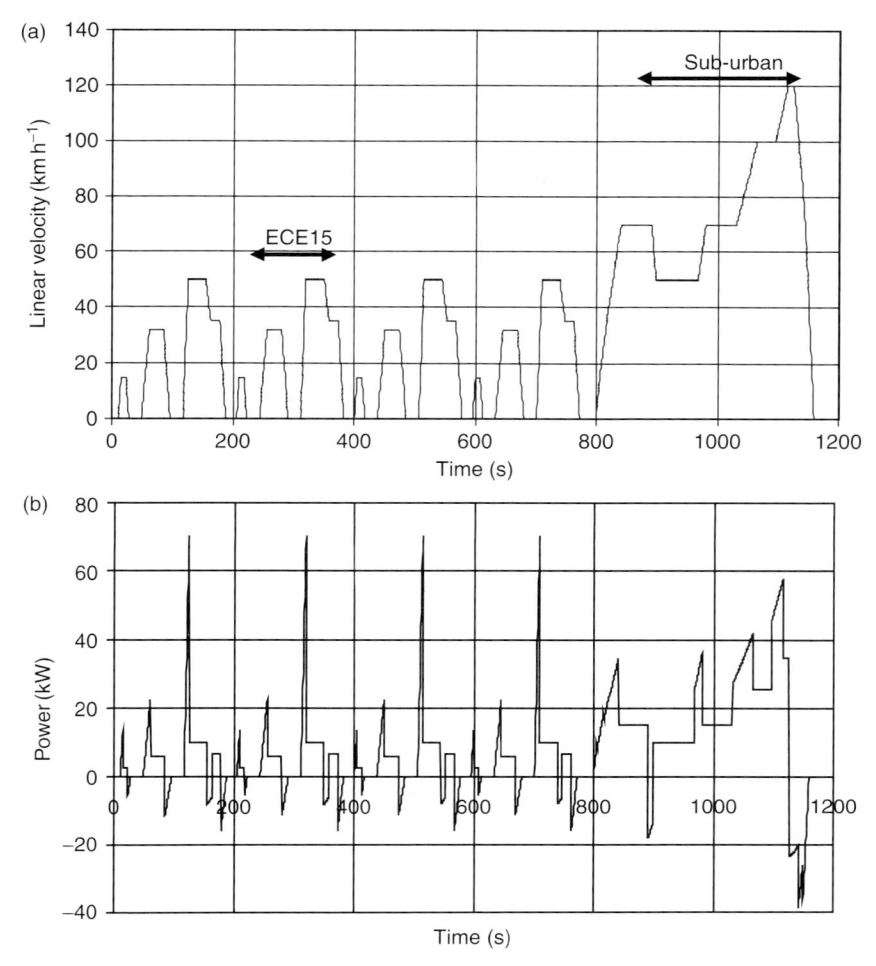

Figure 26 Vehicle linear velocity and associated dynamic power requirements for the London Taxi. (a) NEDC (4 × ECE15 + suburban) driving cycle. (b) Vehicle power vs. time.

making this assessment is in choosing the most appropriate duty rating specification for the vehicle. For example, **Figure 25** illustrates a typical 2.5 ton urban electric vehicle, a London Taxi, which is the reference vehicle for the study. The power required to propel the vehicle over the New European Driving Cycle (NEDC) (**Figure 26(a)**), that comprises 4 × enhanced European Commission R15.04 (ECE15) urban cycles and 1 × EC suburban cycle [32, 41], is detailed in **Table 5**, showing a wide disparity in peak-to-average power requirements, that is, 17:1 and 4:1 for the urban and suburban profiles, respectively.

The data in **Table 5** are calculated via solution of the vehicle kinematics [42] with the NEDC linear velocity driving cycle of **Figure 26(a)**. The vehicle parameter data for the London Taxi are given in Appendix I. The vehicle dynamic power profile calculated over the NEDC driving cycle is illustrated in **Figure 26(b)** and used for subsequent vehicle performance assessment. There is also a

Table 5 Vehicle power requirement

Driving cycle	Power condition	Cycle time (s)	Range (km)	Power (kW)
ECE15	Max. motoring	195	1.13	70.35
	Max. regenerating			−16.16
	Average			4.21
Sub-urban	Max. motoring	400	6.96	57.84
	Max. regenerating			−38.83
	Average			14.57
NEDC	Average	1180	11.47	7.72

similar disparity in the vehicle peak-average power for other driving (or duty) cycles, that is, the Highway Fuel Economy Test (HWFET) schedule, US 1975 schedule (FTP75), and Japanese 11-mode test schedule, hence the potential to oversize the vehicle energy source for single source systems, as discussed in Reference 43. Note that although all sources are a source of energy, reference is made here to energy and power to emphasize the functionality of the vehicle on-board sources with respect to the vehicle energy management philosophy.

4.13.9.3 Fuel Cells for Transportation

4.13.9.3.1 Background

A major advantage of FC-powered vehicles is the development of cleaner, more energy-efficient cars, trucks, and buses that can initially operate on conventional fuels via local reformation, that is, gasoline and diesel, while enabling the technology platform for a future move to renewable and alternative fuels, that is, methanol, ethanol, natural gas, and other hydrocarbons, and ultimately hydrogen, a particularly significant issue when considering the infrastructure and support requirements of a modern transportation network.

With on-board fuels other than pure hydrogen, for example, natural gas, methanol, and gasoline, the FC systems could use an appropriate fuel processor to convert the fuel into hydrogen. Since the FC relies on chemistry and not combustion, local emissions from this type of system should, potentially, be much smaller than emissions from the cleanest fuel combustion process emissions, while offering the advantages of an electric transmission. However, in traction systems, FCs have major operational disadvantages in turns of their voltage regulation and inability to accept vehicle kinetic energy during braking [33, 44], hence the consideration of a hybrid energy/power source.

For the taxi vehicle test platform, 2×3 kW PEMFCs have been chosen to provide a background energy input, essentially acting as a vehicle range extender. The FCs are prototype systems developed by MES-DEA, Switzerland [44], and are designed to realize a very compact, lightweight, and simple fuel stack. The stack has separate forced airflow systems for cooling and reaction air supply, operate close to ambient pressure on the cathode for seal integrity, have a modular layout, but most significantly, has no auxiliary humidification components. A microprocessor manages the associated cooling and airflow fans, steering electronics for membrane hydration, main, and purge valves. **Figure 27** illustrates the 3 kW prototype FC system and control electronics, the main specification details of which are given in Appendix I [44].

4.13.9.4 Fuel Cell Modeling

As with electrochemical batteries, FCs exhibit nonlinear performance characteristics that can significantly influence vehicle drive system operation and component optimization if not considered at the system design stage. The three main FC loss mechanisms can be summarized as

- irreversible/activation polarization loss,
- concentration polarization loss, and
- ohmic or resistance polarization.

The influence of these loss mechanisms on FC performance is illustrated in **Figure 28**, showing measured FC voltage and power output as a function of cell current density (or load current). The FC can be modeled by a semiempirical equation as discussed in Reference 45, for which parameters are calculated through an identification process with experimental data, viz.

Figure 27 Prototype fuel cell system and control electronics. Reproduced with permission from MES-DEA (2003), *Fuel Cell Systems, Technical Information*, Switzerland [44].

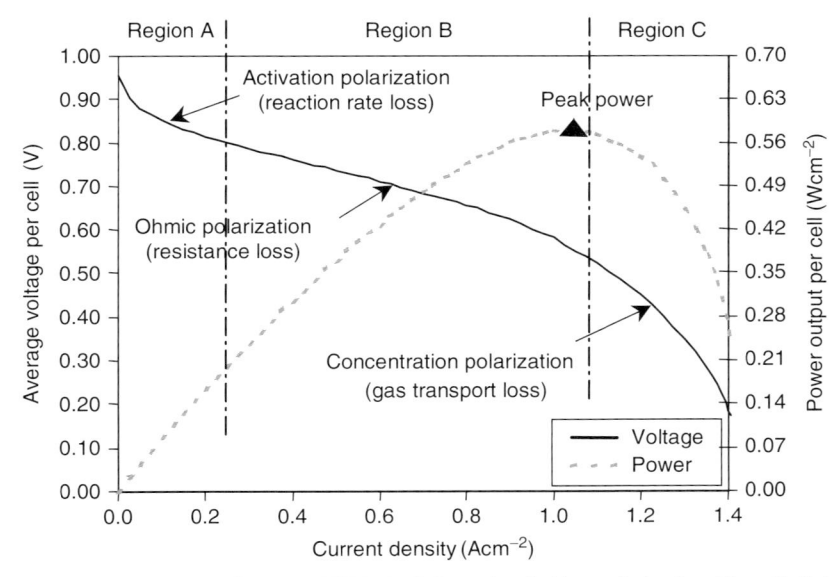

Figure 28 Measured voltage and power data for MES-DEA H₂ PEM fuel cell. Reproduced with permission from Thematic Network on 'Fuel Cells, Electric and Hybrid Vehicles (ELEDRIVE)', a Network funded under Framework V, Contract No. ENK6-CT-2000-20057, Project No. NNE5-1999–20036 [41].

$$V_{cell} = E_o - b \ln(J) - (R_{int} J) - k_1 e^{(k_2 J)} \quad [11]$$

where terms are derived from the associated Nernst, Tafel, and Ohm's laws, and V_{cell} is the FC terminal voltage, E_o the steady open-circuit voltage, b the Tafel's parameter for oxygen reduction, J the current density, R_{int} the cell ohmic resistance, and k_1 and k_2 the diffusion parameters. While the model is not universal with regard to the FC fundamental chemistry, it is much simpler in form and represents the main voltage loss components. Each term in eqn [11] is dominant in each region of the V-J characteristic. In region A, the cell voltage decreases drastically due to the oxygen electrochemical activation reactions, where the logarithm term has the main influence. In region B, the curve is roughly linear, that is, essentially ohmic resistive losses, and Region C corresponds to diffusion losses, that is, exponential term. The five parameters in eqn [11] depend on cell temperature and gas pressures. However, for the FC stack considered, the stack temperature is tightly regulated via forced ventilation and the stack pressure is fixed to 1.4 bar. **Figure 28** shows measured voltage regulation and power capacity with load current for a 3 kW MES-DEA FC.

For modeling purposes, implementation of eqn [11] can be problematic at zero current; hence a simpler quadratic fit to the measured data of **Figure 27** is used.

$$V_{cell} = k_a + k_b J + k_c J^2 + k_d J^3 + k_e J^4 + k_f J^5 + k_g J^6 + k_h J^7 + k_i J^8 + k_j J^9 + k_k J^{10} \quad [12]$$

where V_{cell} is the FC terminal voltage per cell, and J the cell current density. The FC terminal voltage is used in conjunction with the measured stack fuel-to-electrical conversion efficiency, as illustrated in **Figure 29**, to simulate operation and predict performance. Again, a curve fit to the measured data of **Figure 29** is used in the FC model

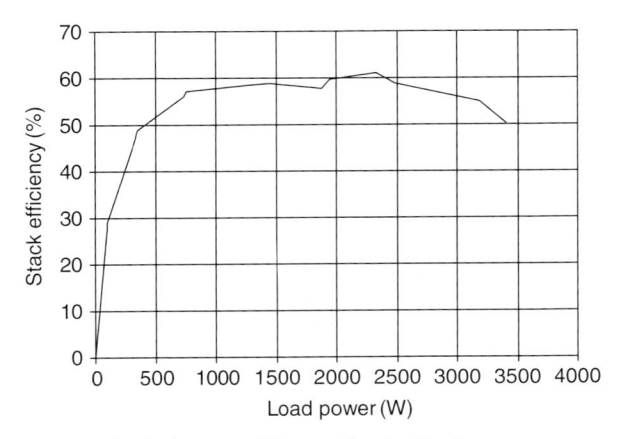

$$\eta = a_a + a_b P_\%^{0.5} + a_c P_\% + a_d P_\%^{1.5} + a_e P_\%^2 + a_f P_\%^{2.5} \quad [13]$$

Figure 29 Measured fuel cell stack hydrogen-to-electrical energy efficiency with output load.

where η is the fuel efficiency and $P_\%$ the FC per unit load power, and the parameter values for eqns [12] and [13] are as given in Appendix I.

4.13.9.4.1 Fuel Cell Operation

For road vehicle applications, the FC system must satisfy or contribute to the load demand of the vehicle traction drivetrain. The decision as to whether the FC system supplies all of the vehicle load or simply the average energy requirements can significantly influence the sizing of the FC system and hence the FC system cost. A vehicle supplied solely via FCs would necessitate operation at low current densities (and hence oversizing of the FC) to minimize the voltage swing on the DC supply to the vehicle traction system. Hence, the taxi vehicle considered were the variation in peak-average power demand is 17:1 and 4:1, respectively, for urban and suburban driving, the FC system would have to be rated much higher than the peak power specified. Additionally, since FCs cannot accept vehicle kinetic energy during braking, some form of transient power buffer can significantly reduce the installed FC power capacity [43]. Note that the time-transient response of the FC fueling also fosters FC operation in a hybrid-energy source configuration.

There are, therefore, clear benefits in terms of FC size and the recovery of vehicle regenerative braking energy for operation of FC systems in hybrid energy source configurations, where the FC supplies the vehicle average energy, or provides a range extension/battery support function, in combination with a peak power buffer, such as supercapacitor or, as for the taxi, a higher power dense battery.

4.13.9.5 Vehicle Traction Battery

4.13.9.5.1 Background

The ZEBRA technology is a serious candidate to power future electric vehicles since it not only has an energy density ~2.5 × that of lead–acid batteries (50% more than NiMH) but also has a relatively flat Peukert characteristic from 0% to 80% depth of discharge (DOD), good power density for acceleration and acceptance of regenerative energy, no maintenance, essentially intolerant to external temperature, ambient, safety, and fault tolerance, and perhaps of greatest significance for the automotive sector, the potential for low cost in volume manufacture. Originally developed by Beta R&D in the United Kingdom, the ZEBRA battery technology is now owned and manufactured by MES-DEA, Switzerland. Commercialization of the battery has made considerable progress in recent years, particularly in the automation of assembly and component optimization. Production is 2000 batteries per year with planned staged increases in capacity to 33 000 batteries, and with space available on site for a further expansion to a maximum of 100 000 batteries [46]. The ZEBRA battery system has been used in many applications, including electric vehicles. So far, the batteries had been installed in cars, buses, and vans from Mercedes, BMW, Opel, VW, Renault, Fiat, MAN, Evobus, IVECO, Larag, and Autodromo [47].

For the taxi traction system, a nominal DC link of 550 V was chosen to minimize the electrical power distribution mass and fully utilize the traction inverter silicon volt–ampere rating. The DC link voltage is realized via 2 × Z5C traction batteries, **Figure 30**, electrically connected in series, details of which are given in Appendix I [48].

4.13.9.5.2 Zebra battery simulation model

Electric vehicle traction duties are typified by high power discharge/charge rates for vehicle acceleration and braking demands, respectively [34, 35], as illustrated by **Figure 26(b)**. Since the traction battery supplies the vehicle traction drive system, the battery voltage regulation with load current is an important aspect of vehicle operation and system performance modeling. Simulation of the ZEBRA battery is facilitated via a detailed analytic model employing nonlinear open-circuit terminal voltage and resistance characteristics derived from cell experimental test data provided by Beta R&D. Since the battery dynamic current loadings are of a relatively low frequency (<100 Hz for the NEDC cycle), the battery equivalent circuit model can be simplified to that illustrated in **Figure 31(a)**. The open-circuit terminal voltage of the battery depends on battery state-of-charge (SoC), or discharged ampere-hour, and is found to be independent of load current (**Figure 31(b)**). The specified maximum discharge ampere-hour (Ah) capacity is taken from the manufacturer's nameplate capacity and collaborated via a series of Peukert tests. The battery internal resistance is similarly determined from test and is a function of discharged Ah and charging/discharging current rate (**Figure 31(c)**).

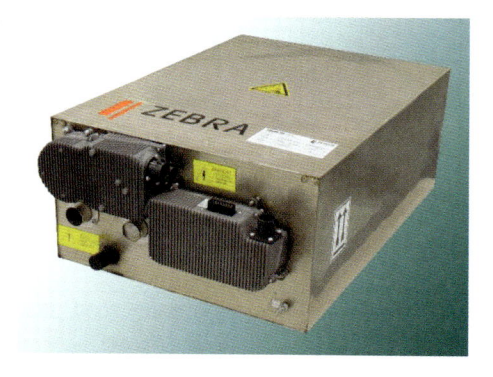

Figure 30 ZEBRA Z5C Traction battery.

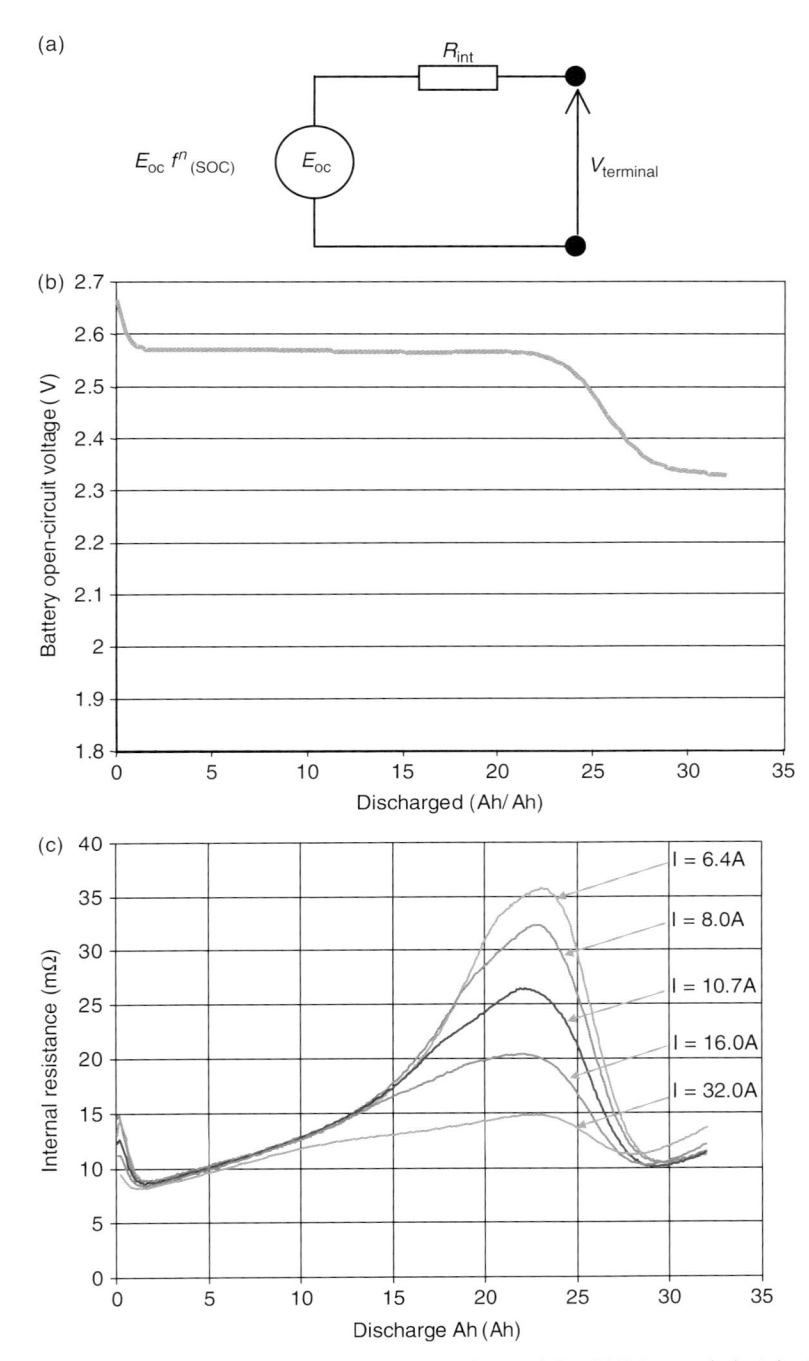

Figure 31 ZEBRA Z5C battery cell equivalent circuit model and model parameter characteristics. (a) Battery equivalent circuit (b) Battery cell open-circuit voltage (c) Battery cell internal resistance.

As with the FC model, functions for the ZEBRA battery open-circuit voltage and internal resistance are derived from curve-fits to measured battery test data. These analytic expressions thus improve on simulation time when solving multiple component drivetrain models. The curve-fit equations and battery model parameters are given in Appendix II.

4.13.9.5.3 Lead–acid battery simulation model
As a comparison of two vehicle battery technologies at the initial vehicle component assessment and specification stage, a similar model is implemented for a sealed lead–acid battery, as discussed in Reference 43. The lead–acid battery details are provided in Appendix I.

4.13.9.6 Vehicle Performance Evaluation

As previously discussed, the two major operational problems with FC systems in electric vehicle drivetrains is their poor regulation with load (**Figure 28**) and inability to accept regenerative currents that, if allowed, would result in excessive chemical fatigue of the stack membranes and hence reduced lifetime [44]. Consequently, if the FC system mass and volume is to be kept within limits commensurate with their utility in the drivetrain, some form of peak power buffering is necessary and hence a hybrid energy source for the vehicle.

The energy management strategy considered for the taxi vehicle is one where the FC provides a range extension function supplementing the battery energy, while allowing all dynamic power demands to be taken by the battery. As an assessment of the on-board energy sources the taxi performance was evaluated via two duty loading regimes, viz.

- repetitive ECE15 cycles, that is, inner city driving, and the more energy demanding,
- repetitive NEDC cycles.

The battery management strategy chosen ensures operation within nameplate voltage and current limits, the minimum voltage limit dictating actual energy utilization, and hence operating time and range. The FC utilization was constrained by the quoted on-board hydrogen storage. However, the FC stack was considered as providing a light mean supply of 2 kW and a mean supply of 4 kW, hence, operating over the most energy conversion efficient region of the stack, **Figure 29**. A number of case studies were considered; Cases 1–4 being for pure battery mode and comparing the ZEBRA and more common sealed lead–acid battery technologies; Cases 5 and 6 assess the performance of the combined ZEBRA battery and FC source. Part (i) of **Table 6** provides the test conditions and battery details for each case, while parts (ii) and (iii) give the simulated data for the two duty cycle regimes.

Table 6 Vehicle performance evaluation

(i) Test conditions

Case	Battery	Battery rated capacity (Ah)	Total battery No	Total battery Volume (l)	Mass (kg)
1	Z5C	66.0	2	266.4	390.0
2	Pb-acid	31.3	36	157.6	390.0
3	Pb-acid	52.9	36	266.4	658.4
4	Pb-acid	73.5	36	365.0	914.8
5	Z5C+FC	66.0	2	266.4	390.0
6	Z5C+FC	66.0	2	266.4	390.0

(ii) Repetitive ECE15 cycles

	Battery	Ave. FC power (kW)	Time duration (h)	Range (km)
1	Z5C	0	5.79	126.7
2	Pb-acid	0	2.48	51.7
3	Pb-acid	0	4.22	87.9
4	Pb-acid	0	5.75	119.9
5	Z5C+FC	2	10.46	218.0
6	Z5C+FC	4	11.95	249.0

(iii) Repetitive NEDC cycles

	Battery	Ave. FC power (kW)	Time duration (h)	Distance (km)
1	Z5C	0	3.42	119.8
2	Pb-acid	0	1.58	32.9
3	Pb-acid	0	2.56	89.8
4	Pb-acid	0	3.42	119.8
5	Z5C+FC	2	4.63	161.9
6	Z5C+FC	4	6.92	242.2

Per cycle values	Duration (s)	Distance (km)
ECE15	195	1.129
NEDC	1180	11.471

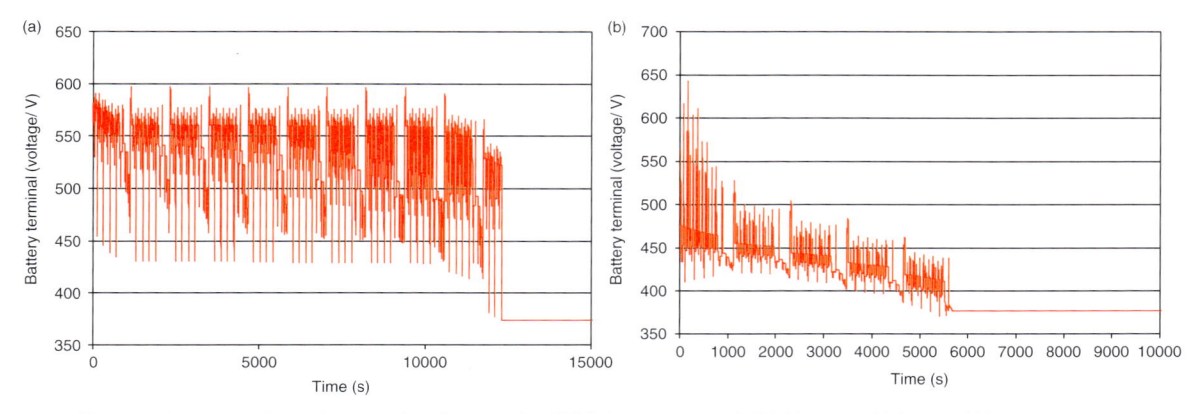

Figure 32 Simulated battery terminal voltage vs. time for repetitive NEDC duty cycles. (a) ZEBRA battery. (b) Lead–acid battery.

4.13.9.6.1 Pure battery electric mode

For both duty regimes, Case 1 gives results for the ZEBRA battery, while Case 2 compares the lead–acid battery performance for the same battery mass as that of the ZEBRA, Case 3 for the same battery volume and Case 4 for the same nameplate energy. These results clearly highlight the benefits of the ZEBRA battery in terms of mass and volume, showing an increased range of 2.4 × based on mass and 1.4 × based on volume. From a vehicle system point of view, minimization of vehicle on-board mass is the primary goal since this equates to drivetrain peak power rating. While component volume is important, it is not as critical for the taxi example given the available vehicle space envelope. The result of Case 4 has been included for interest, but such a mass impact would compromise the vehicle functionality by significantly limiting passenger payload. It is worth noting that the lead–acid simulation assumed a constant battery coolant ambient of 20 °C which would, in practice, necessitate a thermal management system, figures for which are not included in the mass and volume audits. **Figure 32** illustrates simulated battery terminal voltage variation for the repetitive NEDC duty loading, for the Zebra battery (a), and the lead–acid battery (b), corresponding to Cases 1 and 2, respectively.

4.13.9.6.2 Fuel Cell and Battery Hybrid Source

Cases 5 and 6 compare vehicle performance with a mean FC input of 2 and 4 kW, respectively. The results of **Table 6** demonstrate the benefit of the additional energy source in extending the vehicle range, in both cases by a factor of 2, making the vehicle operating times and range attractive for fleet taxi schemes.

4.13.10 Summary

The section has reviewed FC systems for transportation and discussed the main application issues in automotive drivetrains, specifically their poor voltage regulation with load and inability to accept regenerative braking energy. A detailed model of a prototype FC and ZEBRA traction battery suitable for vehicle performance simulation has been presented and vehicle performance assessed for various battery and FC combinations and for typical dynamic urban and suburban driving duty cycle regimes. It has been shown that the FC and battery combination is complementary for such duty loading, extending the vehicle range while minimizing the installed FC capacity. The results demonstrate the utility of combining energy and power sources for electric vehicle propulsion.

Appendix I Model Data and Component Specifications

Table A.1 London Taxi vehicle data

Gross vehicle weight	2500 kg
Drag force coefficient	0.31
Equivalent frontal area	1.75 m^2
Coefficient of rolling resistance	0.03
Road wheel radius	0.274 m
Wheel inertia	0.164 kgm^2
Traction machine inertia	0.57 × 10^{-3} kgm^2

Table A.2 MES-DEA 3.0 kW prototype fuel cell system [44]

Performance data	
Unreg. dc output voltage range	72–114 V
H_2 consumption at full-load	39 ln min^{-1}. (0.2 kg h^{-1})
Max. power output	3 kW
Open-circuit voltage per cell	0.95 V
Number of cells per stack	120
Active cell area	61 cm^2
Operating conditions	
Stack temperature	Max. 63 °C
Hydrogen pressure	0.4–0.7 bar
Air pressure	Ambient
Fuel supply	Pure hydrogen, dead-end mode
Ambient temperature	0 to +35 °C
Gas humidification	none
Working cycle	continuous
Cooling	Force air cooled
Stack volume	410 × 305 × 235 mm
Control unit volume	295 × 155 × 95 mm
Stack weight	9 kg
System weight	11 kg
Vehicle on-board Hydrogen storage	
Gas storage	Compressed H_2 at 230 bar
Storage medium	3x carbon composite cylinders
Total storage capability	90 l

Table A.3 ZEBRA Z5C battery data [47]

Type	Zebra Z5C
Capacity	66 Ah
Rated energy	17.8 kWh
Open-circuit voltage	278.6 V
Max. regen voltage	335 V
Max. charging voltage	308 V
Min. voltage	186 V
Max. discharge current	224 A
Weight	195 kg
Specific energy	91.2 Wh kg^{-1}
Specific power	164 W/kg
Peak power	32 kW
Thermal Loss	< 120 W
Cooling	Air
Battery internal temperature	270–350 °C
Ambient temperature	−40 to +70 °C
Dimensions (WxLxH)	533 × 833 × 300 mm
Number of cells per battery	216
Cell configuration	2 parallel strings of 108 series cells

Table A.4 Fuel cell model parameters

Parameters for eqn [12]:		*Parameters for eqn [13]:*	
k_a	0.950 602 847	a_a	−0.000 558 716
k_b	−2.111 185 823	a_b	1.196 398 539
k_c	18.408 091 8	a_c	4.580 251 356
k_d	−101.455 289	a_d	−17.647 307 9
k_e	333.775 762	a_e	20.456 066 45
k_f	−684.422 768 7	a_f	−8.028 431 982
k_g	892.840 835 4		
k_h	−737.716 086 4		
k_i	371.757 557 3		
k_j	−103.569 900 7		
k_k	12.121 244 03		

Table A.5 Sealed lead–acid battery data

Model	HAWKER Genesis EP Series
Cell number	6 cells per module
Nominal voltage	12 V (2 V per cell)
Max. voltage	13.5 V open circuit (2.25 V per cell)
Max. charging voltage	16 V (2.67 V per cell)
Min. voltage	10.2 V (recommended, 1.7 V per cell)
Max. current	450 A
Rated energy	0.1318 to 0.846 kWh
Rated capacity	70 Ah
Rated temperature	20 °C
Mass	24.2 kg
Volume	9.79 l
Dimension	331 × 168 × 176 mm

Appendix II Zebra Equivalent Circuit Model

The following equations model the ZEBRA battery as a function of discharge Ampere-hour (q) and battery terminal supply current (i). The equation for cell open-circuit voltage is given by:

$$E_{oc} = \frac{v_a + v_c\, q^{0.5} + v_e\, q^1 + v_g\, q^{1.5} + v_i\, q^2 + v_k\, q^{2.5}}{1 + v_b\, q^{0.5} + v_d\, q^1 + v_f\, q^{1.5} + v_h\, q^2 + v_j\, q^{2.5}} \quad [A1]$$

From the experimental test data, the battery internal resistance is found to be a complex function of discharge ampere-hour (or SoC) and current charge/discharge rate. Curve fit functions are used to analytically model the internal resistance. However, due to highly nonlinear relationship, it is not possible to fit one three-dimension equation to the full data set without the model losing accuracy. To overcome this problem, the model uses a set of 11 equations determined by the current rate and discharge ampere-hour. For example, for discharge currents higher than 40 A, a constant resistance of R_{max-2} is used. For all other regions, that is, when discharge current is between 0 and 40 A, the appropriate resistance equation is chosen according to the defined conditions.

The choice of battery cell internal resistance is dictated by the following algorithm:

Loop start
if '$q > ah_{ref}$' then 'simulation stop' else
if '$i \leq 0$' then '$r_{int} = r_{chg}$' else
if '$i > 40$' then '$r_{int} = r_{max-2}$' else
if '$i \leq 15$ and $q \leq 2$' then '$r_{int} = r_{a0}$' else
if '$i > 15$ and $q \leq 2$' then '$r_{int} = r_{a1}$' else
if '$26 < q < 28$' then '$r_{int} = r_{d0}$' else
if '$q \leq 15$ and $2 < i \leq 28$' then '$r_{int} = r_{b0}$' else
if '$q > 15$ and $2 < i \leq 5$' then '$r_{int} = r_{b1}$' else
if '$q > 15$ and $5 < i \leq 22.5$' then '$r_{int} = r_{b3}$' else
if '$q > 15$ and $22.5 < i \leq 28$' then '$r_{int} = r_{b2}$' else
if '$q \leq 15$ and $i > 28$' then '$r_{int} = r_{c0}$' else
if '$q > 15$ and $i > 28$' then '$r_{int} = r_{c1}$'
if '$r_{int} > r_{max}$' then '$r_{int} = r_{max}$'
Loop end

Hence, the equations used to calculate the cell internal resistance, R_{int}, in mΩ are

$$R_{A1} = \frac{a_{1a} + a_{1b}\, q + a_{1c}\, q^2 + a_{1d}\, i}{1 + a_{1e}\, q + a_{1f}\, q^2 + a_{1g}\, i} \quad [A2]$$

$$R_{B0} = \frac{b_{0a} + b_{0b}\, q + b_{0c}\, q^2 + b_{0d}\, i}{1 + b_{0e}\, q + b_{0f}\, q^2 + b_{0g}\, i} \quad [A3]$$

$$R_{B1} = \frac{b_{1a} + b_{1b}\, q + b_{1c}\, q^2 + b_{1d}\, i}{1 + b_{1e}\, q + b_{1f}\, q^2 + b_{1g}\, i} \quad [A4]$$

$$R_{B2} = \frac{b_{2a} + b_{2b}\, q + b_{2c}\, q^2 + b_{2d}\, q^3 + b_{2e}\, \ln i}{1 + b_{2f}\, q + b_{2g}\, \ln i} \quad [A5]$$

$$R_{B3} = \frac{b_{3a} + b_{3b}\, q + b_{3c}\, q^2 + b_{3d}\, q^3 + b_{3e}\, i}{1 + b_{3f}\, q + b_{3g}\, q^2 + b_{3h}\, i} \quad [A6]$$

$$R_{C1} = \frac{c_{1a} + c_{1b}\, q + c_{1c}\, q^2 + c_{1d}\, q^3 + c_{1e}\, \ln i}{1 + c_{1f}\, q + c_{1g}\, q^2 + c_{1h}\, q^3 + c_{1i}\, \ln i} \quad [A7]$$

$$R_{A0} = a_{0a} + \frac{4\, a_{0b}\, e^{\left(\frac{q - a_{0c}}{a_{0d}}\right)}}{\left[1 + e^{\left(\frac{q - a_{0c}}{a_{0d}}\right)}\right]^2} + \frac{4\, a_{0e}\, e^{\left(-\frac{i - a_{0f}}{a_{0g}}\right)}}{\left[1 + e^{\left(-\frac{q - a_{0f}}{a_{0g}}\right)}\right]^2} + \frac{16\, a_{0h}\, e^{\left(-\frac{(q - a_{0c})}{a_{0d}} - \frac{(i - a_{0f})}{a_{0g}}\right)}}{\left[1 + e^{\left(-\frac{q - a_{0c}}{a_{0d}}\right)}\right]^2 \left[1 + e^{\left(-\frac{q - a_{0f}}{a_{0g}}\right)}\right]^2} \quad [A8]$$

$$R_{C0} = c_{0a} + \frac{c_{0b}}{q} + \frac{c_{0c}}{i} + \frac{c_{0d}}{q^2} + \frac{c_{0e}}{i^2} + \frac{c_{0f}}{q\,i} + \frac{c_{0g}}{q^3} + \frac{c_{0h}}{i^3} + \frac{c_{0i}}{q\,i^2} + \frac{c_{0j}}{q^2 i} \quad [A9]$$

$$R_{D0} = d_{0a} + d_{0b} \ln q + d_{0c} \ln i + d_{0d} [\ln q]^2 + d_{0e} [\ln i]^2 + d_{0f} [\ln q][\ln i]$$
$$+ d_{0g} [\ln q]^3 + d_{0h} [\ln i]^3 + d_{0i} [\ln q][\ln i]^2 + d_{0j} [\ln q]^2 [\ln i] \quad [A10]$$

Table A.6 Zebra battery model parameter values

v_a	2.668 550 131	d_{0h}	0.524 300 703	b_{0a}	8.538 290 542	b_{2e}	−5.216 032 308	c_{0h}	−3848.834 185
v_b	−2.161 541 495	d_{0i}	−22.380 784 76	b_{0b}	−0.424 796 912	b_{2f}	0.002 232 179	c_{0i}	−11 139.148 49
v_c	−5.768 152 987	d_{0j}	−412.878 422 8	b_{0c}	0.004 829 31	b_{2g}	−0.452 954 018	c_{0j}	1 204 035.646
v_d	2.478 144 45	a_{0a}	8.296 720 91	b_{0d}	0.035 452 834	b_{3a}	7.344 557 606	c_{1a}	12.199 825 94
v_e	6.543 581 931	a_{0b}	2.654 229 606	b_{0e}	−0.080 780 68	b_{3b}	−0.226 075 522	c_{1b}	−1.200 804 369
v_f	−0.949 315 41	a_{0c}	0.177 295 354	b_{0f}	0.001 643 179	b_{3c}	−0.028 839 16	c_{1c}	0.039 395 17
v_g	−2.506 047 62	a_{0d}	0.241 852 423	b_{0g}	0.005 002 49	b_{3d}	0.001 220 193	c_{1d}	−0.000 437 123
v_h	0.144 557 23	a_{0e}	0.653 017 062	b_{1a}	8.224 355 635	b_{3e}	0.031 523 757	c_{1e}	0.005 384 114
v_i	0.383 236 649	a_{0f}	7.390 945 256	b_{1b}	−0.307 842 076	b_{3f}	−0.102 404 66	c_{1f}	−0.098 137 889
v_j	−0.007 606 508	a_{0g}	1.661 911 031	b_{1c}	0.001 595 691	b_{3g}	0.002 643 072	c_{1g}	0.003 212 432
v_k	−0.020 331 713	a_{0h}	2.974 473 025	b_{1d}	0.053 949 783	b_{3h}	0.004 302 133	c_{1h}	−3.50917E−05
d_{0a}	100 888.7072	a_{1a}	12.842 068 9	b_{1e}	−0.077 968 772	c_{0a}	−1 110.598 606	c_{1i}	0.000 354 365
d_{0b}	−84 923.677 74	a_{1b}	−18.485 908 73	b_{1f}	0.001 550 886	c_{0b}	105 087.929 3	Ah_{ref}	0 to 34
d_{0c}	−5 137.577 354	a_{1c}	20.685 460 45	b_{1g}	0.007 381 905	c_{0c}	943.155 473 7	R_{max}	80.0
d_{0d}	23 809.057 96	a_{1d}	0.035 764 63	b_{2a}	481.917 849 6	c_{0d}	−3 236 953.626	R_{max-2}	7.5
d_{0e}	72.467 753 98	a_{1e}	−1.663 449 676	b_{2b}	−56.515 691 06	c_{0e}	1695.831 45	R_{chg}	5.0
d_{0f}	2917.312 426	a_{1f}	2.272 354 708	b_{2c}	2.238 986 889	c_{0f}	−72 760.137 98		
d_{0g}	−2223.104 357	a_{1g}	0.011 695 949	b_{2d}	−0.029 265 742	c_{0g}	32 930 698.08		

Acknowledgments

Section 4.13.1: Co-authors, Dr. K.J. Dyke and Dr. D. Strickland. The authors acknowledge the UK Engineering and Physical Science Research Council (EPSRC) and Rolls-Royce PLC for provision of an Eng.D. award. The authors would also like to thank Rolls-Royce Fuel Cell Systems Ltd. for their use of laboratory test equipment and access to SOFC data.

Sections 4.13.2 and 4.13.3: Co-author, Mr. H. T. Yap. The authors acknowledge the support of the UK Engineering and Physical Science Research Council (EPSRC), via Grant No. GR/S81971/01; SEMELAB PLC, UK, for provision of a research studentship and Beta R&D, Derby, UK, for provision of test data and technical information.

References

[1] MacLeay I, et al (2008) Digest of United Kingdom Energy Statistics 2008. *Department for Business, Enterprise and Regulatory Reform (BfBER), Report, A National Statistics publication*, pp. 1–399. London, UK: TSO. ISBN 9780115155222.

[2] Dyke KJ, Schofield N, and Barnes M (2010) The impact of transport electrification on electrical networks. *IEEE Transactions on Industrial Electronics* 57(12): 3917–3926. doi:10.1109/TIE.2010.2040563.

[3] Carrasco JM, Franquelo LG, Bialasiewicz JT, et al. (2006) Power-electronic systems for the grid integration of renewable energy sources: A Survey. *IEEE Transactions on Industrial Electronics* 53: 1002–1016.

[4] Ke J and Xinbo R (2006) Hybrid full-bridge three-level LLC resonant converter & a novel DC-DC converter suitable for fuel-cell power system. *IEEE Transactions on Industrial Electronics* 53: 1492–1503.

[5] Selvaraj J and Rahim NA (2009) Multilevel inverter for grid-connected PV system employing digital PI controller. *IEEE Transactions on Industrial Electronics* 56: 149–158.

[6] Bellini A and Bifaretti S (2006) A simple control technique for three-phase four-leg inverters. *International Symposium on Power Electronics, Electrical Drives, Automation and Motion (SPEEDAM 2006)*, pp. 1143–1148. Taormina, Italy, 23–26 May. ISBN: 1-4244-0193-3, DOI: 10.1109/SPEEDAM.2006.1649940.

[7] Backlund B and Carroll E (2006) Product information – Voltage ratings of high power semiconductors. *Web Based Product Support, ABB Library*. ABB Switzerland Ltd., August, ABB Doc. Ref. No. 5SYA2051 Aug 06, pp. 1–11.

[8]   Letor R (1992) Static and dynamic behavior of paralleled IGBTs. *IEEE Transactions on Industry Applications* 28: 395–402.
[9]   Hofer-Noser P and Karrer N (1999) Monitoring of paralleled IGBT/diode modules. *IEEE Transactions on Power Electronics* 14: 438–444.
[10] Tolbert LM and Peng FZ (2000) Multilevel converters as a utility interface for renewable energy systems. *IEEE Power Engineering Society Summer Meeting*, vol. 2, pp. 1271–1274. Seattle, WA, USA, July. ISBN: 0-7803-6420-1, DOI: 10.1109/PESS.2000.867569.
[11] Sommer R, Mertens A, Griggs M, et al., (1999) New medium voltage drive systems using three-level neutral point clamped inverter with high voltage IGBT. In: *Industry Applications Conference, 1999. Thirty-Fourth IAS Annual Meeting. Conference Record of the 1999 IEEE*, vol. 3, pp. 1513–1519.
[12] Baek JW, Yoo DW, and Kim HG (2000) High voltage switch using series-connected IGBTs with simple auxiliary circuit. In: *Industry Applications Conference, 2000. Conference Record of the 2000 IEEE*, vol. 4, pp. 2237–2242.
[13] Busatto G, Cascone B, Fratelli L, and Luciano A (1998) Series connection of IGBTs in hard-switching applications. *IEEE Industry Applications Conference, Third IAS Annual Meeting*, vol. 2, pp. 825–830. October. ISBN: 0-7803-4943-1, DOI: 10.1109/IAS.1998.730241.
[14] Gerster C (1994) Fast high-power/high-voltage switch using series-connected IGBTs with active gate-controlled voltage-balancing. In: *Applied Power Electronics Conference and Exposition, 1994. APEC '94. Conference Proceedings 1994, Ninth Annual*, vol. 1, pp. 469–472.
[15] Saiz J, Mermet M, Frey D, et al. (2001) Optimisation and integration of an active clamping circuit for IGBT series association. In: *Industry Applications Conference, 2001. Thirty-Sixth IAS Annual Meeting. Conference Record of the 2001 IEEE*, vol. 2, pp. 1046–1051.
[16] Sasagawa K, Abe Y, and Matsuse K (2004) Voltage-balancing method for IGBTs connected in series. *IEEE Transactions on Industry Applications* 40: 1025–1030.
[17] Thalheim J, Felber N, and Fichtner W (2001) A new approach for controlling series-connected IGBT modules. In: *Circuits and Systems, 2001. ISCAS 2001. The 2001 IEEE International Symposium on*, vol. 2, pp. 69–72.
[18] Shammas NYA, Withanage R, and Chamund D (2008) Optimisation of the number of IGBT devices in a series-parallel string. *Microelectronics Journal* 39: 899–907.
[19] Abbate C, Busatto G, Fratelli L, et al. (2005) Series connection of high power IGBT modules for traction applications. *European Conference on Power Electronics and Applications*, pp.1–8. Dresden, Germany. ISBN: 90-75815-09-3, DOI: 10.1109/EPE.2005.219697.
[20] Abbate C, Busatto G, Fratelli L, et al. (2007) The robustness of series-connected high power IGBT modules. *Microelectronics Reliability* 47: 1746–1750.
[21] Mohan N, Undeland TM, and Robbins WP (1989) *Power Electronics: Converters, Applications, and Design*, Int. edn. New York: John Wiley. ISBN-10: 0471505374, ISBN-13: 978-0471505372.
[22] Zhenhua J and Dougal RA (2006) A compact digitally controlled fuel cell/battery hybrid power source. *IEEE Transactions on Industrial Electronics* 53: 1094–1104.
[23] Mitsubishi (2012) CM400DY-24NF. Online document. http://www.mitsubishielectric.com/semiconductors/ (accessed 18 January).
[24] Casanellas F (1994) Losses in PWM inverters using IGBTs. *IEE Proceedings – Electric Power Applications* vol. 141: 235–239.
[25] Brown AJ (2000) An Assessment of the Efficiencies of Soft and Hard-Switched Inverters for Application in Power Electric Vehicles. PhD Thesis, The University of Sheffield, UK.
[26] Ang SS and Oliva A (2005) *Power-Switching Converters*, 540pp., 2nd edn. Taylor & Francis; CRC Press. ISBN-10: 0824722450, ISBN-13: 978-0824722456.
[27] Baek JW, Yoo DW, and Kim HG (2001) High voltage switch using series-connected IGBTs with simple auxiliary circuit. *IEEE Transactions on Industry Applications* 37: 1832–1839.
[28] Dongsheng Z and Braun DH (2001) A practical series connection technique for multiple IGBT devices. In: *Power Electronics Specialists Conference, 2001. PESC. 2001 IEEE 32nd Annual*, vol. 4, pp. 2151–2155.
[29] Botto G, Carpita M, Gilardi E, and Tenconi S (1997) Series connected soft switched IGBTs for high power, high voltage drives applications: experimental results. In: *Power Electronics Specialists Conference, 1997. PESC '97 Record, 28th Annual IEEE*, vol. 1, pp. 3–7.
[30] Eckel HG (1997) Series Connection of IGBTs in Zero Voltage Switching Inverter. *Proceeding PCIM'97 Part: Power Conversion*, pp. 327–333. Nurnberg Germany, 10–12 June.
[31] Ju Won B, Dong-Wook Y, and Heung-Geun K (2001) High-voltage switch using series-connected IGBTs with simple auxiliary circuit. *IEEE Transactions on Industry Applications* 37: 1832–1839.
[32] Schofield N, Yap HT, Maggetto G, et al. (2003) A state-of-the-art review and database of fuel cells and their application in electric vehicles useful for education needs. In: *Proceedings of 10th European Conference on Power Electronics and Applications (EPE2003)*, CD ROM, Section 906, pp. 1–10, Sept. 2003.
[33] Appleby AJ and Foulkes FR (1989) *Fuel Cell Handbook*, 762pp. Van Nostrand Reinhold. ISBN 0442319266, 9780442319267.
[34] European Commission funded Fuel Cell and Hydrogen Research and Technical Development Projects (2002-2006) European Commission, http://ec.europa.eu/index_en.htm, Direct link: http://ec.europa.eu/research/energy/pdf/hydrogen_synopses_en.pdf, last visited July 2007.
[35] European Commission funded Fuel Cell and Hydrogen Research and Technical Development Projects (1999-2002) European Commission, http://ec.europa.eu/index_en.htm, Direct link: http://ec.europa.eu/research/energy/pdf/european_fc_and_h2_projects.pdf, last visited July 2007.
[36] Schofield N, Yap HT, and Bingham CM (2005) A H_2 PEM fuel cell and high energy dense battery hybrid energy source for an urban electric vehicle. In: *International Electric Machines and Drives Conference (IEMDC 2005)*, pp. 1–8, May 2005, San Antonio, TX, USA. IEEE Cat. 05EX1023C, ISBN: 0–7803–8988–3.
[37] MES-DEA (2007), *Fuel Cell Systems*, Switzerland, Direct link. http://www.mes-dea.ch/, last visited July 2007.
[38] Van Nguyen T and Knobbe MW (2003) A liquid water management strategy for PEM fuel cell stacks. *Journal of Power Sources* 114: 70–79.
[39] Glises R, Hissel D, Harel F, and Péra MC (2005) New design of a PEM fuel cell air automatic climate control unit. *Journal of Power Sources* 150: 78–85.
[40] Jung SH, Kim SL, Kim MS, et al. (2007) Experimental study of gas humidification with injectors for automotive PEM fuel cell systems. *Journal of Power Sources* 170: 324–333.
[41] Thematic Network on 'Fuel Cells, Electric and Hybrid Vehicles (ELEDRIVE)', a Network funded under Framework V, Contract No. ENK6-CT-2000-20057, Project No. NNE5-1999–20036.
[42] Schofield N, Bingham CM, and Howe D (2002) Regenerative braking for all-electric and hybrid electric vehicles. In: *IMechE Conference Braking 2002*, pp. 175–183, Leeds, UK, July 2002.
[43] Yap HT, Schofield N, and Bingham CM (2004) Hybrid energy/power sources for electric vehicle traction systems. In: *IEE PEMD Conference*, pp. 1–6 May.
[44] MES-DEA (2003), *Fuel Cell Systems, Technical Information*, Switzerland.
[45] Busquet S, Hubert CE, Labbe J, et al. (2004) A new approach to empirical electrical modelling of a fuel cell, an electrolyser or a regenerative fuel cell. *Journal of Power Sources* 134: 41–48.
[46] Dustmann C-H (1998) Zebra battery meets USABC goals. *Journal of Power Sources* 72: 27–31.
[47] Sudworth J (2001) The sodium/nickel chloride (ZEBRA) battery. *Journal of Power Sources* 100: 149–163.
[48] Zeb5 component data (2003) *Beta R&D*, Derby, UK.

4.14 Future Perspective on Hydrogen and Fuel Cells

K Hall, Technology Transition Corporation, Ltd., Tyne and Wear, UK

© 2012 Elsevier Ltd. All rights reserved.

4.14.1	Overview	331
4.14.2	Why Hydrogen?	332
4.14.3	Hydrogen for Transport	333
4.14.4	Stationary Power	334
4.14.5	The Efficiency Debate	335
4.14.5.1	A Holistic Approach	335
4.14.6	From Here to There	337
4.14.7	Conclusions	339
References		339
Further Reading		340

Glossary

Demand-side management (DSM) Modification of consumer demand for energy through education or financial incentives.

Holistic Relating to or concerned with wholes or with complete systems rather than with the analysis of, treatment of, or dissection into parts [1].

Integrated gasification combined cycle (IGCC) Technology that turns coal into a synthesis gas and involves generating electricity from gas turbines as well as steam-powered turbines.

4.14.1 Overview

Population growth is projected to continue in the foreseeable future. (Excerpted from data from US Census Bureau 2009, Population Reference Bureau, and UN Department of Economic and Social Affairs as follows: [2–11]). More and more people are living in metropolitan areas. Roads are becoming more congested [12], with incentives for mass transit and tariffs for driving personal automobiles in crowded cities becoming more commonplace. As ultralow emission vehicles, such as hybrid electric vehicles, do not contribute to the growing production of carbon emissions from vehicles, these are often exempted from congestion charging and are therefore highly sought after vehicles in areas such as London, where congestion-charging policies are in place.

The future presents an image of vehicles that rely less on a diminishing supply of fossil fuels and more on clean energy choices – such as a cleaner energy mix for electricity, clean efficient hydrogen fuel cells, and even hydrogen internal combustion engines. Added to a growing mix of taxis and buses running on cleaner energy technologies [13–16] the near- to mid-term future looks much like the present day, only with cleaner air and fewer harmful emissions from transportation applications (**Table 1**).

Hydrogen energy can contribute significantly to the future energy mix due to its versatility. Not only can hydrogen be produced from fossil fuel feedstocks, it can also be produced from renewable energy resources and nuclear power. The production of hydrogen in any of these ways provides many benefits, including the ability to store intermittent energy (e.g., from wind or PV) for use when demand outstrips supply, or in another application (such as transport) or another location. This solution affords greater options for producing energy using renewable resources and providing this energy in many usable forms in the growing cities, providing clean stationary power as well as transport fuel.

Producing hydrogen from fossil fuels makes sense when and where the fossil fuels are abundant, providing energy to the end user without the carbon. Large-scale power plants, therefore, could sequester the carbon, and provide power as electricity, gaseous hydrogen, or even liquid hydrogen if desired. The ability of large-scale power plants to provide energy in these three forms opens new markets and delivers clean, reliable power.

It is important to understand that hydrogen energy will be used alongside many other forms of energy and enhance the overall efficiency of delivering clean fuel for a variety of applications. How hydrogen will be used in the future depends on the specific needs of the community. This chapter will describe many anticipated needs and how hydrogen can play a role in addressing those needs.

Today, there are many pre-commercial and early market applications of technologies that are critical on the path to a future energy mix that do not rely on imported fossil fuels, and which contribute to carbon-reduction targets and allow communities to make the most of the energy resources available to them. We will explore a number of these technologies and discuss their roles in the transition to a low-carbon energy future where hydrogen energy plays a dominant role alongside clean electricity.

And finally, the chapter will describe the future applications of hydrogen energy with respect to the projected energy supply needs.

Table 1 Projected increases in world population

	United States Census Bureau (2009)[a]	Population Reference Bureau (1973–2008)[b]	UN Department of Economic and Social Affairs (2008)[c]
2010	6 830 586 985		6 908 688 000
2020	7 557 514 266		7 674 833 000
2030	8 202 205 367		8 308 895 000
2040	8 748 743 446		8 801 196 000
2050	9 202 458 484	9 352 000 000	9 149 984 000

4.14.2 Why Hydrogen?

Let us begin by discussing the reasons why hydrogen is of interest. There are many, and in reviewing the key policy drivers for hydrogen energy in a number of countries, The author has selected the predominant drivers that tend to appear in National policy documents more often than not: Security of Energy Supply, Greenhouse Gases/Climate Change, and Air Pollution/Environmental (United Kingdom Hydrogen Association [17], U.S. Department of Energy [18], Canadian Hydrogen Association [19], European Comission [20], Ministry of New and Renewable Energy, India [21]).

By their nature, fossil fuels are used faster than they are produced. Although there continue to be significant resources discovered, the cost of accessing these resources has to be balanced against the cost of obtaining energy from other resources. The issue is not one of scarcity of supply of fossil fuels; it is more about the difficulties of increasing that capacity to keep pace with increasing demand [22]. In addition, carbon-based fuels contribute greenhouse gases to the atmosphere. To ensure future supplies of fuel, and mitigate potential damage to the environment from combustion of fossil fuels, there is a trend toward sustainable supplies of energy.

The World Commission on Environment and Development defined sustainable development as development that "meets the needs of the present without compromising the ability of future generations to meet their own needs" [23].

In practical terms, resources that are used more quickly than they can be renewed and create environmental damage cannot meet the requirement.

Therefore, although it is quite reasonable to expect that fossil fuels will continue to be a key part of our future energy mix, it is also reasonable to expect a growing portion of this energy mix to come from low-carbon and diverse supplies, with a growing emphasis on sustainability.

It is worth noting that indigenous, low-carbon energy supplies tend to be less dispatchable, or less capable of following demand variations, than conventional technologies. Notable exceptions include large-scale hydroelectric and coal with precombustion carbon capture and storage (CCS) [2] (**Figure 1**).

Therefore, a key risk associated with a decarbonized grid is supply variability resulting from the relatively poor dispatchability of many low-carbon generators. This could result in increased difficulty in maintaining grid stability as low-carbon options are taken up.

Demand-side management (DSM) solutions are needed to ensure the necessary grid balancing. There are many DSM solutions available, distinguished mainly by the storage timescales they provide. Batteries, flow cells, flywheels, and supercapacitors are examples of short time-scale energy storage (less than a second to a few hours).

Electricity storage and pumped hydroelectric are examples of medium time-scale energy storage (hours to a few days).

It is important to recognize that the intermittent nature of many renewable energy technologies necessitates longer-term energy storage (can be weeks or more). Hydrogen has a unique role to play in meeting these longer-term needs.

Hydrogen, like electricity, is an energy carrier, rather than an energy source. So, we are concerned with production, storage, and use, as in the case of electricity. Assuming that the end products meet standard quality requirements, neither electricity nor hydrogen retains any 'memory' of the feedstocks or methods used to produce it. Both are flexible that they can be produced from a variety of feedstocks, providing energy in a usable form where and when it is needed. The societal movement to low-carbon options for energy generation is compatible with both electricity and hydrogen; however with this shift comes new issues which must be addressed.

As renewable energy increases penetration in the energy supply, the need for longer-term storage becomes greater [24].

Generators such as conventional coal power plants, flexible combined cycle gas turbines, and open cycle gas turbine power plants are low load-factor generators with a relatively low capital expenditure required.

Adding postcombustion CCS increases both the load factor and capital expenditure. One way this could be offset is to consider precombustion CCS with open cycle gas turbine power plants. Precombustion CCS technologies are being developed. One leading method currently being developed is a system called integrated gasification combined cycle (IGCC), which involves generating electricity from gas turbines as well as steam-powered ones [25]. This approach enables the sale of hydrogen for industrial uses as well as a transport fuel.

As the energy supply becomes decarbonized and gas becomes more expensive, hydrogen from coal plus CCS or from electrolysis becomes a viable option; and in fact becomes a very attractive option [26].

The point at which decarbonized hydrogen is competitive with conventional fossil fuel technologies depends on several factors – including the price of carbon and the price of the fossil fuels. For example, when the CO_2 value offsets the fuel conversion costs for a given application, the use of CCS and hydrogen as an intermediary energy vector becomes competitive with natural gas for energy generation.

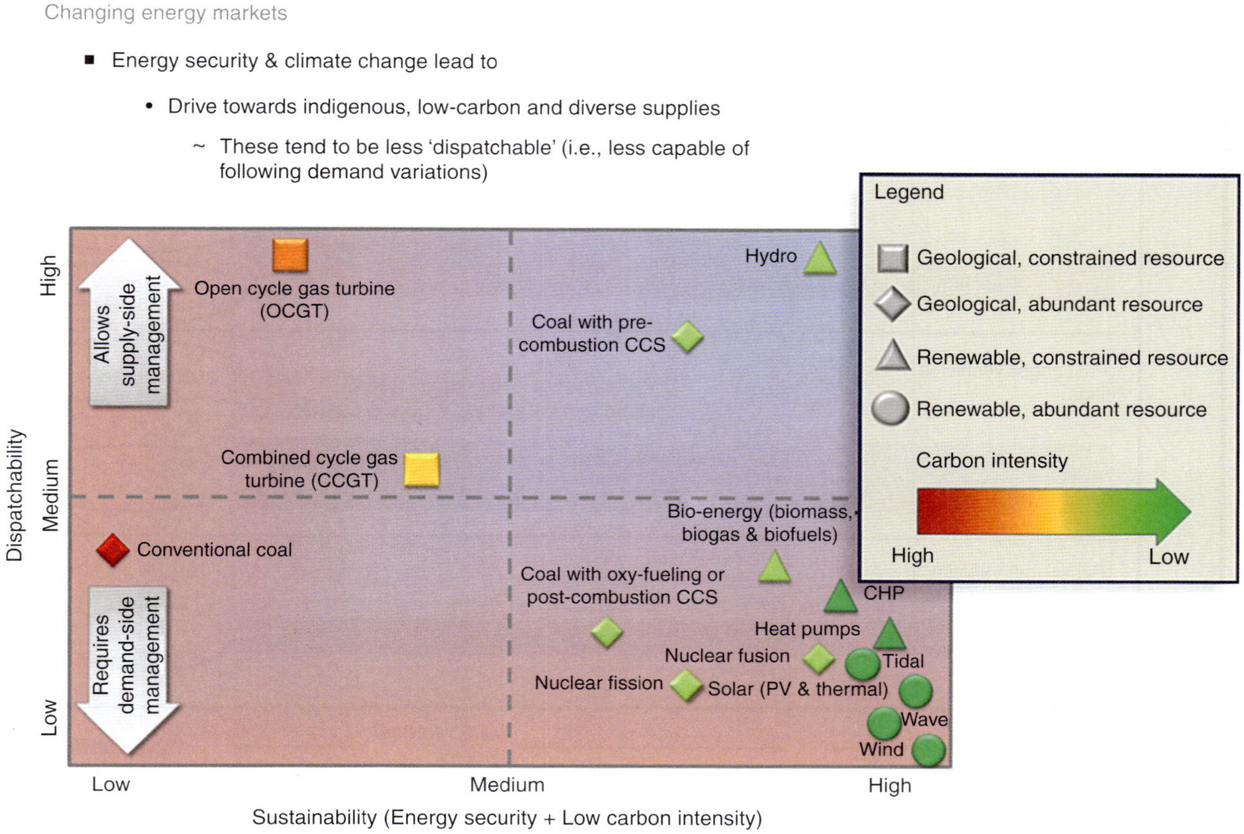

Changing energy markets

- Energy security & climate change lead to
  - Drive towards indigenous, low-carbon and diverse supplies
    - These tend to be less 'dispatchable' (i.e., less capable of following demand variations)

Figure 1 Dispatchability versus sustainability. Reproduced with permission from Gammon R (2010) *Dispatchability versus Sustainability Loughborough.* Leicestershire, UK: Bryte-Energy Limited [2].

4.14.3 Hydrogen for Transport

There are currently many regions demonstrating hydrogen vehicles and refueling technologies. In September 2009, nine major automotive manufacturers signed a letter of understanding to develop and launch fuel cell electric vehicles, with commercialization anticipated in the 2015 timeframe [27].

Development of a hydrogen infrastructure for vehicles is well underway, with hydrogen stations across the world [28]. The author has personally visited operating stations in California, Washington DC, Japan, Korea, the United Kingdom, and Germany. The high energy density of hydrogen and rapid refueling times for hydrogen vehicles provide a distinct advantage to public charge points for electric vehicles. In addition, home hydrogen refuelers are being developed which overcome the early difficulties of deploying widescale infrastructure in advance of mass commercialization of vehicles [29] (**Figure 2**).

Research and development of hydrogen infrastructure is being conducted worldwide. The economics depend on a number of factors including geographical location, hydrogen production techniques, storage technology and timeframe, and distribution methods. Most cost-effective production techniques may vary as each region considers the resources available to them.

Japan is intensely investigating options to provide sustainable stationary and transportation power to large cities and has identified utilization rate as the key factor in making a hydrogen infrastructure economical [30].

Electrification of vehicle power trains is required to decarbonize transport. Batteries and hydrogen are two ways of achieving this and all leading OEMs that have active programs in both areas. It is worth noting that commercial fuel cell vehicles under development are hybrids, combining batteries, and fuel cells. The hybrid electric vehicle operates the fuel cell as an alternative power unit to supply the power required by the vehicle, to recharge the batteries, and to power accessories such as the air conditioner and heater. According to a US training module developed by the College of the Desert,

> Hybrid electric cars can exceed the limited 100 mile (160 km) range-per-charge of most electric vehicles and have the potential to limit emissions to near zero. A hybrid can achieve the cruising range and performance advantages of conventional vehicles with the low-noise, low-exhaust emissions, and energy independence benefits of electric vehicles [31].

2. Hydrogen fuel cell vehicles introduction scenario

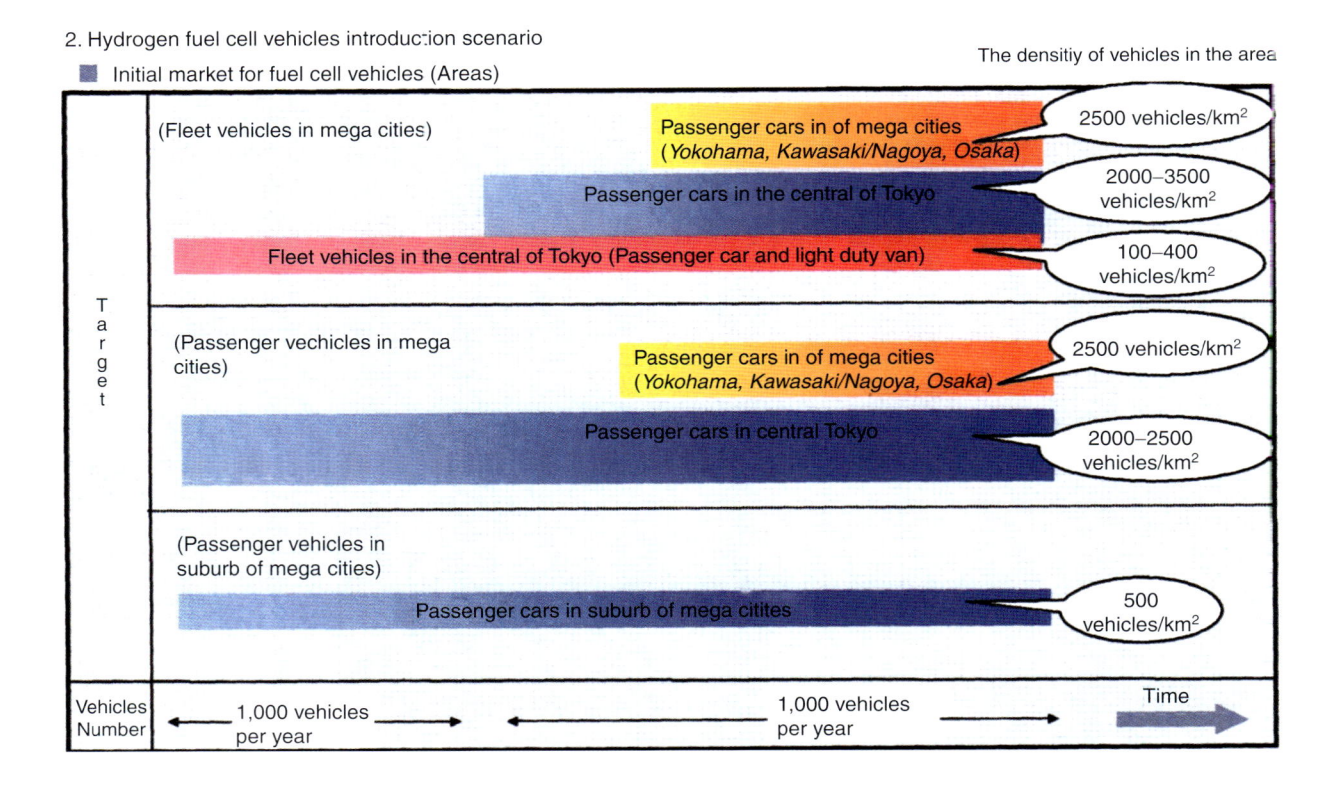

■ Initial market for fuel cell vehicles (Areas)

The densitiy of vehicles in the area

Target:
- (Fleet vehicles in mega cities) — Passenger cars in of mega cities (*Yokohama, Kawasaki/Nagoya, Osaka*) — 2500 vehicles/km²
- Passenger cars in the central of Tokyo — 2000–3500 vehicles/km²
- Fleet vehicles in the central of Tokyo (Passenger car and light duty van) — 100–400 vehicles/km²
- (Passenger vechicles in mega cities) — Passenger cars in of mega cities (*Yokohama, Kawasaki/Nagoya, Osaka*) — 2500 vehicles/km²
- Passenger cars in central Tokyo — 2000–2500 vehicles/km²
- (Passenger vehicles in suburb of mega cities) — Passenger cars in suburb of mega citites — 500 vehicles/km²

Vehicles Number: 1,000 vehicles per year → 1,000 vehicles per year → Time

Figure 2 Honda solar hydrogen filling station in Torrence, California. Reproduced with permission from ENEA (2010) *Vision of a Hydrogen/Electric Energy Scenario*. Rome, Italy: ENEA.

4.14.4 Stationary Power

Fuel cells that operate on hydrogen energy are available on the market today. They come in a variety of sizes for a variety of applications. The solution is carefully matched with the problem that needs to be solved.

There is much more information on the variety of fuel cell technologies available today elsewhere in this volume. They are mentioned here only to provide a brief context for a transition from the energy mix of today, to the energy mix of the future, where hydrogen plays a more dominant role. It is anticipated the market penetration for stationary fuel cells will continue to grow, as hydrogen becomes more widely available.

4.14.5 The Efficiency Debate

Efficiency is a key issue that is often raised by those who believe hydrogen energy has no future. Some ask why we would convert electricity to hydrogen, and then back to electricity. To answer this question, keep in mind that efficiency must not be considered in isolation of the needs of society. In addition, consideration must be given to efficiency gains of capturing energy that would otherwise be lost in order to gain a more complete picture.

How, for example, does one measure the efficiency of a system that allows you to capture renewable energy that otherwise would have not been captured? Rather than turning some wind turbines off at night when supply outstrips demand, the turbines can be allowed to operate fully, thereby increasing the utilization rate of the wind energy system. Wind power that cannot be used for stationary power or exported to the grid could be used in power electrolyzers to produce hydrogen. This hydrogen could then be used in stationary or transport applications where and when needed. Thus, although there will undoubtedly be efficiency losses in each step of transfer or conversion, you are starting with a resource that was not going to be used at all. Therefore, even if you achieve a system efficiency of 45%, for example, does it make sense to imply you are somehow 'losing' 55% of the energy when your starting position was to lose 100% by switching off the wind turbines?

Even so, if we want to simply look at the efficiency of the stack and the electrolyzer system, recent progress reports show electrolyzer stack efficiencies between the low seventies and the upper eighties, depending on the specific components and materials used. System efficiencies, however, vary with the power of the system. Let us take sample data from recent research at NREL [32]. Looking at a 6.5 kW system at 135 A, a measured hydrogen flow of 1.05 Nm^3 h^{-1}, the reported High Heat Value system efficiency is 57.4 and the low heat value system efficiency is 48.5%.

4.14.5.1 A Holistic Approach

Hydrogen is meant to be considered holistically – throughout the energy chain. It complements electricity, allowing for useful energy to be available in an appropriate form where and when it is needed. Both electricity and hydrogen will continue to be important throughout the heat, electricity, and transport sectors; and both will continue to be produced in more sustainable, environmentally friendly ways.

There have been many critics of hydrogen energy who point to narrow applications and show, correctly, that hydrogen may be less efficient or more expensive than other technologies [33]. However, these critics fail to look at hydrogen's role across the energy spectrum, and therefore give any credit for hydrogen serving multiple needs simultaneously.

The following figure from AMEC depicts the potential complex role of hydrogen for providing the capacity, the flexibility, and the sustainability of a future energy system across heat, electricity, and transport sectors (**Figure 3**):

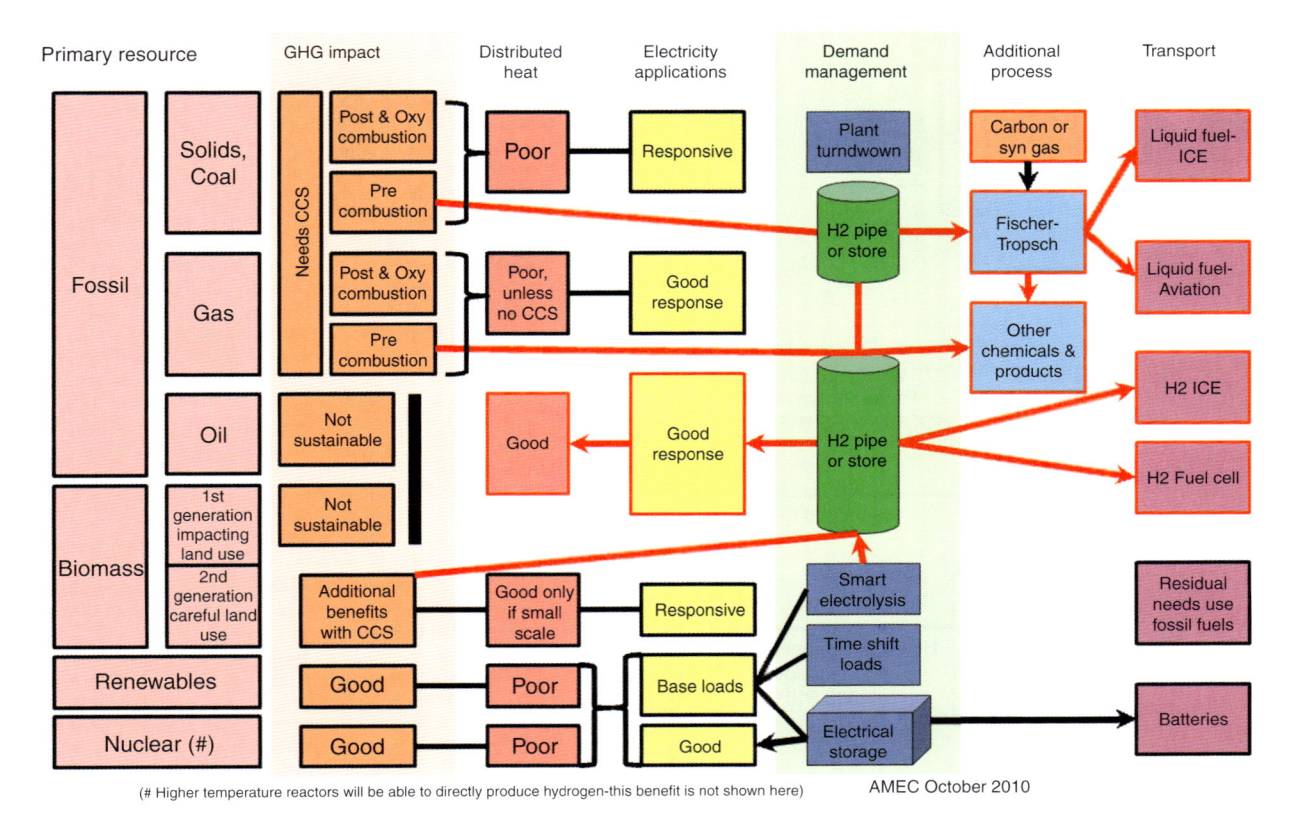

Figure 3 A holistic approach for hydrogen. Reproduced with permission from ITM Power (2010) *Hydrogen Powered Home*. Sheffield, UK: ITM Power

NREL [34] has shown That hydrogen can be produced at the wind site for prices ranging from $5.55 per kg in the near term to $2.27 per kg in the long term. A research opportunity in this scenario is the elimination of redundant controls and power electronics in a combined turbine/electrolysis system.

Hydrogen fuel cells can be used as a buffer for intermittent renewable resources.

There are examples of systems that use solar or wind turbines, coupled with electrolysis for hydrogen production. Renewable energy resources are not distributed equally throughout the world, and require significant areas to deploy technologies to gather sizeable amounts of energy. In order for these types of energy resources to become more practical, the energy needs to be easy to store, transport, and use. Coupling renewable resources with hydrogen not only achieves this, but it also allows this stored energy to be used as a sustainable transport fuel [35]. One such project is the Wind2H2 project in the United States, which links wind turbines and photovoltaics to electrolyzers, which pass the renewably generated electricity through water to split it into hydrogen and oxygen. The hydrogen can then be stored and used later to generate electricity from an internal combustion engine or a fuel cell (**Figure 4**)

The Wind2H2 project seeks to improve the system efficiency of producing hydrogen from renewable resources in quantities large enough and at costs low enough to compete with traditional energy sources such as coal, oil, and natural gas. Some success has already been achieved in optimizing power electronics [36].

Renewable electricity, particularly which is above and beyond the demand for the direct electricity at the time and therefore would not be captured, can be converted via electrolysis to produce hydrogen. This hydrogen can then be used to power the fuel cell during peak demand. Critics will point to the fact that it is more efficient to use the renewable electricity directly – which is true when that is an option. However, the nature of intermittent resources and transmission lines means that there will be times when the system is capable of generating more electricity than is needed. Often, this results in some wind turbines being switched off, for example. The electricity which could be generated by these turbines could be used to electrolyze water to store hydrogen for those times when demand is greater than can be supplied directly from the renewable resources. In a case like this, how does one characterize the efficiency? The system is using energy which otherwise would not have been captured at all. The turbines are already in place.

The efficiency debate applies to all areas of hydrogen production, storage, and use. The same debate can be made of electricity, but rarely is made, because we do not wish to burn coal in our homes to heat water or power our television or computers. Both hydrogen and electricity are used in a form which is clean and quiet easy to use where and when it is needed. Electricity provides electrons, and hydrogen can provide electrons with gaseous or liquid storage. Yes, it takes energy to provide any of these. As society moves to more environmentally sustainable energy resources, the game becomes one of capturing more of this energy, not only how efficiently we use but also what has been captured.

Consider the case of renewable resources where 50% of the available energy is captured, and that is used 80% efficiently versus adding hydrogen storage to capture 80% of the available energy which may be used 50% efficiently. The current efficiency debate focuses only on the efficiency of use after conversion losses; however these two scenarios actually are comparable. Now when 95%

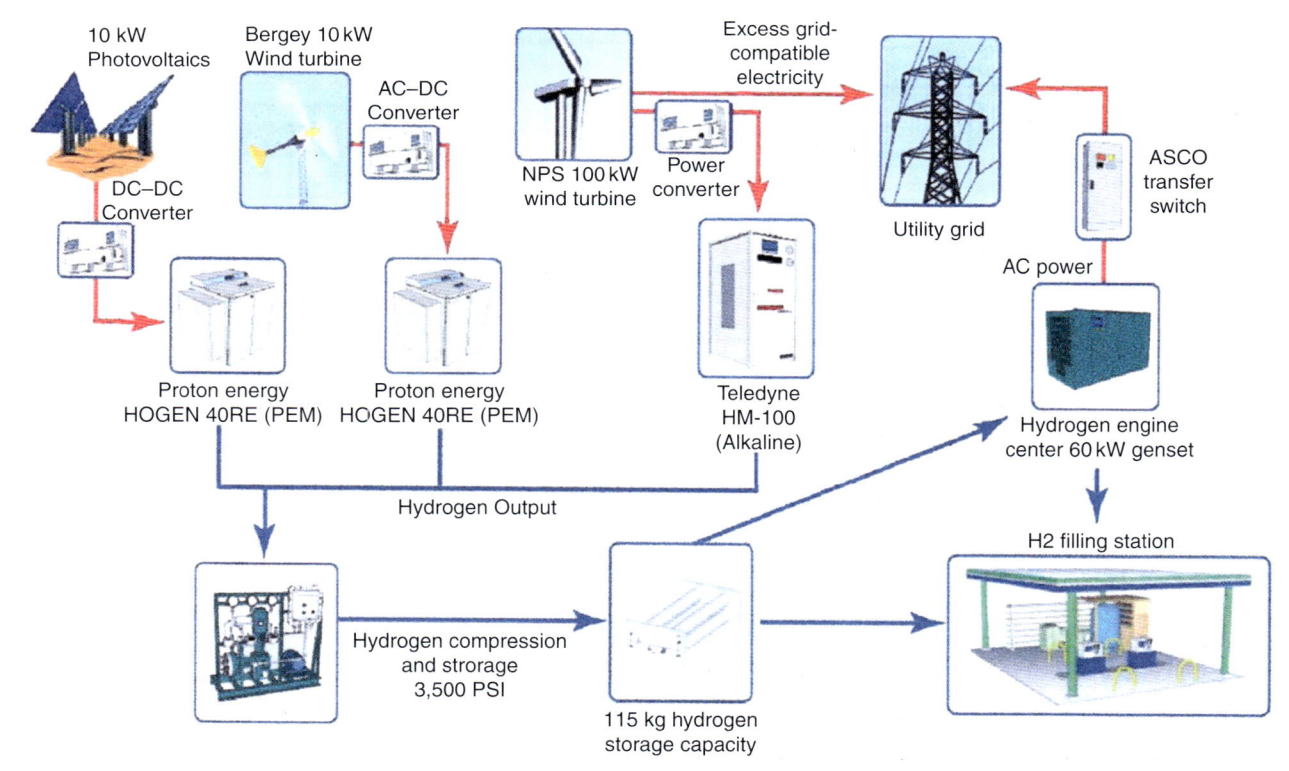

Figure 4 Overall Wind2H2 system diagram.

of the available energy is captured and used 60% efficiently, more overall energy is available for use. So in this case, the efficiency debate needs to include the ability to capture the resource in the first place as well as the conversion losses prior to use.

Recall the need for long-term storage of intermittent renewable energy discussed previously. The addition of electrolysis and hydrogen storage means that the renewable resource need not be turned off overnight or during other times of low demand. Capturing and storing some of this energy for use when demand outstrips supply increases the energy output from the renewable energy system, helps manage supply and demand issues, and creates a store of energy which can be used in a number of applications, including fueling hydrogen vehicles. Farms that operate wind turbines may use the excess hydrogen to power farm equipment, becoming more self-sustaining; or the excess hydrogen can be sold as a commodity. In fact, hydrogen opens new markets for electricity to include fuel for vehicles.

Critics will point out that electricity can be used directly as a vehicle fuel in battery electric vehicles (BEVs). Yes, of course, this is true. The difficulty has been in ensuring the capacity required to provide the electricity to the vehicle while maintaining capacity for other uses. In the case of hydrogen, which can be delivered as a gas or liquid as well as electrons, there are simply more options. When and where it is not convenient to deliver electrons to the vehicle, hydrogen can be delivered as a gas or liquid, reducing refueling/recharging times and avoiding an additional demand on the electrical grid. In areas where there is no electrical grid or no additional capacity, this is especially attractive.

One reason someone may want to suffer the efficiency losses in converting electricity to hydrogen, and then back to electricity, may relate to intermittency of renewable energy. During the times when a photovoltaic system or wind turbine is capable of producing more electricity than the user can use at the time, the surplus renewable power could be used to make surplus electricity. If there is a need to store this electricity, one option for this is through hydrogen production by electrolysis. Although there are efficiency losses in this conversion, we are starting with energy that was not usable. Any energy captured in this way is basically bonus energy that would have been lost otherwise.

What is then done with this energy is a matter of individual needs and circumstances. Someone may choose to store the hydrogen, and then run the hydrogen through a fuel cell to create electricity locally when the demand for the renewable electricity exceeds the supply. In this way, more of the renewable energy is captured than can be used directly, and this helps resolve the intermittency issues with renewable energy. Hydrogen is used as an energy storage mechanism for renewable resource.

Perhaps there is not a need to capture the energy for local use. Or perhaps the renewable energy system is capable of providing more electricity than can be used locally, even accounting for intermittency issues. In this case, the excess energy could still be converted to hydrogen, but now the hydrogen could be sold as a commodity, or used to power vehicles. The ability to gain revenue from this energy as a vehicle fuel may be an attractive option.

The author believes the key to the future of hydrogen energy lies in its flexibility. No single production method is expected to dominate the future of hydrogen production. Precombustion CCS, electrolysis, nuclear, bio-energy, and others all will likely have a role to play. The flexibility in production methods provides greater flexibility in solving a broader array of energy issues than a single production method would.

It is worthwhile to consider the broader energy picture to better understand why energy conversion is not the barrier that it may seem to be at first glance.

Figure 5 depicts a vision of a future hydrogen/electric energy scenario. It shows the flexibility in generation described in this chapter, and how the hydrogen, regardless of how it is produced, can be delivered as electricity, gas, or liquid for a variety of applications.

In this hydrogen vision, hydrogen is produced from all available feedstocks, including fossil fuel power plants that utilize Carbon-Capture technologies. The hydrogen that is delivered to the filling station has no memory – it may have come from any of the available feedstocks. Yet, it is delivered to the grid, fuel cell, or vehicle in a standardized form, ensuring a consistent, robust hydrogen infrastructure throughout the world.

The concept of sustainable energy with hydrogen as a key component is one that is embraced all over the world [38]. Even in countries where hydrogen demonstrations are not yet as prevalent as they are in North America, Germany, and Japan, we are seeing promising advanced research results. Scientists at Korea's S&P Energy Research Institute, for example, are working on chemical processes for manufacturing hydrogen that can reduce the cost of producing hydrogen by 20–30 times [39]. And in the last 3 years, India formed a hydrogen association [40] and installed its first hydrogen fuel-dispensing bunk [41]. In addition, the first hydrogen highway opened in Norway in 2009 [42].

4.14.6 From Here to There

To appreciate the potential of hydrogen energy, it is important to understand from the beginning. The starting point for a transition that includes abundant clean hydrogen is where we are today. Presently, there is a robust electricity network and fossil fuel infrastructure. Electricity is made predominantly from coal and nuclear feedstocks, with a growing portion coming from a variety of renewable energy technologies. Supporters for hydrogen energy point out that as power production in general moves away from fossil fuels, the amount of hydrogen produced from clean resources will also grow. Renewable resources will become the dominating energy source and renewable electricity will require new energy storage capacities [43]. In this way, the carbon footprint of hydrogen tracks the carbon footprint of electricity.

Figure 6 shows a home scenario where the homeowner is using renewable energy for electricity and generating hydrogen gas for home appliances as well as the family car.

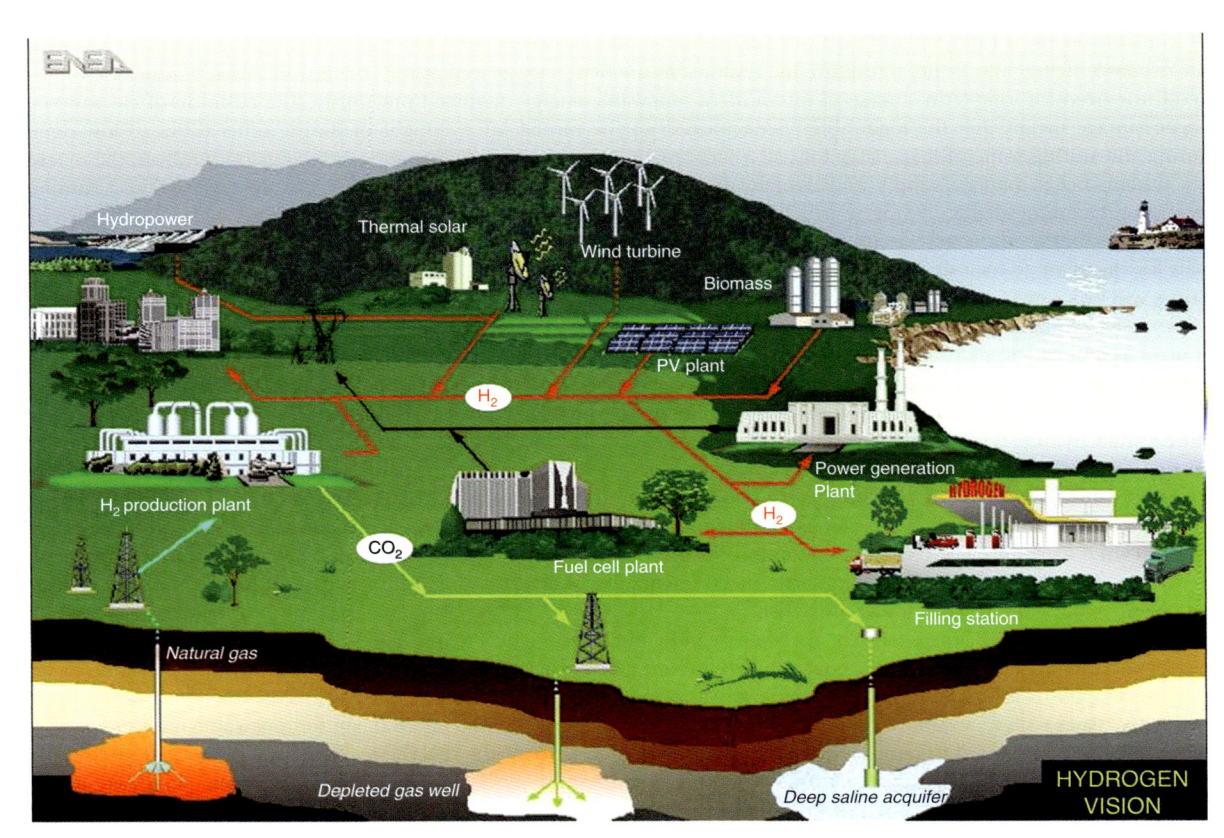

Figure 5 Vision of a hydrogen/electric energy scenario, used with permission from ENEA. Reproduced with permission from ENEA (2010) *Vision of a Hydrogen/Electric Energy Scenario*. Rome, Italy: ENEA [37].

Figure 6 Hydrogen powered home used with permission from ITM Power. Reproduced with permission from ITM Power (2010) *Hydrogen Powered Home*. Sheffield, UK: ITM Power [44].

In this scenario, hydrogen again plays the role of energy buffer with intermittent renewable resources. In addition, it allows for a separate stream of gaseous energy, suitable for home appliances and vehicles.

4.14.7 Conclusions

Hydrogen will have an important role to play in decarbonized transport and electricity generation, as part of a mix that includes a range of other technologies (e.g., biofuel, BEVs, renewable resources, nuclear, and fossil fuel with CCS) (Orion Innovations [45]).

A major decarbonization problem will be heat, in particular season peak loads. Such loads may benefit from hydrogen, which is commercially more attractive over longer-term storage.

The use of hydrogen energy offers benefits (United Kingdom Hydrogen Association [17]) at the large scale, such as hydrogen from precombustion CCS, off-peak and grid balancing of national grid electricity, storage and supply of low-carbon energy for heat, and particularly transport applications, as well as at the small scale, such as community and distributed systems utilizing wind, tidal, wave, photovoltaic, and other renewable resources with hydrogen fuel cell systems, standby and mobile, and auxiliary power, just to name a few.

Hydrogen can contribute by acting as an energy store to balance supply and demand, in a similar manner to batteries with electricity but at a lower storage cost; and providing an energy storage medium or a transport fuel as a sidestream from precombustion CCS power stations.

Hydrogen is available today from refinery gasifiers with a wide range of inputs, natural gas, biogas or waste, and electrolysis of water at overall efficiencies ranging from 50% to 70%. The hydrogen can already be made in large centralized plants or in smaller distributed units located close to refueling requirements.

Construction of a hydrogen infrastructure will follow demand, under normal commercial terms. However, like recharging points, the first refueling stations do need deployment support.

Improvements in utilization of renewable resources and hydrogen, as well as in system efficiencies will make these technologies commercially attractive over a wider range of applications.

Electrolytic hydrogen is an embedded solution and will track the carbon footprint of the grid and the adoption of embedded and off-grid renewable resources.

References

[1] http://www.merriam-webster.com/dictionary/holistic (accessed 19 October 2011).
[2] Gammon R (2010) *Dispatchability Versus Sustainability Loughborough*. Leicestershire, UK: Bryte-Energy Limited.
[3] U.S. Census Bureau (2009) International data base estimates updated. December 2009. (accessed 21 January 2010).
[4] Haub C (2008) 2008 World population data sheet. Population Reference Bureau.
[5] Haub C (2007) 2007 World population data sheet, 2006 estimate. Population Reference Bureau.
[6] Haub C (2006) 2006 World population data sheet, 2005 estimate. Population Reference Bureau.
[7] Haub C (2005) 2005 World population data sheet, 2002 estimate. Population Reference Bureau.
[8] Haub C (2002) How many people have ever lived on earth? *Population Today* 30(8): 3–4 (Estimates prior to 2002).
[9] Haub C (1995) How many people have ever lived on earth? *Population Today* 23(2): 5–6.
[10] 1950–2050 estimates (only medium variants shown): World Population Prospects: The 2008 Revision. United Nations Department of Economic and Social Affairs, Population Division.
[11] Estimates prior to 1950: The World at Six Billion, 1999. United Nations Department of Economic and Social Affairs, Population Division.
[12] Mayerowitz S (2010) America's most congested highways and roads. *ABC News*, 25 February. http://abcnews.go.com/Travel/traffic-delays-americas-congested-highways-roads/story?id=9932888.
[13] Fuel cell transit bus evaluations, joint evaluation plan for the U.S. Department of Energy and the Federal Transit Administration. Technical Report NREL/TP-5600-49342-1, November 2010.
[14] Greater London authority press release: Mayor unveils hydrogen bus fleet for the capital, 10 December 2010.
[15] Hydrogen taxis for London roads from 2012. *Taxi Insurance Cost Auto News*, 22 July 2011.
[16] Motor trend, Tokyo testing: Toyota rolls out hydrogen fuel cell taxis. *Donny Nordlicht*, 31 January 2011.
[17] United Kingdom Hydrogen Association (2007) Policy priorities. UKHFCA. http://www.ukhfca.co.uk/wp-content/uploads/2011/03/policyPaper_adopted.pdf (accessed 19 October 2011).
[18] U.S. Department of Energy (2002) *A National Vision of America's Transition to a Hydrogen Economy – To 2030 and Beyond*. Washington, DC: U.S. Department of Energy.
[19] Canadian Hydrogen Association (2007) *Hydrogen Systems: The Canadian Opportunity for Greenhouse*. Trois Rivieres, Canada: Canadian Hydrogen Association.
[20] Roads2HyCom: Socio-economic conditions for fuel cell and hydrogen technology development, Roads2HyCom project, a deliverable of the European Commission Framework Six Program, January 2009.
[21] National hydrogen energy roadmap: Path way for transition to hydrogen energy for India. National Hydrogen Energy Board, Ministry of New and Renewable Energy, Government of India, 2006.
[22] Boscheck R (ed.) (2007) *Energy Futures*. Palgrave Macmillan.
[23] World commission on environment and development, our common future, Brundland, 1987.
[24] INFORM, Harnessing hydrogen – The key to sustainable transportation, Cannon 1995.
[25] Science and environment. 'Clean' coal plants get go-ahead, *BBC News*, 3 September 2008. http://news.bbc.co.uk/1/hi/sci/tech/7584159.stm.
[26] UK HFCA letter to Prof David MacKay, Chief Scientific Advisor to DECC. http://www.ukhfca.co.uk/wp-content/uploads/2011/03/Meeting-Prof-MacKay-Follow-up-Letter-final.pdf (accessed March 2011).
[27] Doggett S (2009) 9 major automakers sign letter agreeing to develop and launch fuel-cell vehicles. blogs.edmunds.com.
[28] Ludwig-Bölkow-Systemtechnik GmbH and TÜV SÜD, Hydrogen filling stations worldwide – Overview. http://www.h2stations.org/ (accessed 19 October 2011).
[29] Fuel Cell Today (2008) *ITM Power Launches Hydrogen Home Refueller*. London, UK: Fuel Cell Today.

[30] IEA/IPHE Workshop: Building the Hydrogen Economy: Enabling Infrastructure Development: Transition Scenario for Hydrogen Infrastructure for Fuel Cell Vehicles in Japan; Mitsubishi, 11 July 2007.
[31] Fuel cell hybrid electric vehicles: Training module 8, College of the Desert, December 2001. http://www1.eere.energy.gov/hydrogenandfuelcells/tech_validation/pdfs/fcm0&r0.pdf (accessed 19 October 2011).
[32] Harrison KW, et al. (2009) The wind-to-hydrogen project: Operational experience, performance testing, and systems integration. Technical Report NREL/TP-550-44082, March 2009.
[33] Bossel U, Eliasson B, and Taylor G (2004) The future of the hydrogen economy: Bright or bleak? 15 April 2003 – Revised 28 October 2004.
[34] Levene J, Kroposki B, and Sverdrup G (2006) Wind energy and production of hydrogen and electricity – Opportunities for renewable hydrogen – preprint. *National Renewable Energy Laboratory* (accessed 20 October 2008).
[35] INFORM, Harnessing Hydrogen – The Key to Sustainable Transportation, Cannon, 1995.
[36] Harrison K and Ramsden. T (2010) NREL hydrogen and fuel cell technical highlights, NREL improves system efficiency and increases energy transfer with Wind2H2 project, enabling reduced cost electrolysis production. http://www.nrel.gov/hydrogen/pdfs/48435.pdf.
[37] ENEA (2010) *Vision of a Hydrogen/Electric Energy Scenario*. Rome, Italy: ENEA.
[38] Partnership for advancing the transition to hydrogen. Annual Report on World Progress in Hydrogen Energy.
[39] Korean research makes hydrogen manufacture 30 times cheaper. http://gizmodo.com/5065847/korean-research-makes-hydrogen-manufacture-30-times-cheaper (accessed 19 October 2011).
[40] Inauguration of hydrogen association of India (HAI) on 16 December 2010. http://www.hai.org.in/past_events_2.html (accessed 19 October 2011).
[41] Hill K, Gasworld.com, hydrogen bunk means hydrogen cars for India. 14 January 2009.
[42] Navarro X (2009) Green car news, first hydrogen highway opened in Norway, 14 May 2009. http://green.autoblog.com/2009/05/14/first-hydrogen-highway-opened-in-norway/ (accessed 19 October 2011).
[43] Wurster R et al. Energy infrastructure 21 role of hydrogen in addressing the challenges in the new global energy system.
[44] ITM Power (2010) *Hydrogen Powered Home*. Sheffield, UK: ITM Power.
[45] Orion Innovations (2009) *Hydrogen Future Study – HyFuture*. Glasgow, UK: The Scottish Hydrogen and Fuel Cell Association.

Further Reading

[1] Fuel Cell and Hydrogen Energy Association. Renewable hydrogen production using electrolysis. http://www.fchea.org/core/import/PDFs/factsheets/Renewable%20Hydrogen%20Production%20Using%20Electrolysis_NEW.pdf (accessed 19 October 2011).
[2] Renewable Energy Policy Project (2002) Hydrogen and fuel cells. REPP. http://www.repp.org/hydrogen/index.html (accessed 29 October 2010).
[3] National hydrogen energy roadmap: Toward a more secure and cleaner energy future for America, US Department of Energy, November 2002.
[4] The hydrogen commercialization plan. National Hydrogen Association, 1996.
[5] European Comission (2008) *HyWays: The European Hydrogen Roadmap*. Brussels, Belgium: European Commission.
[6] A portfolio of power-trains for Europe: A fact-based analysis – The role of battery electric vehicles, plug-in hybrids and fuel cell electric vehicle.
[7] International Energy Agency (2007) Building the hydrogen economy: Enabling infrastructure development -Part II: Sharing the European vision, 10–12 July 2007, Paris, France: International Energy Agency.